IN A REDWOOD FOREST

A TEXTBOOK

OF

GENERAL BOTANY

FOR

COLLEGES AND UNIVERSITIES

BY

RICHARD M. HOLMAN

*Late Associate Professor of Botany in the College of Letters
and Science of the University of California*

AND

WILFRED W. ROBBINS

*Professor of Botany in the College of Agriculture
of the University of California*

FOURTH EDITION
Seventeenth Printing

NEW YORK

JOHN WILEY & SONS, Inc.

LONDON: CHAPMAN & HALL, LIMITED

PREFACE TO THE FOURTH EDITION

The untimely death of the senior author, Doctor Richard M. Holman, occurred shortly after the issuance of the third edition. In the preparation of the fourth edition there has been adherence to and consideration for his viewpoint in the organization and treatment of subject matter. Many changes, however, have been made in the present edition, made necessary as the result of recent researches. The sections on absorption and conduction by roots have been completely rewritten to be in harmony with investigations of the last few years in plant physiology. The same is true of the sections dealing with the rise of sap in stems, and conduction of foods. The theory of active solute absorption has been given greater weight than in previous editions. Credit is due Dr. A. S. Crafts, of the Division of Botany, College of Agriculture of the University of California, for assistance in the rewriting of the above physiological discussions. Dr. A. S. Foster, of the Department of Botany, University of California, has assumed the responsibility of rewriting the subject matter pertaining to the origin and development of leaves, and for the revised classification of tissues, which lays emphasis on progressive and regressive development as contrasted to the static and rather arbitrary classification of previous editions. A discussion of hormones in their relation to growth phenomena has been included. Attention has been given to the improvement of a number of old illustrations and to the addition of such new ones as have been deemed desirable. In addition to the major changes mentioned above, there are scores of smaller ones, which in many cases correct errors, or make the meaning more understandable. We are grateful to users of the textbook for calling many of these points to our attention. From a number of instructors has come a request for a glossary and, accordingly, such has been added, which not only includes definitions of terms, but the origin of words. This, we believe, will be of considerable use to the student.

In addition to Dr. Crafts and Dr. Foster, whose contributions to the present edition have been extensive, we are also grateful to Dr. Lee Bonar, of the Department of Botany, University of California, who has thoroughly gone over Part II and made valued changes, and to

Dr. T. Elliot Weier and Dr. Katherine Esau, both of the Division of Botany, College of Agriculture, University of California, who, through their use of the textbook over a number of years, have been able to offer important suggestions.

WILFRED W. ROBBINS

DAVIS, CALIFORNIA
 May 11, 1938

PREFACE TO THE THIRD EDITION

In preparing the third edition of this textbook the authors have made those changes which the growth of botanical knowledge during the seven years since the publication of the second edition seems to justify. These changes, and those prompted by the experience of the authors in the use of the book and by the suggestions of other teachers who have used it, have made it necessary to rewrite portions of every chapter. It has proved possible, however, to avoid any considerable addition to the amount of text matter. The increase in the number of pages in the book is largely due to the inclusion of about fifty additional illustrations. A number of the old illustrations have been redrawn or have been replaced by improved figures. In some cases, where no sacrifice of illustrative value was involved, photomicrographs have replaced line drawings.

The authors have sought to increase the ease with which the book may be read, wherever that was possible without sacrificing that logical organization and clarity of statement which intelligent teachers and students recognize as the most essential qualities of a good textbook. In this edition fine print has been used in the body of the text, not only for the statements of physical and chemical principles essential to the understanding of certain physiological processes, but also for certain detailed and special material which some teachers may wish to omit from their reading assignments.

In the chapter on The Relation of the Plant to the Environment, there has been added to the sections on Plant Associations, Invasion, and Succession, an account of the Climax, prepared by Dr. F. E. Clements of the Carnegie Institution of Washington, and a section on Fossil Plants prepared by Dr. Ralph W. Chaney of the Carnegie Institution has also been added. It is hoped that the list of references included in this edition will be found helpful to students and teachers using the book. Limitation of space prevents our listing here the large number of persons to whom we are indebted for assistance in this revision, but we cannot forego expressing our thanks individually to the following persons, who have been of particular assistance: Dr. Joel

The authors gratefully acknowledge the helpful suggestions made and the assistance given by several of their associates in the botanical and agricultural departments of the University of California and by the following teachers in other colleges and universities: Howard C. Abbott, Rimo Bacigalupi, H. P. Barss, E. A. Bessey, Otis F. Curtis, Sarah L. Doubt, Clifford H. Farr, Margaret C. Ferguson, Robert Griggs, J. E. Kirkwood, P. A. Lehenbauer, H. E. McMinn, E. C. Miller, A. D. Oxley, Ethel G. Stiffler, W. I. Witterback and many others.

The authors are particularly indebted to Esther G. Holman for her criticism of the manuscript of the second edition and checking of the proof sheets.

WILFRED W. ROBBINS.
RICHARD M. HOLMAN.

BERKELEY, CALIFORNIA,
    October 7, 1927.

PREFACE TO THE FIRST EDITION

THIS book embodies the material of the lectures to the students in the two courses in General Botany given in the University of California. One of these courses, given at the Branch of the Agricultural College at Davis, is for agricultural students exclusively; the other, given at Berkeley, is attended by both agricultural and liberal arts students. Since there are frequent interchanges of students between the two institutions and since both courses serve as prerequisites for the same advanced courses, it is desirable that the two courses be essentially equivalent. During frequent conferences the authors of the present volume, who are responsible for the two courses, have on the basis of their experience in elementary botanical instruction in several universities and agricultural colleges found themselves in agreement upon the following points:

(1) That the agricultural student will profit more by a broad survey of the whole field of botany, in as far as that is possible or desirable in the elementary courses, than from a special course for agricultural students restricted to those aspects of botany which are capable of the most obvious and direct application to agriculture.

(2) That the general student in an elementary course in botany, no less than the agricultural student, will profit by having the subject related wherever possible to agricultural practices and problems, and by the use of economic plants for illustrative material in every case where they will serve the particular end as well as any other plants.

(3) That the results from such a course are likely to be more satisfactory if a relatively small number of forms and processes are discussed and studied with some degree of completeness than if the work is more superficial and extensive.

(4) That the usual procedure of presenting the subject matter of such a course largely by means of formal lectures leaves much to be desired and that a textbook which presented practically the whole content of the usual lectures on the fundamentals of general botany would result in better teaching, since it would make it possible for the instructor to devote more of his time and energy to the more effective work of recitation, conference, and quiz.

(5) That, although an acquaintance with the activities of the plant, rather than with its structure, should be the primary aim of such a course, a knowledge of structure is essential to an intelligent understanding of function.

(6) That the text for such a course should be as fully illustrated as possible and that the usefulness of the illustrations would be greatly increased by direct labeling, wherever possible, of the parts of each structure illustrated.

We have endeavored to embody all of these considerations in the present text.

The text is designed for a year's course, the material covered by Part I to be taken up in one semester and by Part II in a second semester. However, Part I may be used alone. With the exception of the first and second, the Chapters of Part I have been so written that they may be taken up in any order desired by the instructor. If it is thought desirable to use Part II without taking up all the material in Part I, Chapters I and II may be used as introductory to Part II.

ACKNOWLEDGMENTS

Although the authors are indebted to a number of their colleagues, who have read certain chapters and made suggestions for their improvement, they accept sole responsibility for the contents of the book. Among those who have read certain chapters, especially those touching on their own particular field of study or interest, or who have made helpful suggestions during the preparation of the book are:

Professor C. B. Hutchison, Director of the Branch of the College of Agriculture at Davis, and Professor of Plant Breeding; Professors W. A. Setchell, N. L. Gardner, T. H. Goodspeed, and O. L. Sponsler, Dr. Lee Bonar, and Miss Lucile Roush of the Department of Botany of the University of California; Professors C. B. Lipman, P. B. Kennedy, R. E. Clausen, and J. P. Bennett of the Agricultural College of the University of California; Professor Francis Ramaley of the University of Colorado; and Professor D. H. Campbell of Stanford University.

The majority of the illustrations are original, and for their assistance in the preparation of these we wish especially to thank Miss Elisabeth Pratt, Miss Mildred Hollis, Miss Jane Mackie, Mr. Charles Quibell, Miss Ruth Seely.

In the case of illustrations which have been borrowed acknowledgment of the source has been made in the legend of each cut but we wish to express here our thanks to the following authors and publishers for their courtesy in permitting the use of figures: Professor A. H. H. Buller,

University of Manitoba; Professor D. H. Campbell, Stanford University; Professor Charles J. Chamberlain, University of Chicago; Professor John M. Coulter, University of Chicago; Professor C. C. Curtis, Columbia University; Professors Woodbridge Metcalf and E. Fritz, of the Division of Forestry, University of California; Professor C. S. Gager, Brooklyn Botanic Garden; Professors W. A. Setchell, W. L. Jepson, N. L. Gardner, and H. M. Hall, University of California; Professor John W. Harshberger, University of Pennsylvania; Professor E. C. Jeffrey, Harvard University; Professor William A. Locy, Northwestern University; Professor Edwin C. Miller, Kansas Agricultural College; Professor D. M. Mottier, University of Indiana; Professor John Percival, University College, Reading, England; Professor C. S. Sargent, Yale University; Professor Lester W. Sharp, Cornell University; Professor E. W. Sinnott, Connecticut Agricultural College; Professor W. C. Stevens, University of Kansas; Professor Warren P. Tufts, of the Division of Pomology, University of California; Professor J. E. Weaver, University of Nebraska; P. Blakiston's Son & Company, Figs. 46, 55, 56, 95, 100, 114, 120, 127, 172, 173, 174, 175, 176, 177, 178, 179, 181, 182, 183, 195, 198, 199, 200, 202, 209, Robbins' *Botany of Crop Plants*; Figs. 60, 68, 75, 136, Stevens' *Plant Anatomy*; Figs. 145, 146, 147, 148, Palladin's *Plant Physiology*; Figs. 165, 268, 279, Gager's *Fundamentals of Botany*; Fig. 258, Harshberger's *Mycology and Plant Pathology*; E. P. Dutton, Figs. 44, 45, 106, 357, 358, 367, 368, 369, Percival's *The Wheat Plant*; Ginn and Company, Figs. 123 and 188, H, from Bergen and Caldwell's *Practical Botany*; Henry Holt and Company, Figs. 12, 13, 14, Locy's *Biology and Its Makers*; Figs. 59, 156, 157, 186, 274, Kerner's *Natural History of Plants*; Figs. 74, 278, 323, 324, 355, Curtis' *Nature and Development of Plants*; The Macmillan Company, Fig. 54, Bailey's *Lessons with Plants*; Figs. 83, 107, 137, 138, 151, Haberlandt's *Plant Anatomy*; Fig. 180, Ganong's *A Textbook of General Botany*; Figs. 211, 237, C. Strasburger's *Textbook of Botany*; McGraw-Hill Company, Fig. 4, Sharp's *Cytology*; Fig. 262, Sinnott's *Botany-Principles and Problems*; University of Chicago Press, Fig. 109, Jeffrey's *The Anatomy of Woody Plants*; Figs. 162, 347, 348, 349, 350, 351, 354, Coulter and Chamberlain's *Morphology of Gymnosperms*; Fig. 263, Chamberlain's *Methods in Plant Histology*.

RICHARD M. HOLMAN.
WILFRED W. ROBBINS.

DAVIS, CALIFORNIA,
August 29, 1924.

CONTENTS

PART I

THE STRUCTURE AND PHYSIOLOGY OF SEED-BEARING PLANTS

PART II

A SURVEY OF THE PLANT KINGDOM WITH PARTICULAR EMPHASIS UPON DEVELOPMENT, REPRODUCTION, AND RELATIONSHIPS, INCLUDING ALSO A CHAPTER ON EVOLUTION AND HEREDITY

TEXTBOOK OF GENERAL BOTANY

PART I

THE STRUCTURE AND PHYSIOLOGY OF SEED-BEARING PLANTS

CHAPTER I

INTRODUCTION

The Sciences.—Botany is one of the great divisions of knowledge which we call **the sciences**. Botany and the various other sciences, taken collectively, are spoken of as **science**. Science is often defined as **classified knowledge**, but science means much more than a mere orderly arrangement of facts. Science includes properly only such facts as can be conveyed to the minds of others by definite and precise statement. It does not properly include any facts which have not been verified and subjected to the test of experimentation or repeated accurate observation.

Through classification and comparison of such facts, there are often brought to light certain broad and general truths which enable us to embody in one statement a great many known facts and to predict, with great certainty and without repetition of observations or measurements, a great many other facts. The discovery of these general truths, or **natural laws**, as they are called, is the most important goal of science. In the search for such laws, scientists make use of certain tentative explanations, or **hypotheses**, which are products of the imagination of the scientific worker and are in agreement with many of the facts which are known about the subject under consideration. Many hypotheses are soon shown to be wrong, but a hypothesis which survives the test of newly discovered facts and is not displaced by some more reasonable hypothesis attains in time to the dignity of a **theory**. A theory is not recognized, however, as a natural law until it has long stood the test to which it is constantly being put by the discovery of new facts. Many theories which have finally been abandoned because of their failure to meet this test have, nevertheless, by reason of the stimulus which they

1

have given to the imagination of scientific workers and to experimentation, greatly contributed toward the advancement of science.

The methods of science are intellectual; they are based upon reason and logic, not upon prejudice, sentiment, or emotion. Accurate observation, measurement, and experimentation, verification of the facts thus revealed, the classification and comparison of these facts, and, finally, strictly logical inference from these facts—these are the methods of science. Science is the concern of the head, not the heart. *Knowing*, in the intellectual sense, may not be the most important thing in life, but it is the only thing with which science is concerned. The critical student will always be on his guard against those who, through ignorance, superstition, sentimentality, or self-interest, present as scientific truth, statements which have not been properly verified or are utterly false.

On the other hand, although there is no valid reason why any field of human knowledge or experience should be closed against scientific inquiry, yet many of the most important facts of human experience, having to do with emotion, sentiment, and faith, are by no means purely intellectual in their nature, and their worth is not necessarily to be judged by the purely intellectual standards of science. To insist that their value be judged by such standards is no more justifiable than to permit emotion and sentiment to enter into scientific thinking.

In this age in which we are able to converse with each other half way around the world, to travel hundreds of miles an hour through the air, to make machines perform most of our former drudgeries, and to avert, by the application of scientific knowledge, many of man's most dread diseases, it is quite unnecessary to emphasize the importance of science.

The constantly increasing store of truth which it furnishes and its great practical utility in our modern life are recognized by all. Nor are its benefits entirely material. From the pursuit of scientific truth many persons secure satisfaction of a very keen and elevating sort; and a knowledge of the laws of the universe which surrounds us has led many to a finer appreciation of the order and beauty of nature.

Most of the sciences have to do with material things, the substances of which they are made, their form and structure, and the changes which they may undergo. These sciences are sometimes spoken of as the **concrete sciences**, to distinguish them from mathematics and certain other sciences which are called the **abstract sciences** and which are not concerned primarily with materials or objects. The concrete sciences may be divided into those which are concerned chiefly with non-living things (the **physical sciences**) and those which are concerned with living things or **organisms** (the **biological sciences**). To the group of the physical sciences belong chemistry, physics, geology, astronomy and many others.

Botany and Zoology—Distinctions between Plants and Animals.— It is customary to divide all organisms into the two groups or kingdoms, plants and animals, and, accordingly, we recognize two major biological sciences, botany and zoology. However, certain branches of the study of animals, such as human anatomy, physiology, and psychology, and, similarly, certain divisions of the study of plants, such as bacteriology and plant pathology, are commonly spoken of as if they were independent sciences because of their great significance in relation to human affairs. To define botany as the science of plants and zoology as the science of animals seems at first thought to distinguish clearly between the two biological sciences. On looking further into the matter, however, we find that the distinction is not so clear as it seemed, for it is by no means easy to define the familiar words, plants, and animals. Indeed, it is impossible to draw a sharp line of distinction which will separate all plants from all animals, but the following points of difference apply to most plants and animals:

PLANTS	ANIMALS
1. The great majority of plants are not able to move from place to place. Many simple plants are, however, capable of such movement (locomotion).	1. Locomotion (movement from place to place) is characteristic of most animals, although many animals, such as the sponges and the sea anemones, grow attached throughout most of their life.
2. In most plants each of the cells, or minute masses of living substances of which the bodies of all organisms are made up, is surrounded by a relatively rigid wall.	2. The cells of animals are generally without such surrounding walls.
3. Most plants have the power of building up from very simple substances, secured from the soil and from the atmosphere, the complex substances called foods which are used by all plants and animals to increase and replace living substance and for other life processes. Plants, therefore, could exist in a world devoid of animals.	3. Animals are unable to make their own foods. They must secure them from plants, either directly or through other animals. In a world devoid of plants, animals could not long continue to live. This, which is the most important distinction between typical plants and typical animals, does not, however, distinguish all plants from all animals, for there are several large groups of simple plants which are unable to make foods.
4. In most plants growth and development proceed in an unlimited fashion. New organs and tissues continue to be produced throughout the life of the plant.	4. In animals, on the other hand, organs are fairly well formed in the embryo, and growth and development consist chiefly in their enlargement and maturing.

Among the larger and more complex organisms, such as trees, shrubs, reptiles, birds, and mammals, for example, there is little difficulty in distinguishing which are plants and which are animals, but among the simplest organisms, such as certain one-celled aquatic forms, it is often very difficult and sometimes apparently quite impossible to maintain any distinctions between them. We do not know just what kind of organism was the first to come into existence on this earth or whether such kinds of organisms still exist or have become extinct. Certainly these first organisms must have been plant-like, since only plants are able to combine the simple substances, water and certain constituents of the soil and the atmosphere, into the complex substances which we call foods without which animals can not exist. According to the **theory of evolution** it is from these first simple plant-like organisms that there have developed by relatively slow changes all the hundreds of thousands of different kinds (species) of plants and animals which now exist upon the earth. The first somewhat animal-like organisms which evolved from these original plant-like organisms were probably much like the latter. The differences could only have been distinguished by very careful study of their behavior. The simplest living things which exist today are doubtless very like those early forms and it is accordingly no easy matter to distinguish among them the plants from the animals. They include organisms which are considered by some to be plants and by others to be animals. Because of this, these organisms have come to be studied by both botanists and zoologists. As evolution went on, and more and more complex and larger organisms evolved, the distinctions between plants and animals became more and more marked.

The name **protoplasm** has been given to the living substance of both plants and animals. It is essentially similar in these two groups of organisms, and the principles which underlie the structure, development, and activities of these two groups are fundamentally the same. Botany and zoology are, therefore, not unrelated sciences but have much common ground and are to a large degree interdependent.

Similarly, every science overlaps and shares part of the field of other sciences. Thus, the biological sciences, botany and zoology, meet physics in the field of bio-physics, chemistry in the field of bio-chemistry, and geology in the field of paleontology, which is the study of the fossil remains of plants and animals. In such cases each of the sciences concerned may contribute new facts to the other. Thus the information which the botanist is able to supply as to the structure and relationship of the plants whose fossil remains are found in the rocks may assist the geologist in judging the age and origin of those rocks. The botanist, on the other hand, is indebted to the geologist for help in locating fossils of extinct plants and in gaining knowledge of the ancestors of present-day plants.

Pure and Applied Science.—Science is often divided into **pure science** and **applied science.** By pure science is meant scientific knowledge pursued without regard to its practical application to agriculture, industry, medicine, or other material interests. The worker in the field of pure science believes that the search for new facts and new laws is worth while for itself. The worker in the field of applied science prefers to direct his effort toward the securing of scientific facts which can be utilized to improve the quantity or quality of some crop, to better the breeds of domestic animals, to develop improved methods in hygiene or medicine, to make more economical some manufacturing process, or to add in some other way to man's comfort or material well-being. Science had its beginnings, it is true, in the observations and speculations of the ancients relative to things which were of immediate and practical interest and importance to them. Historically interesting as are these earliest recorded observations of the plants and animals which furnished the ancients with food, clothing, and medicine, there was little real scientific progress until late in the Middle Ages, when there came into the world that spirit of pure scholarship which seeks to learn the truth without regard to its practical worth. Many of those who laid the groundwork of modern chemistry, physics, and the biological sciences, as well as of scientific agriculture and medicine, were not in the least concerned with the economic importance of what they learned. Workers in pure science are constantly enlarging our fundamental knowledge, and incidentally revealing much of which the worker in applied science can make practical use. On the other hand, those who are seeking to solve practical problems have made many discoveries of great fundamental importance to pure science.

Fields of Botany.—Pure botany is commonly divided into **systematic botany, plant morphology,** and **plant physiology.**

Systematic botany, or **taxonomy** of plants, is concerned with distinguishing the different kinds of plants, describing each kind accurately, giving to each a name, and seeking to classify the different kinds so that those which are most closely related will be within the same group.

Plant morphology, which is concerned with the structure of plants, is generally subdivided into **external morphology** and **anatomy.** The first of these subdivisions has to do with the form, arrangement, and relationships of the organs of the plant and with their structure in so far as these things can be studied without cutting into the plant body. Anatomy, which is the study of the internal structure of the plant, includes **histology** and **cytology.** Anatomy is the study of the internal

structure of the plant.   A phase of anatomy is **cytology** which is concerned with the structure of the minute masses of living material (protoplasm) by which the walls are built up and which are responsible for the
growth of the plant and for all other life processes.   It is obvious that it is
necessary to know the structure of a plant if we are to classify it properly,
or to understand its activities; just as it is necessary, for example, to
know the structure of the eye, if we are to understand the function, sight.
More specifically, to know adequately how a leaf manufactures food, it is
essential to have an understanding of its structure, that is, its morphology.

Plant physiology is the study of the activities of plants, the principal
ones of which are growth, methods of getting the materials from which
they make foods, the building up of these foods, and the processes by
which they produce other plants like themselves. The plant physiologist
seeks not only to describe, measure, and analyze these processes but to
reduce them to the terms of physics and chemistry.   In **plant ecology,**
which is a branch of plant physiology, particular attention is given to the
relations between plants and their environment in nature, that is to the
soil, to temperature, to moisture supply, to light, and to the influences of
the other plants and the animals which are associated with them.   Plant
ecology seeks to determine, among other things, why certain plants are
restricted to particular locations and why they are generally found growing with certain other plants and with certain animals.   There are many
other special fields of pure botany which it is impossible to discuss here
on account of limitation of space.

Applied botany, or economic botany, includes forestry, plant breeding, plant pathology (the study of the diseases of plants), horticulture
(the study of orchard and garden crops), agronomy (the study of
field crops), and in fact all those branches of scientific agriculture which
have to do with plants.   The Government of the United States, through
the Bureau of Plant Industry and other agencies, and the different
states, through their experiment stations, provide for the investigation
of a large number of problems in applied botany and for the dissemination of the results of these investigations among farmers and others.

**Physical and Chemical Principles Fundamental to the Biological
Sciences.**—It is impossible to study plants understandingly without
some knowledge of fundamental physical and chemical facts and principles.   Particularly is this essential in considering the activities of the
plant and of its constituent cells, that is, in the study of plant physiology.
It can not be expected that all of those who use this book will have
received instruction in physics and chemistry.   For the sake of those
students who have not had such instruction, and by way of review for
those who have, there will be introduced in this book, from time to time,

brief statements of the physical and chemical conceptions essential to a proper understanding of what follows. To set off these parts of the text from the purely botanical portions finer print will be used. The parts in fine print, however, are not to be considered of less importance than the rest of the book. They are absolutely essential to a proper understanding of the rest.

By way of introduction to these scattered notes are the following statements of fundamentals.

Through his senses man is aware of the existence of the universe about him. He sees, hears, feels, tastes, and smells it. If sight, hearing, sense of touch, taste, and smell were lost he might through his memory still be aware that various features of the universe had existed about him but would have no way of learning whether any particular feature still existed. The universe is then to man but the sum total of all the features which may affect one or more of his senses. All these features generally are spoken of in terms either of *matter* or of *energy*.

Definitions, Their Use and Abuse.—It is necessary that these terms, matter and energy, be defined here, but before that is done a note of warning must be sounded relative to the use of definitions. Definitions are essential if a writer or speaker is to express himself exactly and to be clearly understood by the reader or hearer. These definitions should be worded so as to express the meaning of the term in question as completely and precisely as possible. The student is, however, likely to fall into two very serious errors in the use of definitions. First, he is likely to take definitions too seriously and be satisfied with mere definitions; and second, he is likely to commit definitions to memory and be satisfied with mere words without regard to their real meaning.

A concise statement, such as a definition, can seldom make clear the full extent and the precise limitations of the meaning of a term. On that account the student should make his definitions as nearly perfect as possible and at the same time never be satisfied without knowing more than mere definitions.

It is the ideas involved, not the words, which are the essential things about a definition, and when a student learns the words by rote he is simply degrading his mind to the level of a mere automatic machine like the phonograph or the telephone receiver. Any tendency to do this may be avoided by trying, each time a given term is defined, to state the definition in different words.

Matter and Energy.—Matter is whatever has mass or occupies space. Energy is the capacity to do work. Different kinds of matter are called *materials*. Sandstone, oxygen, salt, cane sugar, and water are materials. We distinguish different materials from each other by the way they affect our senses, that is to say by their different *properties*. Thus we recognize as sugar a white, sweet-tasting material which dissolves when placed in water. Man has learned that he can, when he wishes to identify a substance, supplement his senses by other tests, which are often more conclusive than the direct evidence of the senses. Thus the chemist might make doubly sure that the sweet, white, soluble material was sugar by determining at what temperature it melts (melting-point) or how the substance in question behaves when treated with some other known substance (reagent).

Light, heat, mechanical energy, and electricity are different forms of energy. Any one form of energy may be transformed into any other, and such transformations are constantly going on within our own bodies and all around us, but these changes from one form to another are never attended by any loss or gain in the quantity of energy.

Transformation of One Form of Energy into Other Forms.—The statements in the preceding paragraph will be made somewhat clearer by means of illustrations taken from everyday life. The mechanical energy of a waterfall directed against a water wheel or turbine which rotates a dynamo is transformed into electrical energy. In our homes this electrical energy is transformed by the toaster or electric stove into heat energy, by the electric light bulb into light energy, and by the motor into mechanical energy again. The decomposition of water by an electric current into oxygen and hydrogen involves a transformation of electrical into chemical energy which may be said to be stored in the oxygen gas and the hydrogen gas. The hydrogen and oxygen if mixed and lighted will burn and the chemical energy will be transformed into heat energy and light energy. If the mixture of gases were ignited in the cylinders of an automobile, part of the resulting energy would be in the form of mechanical energy just as when gasoline vapor and oxygen explode in the operation of an automobile. Such transformations are of great importance, for the activities of plants and animals, including man, and all the operations of industry consist largely of such transformations.

Materials and Objects.—In considering matter it is important to distinguish clearly between a material (or substance) and an object (or body). An object is a certain quantity of material having a characteristic form. Thus a quantity of (the material) water, having a rounded (generally spherical) form, is a water drop and a water drop is an object. Similarly a round mass of air, visible of course only when surrounded by a liquid or a solid, is a bubble. Air is a material, a bubble is an object. The material (kind of matter) of which an object consists is generally secondary in importance to its form and dimensions. Thus, cups may be of iron, silver, wood, glass, or clay; and from a single material, iron, for instance, nails, rails, knives, hooks, beams, screws, and a great variety of other objects may be made.

States of Matter.—All the materials with which we are familiar are solids, liquids, or gases. By a solid we mean material in such a state that a continuous mass of it can not flow or be poured. A solid does not take on the form of any vessel in which it is placed. A liquid, on the other hand, can be poured and always accommodates itself, in as far as it fills it, to the form of any empty vessel in which it is placed. A gas is invisible unless it has a characteristic color. Furthermore, it not only takes on the shape of any empty vessel (one containing not even gas) in which it is placed but will expand to fill the vessel completely no matter how little the quantity of the gas. Solid, liquid, and gas are not different materials but merely different states, for the same material may exist in the three different states as in the case of ice, water, and water vapor. The three states are characteristic of the material at low, intermediate, and high temperatures. Thus butter at the temperature of a warm summer day becomes a liquid, kerosene heated to a high temperature becomes a gas, and oxygen reduced to a very low temperature becomes first a liquid and then a solid. A very remarkable fact having to do with the change from one state to another, is that a considerable quantity of heat energy is liberated when a gas becomes a liquid or a liquid changes to a solid. When the transformations are in the opposite order corresponding quantities of heat energy are absorbed.

Density.—Every object has a certain weight. Its weight is an expression of the degree to which it is attracted by the earth (attraction of gravity). We determine its weight by comparing its attraction by the earth with the earth's attraction for one or more standard objects (one or more of a set of weights) arbitrarily chosen. Weight is a property not of particular **kinds** of matter, but of **a given object** or a certain volume of any particular kind of matter. We do not say that iron weighs 8 grams and gold 19 grams. That is meaningless. We say rather that a cube of iron 1 centimeter on each edge weighs about 8 grams or that a cubic centimeter of gold weighs about 19 grams.

The weight in grams of a unit volume (1 cubic centimeter) of different materials is its density. It is this differing weight of equal volumes of different materials which we have in mind when we say that lead is a heavy metal and aluminum a light metal, or that cork is lighter than water. We should say that, of the two metals, lead and aluminum, lead has a density of 11.3, which is greater than the density of aluminum, 2.7; or that the density of cork is less than 1 (the density of water). We have then only to weigh a cubic centimeter of a solid or liquid material to determine its density. Since given weights of matter almost always occupy a greater volume at higher temperatures than at lower temperatures, that is to say expand and contract as the temperature rises and falls, the density of a material varies with temperature. In the following table of some common substances the densities, except where otherwise specified, were determined at 18° C.

Aluminum	2.7	Lead	11.2
Cane sugar	1.59	Platinum	21.4
Common salt	2.16	Glycerine	1.26
Cork	0.2	Petroleum	0.8
Gold	19.2	Quicksilver	13.55
Iron	7.8	Water	0.998

(at 4° the density of water is 1; at a lower temperature or at a higher temperature it is less than 1.)

Gases also differ in density. Hydrogen has a lower density than any other gas.

Elements and Compounds and Mixtures.—In the case of most materials, such as water, salt, cane sugar, etc., it is possible to decompose the substance into two or more different simpler substances. For instance, by the passage of an electric current through it, water may be decomposed into the two gases, oxygen and hydrogen. It is not possible by ordinary chemical reactions to break down oxygen and hydrogen into simpler substances.[1] Similarly cane sugar can be decomposed or broken up into oxygen, hydrogen, and carbon, but carbon also has resisted all attempts to break it down into simpler component substances.

Although chemists have analyzed thousands of different kinds of materials, they have found only about ninety of these simple elementary substances or elements. A few of the best known or most widely distributed of the elements are oxygen, nitrogen, hydrogen, carbon, sulphur, phosphorus, potassium, sodium, chlorine, calcium, magnesium, iron, aluminum, gold, silver, tin, platinum, and copper. Any of the elements can exist in a pure condition, uncombined with other elements.

All materials except such pure elements are either *compounds* or *mixtures* of two or more compounds or elements. A compound always consists of two or more elements united in certain definite and constant proportions. Such materials as

[1] There are, however, several elements (the radioactive ones) which break down spontaneously into other elements. Thus radium yields helium and lead. There is in the case of most of the elements no evidence of any spontaneous disintegration into other elements. Recently methods have, however, been devised, much more violent than ordinary chemical reactions, by which certain elements have been artificially disintegrated and synthesized.

water, cane sugar, and common salt are examples of compounds. Water, as we
have already learned, is composed of the elements hydrogen and oxygen. When
any quantity of water is decomposed the proportions of the two elements are always
the same, two parts by weight of hydrogen to sixteen of oxygen. Similarly common salt is composed of sodium and chlorine in the proportions by weight of 23 to
35.5. It is this unvarying proportion between the quantities of the different elements which distinguishes a compound from a mixture, for in the latter case the
ingredients may exist in all conceivable proportions.

Atoms and Molecules.—If it were possible to divide a piece of some compound
into smaller and smaller pieces, we would find sooner or later that we had particles
so fine that further division was impossible without separating them into simpler
compounds or into the component elements. Such particles, the smallest particles
of any particular compound, are called molecules.

All the molecules of a given pure compound are alike and so have the same weight.
If we attempted to divide a molecule of water we would get oxygen and hydrogen
instead of water. Molecules of a compound are composed of one or more units of
each element present. These unit particles of any element are all of the same weight
or very nearly the same weight.

The following statements will serve to illustrate the relation of the terms just
explained. A piece of cane sugar consists of a great many sugar molecules all of
the same weight. Each such molecule is made up of twelve carbon atoms, twenty-
two hydrogen atoms and eleven oxygen atoms. A single atom of carbon weighs
almost exactly twelve times as much as a hydrogen atom.

Several atoms of a single element can combine to
form a molecule of that element. Thus oxygen gas
under ordinary conditions is made up of oxygen
molecules, each consisting of two oxygen atoms and
similarly the molecules of hydrogen consist of two
atoms each.

Pure Substances.—A material made up of only
one kind of molecules or of only one kind of atoms
is called a *pure substance*. If only one kind of atom
is present in a pure substance the substance is an
element. If more than one kind of atom is present
it is a compound.

Classification of Plants.—There exist
today upon the earth over a quarter of
a million different kinds of plants. A great
many kinds which flourished in the past
are now extinct. Among the many kinds
now existing there are clearly certain ones,
such as the different kinds of oak, which
resemble each other more closely than they
do any other kinds of plants. From very

Fig. 1.—Theophrastus, the
Father of Botany, born in
Asia Minor (Lesbos) 370
B.C., died in Greece 285 B.C.
(From Wittrock's *Cata-
logus Illustratus Iconothecae
Botanicae*.)

early times, certain of these clearly marked groups of plants have been
recognized and men have tried to classify such small groups of plants
and animals in various ways.

The first serious attempt at the classification of plants of which we have record was made by Theophrastus, a Greek philosopher and pioneer in the field of science. He lived between 370 and 285 B.C. and was a student of both Plato and Aristotle. In his principal botanical work, *The Enquiry into Plants*, Theophrastus shows such a keen perception of the essential differences between different kinds of plants, and such a genius for their classification, that he has been very properly called the first systematic botanist. His works include descriptions not only of the plants of Greece and adjoining countries but also of plants found only in countries much farther east.

His knowledge of these plants he owed largely to Alexander the Great, who took with him, on his expeditions into the East, trained men who could make accurate observations of the plants they saw.

[1] No very important advance over the work of Theophrastus was accomplished by other classical botanists or by those of the Middle Ages, although Dioscorides about A.D. 80 described some four hundred medicinal plants in his *Materia Medica*, which was in general use even up to the seventeenth century. From about 1600 to the middle of the last century, great

FIG. 2.—Linnæus (Carl von Linné) (1707–1778), the Founder of Modern Taxonomy.

advance was made in the field of plant classification, the most important representative of the period being the Swedish botanist, Linnæus. Since his time there have been put forward several systems of classification, each representing a distinct advance over the preceding. The most important of these were the classifications of Bernard and Antoine Laurent de Jussieu, that of A. P. de Candolle and his fellow-workers, embodied in the *Prodromus Systematis Regni Vegetabilis*, that of Bentham and Hooker, published in their *Genera Plantarum*, and the system put forward by Engler and Prantl in their *Natürlichen Pflanzenfamilien* (The Natural Plant Families). Limitation of space prevents even the

[1] Some of the material of this and the previous paragraph is drawn from Jepson's *Economic Plants of California*.

mention of many men who made outstanding contributions to this field.

All systems of classification of plants are either **artificial** or **natural classifications,** or a combination of both. An artificial classification is one in which there is no recognition of any actual relationship between different kinds of plants, in the sense of common descent. An artificial classification may be based upon such superficial characteristics as flower color or leaf form, although plants with the same flower color or leaf form may be much less closely related to each other than they are to certain plants having very different colored flowers, leaves of entirely different form, or both. All the earlier classifications were very largely artificial, for those who made them believed that each kind of plant or animal had been specially and separately created (the **theory of special creation**) and that once created, no kind of organism could ever give rise to any other kind (the **theory of constancy of species**).

As long as those beliefs were held it was inconceivable that there could be any relationship, in the sense of common descent, between different species, no matter how many points of resemblance there might be between them. With the acceptance of the doctrine of evolution, botanists came to look upon all plants as being related and attempted to classify them so that each group included kinds of plants more closely related to each other than to any other kinds (closely related plants being plants having a great part of their ancestry in common). Such a classification is called a natural classification.

Because of the incompleteness of our knowledge of the relationships of plants and for other reasons, it is not possible for us to classify plants so as to show all their relationships. Accordingly, our present-day classifications are partly artificial and partly natural. The principal goal of the systematic botanist is, however, to work out a classification of plants which will correspond as closely as possible with their actual evolution.

Plant Characters Used as a Basis of Classification.—In all higher plants there are reproductive organs, such as flowers and fruits, and vegetative organs, such as roots, stems, and leaves. Reproductive organs are less influenced by environmental conditions than are vegetative organs. There may be little resemblance between the vegetative portions of two species, although their reproductive structures may be very similar. For example, the strawberry and the raspberry, although closely related, have quite different growth forms, that is, their vegetative organs are quite dissimilar. However, the flowers of the two are constructed on the same general plan. On the other hand, two plants with very dissimilar reproductive structures may resemble each other very closely in their general vegetative appearance, especially when they grow under the same external conditions.

A very striking example of close resemblance of the vegetative organs of plants which have very dissimilar reproductive organs (flowers and fruits) is furnished by the cactus family and certain species of the spurge and milkweed families. Most of the cacti, all of which are native to America, have peculiar, leafless, fleshy stems covered with sharp spines or bristles. Certain African species of the milkweed family and several species of the spurge family, although these families are certainly not closely related to the cacti, are so similar to cactus plants that only those very familiar with such plants could distinguish them from certain members of the cactus family.

Although vegetative structures may be modified to a great degree under diverse environmental influences, these same influences do not

Fig. 3.—Three different types of xerophytic plants, showing the close resemblance of the vegetative organs of these plants which belong to different plant families and thus have dissimilar reproductive organs. *A, Trichocereus bridgesii* (Cactus Family), native to America; *B, Euphorbia fimbriata* (Spurge Family), native to Africa; *C, Trichocaulon flavum* (Milkweed Family), native to Africa.

modify, to an equal extent, the reproductive organs. On account of this greater stability of the reproductive structures, they are of relatively greater value than the vegetative structures in showing actual relationships, and are of prime importance in classification.

The Groups Making up the Plant Kingdom.—There is on the earth an immense number of individual plants. A careful examination of any two plants will show that, even though they may be very much alike, there are individual differences between them. Every one of these individuals is the offspring of one or, in most plants, of two parents. Every individual is a point in one of the many long lines of descent leading back into remote time. If we could trace these lines back we would find that at each generation they merged with other lines, just as we find in tracing the genealogies of human individuals. According to the theory of evolution, if we could follow these lines of descent back far enough we would find that all the individuals had descended from one or a few very simple organisms. This means that perhaps all plant individuals are related or at least that within each of a few great groups of plants all individuals past and present have descended from the same remote ancestors.

Species.—Everyone recognizes that among the myriads of individual plants about us there are different kinds such as the oaks, the roses, or the pines. If the oaks are studied with some care it is found that there are many recognizable kinds of oaks, and so it is with the roses, the pines, and other plants. Now it has been generally agreed to speak of each recognizable kind as a **species** (plural also **species**). Each species consists of a group of individuals which are very much alike. Most of the differences between the individuals of a species are due to the effect of external conditions. Any two individuals of a species are assumed to be more closely related, that is, more recently descended from the same ancestor, than are two individuals of different species.

The differences between two closely related species are supposed to have originated through new characteristics which arose among the individual progeny of their common ancestors and which were inherited.

Genera and Larger Groups.—Species which are similar in many respects and which are presumably more closely related to each other than to other species constitute a **genus** (plural, **genera**). For example, all the species of oats belong to a single genus, *Avena*; all the species of wheat to a single genus, *Triticum*. Closely related species are grouped into genera. Similarly closely related genera are grouped into larger groups and these into still larger groups as shown in the following arrangement.

Species are composed of individual plants.
Genera are composed of species.
Families are collections of genera.
Orders are collections of families.
Classes are collections of orders.
Divisions are collections of classes.
Subkingdoms are composed of divisions.
The Plant Kingdom has two subkingdoms.

It is important to bear in mind that individual organisms, plants and animals, are the only things in the plant or animal kingdom which actually exist. A species is merely a mental conception of a group of individuals sufficiently alike and closely enough related to be considered as one kind. A genus is a conception of a group of similar and related species, etc. Such groupings of plants or animals are nevertheless of great practical and theoretical importance in botany and zoology.

The classification of the Plant Kingdom which we shall use in this book includes the following groups:

SUBKINGDOM I.

THALLOPHYTA	Includes a great variety of simple plants such as the pond scums, bacteria, molds, and mushrooms and some larger and more complex plants such as the seaweeds.
Division 1. **Algae**	Thallophyta which possess chlorophyll.
Division 2. **Fungi**	Thallophyta which do not possess chlorophyll.

SUBKINGDOM II.

EMBRYOPHYTA

Division 1.	**Bryophyta**	Mosses and related plants.
Division 2.	**Pteridophyta**	Ferns and related plants.
Division 3.	**Spermatophyta**	Seed-bearing plants.

The method of classifying plants is illustrated below by the complete classification of a cinnamon rose and of wheat.

Division	Spermatophyta	Spermatophyta
Class	Angiospermae	Angiospermae
Subclass	Dicotyledonae	Monocotyledonae
Order	Rosales	Graminales
Family	Rosaceae	Gramineae
Genus	Rosa	Triticum
Species	cinnamonea	aestivum

Cinnamon Rose (*Rosa cinnamonea*)   Common Wheat (*Triticum aestivum*)

Naming of Plants.—The name of the genus to which a plant belongs taken together with the name of the species of the plant are spoken of as a **binomial**. This combination of generic and specific names is used as the scientific name of the kind of plant in question. The generic name has the form of a Latin noun; the species name is an adjective. This method of naming plants or animals is called "**binomial nomenclature.**" Systematic botanists and zoologists do not consider a scientific name complete unless there is placed after the binomial an abbreviation

óf the authority for the binomial, that is to say the name of the man
who named the plant or animal. Among the first to employ binomial
nomenclature was the great Swedish naturalist, Linnæus, throug

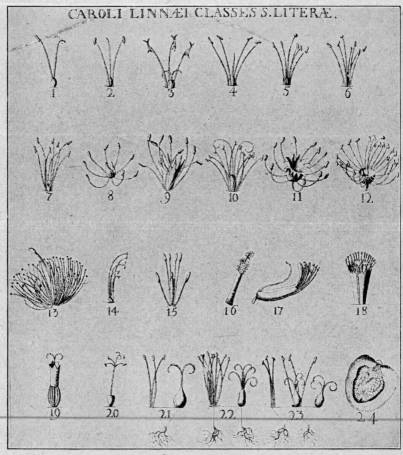

Fɪɢ. 4.—Portion of a page from Linnæus' *Systema Naturae* published in 1737, with
his diagrams illustrating the 24 classes into which he divided the Plant Kingdom.
These classes were based principally upon the number of and variations in the
stamens. The classes were divided into orders based mostly on the number and
variations in the pistils. Thus Class V, "Pentandria" included all plants having
5 stamens free and of equal length in the flower. The first order of this class was
"Monogynia" characterized by the presence of a single pistil. Compare Fig. 5.

whom it came into general use among botanists and zoologists. He
was born in 1707 and was the son of a village pastor. In spite of great
poverty and other obstacles he persisted in his efforts to secure a medical
degree and to acquaint himself with natural history. He became a

practicing physician in Stockholm but devoted his time largely to botanical studies, the results of which soon made him famous throughout Europe. In 1741 Linnæus became professor of natural history at the University of Upsala, where he had the most favorable opportunities to continue his systematic studies of plants, animals, and minerals. He was an excellent teacher and attracted many students to Upsala.

(From 1st Edition *Flora Suecica* 1745)

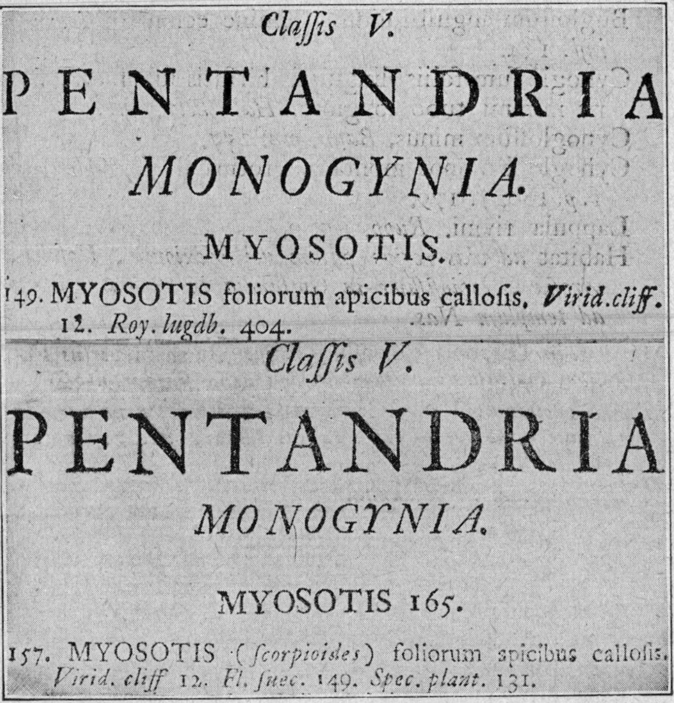

Claſſis V.

PENTANDRIA

MONOGYNIA.

MYOSOTIS.

149. MYOSOTIS foliorum apicibus calloſis, *Virid.cliff*.
12. *Roy. lugdb.* 404.

Claſſis V.

PENTANDRIA

MONOGYNIA.

MYOSOTIS 165.

157. MYOSOTIS (*ſcorpioides*) foliorum apicibus calloſis.
Virid. cliff 12. *Fl. ſuec.* 149. *Spec. plant.* 131.

(From 2nd Edition *Flora Suecica* 1755)

FIG. 5.—Photographs of parts of two pages, one from the 1st and one (below) from the 2nd Edition of Linnæus' "Flora Suecica" (Flora of Sweden), giving the name and brief description of a species of forget-me-not (*Myosotis*). In the upper part of the figure, from the older edition, the species (particular kind of forget-me-not) is designated by a description (3 words—foliorum apicibus callosis) whereas in the later edition a single word (scorpioides) italicised and in parentheses, designates the species. In the interim between the dates of publication of the two editions the practise of "binomial nomenclature" (naming organisms by using two names, a genus name and a species name) had become definitely established in Linnæus' mind.

Linnæus named a great number of our now commonly known plants and animals, as well as many rarer ones, and accordingly we find the initial letter of his name attached to many scientific names. Among these Linnean species of plants are *Beta vulgaris* L. (common beet),

Brassica rapa L. (turnip), *Pyrus malus* L. (apple), *Pyrus communis* L. (pear), *Pisum sativum* L. (garden pea), *Trifolium pratense* L. (red clover), *Medicago sativa* L. (alfalfa), *Daucus carota* L. (carrot), *Solanum tuberosum* L. (potato), *Avena sativa* L. (cultivated oat), and there are hundreds of others.

Origin and Meaning of Scientific Names of Plants.—The specific name is often descriptive of some feature of the plant which was thought by the person who originally described and named it to be characteristic. Examples of such descriptive specific names are *sativus*, meaning sown or cultivated; *communis* and *vulgaris* meaning common; and *alba* and *nigra*, meaning respectively, white and black. The last two specific names are very frequently used. For example, in the genus *Brassica* both of these specific names are employed, *Brassica alba* being white mustard and *Brassica nigra* being black mustard. Not infrequently a specific name is formed from the name of the person who first collected the plant in question or of some person whom the botanist naming the plant wished to honor. For example, a western sand cherry is named *Prunus besseyi*, the specific name being formed from that of the botanist, Bessey. Generic names are often merely the words by which the plants in question were known to those who spoke the Latin language. Examples of such names are *Avena* (oat), *Pinus* (pine), *Quercus* (oak), *Phaseolus* (certain kinds of beans), *Pisum* (pea), and *Ficus* (fig). In other cases the names of genera are descriptive, as in *Trifolium* (*tres*, three, and *folium*, leaf), the name of certain clovers whose leaves are three parted; and *Saccharomyces* (*Saccharon*, sugar, and *Myces*, fungus) a generic name used for the common yeasts which are fungi (Thallophyta which are unable to make their own food) living largely upon sugars. Genera are also sometimes named after persons, for example, *Eschscholtzia* (California poppy) named after the naturalist, Eschscholtz.

The names of plant families are usually based upon some outstanding characteristic of most of the genera of the family, as in the case of the *Leguminosae* which bear their seeds in a legume or pod; or upon the name of one of the principal genera of the family, as in the case of *Solanaceae* which are named after the genus *Solanum*.

Use of Common Names and Scientific Names.—Though it is often convenient to use the common names of plants instead of the scientific names, there are many reasons for employing the latter whenever we wish to avoid all uncertainty as to the particular plant to which we refer. Many common names are strictly local in their use and in other regions are either not used at all or are applied to some other plant. Several distinctly different plant species, which may or may not be related, are often included together under one common name.

The settlers in the North Coast ranges of California apply the name Post Oak to *Quercus garryana*; the ranchmen in certain parts of the Sierra foothills ascribe the name Post Oak to *Quercus Douglasi*; and in the eastern states the same common name is given to an entirely different species, *Quercus stellata*. In other cases, a great number of common names are used for a single species. For example, *Pinus ponderosa* is given such common names as "Bull Pine," "Black Pine," "Yellow Pine," and many others. It is scarcely to be expected that a Russian, French, or Japanese common name will be accepted and generally used by persons who speak mother tongues other than these. It is therefore best to employ for scientific purposes the universally accepted binomials which, being in the Latin form, belong to a language not spoken by any living people but probably more familiar to educated people in general than any living language. The use of **one** scientific name does away with much misunderstanding as to what the plant is to which reference is made.

CHAPTER II

THE PLANT BODY

The Individual Plant.—The Plant Kingdom is made up of a great number and variety of individual plants. Each individual plant—whether it be a single wheat plant among millions in a field, or a single bacterium among countless others in the soil, or a single tree among its many neighbors in a forest—is a distinct and individual organism which is able to carry on all the life processes necessary to maintain its life and perpetuate the species. It has a parent or parents, and a long line of ancestors behind it.

Each individual plant must carry on the different processes which are necessary to maintain its life; at times it must undergo unfavorable environmental conditions such as extremes of temperature and water shortage; it must compete with its neighbor plants for space in which to grow, and for light and water; it must often be subjected to the attacks of insects or other parasites; and finally, it must produce offspring.

The activities of the individual plant are two-fold: **vegetative activities** and **reproductive activities.** The vegetative activities are **those which have to do with the growth and preservation of the individual.** Important vegetative activities are the (1) **absorption** of raw materials from the soil and air, (2) **transfer** of the raw materials in the plant, (3) **food manufacture,** (4) **assimilation** (the process by which foods are transformed into living material—protoplasm) (5) **respiration** (a "breaking down" of substances in the cell, which provides energy for the work of the plant and in which oxygen is taken in and carbon dioxide given off), and (6) **transpiration** (escape of water—as water vapor). Reproductive activities are **those which have to do with the continuation of the species of plants to which the individual belongs.** These activities include the production of many new individuals of the species which will survive the parent plants and thus tend not only to insure the survival of the species but also to increase its numbers and spread the species over wider areas of the earth's surface.

Organs and Tissues.—We speak of the human body as being made up of a number of organs, each performing a function necessary to the whole organism. There are organs of sight, of hearing, of digestion, etc. Just so, we may speak of the **plant body.** It, too, is composed of various organs, with which it carries on its different activities. An **organ** is a part or member of the plant with a particular kind of work to do. For example, the roots are absorbing and anchoring organs, the stems are conducting and supporting organs, the leaves are food-making and transpiring organs, and the flowers are groups of reproductive organs. If we study microscopically the structure of any of these organs, we find that they are made up of many small chambers with walls which are usually thin. Each of these small chambers or compartments is called a **cell.** Just as a brick house is made up of separate units, the bricks, so is the plant body made up of separate units, the cells. **It is in the cells that the complex physical and chemical changes of the living body go on.** Cells of similar structure which together perform a special function constitute a **tissue.** Thus the leaf is composed of several different kinds of tissues such as conductive tissue, protective tissue, and food-making tissue.

Some plants have plant bodies each consisting of a single cell; and others, though they consist of many cells, have but few distinct organs, or a few tissues, with which to carry on the different functions. Such plants, most of which belong to the Thallophyta, are said to be simply organized and include the bacteria, the pond scums, seaweeds, molds, mildews, rusts, smuts, etc.

Many plants have numerous distinct organs, and many tissues which carry on the separate functions. This is true of the commoner plants of orchard, garden, field, and forest. Such plants are said to be highly organized.

Different Kinds of Plant Bodies.—In the simplest plants the plant body consists of a single cell within which all the life activities are carried on. Examples of such one-celled organisms are bacteria (Figs. 291–293); *Protococcus* (Fig. 262) which constitutes the green growth commonly found (in the northern hemisphere) on the north side of tree trunks, fence posts, and walls; and *Spharella nivalis* ("red snow"). The plant body of such organisms is surrounded, at least during part of the life of the plant, on all sides by water and a supply of materials from which food can be absorbed or built up.

A plant body in which cells are joined end to end to form a thread or filament represents an advance in complexity over the unicellular forms. There are numerous filamentous or thread-like algae, such as *Spirogyra* (Fig. 265) (one of the pond scums), and *Oedogonium* (Fig. 274); and also many filamentous fungi (Fig. 310), such as certain molds, mildews, rusts, and smuts. In *Oedogonium*, a basal cell of the filament may become differentiated as a holdfast cell (Fig. 271); and certain other special cells of the filament may take on, in addition to nutritive functions, the reproductive function, whereas the majority of the cells have only nutritive functions. Here there is a slight degree of specialization among the cells of the plant body.

In some of the seaweeds (*Ulva*, or sea lettuce) the plant body is flattened. It consists of a plate of cells, two cells or more in thickness. In other more complex seaweeds (Fig. 282) and in such fungi as mushrooms (Fig. 349), there is a rather complex and extensive plant body. The molds, mildews, rusts, smuts, and fleshy fungi, such as the mushrooms, have various forms of plant bodies, but in none of them, nor in any of the algae, are there true stems and leaves.

The Plant Body of Seed Plants.—In the plant body of seed plants (Spermatophyta), which include almost all our common cultivated plants (Fig. 6), the stems, foliage leaves, and roots are chiefly concerned with maintaining the life of the individual; that is, they carry on the vegetative functions (such as absorption of materials from the soil, manufacture of foods, respiration, transpiration, and assimilation), whereas the flowers (which produce seeds) carry on the reproductive activities, and thus assure the continuance of the race.

The plant body of the seed plant is composed of **shoot** and **root.** The shoot, which is made up of two kinds of organs, stems and leaves, generally grows upward into the air, whereas the root grows downward into the soil. But there are plants, such as the common potato and many others, which have in addition to stems above the ground (aerial stems) other stems which grow beneath the ground (subterranean stems); and there are still other plants, such as the banyan and the woodbine, which have aerial roots as well as subterranean ones. The stem is divided into nodes and internodes, regions which alternate throughout the length of the stem. **Nodes** are slightly enlarged portions of the stem where leaves and buds arise, and where branches originate. An **internode** is the region between two successive nodes.

Principal Distinctions between Stem and Root.—The stems and roots are both cylindrical structures which, in some cases, are distinguished only with difficulty. The following are the principal differences between stems and roots:

1. Normally, branch stems arise only at nodes, and in the axils of leaves, whereas roots branch irregularly, there being no division of roots into nodes and internodes.

2. The internal structure of the stem differs (as we shall learn in Chapters IV and V) from that of the root.

3. Normally stem branches originate at the surface of a main stem

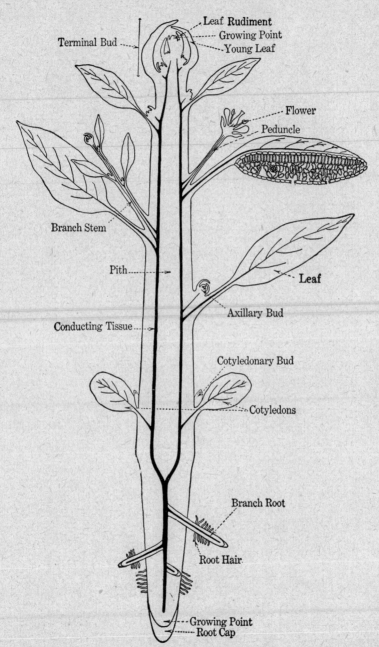

FIG. 6.—Diagram showing the principal organs and tissues of a typical seed plant. (Modified after Sachs.)

and near its extreme tip; branch roots arise, not at the surface, but within a larger root and at some distance from its tip.

4. The growing point at the extreme tip of the stem is covered and

Fig. 7.—Excurrent type of branching (pine).   (Photograph by Emanuel Fritz.)

protected by rudimentary foliage leaves and in some cases by modified leaves, the bud scales. The growing point of roots, however, is protected by a special thimble-shaped structure, the root cap.

Functions of Stem, Root, and Leaf.—The primary functions of the stem are (1) the **support** of foliage leaves and floral leaves (petals, sepals, and other flower parts); (2) the **conduction of water and mineral substances** from the soil; and (3) the **conduction of plant foods** from the points where they are manufactured to points where they are needed in growth, or where they are to be stored for future use.

In addition to these primary functions of stems there are certain secondary ones, such as **food manufacture, storage** of food or water, and **vegetative reproduction** which are sometimes performed by stems. The stems of most non-woody plants and the youngest stems of woody plants are green and share with the leaves the function of food manufacture (photosynthesis).

Some stems act as storage organs. For example, in the underground, enlarged stem (tuber) of potato (Fig. 105), a large amount of starch is stored; also, in the twigs of the common orchard trees considerable quantities of reserve food are stored in the form of starch and sugar. The cacti and various other plants of desert regions have thick fleshy stems within which water is stored.

In some plants the stems act as organs of vegetative reproduction (reproduction without the formation of flowers and seeds). For example, the underground stems (rootstocks or rhizomes) of such plants as Bermuda grass (*Cynodon dactylon*) (Fig. 104), bindweed (*Convolvulus arvensis*), and iris are capable of sending out aerial stems and roots from the nodes. When such underground stems are cut or broken into a number of pieces, each piece, if it includes one or more nodes, may send out new stems and new roots and thus produce a new plant. Likewise, some aerial stems have this power. The runners (creeping stems) of the strawberry (*Fragaria*, Fig. 109), the tubers of the potato (*Solanum tuberosum*), the bulbs (short stems with fleshy leaves) of onion (*Allium cepa*, Fig. 107), the corms of Crocus (fleshy stems, Fig. 108) of cyclamen are examples of stems which serve to reproduce these plants vegetatively and are used by farmers and gardeners to multiply such plants.

The primary functions of the root are (1) **anchorage** and (2) **absorption** of (*a*) water and (*b*) certain mineral (inorganic) salts. A secondary function is **food storage.** Common examples of roots which act as storage organs are those of sugar beet (*Beta vulgaris*), turnip (*Brassica rapa*), and sweet potato (*Ipomaea batatas*).

The primary functions of the leaf are the (1) **manufacture of carbohydrate foods** (photosynthesis), the (2) **synthesis of nitrogenous foods,** and (3) **transpiration** (escape of water in the form of water vapor).

Balance between Shoot and Root Systems.—In an earlier paragraph it was stated that the plant body consists of two main parts: (1) **shoot**, and (2) **root**. These two differ not only structurally, but also in the work they have to do. The shoot is chiefly concerned with the manufacture of food and the development of reproductive structures. The root is chiefly concerned with absorption and anchorage.

It is well recognized that, in transplanting plants and in pruning, a balance must be maintained between the root and the shoot. The root system must be extensive enough to supply the shoot with sufficient water and mineral nutrients. The shoot must be adequate to manufacture sufficient food for the maintenance of the root system. For example, when a young orchard tree is transplanted, many of the roots of the young plant are necessarily destroyed; consequently the absorbing surface is reduced. The approved practice is to cut back or thin out the shoot (remove branches here and there) and thus attempt to re-establish

Fig. 8.—Deliquescent type of branching (elm). (Photograph by Emanuel Fritz.)

the balance between the root system and shoot system. The reduced root system will be unable adequately to supply the tissues of the shoot with water and salts unless the shoot is also reduced. On the other hand, a too severely pruned shoot does not permit of normal growth and development, for the few green leaves which it will bear will be insufficient to supply food for the relatively large root system, which is itself incapable of making food. Either condition will retard the plant's development and, if extreme, may cause its death.

General External Features of the Shoot, Especially of Woody Plants. —Shoots may be **erect, prostrate,** or **climbing.** The shoots of most plants grow erect, but the shoots of such plants as the cucumber, squash, watermelon, and strawberry generally grow prostrate on the ground. Plants which climb upon other plants and thus depend upon them for mechanical support, that is, plants with climbing shoots, are known as **lianas.** Examples of lianas are the scarlet runner bean (*Phaseolus*), hop (*Humulus*), and grape (*Vitis*).

Erect shoots may be **excurrent** or **deliquescent.** Pines, spruces, and firs, and most other cone-bearing trees, have an elongated or cone-shaped shoot system. In these there is a single main stem with many lateral branches. Also, in the Carolina poplar there is a " leader "—one main stem which throughout the life of the plant holds this leadership. This type of stem is said to be **excurrent.** In the oak, cottonwood, apple, peach, and many other deciduous trees, the principal stem may stop growing and be replaced by upper lateral branches which then grow more or less erect so that it is impossible to pick out any one main stem. This type of shoot is called **deliquescent.**

Trees, Shrubs, and Herbs.—The classification of plants into trees, shrubs, and herbs is very commonly used, although there is no very sharp line of distinction among these three classes. Trees and shrubs include those plants whose stems are largely made up of wood and which remain strong and erect when they undergo great water shortage or in fact even after they are dead. By **trees** we mean tall woody plants having generally a single main stem or trunk, at least for some distance above the ground. **Shrubs,** on the other hand, are shorter woody plants more freely branched than trees and frequently having no single main stem, even at the base. In practice the principal distinction between shrubs and trees is one of size. Plants whose stems develop very little wood but are made up mostly of soft tissue, and which droop or collapse (wilt) when they die or are unable to secure sufficient water, are spoken of as **herbs.** The shoots of trees and shrubs generally persist for years whereas those of herbs (at least the parts above ground) generally die each year except in regions where there is no very cold or very dry season. Within a single plant family, or even within a single genus, there may be species which are herbs, others which are shrubs, and still others which are trees. For example, in the pea family (Leguminosae) there are many herbs such as peas, beans, and clovers; shrubs, such as Scotch broom (*Cytisus*), and bladder senna

(*Colutea*); and trees, such as honey locust (*Gleditsia*) and carob (*Cera-tonia*). Individuals of a single species may be trees or shrubs according to the conditions under which they have grown.

Buds.—In seed-bearing plants the shoot system is often extensive and elaborate, and its continued development provides a graphic illustration of the unlimited scheme of growth characteristic of higher plants. This open method of growth is made possible through the continuous formation and growth of numerous buds. In the seed-bearing plants (Spermatophyta) there is a bud, called the **terminal bud,** at the end of every stem. There are also buds, called **lateral buds,** which grow out from the sides of the stems. The lateral buds generally occur just above a leaf and in the angle (**leaf axil**) formed by the leaf stalk (**petiole**) and the stem. Such lateral buds are called **axillary buds.** In trees and

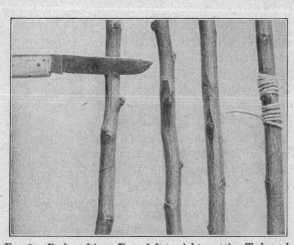

shrubs a relatively conspicuous axillary bud is generally to be found in the axil of every leaf, but in herbs these buds may be very small and often they are so completely buried in the tissue of the stem that they seem to be lacking entirely. Lateral buds which arise anywhere on the

FIG. 9.—Bud-grafting. From left to right: cutting T-shaped cleft in the bark of the stock, bud partly inserted in the cleft; bud inserted and ready to be bound; bud bound tightly, bringing cambium of bud into contact with that of the stock. (Photograph furnished by the Division of Pomology, College of Agriculture, University of California.)

plant, except in the axils of leaves, are called **adventitious buds.** They may arise on stems or roots, or even leaves. Their formation is usually stimulated by injury. For example, when a branch is cut back, as in pruning, numerous adventitious buds may arise at the edges of the cut surface.

Most buds, when they develop or " grow out," produce leafy branch stems. Such buds are called **leaf buds.**

Although the occurrence of buds and the fact that they may grow into leaves and branches are familiar to all, most people do not realize that leaf buds have a rather complex internal structure. **A leaf bud** is a leafy branch in miniature, consisting of a delicate growing point, several very short internodes, and, alternating with these, a number of nodes, each bearing one or more small rudimentary leaves.

That a bud is actually a partially developed shoot is clear when we cut it lengthwise and study its structure. (See Figs. 57 and 58.) It is also shown by the fact that branches always develop from buds. Buds may, in the case of many species of plants, be removed from the stems on which they originated and with certain precautions set into the stems of other plants where they will subsequently develop into branches. Such bud grafting is a common horticultural practice.

The delicate growing point (extreme tip of the stem within the bud) and the rudimentary leaves, especially in the case of most trees and shrubs of cold and arid climates, are usually protected by several layers of overlapping scales (**bud scales**) which are modified leaves (scale leaves, Fig. 10). Bud scales may be covered with hairs, as in the willow, or with a waxy secretion, as in the cottonwood. These coverings very effectively protect the enclosed tender structures from rapid drying out as well as from mechanical injury. Such series of structures intermediate between typical bud scales and typical leaves give strong support to the assumption that bud scales represent reduced and modified leaves. The buds of certain plants are not provided with protective scales. In these cases the outermost organs of the buds are foliage leaves. Buds of this sort, sometimes called naked buds, are common in woody plants of the moist tropics and in most herbaceous plants the world over.

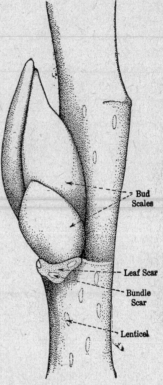

FIG. 10.—External view of a portion of a stem of cottonwood (a species of *Populus*) showing an axillary leaf bud, leaf scar and lenticels.

Although most of the buds on a plant are leaf buds, some buds contain not rudimentary nodes, internodes, and foliage leaves but the stem and the more or less fully developed floral leaves (sepals, petals, stamens, and carpels) which will form one or more flowers when the bud opens. Such buds are called **flower buds,** or by some **fruit buds,** inasmuch as flowers produce fruits. When a bud contains both rudimentary leaves and flowers it is called a **mixed bud.** When a bud of this type unfolds, there is produced a leafy shoot which either (*a*) terminates in a flower cluster, or (*b*) bears flowers or flower clusters in the leaf axils. Examples of the first-mentioned type of mixed bud are apple (Fig. 11), blackberry (*Rubus*), and grape (*Vitis*); whereas the second type is found in such plants as mulberry (*Morus*), fig (*Ficus*), oak (*Quercus*), and a number of others.

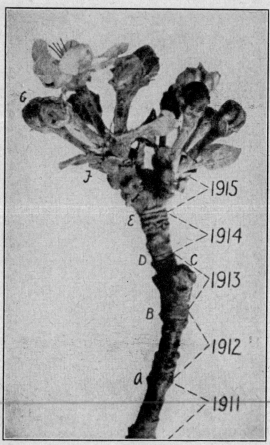

According as there are one, two, or three or more leaves at each node we speak of **alternate, opposite (decussate)** or **whorled** leaf arrangement. Axillary buds are also commonly classified as **alternate buds** (apple, plum, poplar, etc.), **opposite (decussate) buds** (horse chestnut, maple, elderberry, etc.), and **whorled buds** (catalpa, bedstraw, etc.). Obviously, plants with alternate leaves will have alternate bud arrangement; opposite-leaved plants, opposite buds, etc.

Fig. 11.—Fruit spur of apple. Two opened terminal buds are shown. These terminal buds are mixed buds. (After Robbins, from *Botany of Crop Plants.*)

Although generally there is but a single bud in the axil of each leaf, some plants have several buds in or near the leaf axil. Sometimes these are in a group of three which lie side by side. In other cases they lie one above another. All but the central one or the basal one are called **accessory buds.**

Although every axillary leaf bud or mixed bud is potentially a leafy branch and may develop into such a branch in the next growing season, not all these buds do actually develop into branches. Some of them may remain dormant or latent. All buds which do develop into new branch

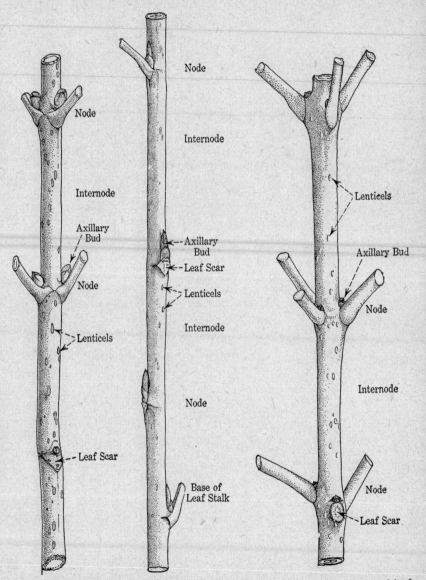

Fig. 12.—The twigs of three different plants showing three methods of bud and leaf arrangement. The base of each leaf stalk is shown. Left, ash (*Fraxinus*), opposite arrangement; middle, poplar (*Populus*), alternate arrangement; right, *Catalpa*, whorled arrangement.

stems or (in the case of terminal buds) into an elongation of an already
existing stem are, in contrast, active buds. The terminal bud of a
branch, in most trees and shrubs, is almost always the most active, and
grows more vigorously than any of the axillary buds. The latter generally decrease in vigor and activity the farther they are from the
terminal bud. Those buds which are several internodes distant (varying with the species and with the conditions) from the apex of the
stem, are dormant and normally do not develop at all into branches.
In most plants the removal of a terminal bud or of the upper end of a
branch stem increases the activity of the remaining axillary buds and
as a result some of the dormant buds may become active. This
" awakening " of dormant buds by the removal of the terminal part
of the stem is less complete the farther the buds are down the stem.
Thus it may be said that the degree of activity of active buds decreases
and the " depth " of dormancy of dormant buds increases the greater
the distance from the end of the branch.

Many buds which are apparently adventitious are often in reality
axillary buds which have remained dormant for so long that their
original position relative to a leaf, long since dead, is difficult to determine. It is such dormant buds buried in the bark of the oldest part of
the tree (near the base of the trunk) which sometimes become active and
grow out into leafy shoots and thus produce short branches from a part
of the tree where branches very rarely occur.

Bud Arrangement and Branching.—The branching system of the
shoot is largely determined by the arrangement of the buds. If the
bud arrangement is alternate, opposite branching can not occur. Similarly whorled branching will not be found in plants with opposite or
alternate bud arrangement. It does not follow, however, that branches
will always occur two at a node in a plant with opposite buds, one at
every node in plants with alternate bud arrangement, etc.

Not all of the leaf buds on a stem develop. Many remain dormant
while others make a short growth and then die as the result of insufficient nutrition or of the attacks of insects or disease. There is competition among the different buds and young branches for light and
for food materials, and the less vigorous of the active buds and young
branches may fail to develop further. Moreover, not all the axillary
buds are leaf buds. One or more at a node may be fruit buds which
do not develop into permanent branches. For these reasons, branches
are much less numerous than axillary buds, and branching is much less
constant and regular than is bud arrangement.

It is a common and well-known practice of orchardists and gardeners
to change the form of plants while they are still young by pruning,

which is the judicious removal of buds or branches. The removal of terminal buds or terminal portions of branches will stimulate the development of axillary buds which would otherwise remain dormant or not grow so vigorously. There results a " spreading " of the plant, and the production of a broad tree with a " low head." A cylindrical or pyramid type of tree may also be secured, by removal of a certain number of lateral buds or branches. Thus, by the removal of buds and branches, a tree or shrub may be forced or " trained " to assume almost any desired form.

The Stems of Woody Deciduous Plants in their Winter Condition.—Most orchard trees, ornamental trees and shrubs, and forest trees, except pines, firs, spruces, and other gymnosperms, are **deciduous,** that is, they lose their leaves in the fall and remain bare of leaves for some months each year. Such plants in their leafless winter condition are particularly favorable for the study of branching, various types of buds and other features of the shoot. A several-year-old twig of such a plant is illustrated in Fig. 13. At the tip is the large terminal bud and at each node an axillary bud. If the brown bud scales are removed from the terminal bud, or certain lateral buds, young overlapping foliage leaves may be found within. In the spring, the short internodes within each active bud will elongate, thus

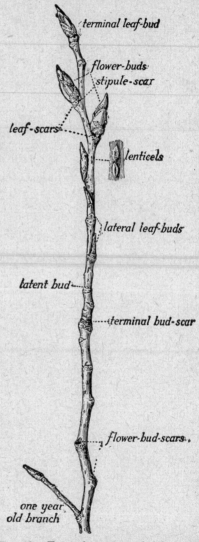

Fig. 13.—Twig of cottonwood (a species of *Populus*) showing two years' growth. (From Robbins' *Botany of Crop Plants,* after Longyear.)

bringing the rudimentary leaves out of the bud and adding to the length of the main twig or branch (if it is a terminal bud) or producing a new branch. Within some of the axillary buds partially developed flowers may be found.

Classification of Buds.—According to their position buds may be classified as terminal, axillary, and adventitious; according to organs developing from them, as leaf buds, flower buds, and mixed buds; according to the presence or absence of special protective structures, as scaly and non-scaly buds; and according to activity, as active and dormant.

Below each bud is a semicircular to elliptical **leaf scar.** This was left when the leaf, in the axil of which the bud was formed, became detached from the twig. The number of these scars at a node shows whether the leaves were alternate, opposite or whorled. If a hand lens is used, one may find within each leaf scar a number of slightly raised areas. These are the **bundle scars** left where the conducting strands passing out from the stem into the leaf stalk (petiole) were broken off when the leaf fell.

In such a twig the growth in length during each of the last few years can be easily determined, for a ring or **girdle** of **bud scale scars** marks the end of one year's growth and the beginning of the next. When the closely set bud scales of a terminal bud fall off in the spring they leave a number of scars so close together as to form a distinct ring. The spacing of these rings often reveals striking differences in the amount of growth produced each year, for there is practically no increase or decrease in the length of any portion of a stem after that portion is a year old.

On some twigs flower bud scars may also be found where the short branch which developed from a flower bud became detached from the stem after the fruit had matured.

Close examination of the twig surface where there are none of these various kinds of scars will reveal numerous lighter colored, slightly raised spots on the bark. These are **lenticels,** regions which permit the passage of gases inward and outward. Were it not for these lenticels the bark would very effectively prevent the passage of air and also the loss of water from underlying stem parts. The lenticels are particularly conspicuous even on old stems of the white birch and the cherry.

Different Kinds of Stems and Roots.—In some plants having roots, stems, and leaves, certain of these organs may be modified to such an extent as to be scarcely recognizable. For example, the tendril of the garden pea (*Pisum sativum*) is morphologically a leaf part; the Irish potato tuber, a modified stem; and the sweet potato, a modified root.

Some seed plants do not possess all of the usual parts of the plant body, namely, roots, stems, leaves, and flowers. For example, in the common water bladderwort (*Utricularia vulgaris*) the roots are lacking; in the floating *Wolffia*, both leaves and roots are absent; and in *Rafflesia arnoldii*, a tropical parasite, which has the largest flowers of any plant in the world, the plant is reduced to a flower and a mass of undifferentiated cells within the tissue of the host and accordingly may be said to be without roots, stems, or foliage leaves.

The Movements of Plants.—In the previous chapter where plants and animals were contrasted it was said that most plants are not capable of locomotion (movement from place to place), and that most animals are capable of locomotion. But, as was there remarked, many simple plants, more primitive than those with which we are more familiar, remain unattached throughout most of their lives, and can move freely in the water in which they live.

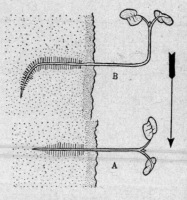

Fig. 15.—Geotropic curvature of a seedling of mustard (*Brassica*). *A*, just after being placed in the horizontal position. *B*, about 24 hours later. The positively geotropic root has bent downward, the negatively geotropic stem upward. (After Sachs.)

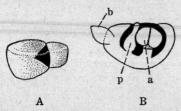

A   B

Fig. 14.—*Wolffia arrhiza*, a plant lacking both leaves and roots. *A*, plant with branch; *B*, flowering plant in longitudinal section. *a*, anther; *b*, branch; *p*, pistil. (Redrawn from Hegelmaier.)

All these motile plants belong to the Thallophyta. But some attached, non-motile plants of the Thallophyta, Bryophyta, Pteridophyta, and the Spermatophyta produce certain reproductive cells which can move about freely and rapidly. Moreover, almost all plants can move in the sense that their organs can elongate; thus the tip of the root moves downward into the soil as it grows, and the stem and leaves move upward into the air. They can also execute curvatures, as when a seedling plant (Fig. 15) placed in a horizontal position bends downward at the root end and upward at the stem end. Ordinarily we think of plants as motionless, but this is only because the movements of plants are slow. By means of the cinematograph camera it is possible to make exposures at intervals of 15 minutes or half an hour and later project them so rapidly that the development and movements of weeks are seen on the screen in a few minutes. Then it becomes apparent that all the parts of the plant above ground are actually in constant motion, so that branches, leaves, and flowers execute a veritable dance.

Some plant movements, such as the spiral upward movement of the tip of the stem as it grows, are due to **internal factors,** or as we might say " to the nature of the plant." Such movements are not due to any outside influences, as is clear from the fact that they go on just the same even though all the external factors (light, temperature, composition of the soil and atmosphere, etc.) which make up the plant's environ-

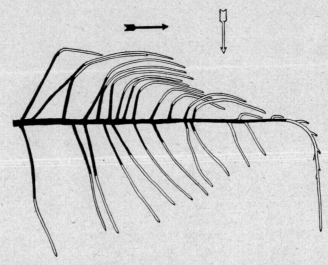

FIG. 16.—Diagram of the root system of the broad bean (*Vicia faba*) showing the orientation of the secondary roots as contrasted with the orientation of the primary root. Originally the whole primary root was growing parallel to the direction of gravity, shown by the solid black arrow. Then the root system was turned through 90° so that it was at right angles to the direction of gravity (outlined arrow). Growth of the root system before and after the change of position is indicated respectively by solid black and outline portions of the figure.

ment are kept constant or unchanged. Such movements are called **autonomic movements.**

Other movements, such as the outward curvature of the petals of a flower bud which opens when, after a period of darkness, light falls upon it, are caused by a change in external conditions, and will not take place at all if the external conditions are kept constant. Other examples of movements due to a change in the external conditions are the curvatures of the stem and root of a seedling plant which has been placed in a horizontal position so that the force of gravity acts upon it in a direction at right angles to what might be called its normal direction, which is " lengthwise " or parallel to the long axis of the root and stem. Such movements, due to a change in some external condition, are called **paratonic movements.** They are **sensitive reactions.**

Any change or difference in the external conditions (environment) of the plant which causes the plant or any of its organs to " do something " (**react**) is spoken of as an **external stimulus.** What the plant does in response to any stimulus is a **reaction.** Paratonic movements are reactions in response to an external stimulus. All such stimuli involve either differences (or changes) of a particular external condition (**factor**) (*a*) **in time** (i.e., differences **between " then and now "**), as when the darkness of night changes to the light of morning and the tulip bud opens, or differences (*b*) **in space** (i.e., differences **between " there and here "**), as when a shoot, lighted from one side only, bends toward the source of light.

All the curvatures or other movements of plants or plant organs in response to external stimuli (paratonic movements) fall naturally into one or the other of two groups. The first of these includes all these movements in which an external stimulus initiates the movement, but in which

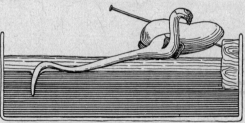

Fig. 17.—Diagram showing penetration of mercury by a downward curvature of the primary root of broad bean (*Vicia fava*). This shows that the geotropic curvature is not a mere passive bending of the root-tip under its own weight. (Redrawn from Sachs.)

the **direction** of the curvature or movement depends upon the kind of plant or organ and not upon the direction of the stimulus. For example, in the case of flowers which open only in the light, the petals of a bud lighted from one side only do not curve toward the source of illumination but bend outward (away from the center of the flower bud). The bud will open just the same in the same manner whether the light falls upon it from one side, from two sides, or from all sides. In short, direction of such movements is independent of the direction of the stimulus. Beside the example already cited many others could be given, such as the opening of the flowers of the night-blooming cereus, the evening primrose, or certain species of daturas, and the " going to sleep " (folding of the leaflets) of clover when with the coming of nightfall the light fails or the temperature becomes lower. (Fig. 18.) One might say that in these cases the external stimulus (change of illumination or of temperature) causes the organs to move but the plant itself (that is, **internal stimuli**) determines in what direction the movement will be. Such movements, the direction of which does not depend upon the direction of the external stimulus, are called **nastic movements.**

The other group of paratonic movements includes those in which the external stimulus not only causes the movement to take place, but also determines its direction. In such cases the stimulus—let us say light—must itself have a direction. If it acts in all directions equally there will be no movement. If it acts in one direction only or if it is much more intense in one direction than any other, the plant or organ will move until it reaches a certain, definite, and, to the experienced observer, predictable position relative to the stimulus. Thus when the stem of

Fig. 18.—Two series of photographs, from a cinematograph film showing the nastic movements of the leaflets of *Oxalis*. The upper row shows the leaf "going to sleep" between noon and 5:50 P.M. The lower row, the leaf unfolding between 2:20 A.M. and 10:40 A.M. (Photographs furnished by George Stone.)

a plant which has been equally illuminated on all sides is shaded so that light comes only from one side it tends to bend so that it points toward the source of light. Its leaves, on the other hand, will tend to place themselves at right angles to the light. The stimulus, light, not only causes the stem and leaves to bend, but also determines what position they shall have when the reaction has been completed and they have come to rest. Such movements are called **movements of orientation.** If the movement of orientation consists of a curvature, as when an organ bends toward or away from the light or toward or away from the center of the earth (downward or upward) this reaction is a **tropism.** If the reaction involves movement of the whole organism (locomotion), as when free-swimming unicellular algae, formerly in the dark and scattered uniformly through a glass of water, collect on the side farthest from the light, when they are lighted from one side, we speak of the movements as **tactic movements.**

Fig. 19.—Mustard (*Brassica alba*) seedling growing in water showing the positively phototropic curvature of the hypocotyl and the negatively phototropic curvature of the root. The arrows show the direction from which light is falling upon the plant. (After Noll.)

Fig. 20.—Diagram, illustrating the hydrotropism of roots. For explanation see text. (Redrawn from Sachs.)

To summarize: Plant movements may be classified thus:

I. Those due to internal factors—they persist under constant external conditions. (**Autonomic.**)
II. Those due to an external stimulus—do not occur at all under constant external conditions. (**Paratonic movements.**)
   1. Those in which the external stimulus does not determine the direction of the movement. (**Nastic movements.**)
   2. Those in which the external stimulus determines the direction of the movement. (**Movements of orientation.**)
      A. Movement is a curvature. (**Tropisms.**)
      B. Movement by locomotion. (**Tactic movements.**)

In the case of the various kinds of tropisms which occur in plants the actual bending of the organ is the result of more rapid elongation (growth) on the side of the stem, root, tendril, or other organ which becomes the convex side of the organ after it bends. A tropism is never

the mere passive curvature of an organ under its own weight, such as
occurs when a long piece of wire or a slender branch, whether dead or
alive, is placed in a horizontal position and held by one end only. In
the case of a tropism a "one-sided" external stimulus is responsible
for the occurrence as well as the direction of the curvature, but the plant
itself curves by reason of a different rate of growth on the two sides of

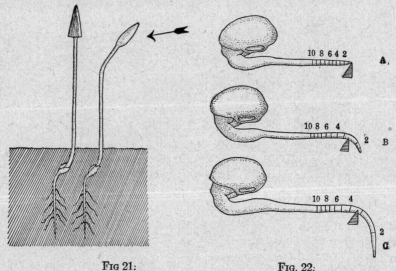

FIG 21:   FIG. 22:

FIG. 21.—Diagram showing that the region of light perception and that of reaction
to light stimulus in the seedling of millet (*Setaria*) are at some distance from each
other. In both seedlings the region of reaction is illuminated but in the case
of the seedling to the left the light sensitive tip is shaded by an opaque paper cap.
(Redrawn from Sachs.)

FIG. 22.—A seedling of white lupine (*Lupinus albus*) at the time it was placed in the
horizontal position (*A*), and after a shorter and longer period (*B* and *C*) in the
new position. The end of the root is marked off into zones beginning with the
extreme tip of the root and each originally one millimeter long. Note that the
region of curvature corresponds with the region of most rapid elongation and
that the sensitive region (included in the first two millimeters) does not elongate
much during the curvature. (Redrawn from Sachs.)

the organ. Accordingly, the curvature of roots generally takes place
near the tip; of stems, throughout the region of elongation.

The question now occurs: what causes a difference in the rate of
growth on the two sides of the organ? It has been demonstrated that
growth hormones play an important rôle in this phenomenon. A hormone is a substance which is produced in one part of the organism, is
moved to another part, and there is capable of influencing a specific
physiological process, even though the substance is present in very
minute quantities. In the case of stems, growth hormones must be
present in the growing regions in order that the enlargement of the cells

shall occur.   When the shoot, for example, is illuminated from one side, these growth hormones accumulate on the shaded side of the stem tip, move down the stem, and stimulate a greater elongation of the cells on the shaded side than of those on the illuminated side.   As a result the stem bends toward the light.   Or, as another example, if a shoot is placed horizontally, then growth hormones accumulate on the under side of the stem tip, thus stimulating a greater enlargement of the cells there than on the upper side, with the result that the stem tip bends upward.   Peculiarly, roots react differently from stems to these hor-- mones; they retard rather than accelerate the enlargement of root cells. For example, when a root tip is placed horizontally, as in Fig. 22A, the growth hormones accumulate on the lower side of the organ, thereby retarding rate of growth of the cells on that side, and as a result the root tip bends downward.

It is the practice of botanists to designate the different kinds of tropisms or tactic curvatures by using prefixes indicating the nature of the external stimulus.   Thus: **geo-** when the earth's attraction (gravity) is the stimulus, **photo-** when light is the stimulus concerned, etc.   We speak of the tropism as being **positive** when the curvature is toward the source of the stimulus, and **negative** when it is away from the source of the stimulus.   Thus the main root is positively geotropic and the main stem is negatively geotropic.   Some of the principal move- ments of orientation which may be observed in plants are:

Negative geotropism.   Examples: Main stems of most plants generally negatively geotropic.

Positive geotropism.   Examples: Main roots of most plants are positively geotropic.   (However, branch roots and stems, many leaves, and special underground stems called rhizomes grow at right angles or at an oblique angle to the direction of gravity.)

Positive phototropism.   Examples: Main stems of seedlings and older plants tend to bend toward the direction of most intense illumination; when the light comes principally from the side, their position is the resultant of negative geotropism and positive phototropism.

Negative phototropism.   Examples: The main root of mustard seedlings is nega- tively phototropic but most roots are not sensitive to light stimulus.   (Leaves and some branch stems tend to grow not toward or away from the principal source of illumination but at a characteristic angle to the light direction.)

Thermotropism.   Examples: Some roots and some other plant organs have been shown to bend and grow toward or away from a region of higher temperature.

Hydrotropism.   Examples: Roots (as shown in Fig. 20) can be shown to curve away from a region where the soil or air is relatively dry and toward a region which is relatively more moist.

Chemotropism.   Examples: Fungus filaments and the tubes which grow out from pollen grains when they germinate may have the direction of their growth determined by the presence of some chemical substance in higher concentra- tion in one part of the surrounding medium than in other parts.

Thigmotropism.   Examples: The tendrils of various climbing plants, such as the squash (*Cucurbita*), the wild cucumber (*Echinocystis*), and the grape

(*Vitis*), are stimulated by contact with solid objects of small diameter to bend so that the place of contact is on the concave side of the resulting curvature. The curvature continues, in most cases, until the object which caused the stimulation is encircled by the tendril and thus the vine secures attachment.

Importance of the Tropisms in the Life of the Plant.—Clearly the negative geotropism and positive phototropism of the stem are advantageous to the plant since they result in the stem growing upward and thus cause the leaves to be favorably placed for the performance of their functions. The more or less horizontal position of the leaves which results, in part at least, from their phototropic and geotropic reaction is also of obvious advantage to the plant. Similarly the positive geotropism and positive hydrotropism combine to direct the young root downward into the soil where its functions can best be carried out.

A further illustration of the advantage to plants of certain tropisms is furnished by the recovery of the normal position by grain which has "lodged" owing to heavy rains or high wind. Such lodged grain is at first prostrate on the ground, or semiprostrate. If the plants are not too old, geotropic curvature takes place at the joints, which retain their power of growth for a long time, and the upper parts of the plants are thus brought again into the normal, perpendicular position. In the case of wheat, oats, barley, and other grains, the stem is surrounded just above each node by a thick cushion of thin-walled tissue which is really part of a leaf base. As long as the stem remains perpendicular this tissue does not grow. However, when the stem is placed in a horizontal position or is much removed from the perpendicular, the tissue of the underside of this cushion is stimulated by gravity to renewed growth so that the stem is bent upward at that place and the upper side of the cushion somewhat compressed. If several such cushions react this way, the upper part of the shoot may be brought into the normal position.

Heredity and Environment.—The plant is a working, living machine with structures for carrying on its various life activities. It is well to keep in mind that the way the plant is constructed and the manner in which it does its work are determined by its inheritance on the one hand, and by the environment in which it lives on the other. The general shape and structure of an apple leaf, for example, is largely determined by inheritance; but slight variations in the shape and thickness of the leaves may be due to the influence of environmental factors, such as moisture and light.

Although the environment has a marked effect upon the structure and behavior of living things, the effect is always limited by the inherited tendencies of the organism. It appears that certain structures of the plant are more susceptible to environmental changes than others. For example, leaf structure seems to be more responsive to the light and conditions of atmospheric moisture than is flower structure. Hence, the plant comes into the world with certain inherited structures and certain physiological activities, and it is well that we know these and reckon with them. On the other hand, the plant is subject to some change—can be trained, so to speak—and such change may be brought about by modifying the conditions under which it lives. The problem of the farmer or others concerned with growing plants, then, is just this: to know the plants he is growing, their inherited structures and activities; to know the environmental factors operating upon the plants; and to seek to find out what environmental changes will give him the desired response on the part of the plant. The response may be expressed in boxes of fruit, in pounds of tubers, in number or size of the flowers, in flavor of fruit, or in percentage of protein in grain; but whatever the particular response on the part of the plant may be, it is one of the grower's chief prob

FIG. 23.—Plant of *Begonia* which grew where the most intense illumination fell upon it obliquely from the right. The leaves by phototropic reaction have placed themselves at right angles to the direction of the light.

lems to find out just what temperature, light, moisture, soil, and other conditions will give the desired response.

The plant, then, is a living thing, with various structures definitely organized into a plant body, and this body is living in an environment by which it is influenced in a great variety of ways.

The Life Cycle.—By life cycle in the plant is meant that series of changes through which it passes in the course of its development.

Every plant, like every animal, begins its life as a single cell. In the simplest plants like bacteria and certain blue-green algae, this single cell is the individual plant itself. It divides, resulting in two individual one-celled plants; these in turn grow and divide, and soon the progeny of the single one-celled plant reaches into the hundreds. The life cycle of such a plant is simple and brief. In such simple unicellular plants which reproduce by fission of one whole, old plant into two new and therefore young individuals, complete rejuvenation takes place with each division (fission). None of the protoplasm ever dies except, as we might say, by some such " accident " as mechanical injury or shortage of water, of raw materials for food manufacture, or of oxygen.

There are a few species of higher plants, like common chickweed (*Stellaria media*) and common groundsel (*Senecio vulgaris*), which complete their life cycle, from seed germination to flower and seed production, in so short a time that there may be several to many generations in a single year. Most of the higher seed-bearing plants do not, however, complete more than one life cycle in a year, and many species require two or more years for the completion of their life cycle. According to the length of the life of the individual, plants may be divided into **annuals, biennials,** and **perennials.**

An **annual** is a plant which completes its life cycle within one year's time and then dies. For example, in wheat, which is an annual, the seed germinates; the roots, leaves, and stems are produced; the plant reaches adult size within a few months; flowers appear and seeds develop. Each seed containing a rudimentary wheat plant, the embryo, is prepared to complete a new generation.

A **biennial** is a plant which completes its life cycle within two years and then dies. The beet plant is a biennial. When the beet seed germinates, the embryo plant resumes its growth and during the first season produces a number of large leaves crowning a fleshy root which we call the " beet." Flowers and seed are not produced the first year, as in annual plants. The plant during the first year is engaged chiefly in storing food in the root. In the fall the leaves die but the " beet " (root) remains alive. In temperate climates the beet must usually be dug and stored where it will not freeze during the cold season and the next season the " beet " is set in the ground, and it sends up a branched stem to a height of three or four feet which gives rise to flowering branches. Seed is finally produced, and soon afterward the plant dies. As in the case of the wheat plant, the beet plant has but one period of seed production, after which the whole plant dies, but the beet requires two vegetative seasons to complete its cycle, whereas the wheat plant requires but one.

There are a number of flowering plants including many biennials in which, at least for a part of the life cycle, the internodes remain very short, so that leaves form a cluster or **rosette** near the ground. This is the case in shepherd's purse (*Capsella*), certain evening primroses (*Oenothera*), *Centaurea*, and many other plants.

All plants which live more than two years are called **perennials.** All the familiar trees and shrubs are good examples of plants which live more than two years. Thus in the apple, after seed germination there is a succession of annual growth periods without production of flowers and seed. At an age of four or five years, depending upon the variety of apple and the environmental conditions, flowers and seeds are produced. Thereafter the vegetative activity of the plant continues year after year and both vegetative organs (new roots, branches, and leaves) and reproductive organs (flowers and seeds) are produced. Though in the apple flowering seldom occurs until the plants are three or four years old, there are many perennials which blossom the first season and yet live for many years bearing flowers each season. There are some species of perennial plants, such as *Agave* (Fig. 24), incorrectly called the century plant, which grow for from ten to twenty-five years before they flower. After flowering such plants generally die.

Fig. 24.—A plant of *Agave* in flower. (Photograph furnished by Mrs. Leslie Moore.)

Vegetative activity necessarily must precede reproductive activity. In all plants there is a period, of varying length, when the plant is accumulating food as if in preparation for reproduction. In annuals and biennials, the plant ordinarily dies after producing seed. In many perennials, like the birches and willows, flowers appear before leaves in the spring of the year. In this case, as in annuals and biennials, the flowers and seed are produced at the expense of food made by leaves and stored in some part of the plant. The food used by the birches, elms, and willows, for example, in their production of flowers and seeds early in the spring before leaves are formed, was made and stored up by the plant during the previous growing season.

So it is that, in perennial plants, periods of vegetation and reproduction alternate, although there are species such as have been cited above in which there are several periods of vegetative activity before the first flowering, and others where flowering occurs but once after many years of vegetative activity.

Certain environmental factors may considerably alter the duration of these periods. For example, favorable temperature and an abundance of water and of available nitrogen in the soil tend to prolong the vegetative period; and, on the other hand, unsuitable temperature conditions, a scarcity of water, and a deficiency of nitrogen in the soil tend to shorten the vegetative period and hasten the time of flowering and seed production.

CHAPTER III

THE CELL

If we cut a thin slice from a root, stem, leaf, or any other living plant structure and examine it under the microscope we find that it is made up of many small chambers separated from one another by walls which are generally thin and transparent. More careful study reveals that within each of these chambers there is a viscous, almost transparent, substance. This is **protoplasm,** the living material of the plant, and the mass of protoplasm in a single such cavity is called a **protoplast.** The protoplasts with their surrounding walls are called

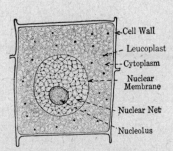

FIG. 25.—A cell from the tip of a root of onion (*Allium cepa*).

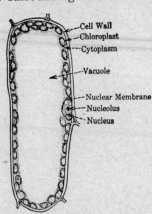

FIG. 26.—A cell from the palisade parenchyma of a leaf.

cells. Cells are in fact the units of structure and function in all organisms. They vary greatly in size but in relatively few cases is the longest diameter greater than 0.25 millimeter, or less than 0.025 millimeter. Plant cells also differ greatly in shape, in the thickness of their walls, and to a certain extent in the nature of the material of which the walls are made. The three principal parts of the cell will be discussed in the following order:

The Cell Wall.
The Protoplast.
The Inclusions.

But before proceeding to our account of these different parts which make up the cell we turn aside here to discuss certain physical and chemical facts and principles, acquaintance with which is essential to an understanding of the structure and particularly of the physiology of the cell.

In the preceding chapter there was inserted a brief discussion of the two kinds of pure substances, elements and compounds, and of the unit particles, atoms and molecules, of which pure substances are composed. It is necessary at this place to extend that discussion somewhat and to take up a number of other physical and chemical conceptions.

Essential Elements and Chemical Symbols.—The known elements are about ninety in all; twenty-seven of the most abundant are listed below in the order of their abundance in the earth's crust, including the atmosphere. The nine most abundant, oxygen, silicon, aluminum, iron, calcium, sodium, potassium, magnesium, and hydrogen, make up 98 per cent of the earth's crust. The remaining elements, about eighty, constitute approximately 2 per cent. The ten elements printed in italics in the list below are those which have long been recognized as essential to the normal development of seed-bearing plants. There is considerable evidence, however, that several other elements, for example, manganese and boron, are also essential. Opposite each element in the list is placed the corresponding symbol. These symbols are international in their use and each one is an abbreviation of the English or Latin name of the corresponding element.

Oxygen . . . . O	*Nitrogen* . . . . N	Gold . . . . Au
Silicon . . . . Si	*Sulphur* . . . . S	Iodine I
Aluminum . . . . Al	*Phosphorus* . . . . . . P	Lead . . . . Pb
Iron . . . . Fe	*Carbon* C	Manganese . . . . . . Mn
Calcium . . . . Ca	Argon . . . . A	Mercury . . . . Hg
Sodium . . . . Na	Barium . . . . Ba	Nickel . . . . Ni
Potassium . . . . . . K	Bromine . . . . Br	Platinum . . . . : Pt
Magnesium . . . . Mg	Chlorine Cl	Silver . . . . Ag
Hydrogen . . . . H	Copper . . . . Cu	Boron . . . . B

Chemical Formulae and Chemical Equations.—Instead of writing out the full name of a compound, its formula is often used. The formula of a compound consists of the symbols of the different elements of which it is made up placed one after the other. When more than one atom of any element is present in a single molecule of the compound the number of atoms of that element in the molecule is indicated by a figure placed just after the symbol of that element. Thus the formula for water is H_2O, which shows that a molecule of water consists of two atoms of hydrogen and one of oxygen. The formulae of several other common compounds are given below.

Carbon dioxide . . . . CO_2 Sodium bicarbonate. $NaHCO_3$
                                                (baking soda)

Sodium chloride . . . . $NaCl$ Cane sugar . . . . $C_{12}H_{22}O_{11}$
(common salt)

Sulphuric acid......... H_2SO_4	Acetic acid....... $C_2H_4O_2$
	(acid of vinegar)
Calcium nitrate......... $Ca(NO_3)_2$	Stearin........... $C_{57}H_{110}O_6$
	(a fat)
Potassium hydroxide.... KOH	Haemoglobin...... $C_{758}H_{1203}N_{195}S_3FeO_{218}$
(potash lye)	(a protein)

When one or more substances undergo a chemical change with the formation of different substances, the change is spoken of as a chemical reaction. It is convenient to represent such a reaction in the form of an equation, giving on the left-hand side the original substance or substances and on the right-hand side the product or products of the reaction. For instance, the reaction which takes place when the element sodium comes in contact with water may be written as follows:

$$2H_2O + 2Na = 2NaOH + H_2$$

which means that two molecules of water plus two atoms of sodium react with the formation of two molecules of sodium hydroxide (soda lye) plus a molecule of hydrogen. When a solution of common salt and one of silver nitrate are mixed, a white insoluble substance, silver chloride, is formed. The equation for this reaction will serve as another example of the use of chemical equations.

$$AgNO_3 + NaCl = AgCl + NaNO_3$$

Silver   Sodium   Silver   Sodium
nitrate chloride chloride nitrate
                  (insoluble)

Carbon Compounds.—The element carbon is remarkable for the great number and variety of compounds which it forms with other elements. In fact, as many as two hundred thousand different compounds of carbon are known. With the exception of such very simple carbon compounds as carbon dioxide and the carbonates (e.g., sodium bicarbonate—baking soda, $NaHCO_3$; and sodium carbonate, Na_2CO_3, washing soda) these compounds exist in nature only as the products of living plants and animals, and are accordingly spoken of as organic compounds. A number of the simpler of such compounds have already been made in the laboratory, and it is not unlikely that we shall eventually be able to produce artificially many of the more complex ones. Among the thousands of carbon compounds, many groups of somewhat similar ones are recognizable, such as alcohols, organic (carbon-containing) acids, etc.

Carbohydrates, Fats, and Proteins.—Three groups of substances which include carbon compounds of very great importance to both animals and plants are the carbohydrates, fats, and proteins. It is possible here only to give a few of the more general characteristics of each of these groups of compounds and to name a few examples.

All **carbohydrates** consist of carbon, hydrogen, and oxygen. No other elements are found in them. The oxygen and hydrogen are generally present in the molecules of carbohydrates in the same proportions as in water, that is, one atom of oxygen to two of hydrogen. The carbohydrates include the sugars (grape sugar—$C_6H_{12}O_6$, cane sugar—$C_{12}H_{22}O_{11}$, and many other sugars), starch, and cellulose. The latter two may be represented by the same formula, $(C_6H_{10}O_5)_n$. In the case of starch and cellulose, as is frequently true among carbon compounds, the difference between the compounds may rest not upon any difference in kind or number of atoms present but upon different arrangements of the atoms within the molecules.

Fats also contain carbon, hydrogen, and oxygen atoms in their molecules. They differ greatly from carbohydrates in the arrangement of the atoms within the molecule. They also differ in that the number of oxygen atoms in the molecule of fat is relatively smaller in proportion to the number of carbon and hydrogen atoms than it is in a carbohydrate molecule. Fats are very abundant in the seeds of cotton, peanut, coconut, corn, and flax but are present in all living cells. Palmitin ($C_{51}H_{98}O_6$) and stearin ($C_{57}H_{110}O_6$) are examples of fats.

Proteins are very complex carbon compounds, containing, in addition to carbon, hydrogen, and oxygen, the elements nitrogen and sulphur. Some proteins also contain phosphorus. Gelatine and egg white consist almost entirely of proteins. Haemoglobin, the red pigment (colored material) of the blood, is also a protein with the formula, $C_{758}H_{1203}N_{195}S_3FeO_{218}$.

Mixtures.—A quantity of matter in which more than one kind of molecule is present is spoken of as a mixture; that is to say, any material consisting of two or more pure substances not united into a compound is a mixture. The elements in a compound, it will be recalled, are always present in certain definite and constant proportions, but a mixture may vary greatly as to the proportions of its constituents. Mixtures are of two principal kinds: **solutions** and **heterogeneous mixtures.**

Solutions.—If a small quantity of the pure substance, sugar, is added to the pure substance, water, and the container is shaken or its contents stirred, the sugar disappears. As the sugar goes into solution in the water, the sugar molecules become separated from one another and uniformly distributed through the resulting solution. The largest particles in such a solution are molecules; and since molecules are too small to be seen with even the highest power of the microscope, the different constituents of a true solution can not be distinguished by the eye. By its appearance such a solution is not to be distinguished from pure water.

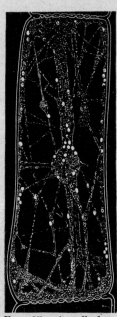

Fig. 27.—A cell from a squash (*Cucurbita*) as seen in optical section, showing the cytoplasm lining the wall, the vacuole, and the strands of cytoplasm crossing the vacuole and supporting the mass of cytoplasm which surrounds the nucleus. (After Sachs.)

A solution differs from a compound in two respects: first, in that it consists of at least two kinds of molecules; and second, in that the proportions of the components may vary continuously. That is, sugar solutions may contain any concentration of sugar from only a trace to a hundred parts or more of sugar to one hundred of water.

The different substances making up any solution are spoken of as the components of the solution. When one of the components is water or some other liquid, it is generally spoken of as the solvent, while the components which are dissolved in the solvent are spoken of as solutes. In most familiar solutions water is the solvent. The solute may be a solid substance, such as salt or sugar, another liquid such as alcohol, or a gas. "Soda water" is a solution in which water is the solvent and carbon dioxide the solute.

Most solutions are liquid, but there are also solutions (air, for example) of several gases. There are also solid solutions such as glass, certain alloys, and solutions of several metals.

Heterogeneous Mixtures.—If the particles of one or more of the substances in a mixture are considerably larger than molecules the mixture is a heterogeneous mixture. A piece of granite is an example of such a mixture, consisting of particles of different kinds of rock clearly distinguishable by the naked eye. Similarly a mixture of white sand and sugar is a heterogeneous mixture. The particles can be readily distinguished by the use of a lens or a microscope, and are many times larger than molecules. Generally the different constituents of such a mixture can be separated by mechanical means.

Colloidal Mixtures.—A peculiar kind of heterogeneous mixture, which is of great interest especially to botanists and zoologists, is the colloidal mixture. In most colloidal mixtures one or more of the components is mixed with a liquid and is in so fine a state of division (tiny solid particles or droplets) that it settles out, if at all, very slowly. The suspended particles of a colloidal mixture may be too small to be seen by the most powerful microscopes but are larger than molecules. In such cases a colloidal mixture may appear perfectly clear like a true solution. If an intense beam of light is passed through a colloidal mixture, however, the path of the beam will be distinctly visible where it passes through the solution. This is due to the fact that the colloidal particles in suspension are large enough so that they appreciably scatter the light just as do dust particles when a beam of light enters a darkened room. If a true solution, for example, salt in distilled water, is used, the path of the light through the solution will not be visible because the particles of dissolved substance are not large enough to scatter light to an appreciable extent.

Familiar examples of colloidal mixtures are egg white, glue, or gelatine mixed with water. Even such substances as common salt, which form a true solution with water, may form a colloidal solution in some other liquid. When a substance such as dry glue is placed in contact with water, with which it can form a colloidal mixture, it absorbs the liquid and swells. This absorption of water with attendant swelling is spoken of as **hydration**. As the result of hydration, a jelly-like colloidal mass, called a **gel**, is formed. In many cases, as more and more water is absorbed, the gel becomes a liquid. In this condition it is spoken of as a **sol**. Gelatine can take up by hydration thirty to forty times its weight of water and still remain a gel. Lowering the temperature of a sol may change it into a gel, and vice versa, as when a pot of glue is heated or allowed to cool. Some sols are changed by heat or certain chemicals into gels and can not be changed back to sols again.

The relation of some of the subjects just discussed to the structure and functions of the cell may be made clearer by the following statements in which some of the terms explained above are used. The protoplast of a plant cell is generally surrounded by a wall composed principally of the *compound*, cellulose, whose molecules are made up of *atoms* of the *elements*, carbon, hydrogen, and oxygen. Everything that enters the plant cell must be in the form of a true solution, for substances in *colloidal solution* can not pass through the wall or enter the cytoplasm. The cytoplasm itself is a colloidal solution in which many small particles (but larger than most molecules) of proteins and other substances are suspended in a watery true solution.

THE CELL WALL

The wall is secreted by the protoplast which it encloses. Where the wall separates the protoplasts of two cells, as it does in most cases, it is produced in part by each of these two masses of protoplasm. When the cells are young, a very thin wall common to both of them separates adjoining protoplasts; but as they grow older, successive layers of new cell-wall material are laid down by both protoplasts so that the wall may finally come to have a thickness many times as great as when it was first formed. The original thin wall separating two adjacent protoplasts is called the **middle lamella**. It is largely composed of a substance called pectose or of a compound of a related substance (pectic acid) and lime. The rest of the cell wall, except in cells of the wood, cork, epidermis (single layer of cells forming the surface tissue), and a few other tissues of stems and leaves, is made up almost entirely of the carbohydrate cellulose $(C_6H_{10}O_5)_n$. Cane sugar, glucose, or grape sugar, and starch are other familiar examples of carbohydrates. The pectose present in large quantities in the middle lamella and in small quantities in the rest of the cell wall easily changes into pectin. Pectin is a substance which causes fruit jellies to stiffen if it is present in sufficient quantities, and if it is accompanied by proper proportions of fruit acid and sugar. Cellulose is a material which is probably of greater economic

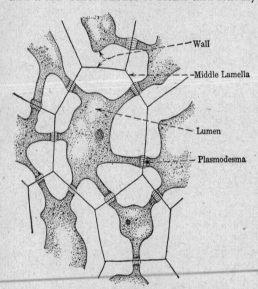

Labels: Wall — Middle Lamella — Lumen — Plasmodesma

FIG. 28.—Section of endosperm of date seed showing plasmodesma.

importance than any other organic material not used as food by man. Cotton, linen, hemp, and wood consist of pure cellulose or of cellulose mixed with other substances which will be discussed later. Man is unable to use cellulose for food, but it can be digested and utilized by cattle and other herbivorous animals. It has also come to be used as a raw material in the chemical industries which produce such substances as guncotton and other explosives, celluloid, artificial silk (rayon), lacquer, and other materials of great commercial importance.

THE PROTOPLAST

Each protoplast is a more or less independent unit. However, it has been demonstrated that there are very minute perforations in the walls separating adjacent protoplasts, and that through these openings extend fine threads of protoplasm, each thread being called a **plasmodesma.**

Protoplasm is not a single chemical compound, but a very complex mixture of many different compounds. These include carbohydrates, water, fatty substances, proteins, and simple compounds of the metals calcium, potassium, and magnesium, and of phosphorus, sulphur, and iron. With the exception of the water, the proteins are present in larger

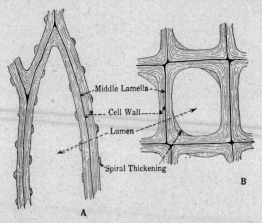

Fig. 29.—A tracheid (dead conducting cell of wood), showing the lumen, which is the cavity formerly occupied by the protoplast, the cell wall and spiral thickening, both originally of cellulose, and the middle lamella. *A*, a portion of a tracheid in longitudinal section; *B*, a tracheid in cross section. (Redrawn from Sharp's *Cytology*, McGraw-Hill Book Co., Inc.)

quantities than any of the other substances. Familiar examples of proteins are gelatine and egg white. In addition to carbon, oxygen, and hydrogen, the proteins contain nitrogen and sulphur, and in some proteins phosphorus is also present in the molecule. The protoplasm generally seems to be of the consistency of a viscous liquid, though in some cells and under certain conditions it is more like a stiff jelly. It is a colloidal mixture (see page 51) of particles and drops, usually too minute to be visible, suspended in a fluid. The living protoplasm of most cells contains from 60 to 90 per cent of water. When a cell dies the protoplasm loses its liquid or viscous consistency and coagulates or sets into a firm mass.

The protoplasm of the cell is not uniform but is differentiated into a number of cell organs and regions. These different parts of the proto-

plast and their relations to one another are shown in the following
outline:

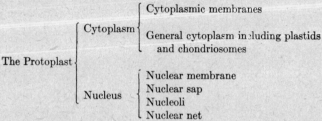

The Cytoplasm.—In the protoplast of every typical cell there is a
round or oval structure called the **nucleus.** All of the protoplasm outside of the nucleus is called cytoplasm. The cytoplasm forms, in most
cases, the greater part of the protoplast. Non-living **inclusions** (granules, crystals and vacuoles) may be found within the cytoplasm. The
most common of these are the **vacuoles,** which may be thought of as
drops of a watery solution of various substances embedded in the cytoplasm. Vacuoles vary greatly in size. They sometimes make up by far
the greater part of the volume of the cell.

In some cases there may be distinguished at the outer surface of
the protoplast, where it is in contact with the cell wall, a thin layer
which is not finely granular like the rest of the cytoplasm but clear
and highly transparent. Although it is impossible to see such a layer
in many plant cells, there are other grounds for believing that, wherever
the cytoplasm is in contact with the cell wall or with the contents of the
vacuole, there is a surface layer differing considerably in its properties
from the rest of the cytoplasm. We shall speak of such layers, which
are no doubt generally too thin to be visible even under the microscope,
as **cytoplasmic membranes.** It is generally assumed by botanists that
these layers are semipermeable or, perhaps better, differentially permeable membranes. Such membranes permit the free passage through
them of water and some dissolved substances but prevent, or at least
very greatly hinder, the passage of certain other dissolved substances.
These cytoplasmic membranes have long been thought to be of great
importance because of their supposed control over the entrance and exit
of substances into and from the cell.

Plastids and Chondriosomes.—In many cells there are specialized
cytoplasmic (living) structures called plastids. These are generally
spherical or ellipsoidal in form and may be considered to be portions
of the cytoplasm which are specially differentiated to perform a particular function in the cell. The plastids are of three kinds, differing in
color and in the nature of the work which they perform. There are

green plastids, which are called **chloroplasts**; colorless ones known as **leucoplasts**; and **chromoplasts,** which may be yellow, brown, or red in color. The green color of the chloroplasts is due to the presence of pigments (colored compounds) which may be dissolved out by means of alcohol, ether, acetone, and other organic solvents. Two of these pigments (**chlorophyll a** and **chlorophyll b**) are green; the other two (**carotene** and **xanthophyll**) are yellow. Frequently the term chlorophyll is applied to the mixture of chlorophyll a and chlorophyll b which always occur together or erroneously to the mixture of all four pigments which can be dissolved out with alcohol. From this mixture of the four pigments it is pos-

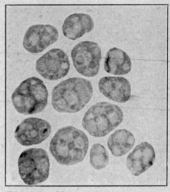

Fig. 30.—Chloroplasts from a tobacco leaf, X1200. The larger granules are starch; the chlorophyll is localized in the smaller granules. (From Weier.)

sible, though, to separate the four different colored compounds, the chemical formulae of which are:

Chlorophyll a............................$C_{55}H_{72}O_5N_4Mg$
Chlorophyll b............................$C_{55}H_{70}O_6N_4Mg$
Carotene.................................$C_{40}H_{56}$
Xanthophyll.............................$C_{40}H_{56}O_2$

It is an interesting fact that the presence of the element iron in a plant is essential to the formation of chlorophyll. Because plants deprived of iron failed to form chlorophyll, it was formerly believed, before the composition of chlorophyll was known, that iron must be a component of chlorophyll. As the formulae show, that is not the case. Not iron but another element, magnesium, is the only metallic element in chlorophyll.

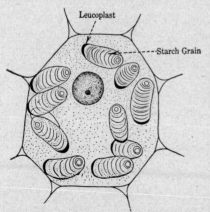

Leucoplast

Starch Grain

Fig. 31.—Starch-storing cell of *Pellionia* showing leucoplasts and contained starch grains. (Redrawn from Gager.)

The quantity and color intensity of the green pigments are such as largely to mask the yellow pigments. It is the chloroplasts which give the color to the green cells of leaves and of the young parts of stems. Organs which do not normally possess chloroplasts, such as the tubers of the potato, may develop green plastids when exposed to the light. In such cases leucoplasts which were present in the cells before exposure to light are stimulated to produce pigments and are thus transformed into chloroplasts.

The green plastids (chloroplasts) are the centers of the process of photosynthesis, by which the simple compounds, carbon dioxide and water, secured from the air and from the soil, are built up, first into sugar, and then into starch. In most green cells, starch grains make their appearance within the chloroplasts soon after photosynthesis begins. During the night when photosynthesis can not go on, these starch grains disappear. In the cells of starchy seeds (rice, wheat, etc.), in the tubers (modified underground stems of white potatoes), in sweet potato roots, and in the non-green cells of other organs, starch is often stored. The starch-storing cells of such organs are able to change certain sugars (which were originally produced by photosynthesis in the chloroplasts of the leaves and then transferred to the storage organs) into starch. The starch is built up inside the leucoplasts into starch grains. As these grains

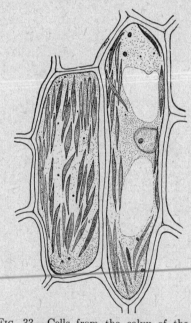

FIG. 33.—Cells from the calyx of the Bird-of-Paradise flower (*Strelitzia*), showing chromoplasts. The cell on the left is shown in surface view, the one on the right in median optical section. (Drawing by A. W. Bell.)

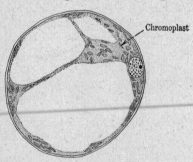

Chromoplast

FIG. 32.—Cell from the flesh of a tomato (*Lycopersicum esculentum*), showing the chromoplasts which give the tomato its red color. (After Frank.)

increase in size the leucoplasts stretch to many times their "normal" size.

Chromoplasts are responsible for the red, yellow, or orange color of many flowers and fruits. They owe their color principally to the two pigments, carotene and xanthophyll. These two closely related pigments occur in the tissues of animals; the yellow color of egg yolks and of butter fat is due to them. There is evidence that the fat-soluble vitamin A in the animal body is converted from carotene. In many cases the colors of flowers or fruits are due, not to pigments contained in plastids, but to colored substances dissolved in the solution contained in the vacuoles of the cells. A single plastid may be in turn a leucoplast, a chloroplast, and a chromoplast. This is the case in the cells near the surface of many fruits, such as the red pepper or tomato, but the leucoplasts of tissue not normally exposed to the light never become chloroplasts or chromoplasts. In the young flower of these plants, the ovary, that part of the flower which develops later into the fruit, is almost colorless and the cells near the surface contain numerous leucoplasts. Later, the ovary, as well as the young fruit which develops from it, will become green and chloroplasts will be found to have developed from the leucoplasts. As the fruit ripens, the chloroplasts are transformed to chromoplasts, and the color of the fruit changes from green to red.

Plastids probably arise by division of pre-existing plastids; their division can be observed in algae and in thin leaves, such as those of moss.

Small rod-shaped bodies, granules, or filaments are found in the cytoplasm of the cells (particularly young cells) of both plants and animals. These are called **chondriosomes** or **mitochondria**. Special staining methods are necessary to make these

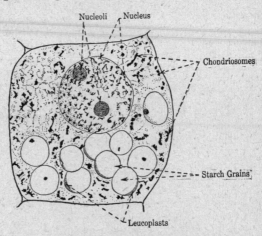

FIG. 34.—A cell from the root of a garden pea (*Pisum sativum*), showing chondriosomes scattered through the cytoplasm. (Redrawn from Mottier.)

visible. Though of almost universal occurrence, there is no general agreement among cytologists as to their nature and function.

The Nucleus.—The nucleus apparently controls in some way most of the activities which go on in the living cell, and its removal is soon followed by the death of the cell. There is abundant evidence that it is material within the nucleus which is principally responsible for the inheritance by organisms of the characteristics of their ancestors.

Typically, the nucleus is a spherical structure (although ellipsoidal, disc-shaped, or considerably elongated nuclei occasionally occur), surrounded by a **nuclear membrane** and containing a highly transparent material called the **nuclear sap.** This may be a sol or a gel.

Within the nuclear sap are the **nucleolus** (plural, **nucleoli**) and the **nuclear net.** The nucleolus is another cell structure concerning the function of which cytologists differ. It seems likely that one of its functions is the storage of reserve material of some sort. Usually the nucleus contains only one nucleolus, two or more may occur in a single nucleus, but rarely are they lacking altogether. The nucleoli are usually spherical in form. During the division of the nucleus into two nuclei at the time of cell division, the nucleoli disappear entirely and reappear again in the two new nuclei when the process of division is complete.

The **nuclear net** may, in some cases, be quite clearly seen in living cells examined under the microscope. Usually it is necessary to fix and stain the cell before the net can be made out. When the cell is thus treated, certain deeply stained granules are found here and there along the thread of the nuclear net, while the thread itself is found to be very slightly or not at all affected by the staining solution. Though it was formerly assumed that the net consisted of two different kinds of materials, **linin** and **chromatin,** it now seems more likely that the whole nuclear net consists of chromatin, which stains more distinctly at the intersections of the threads than elsewhere. The chromatin is without question a substance of very great importance. There is very conclusive evidence that it is this substance which bears the characteristics which the plant is able to pass on to successive generations. There can be no doubt that the resemblance of a plant to its parents is due to the fact that in the process of reproduction some of the chromatin of each parent plant is contributed to the new individual. It should be borne in mind that these and all the other parts of the nucleus and cytoplasm which have been mentioned, though they may differ in consistency, in staining properties, in chemical composition, and in other particulars, are included under the general term protoplasm.

INCLUSIONS

Within the cytoplasm may be found various non-living structures which are called **inclusions.** These may be drops of (1) liquid (vacuoles), or (2) crystals, or (3) solid bodies of various non-crystalline forms, chiefly starch grains and protein bodies. When they are small it may be difficult in some cases to determine whether they are part of the cytoplasm or actually non-protoplasmic in nature. The inclusions may be (*a*) accumulations of raw materials for food manufacture, (*b*) food, (*c*) by-products and waste materials. They are generally absent from very young cells but appear in increasing number as the cells grow older and are particularly conspicuous in cells which serve for food storage.

Vacuoles.—These are inclusions in the form of drops of liquid which are found in all but the very youngest cells. As a young cell grows, its volume increases much more rapidly than does the quantity of protoplasm within it. As a result there is not sufficient protoplasm to fill completely the cell cavity. The water which is absorbed by such cells as they grow makes up the difference in volume. Although the cytoplasm may be somewhat diluted by the absorbed water, much of the latter forms droplets or small vacuoles which are numerous at the time of their first appearance. As the cell grows these increase in size and some of them come into contact with each other and fuse. Thus they become fewer in number but larger in size in the older cells than in the younger ones. By the time the cell has reached its greatest size there is generally only a single large vacuole. This is commonly larger in volume than the protoplasm and occupies the center of the cell so that the protoplast in old cells has the form of a closed sac. In such cells the nucleus lies near the cell wall, embedded in the cytoplasm, or is suspended in the large central vacuole by fine threads of cytoplasm which are connected with the cytoplasm lining the cell wall. In the latter case the nucleus is surrounded by a layer of cytoplasm. It is never in direct contact with the vacuole.

The vacuole contains, not pure water, but a solution of many substances dissolved in water. Among these substances are (1) the gases of the atmosphere, including nitrogen, oxygen, and carbon dioxide; (2) inorganic salts (such as nitrates, chlorides, sulphates, or phosphates of the metals potassium, sodium, calcium, and magnesium); (3) organic acids (such as malic, formic, acetic, and oxalic acid); (4) compounds of some of these acids with the metals named above; (5) sugars (such as cane sugar, grape sugar, and malt sugar); (6) soluble proteins and simpler nitrogenous compounds; and (7) other substances. The cell sap is generally slightly acid. In the cells of beet roots and of the flowers, leaves, or other parts of many plants, the cell sap frequently contains dissolved **anthocyanin pigments** which give them a red, purple, or blue color. The anthocyanins belong to a chemical group known as the glucosides; these are compounds which, when broken up into less complex substances, yield the sugar glucose or some other monosaccharose, and certain other compounds. The reaction of the cell sap determines the color of the anthocyanins; for example, when the cell sap is alkaline, the color is blue, and when the cell sap is acid, the color is red. The function of anthocyanins is still a matter of dispute. In the carrot, on the other hand, the yellow color is due to pigments in the chromoplasts. In some colored flowers the two methods of coloration are combined, both colored cell sap and chromoplasts being found in the same cell.

In addition to vacuoles containing a watery cell sap, there are found in certain cells oil drops of considerable size which are sometimes spoken of as **oil vacuoles.** They never reach the size of the cell-sap vacuoles of mature cells.

Crystals.—Cells with crystal inclusions can be found in almost all plants. The crystals may be large ones occurring singly in the cells, or numerous very fine crystals scattered through the cytoplasm and often called crystal sand, or bundles of fine sharp needles (**raphides**), or spherical groups of radiating crystals. The crystals are formed in vacuoles, which, in cells containing raphides, have cell sap of a mucilaginous nature. In many cases the crystals consist of calcium oxalate.

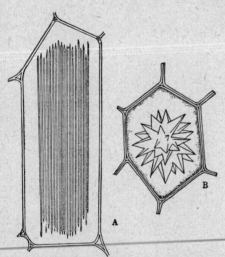

Oxalic acid is a by-product of certain activities of the plant. It is a soluble substance and one which is toxic to the protoplasm, if it reaches a high concentration in the cell. When united with calcium, the soluble oxalic acid is converted into the highly insoluble calcium oxalate which can not injure the protoplasm. Sometimes the crystals found in living cells consist of calcium carbonate. Protein crystals are also found as inclusions in plant cells as well as noncrystalline protein particles.

FIG. 35.—Crystal inclusions. *A*, a cell from the stem of spiderwort (*Tradescantia*) showing a group of raphides. *B*, a cell from the leaf-stalk of dock (*Rumex*) showing a crystal cluster. In *A* the cytoplasm has been omitted.

Starch Grains.—These inclusions are generally to be found in green cells after a period of active photosynthesis, and in various food-storing cells, such as those of the potato tuber and of many seeds. The stored starch of plants is perhaps the single most important compound used as food by man. The starch grains which are produced in green food-making cells are formed within the chloroplasts. Those found in food-storage cells are produced within the leucoplasts.

The grains of stored starch consist of successive layers, which are often thicker on one side of the grain than on the other. This is conspicuously the case in the starch grains of potato. Sometimes a number of small grains are united into a group which is called a compound grain. Compound grains occur in rice, oats, and some other cereals.

The starch molecule consists of carbon, hydrogen, and oxygen atoms united in the proportions of six of carbon to ten of hydrogen and five of oxygen. Starch grains are insoluble in water. The plant is able to change starch into certain sugars which are soluble in the cell sap and which can pass from one part of the plant to another.

When a green cell which contains starch within its chloroplasts discontinues photosynthesis, as it does when night comes on, the starch is changed into sugar which passes to parts of the plant where it will be used or stored.

The sugar which reaches the storage tissues may be stored in the cells in the form of sugar, as in the sugar beet, or may be converted again by leucoplasts into starch, as in white potatoes and sweet potatoes, and remain in this form until it is needed by the plant. It is then changed back into sugar and passes to the parts of the plant where it is to be used as food.

When starch grains are treated with a solution of iodine they become blue in color. The form of the grains of stored starch is different in different plants, a fact which often makes it possible to determine, by microscopic examination of a sample of starch, from what plant it was secured.

HISTORY OF OUR KNOWLEDGE OF THE CELL

Cells were first seen by Robert Hooke, an Englishman, who in addition to being a professor of geometry, an architect, and an experimenter with flying machines, was also interested in optics, and greatly improved the compound microscope, an instrument

FIG. 36.—Robert Hooke's illustrations of cork cells in longitudinal and cross section as he saw them under his microscope. Reduced facsimile reproduction from his *Micrographia* published in 1665.

which had been invented by Zacharias Jansen, a spectacle maker of Middleburg, Holland, in 1590. The compound microscope soon became a most important tool of biological science and such it has remained. Hooke, who lived from 1636 to 1703, examined a great number of natural objects with his improved microscope. It was when he placed a small fragment of cork (the dead outer bark of woody plants) under his microscope that he first observed the numerous cavities which we now know to be characteristic of the structure of all plant parts. He gave the name **cells** to the cavities. In the cells of cork there is no protoplasm, and even when Hooke examined slices of living plant tissue the contents of the cells escaped his notice on account of the transparency of the protoplasm and the imperfections of his microscope. The term cell is still, and perhaps always will be, generally used for the structural units of plants and animals although it is now recognized that the protoplast is the essential part of the cell and that the wall is merely a product of the protoplast. Hooke made no systematic study of the cellular structure of plants. This was first attempted by the Italian professor of medicine, Marcello Malpighi (1628–1694), who published an *Anatomy of Plants* in 1675, and by Nehemiah Grew (1641–1712), an English physician, who worked out the form of the cells and their arrangements in different parts of the plant. These men did not, however, see the protoplasts of the cells which they studied, and had no idea how the cell walls were formed.

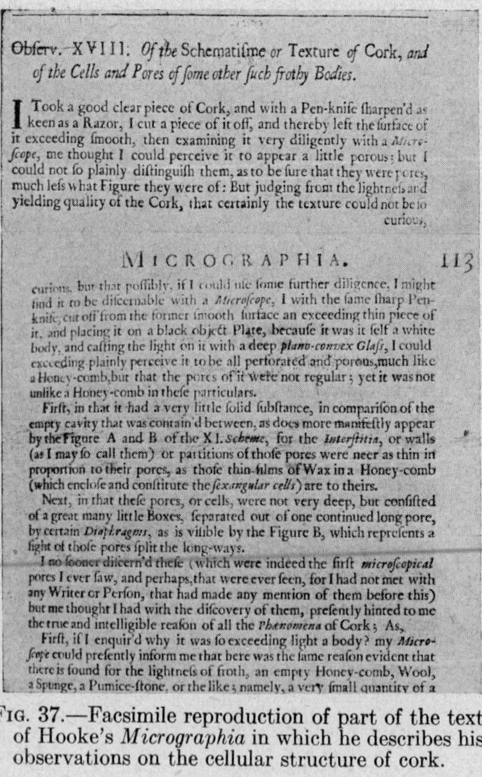

The Cell Theory.—No incident in the history of our knowledge of the cell is of greater importance than the putting forward of the cell theory by Schleiden and Schwann. These two men, the former a botanist who had given up the practice of law to devote himself to the study of the structure and physiology of plants, and the latter a student of animal anatomy, attempted to put into the form of a general statement or theory the facts which they and earlier workers had discovered as to the structure of plants and animals. The theory had its origin in a conversation held between these two friends while they were dining together

Observ. XVIII. *Of the Schematisme or Texture of Cork, and of the Cells and Pores of some other such frothy Bodies.*

I Took a good clear piece of Cork, and with a Pen-knife sharpen'd as keen as a Razor, I cut a piece of it off, and thereby left the surface of it exceeding smooth, then examining it very diligently with a *Microscope*, me thought I could perceive it to appear a little porous: but I could not so plainly distinguish them, as to be sure that they were pores, much less what Figure they were of: But judging from the lightness and yielding quality of the Cork, that certainly the texture could not be so curious,

MICROGRAPHIA.   113

curious, but that possibly, if I could use some further diligence, I might find it to be discernable with a *Microscope*, I with the same sharp Pen-knife, cut off from the former smooth surface an exceeding thin piece of it, and placing it on a black object Plate, because it was it self a white body, and casting the light on it with a deep *plano-convex Glass*, I could exceeding plainly perceive it to be all perforated and porous,much like a Honey-comb,but that the pores of it were not regular; yet it was not unlike a Honey-comb in these particulars.

First, in that it had a very little solid substance, in comparison of the empty cavity that was contain'd between, as does more manifestly appear by the Figure A and B of the XI. *Scheme*, for the *Interstitia*, or walls (as I may so call them) or partitions of those pores were neer as thin in proportion to their pores, as those thin films of Wax in a Honey-comb (which enclose and constitute the *sexangular cells*) are to theirs.

Next, in that these pores, or cells, were not very deep, but consisted of a great many little Boxes, separated out of one continued long pore, by certain *Diaphragms*, as is visible by the Figure B, which represents a sight of those pores split the long-ways.

I no sooner discern'd these (which were indeed the first *microscopical* pores I ever saw, and perhaps,that were ever seen, for I had not met with any Writer or Person, that had made any mention of them before this) but me thought I had with the discovery of them, presently hinted to me the true and intelligible reason of all the *Phenomena* of Cork; As,

First, if I enquir'd why it was so exceeding light a body? my *Microscope* could presently inform me that here was the same reason evident that there is found for the lightness of froth, an empty Honey-comb, Wool, a Spunge, a Pumice-stone, or the like; namely, a very small quantity of a

FIG. 37.—Facsimile reproduction of part of the text of Hooke's *Micrographia* in which he describes his observations on the cellular structure of cork.

one day in October, 1838. After dinner Schleiden accompanied Schwann to the latter's laboratory where he examined some of Schwann's microscopic preparations and was struck with the many points of resemblance between the animal cells which he saw there and the plant cells which he had himself studied. Schwann was largely responsible for the publication of the theory which grew out of this and later discussions, but it is doubtful whether the theory would have been put forward at all but for Schleiden's contributions. In its main features the theory was correct, but more important than its truth or falsity is the fact that it proved to be a stimulus to renewed and more searching investigations and thus marked the beginning of a new epoch in the study of anatomy of plants and animals. In the words of Schwann, this theory set forth that **the elementary parts of all tissues are formed of cells in an analogous, though very diversified, manner, so that it may be asserted that there is one universal principle of development for the elementary parts of organisms, however different, and that this principle is the formation of cells.**

Discovery of the Nucleus and of Protoplasm.—Robert Brown in 1831 first recognized the importance of the nucleus and its constant occurrence in living cells. He is generally given the credit for its discovery.

The protoplasm of the cell was observed by Corti as early as 1772. Dujardin, in 1835, noted the constant occurrence, in the cells of certain simple animals, of a jelly-like substance for which he proposed the name, **sarcode,** and which he recognized as the living material of these animals. Eleven years later the botanist von Mohl

Fig. 38.—Matthias Jakob Schleiden (1804–1881) the German botanist who together with the zoologist, Schwann, propounded *The Cell Theory.*

proposed the name protoplasm for a substance which he found in the cells of plants, and in 1861 Max Schultze showed by his studies that a substance such as Dujardin had observed in simple animals was also present in the cells of higher animals, and thus established the close similarity of the living substance of plants and animals. He formulated what is now generally known as the **protoplasm doctrine, i.e., that each unit of organization of living things consists of a mass of protoplasm surrounding a nucleus and that the protoplasm of plants and that of animals are not essentially different.**

Since the appearance of the protoplasm doctrine, our knowledge of plant anatomy and cytology has increased enormously. To recount here even the most outstanding discoveries which have been made during this period would make too large a demand upon our space. Among those who have contributed during the past fifty years to the great store of information about the structure and functions of the cell, one of the most outstanding figures is that of Strasburger, for many years professor of botany at the University of Bonn, Germany. His fame rests not only on his many and important discoveries relative to the structure and behavior of the nucleus and other parts of the cell, but also upon the fact that he taught and inspired many students who later, by their investigations, greatly advanced our knowledge of cell structure and physiology.

Fig. 39.—Theodor Schwann (1810–1882) the German zoologist, who was with Schleiden co-author of *The Cell Theory.*

THE PHYSIOLOGY OF THE CELL

Most plants are multicellular, that is, are made up of many cells—hundreds, thousands, or even millions of them—and the organs in which the various essential activities of the plant go on are, in most plants, also multicellular. **Yet every function which the plant performs is but the expression of the activities of individual cells,** and in unicellular (one-celled) plants all of the physiological processes are carried on within a single protoplast. The most important of these processes, namely, absorption, photosynthesis, assimilation, growth, and reproduction, as they go on in a single cell, are discussed below.

In reading the following account of these physiological processes the student may well keep in mind one of the many different species of green unicellular plants which may be found by microscopic examination of the water of ponds or streams, of moist soils, or of the wet surfaces of stones.

Absorption. *Solution.*—Since it is impossible for substances to enter the plant cell except in solution in water, it is necessary to learn something of the properties of solutions before we can understand the process of absorption.

On pages 50 and 51 a solution was defined and the distinction pointed out between true solutions and colloidal solutions. Except where otherwise stated we shall here use the term solution to designate a molecular solution, that is, a solution containing no particles larger than molecules. In every solution two or more substances are present. They are spoken of as the *components* of the solution. It is customary to speak of the liquid component, or, if there is more than one liquid component, of the one which is present in largest quantity as the *solvent*, and of the other component or components as the *solute* or *solutes*. That the distinction between solvent and solute, though a convenient one, is an entirely arbitrary one, is clear when we consider a solution consisting of equal volumes of water and alcohol. In such a solution, we may well ask ourselves which would be the solvent. In the case of the solutions from which plants absorb substances the solvent is water. It is true that the atmosphere, a solution of several gases, supplies substances, oxygen, and carbon dioxide, which are absorbed by plants, but these gases must go into solution in water before they actually enter the cells. All other substances besides carbon dioxide and oxygen are absorbed, in the case of typical seed-bearing plants, ferns, and mosses, from the water solution existing in the soil. In the case of the unicellular green plants, which we have mentioned, all materials are absorbed from the water (of the sea or of streams, lakes or ponds) in which they are submerged. Soil water, sea water, and the water of rivers, ponds, and lakes are dilute solutions. That is to say, they are solutions in which the number of molecules and ions of solutes is very small relative to the number of water molecules.

A great many of the compounds which are soluble in water exist in solution in water not only as molecules but also as parts of molecules which are called *ions*. Thus a crystal of common salt, NaCl, when dissolved in water yields not only NaCl molecules but also Na^+ and Cl^- ions. These sodium ions and chlorine ions are not the same as atoms, for, as the plus and minus signs written after the symbols indicate, they are electrically charged, the sodium ion with a unit positive charge and the chlorine ion with a unit negative charge. When the water of the solution is removed by evaporation or boiling, the ions unite again to form salt molecules and the molecules again become arranged so as to form salt crystals. In their properties and behavior, ions are quite different from the molecules which produce them. Ions may consist of groups of atoms. Thus when caustic potash, KOH, goes into solution in water some of the molecules break up into K^+ ions and OH^- ions. Similarly sulphuric acid (H_2SO_4), in water may give H^+ ions, HSO_4^- ions, SO_4^{--} ions, and some H_2SO_4 molecules in the solution.

Most of the substances which green plants absorb from outside are more or less ionized (broken down into ions) when in solution in water. Many substances, cane sugar, glucose and glycerine, for instance, do not ionize at all. In the case of compounds which do undergo ionization in water, the process is more complete the more dilute the solution. Thus in a very concentrated solution of such a compound relatively few of the molecules of the solute break up into ions, but in a very dilute solution almost all of the molecules are ionized and very few molecules of solute remain. We shall use the expression *dissolved particles* to include both molecules and ions of a solute.

Diffusion.[1]—This is a process which plays a very important part in the life of the plant. If a piece of any soluble substance be dropped into a glass of water it will gradually go into solution (Fig. 40). If a crystal of copper sulphate (blue vitriol) or other deeply colored substance is used we more easily follow the process of solution and diffusion. For some time the solution will be more deeply colored in the vicinity of the crystal, indicating that the dissolved particles of solute are nearer together there than in more distant parts of the solution. In time the whole solution will become uniform in color, indicating that the dissolved particles of the solute have become uniformly distributed among the water molecules.

FIG. 40.—Diagrammatic-representation of the diffusion of dissolved particles from a crystal of a colored solute undergoing solution in water.

Such scattering of the molecules or ions of one component of a solution among those of the other components, resulting in a uniform distribution of the particles of all components throughout the solution is called **diffusion.**

Diffusion is not restricted to solutions in water or other liquids but takes place also in solutions in which one or all of the components are gases. If even a small quantity of gas of strong and characteristic odor is introduced into the air in one corner of a room, it is soon detectable throughout the room no matter how undisturbed the air has remained. This is due to the diffusion of molecules of the gas throughout the air of the room, the air itself being a solution of oxygen, nitrogen, carbon dioxide, and other gases. Diffusion is much more rapid in gases than in liquids.

Diffusion of solutes in liquids is not a rapid process, and when we make a solution we do not ordinarily wait for diffusion to become complete but hasten it by shaking or stirring the mixture.

[1] What appears to be a very satisfactory explanation of diffusion in liquid solutions and solutions of gases is furnished by the kinetic theory. According to this theory molecules of gases or dissolved particles of any substance in liquid solutions are in constant and rapid motion. Any such particle moves in a straight line until it strikes another such particle or the wall of the container. In either case it rebounds and again moves in a straight line until it again collides and rebounds. This goes on indefinitely. A moment's consideration will make it clear that such "jostling" of particles will tend to result in a uniform distribution of each kind of particle throughout the volume of solution, and this process of forming a uniform distribution is what we call diffusion.

Passage of Solvents through Membranes.—If water is carefully poured upon a quantity of sugar syrup (a concentrated solution of cane sugar in water) the two fluids will at first form two distinct layers. Soon, however, the molecules of water will diffuse into the concentrated sugar solution and those of the sugar will diffuse into the water, so that finally a uniform solution results. If the syrup and water are separated by a membrane like an ordinary cell wall or a piece of filter paper through which the dissolved particles of sugar and water can pass freely, water will diffuse into the syrup and sugar into the water so that the solutions on the two sides of the membrane will eventually become of equal concentration. Such a membrane which permits water and all solutes to pass freely through it is called a **permeable membrane.**

There are membranes which permit water to pass freely but prevent or, what is more common, restrict the passage of solutes in general or of some solutes at least. Such a membrane is called a **semipermeable membrane.**

When pure water or a dilute solution of a solute is separated from a concentrated solution by a semipermeable membrane through which the solute can not pass, an interesting change results. This will be more easily understood if we think of the membrane as stretched across the U-shaped tube shown in Fig. 41, *A* and *B*. The left arm of

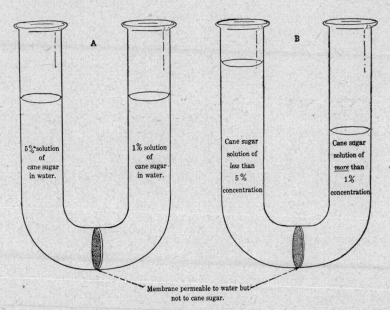

FIG. 41.—Diagram illustrating diffusion through a semipermeable membrane. For explanation see text.

the tube, in *A*, has been partly filled with a solution of 5 grams of **cane sugar** in 95 grams of water (what is spoken of as a 5 per cent solution by weight).[1]   Into the right arm an equal volume of a dilute solution (say 1 per cent) of cane sugar has been poured.   The level of the liquids in the two arms is the same, and the two solutions are separated by a membrane which is impermeable to cane sugar molecules but permeable to water molecules.   Fig. 41, *B*, shows the same U-tube and its contents after the lapse of sufficient time to allow an equilibrium to be reached between the solutions on the two sides of the membrane. The changes which result in this equilibrium are as follows.

Water diffuses from the more dilute solution on the right through the membrane to the more concentrated solution on the left.

The solute, cane sugar, *tends to diffuse* from the more concentrated solution on the left of the membrane to the more dilute solution on the right but **the cane sugar will not pass because the membrane is not permeable to it.**   As a consequence of water passing through the membrane from right to left the following changes occur:

1. The solution in the right arm becomes more concentrated as the result of the loss of water.   Its volume becomes less for the same reason.

2. The solution in the left arm becomes more dilute as the result of the addition of water from the other arm.   Its volume becomes greater for the same reason.

3. The level of the solutions becomes different, as shown in *B*, the level rising in what was originally the more concentrated solution and falling in what was originally the more dilute.

The difference in level of the solutions in the two arms of the U-tube necessitates the conclusion that there is a pressure supporting the column which stands at the higher level.   The existence of the pressure wherever two solutions of different concentrations are separated by a membrane not permeable to the solute is still more clearly demonstrated in what follows.

---

[1] Ordinarily when we speak of the concentration of solutions we have in mind the percentage composition, a 1 per cent salt solution being one containing 1 gram of salt in 99 of water.   In this sense it is quite correct to speak of a 1 per cent solution of cane sugar as having the same concentration as a 1 per cent solution of grape sugar or glucose.

It is important to keep in mind, however, that the term concentration, when used in discussions of diffusion and osmosis, refers to the relative numbers of dissolved particles of solute (molecules and ions), not to the number of grams, in a given volume of solution. When concentration is used in this sense it is not correct to speak of a 1 per cent solution of cane sugar as having the same concentration as a 1 per cent solution of grape sugar. A grape-sugar molecule weighs only about one-half as much as a cane-sugar molecule, and therefore, there are almost twice as many dissolved particles of grape sugar in a cubic centimeter of 1 per cent solution as there are in the same volume of a 1 per cent solution of cane sugar.

The passage of the solvent (water in this case) from a quantity of pure solvent or a dilute solution through a semipermeable membrane into a more concentrated solution is one of the processes which has been included under the term **osmosis** [1] and the pressure of which we have just spoken is called **osmotic pressure.**

The tissue forming the wall of a pig's bladder prevents, or at least greatly hinders, the passage of some solutes through it. That is to say, it is more or less semipermeable. If such a bladder is filled with a concentrated solution, say of sugar, and the bladder tied shut and immersed in water or a very dilute sugar solution, it soon swells up and becomes stretched and inflated as the result of water passing inward through the semipermeable wall into the concentrated solution within the bladder. It soon becomes clear that a high hydrostatic pressure has developed within. This pressure may become sufficient to burst the bladder or, if a long tube of narrow bore be fastened firmly into the mouth of the bladder, sugar solution may rise in the tube to a height of many meters (a meter is 39.37 inches).

The experiment shown in Fig. 41 *A* and *B,* and the experiment with the pig's bladder, demonstrate the existence of osmotic pressure. Such a pressure results only when:

1. The membrane is permeable to the solvent.

2. Solutes are present which can not pass freely through the membrane.

3. The number of dissolved particles of these solutes in a given volume of the solution is greater on one side of the membrane than on the other.

Diffusion of Solutes through Membranes.—Thus far we have spoken only of the passage of the solvent, generally water, through semipermeable membranes. Many semipermeable membranes permit the dissolved particles of some solutes to pass freely but are relatively impermeable to other solutes. In plants and animals such so-called " selective " membranes are of great importance. Fig. 42 (identical with Fig. 41, except for the composition of the solutions) illustrates what takes place when two solutions are used each with two solutes, one of which can pass through the membrane.

The *A* portion of Fig. 42 shows a U-tube with the right arm filled with a solution of 5 per cent of cane sugar and $\frac{1}{20}$ per cent of common salt and the left arm filled with a solution of 10 per cent cane sugar and $\frac{1}{60}$ per cent solution of common salt. The volumes of the two solutions

---

[1] The word osmosis has been given such a variety of meanings by those who have used it that it has lost any precise meaning whatever. As far as possible we shall avoid its use.

are the same. The membrane, M, separating the two solutions is permeable to water and common salt but not to the cane sugar. The B portion of the figure shows the contents of the same U-tube some time later. The following changes have taken place:

1. The concentration of salt has become the same on the two sides of the membrane due to salt particles having diffused from the solution where there were more in a given volume ($\frac{1}{20}$ per cent) to the solution where they were fewer ($\frac{1}{60}$ per cent).

2. In Fig. 42 B the concentration of sugar in the left arm has become less than 10 per cent cane sugar, and that in the right arm more than

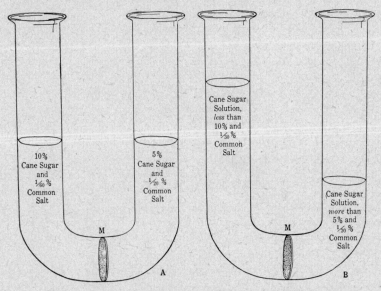

Fig. 42.—Diagram illustrating diffusion through a semipermeable membrane. For explanation see text.

5 per cent cane sugar. This has resulted not from sugar molecules passing through the membrane but from water passing from the more dilute solution (and thus concentrating it) to the more concentrated (and thus diluting it).

3. Diffusion of water has raised the level of what was the more concentrated solution above the level of the solution which was at first the less concentrated.

It is the first of these changes which should be emphasized here. As illustrated by Fig. 42 any solute will pass through a semipermeable membrane from one solution to another provided:

(a) That the membrane, though not permeable to some solutes, is permeable to this particular solute.

(b) That this particular solute, present in one of the solutions, is absent from the other solution or present in lower concentration.

In general, the movement of a particular solute is not affected by the concentrations of other solutes present.

Diffusion in Relation to Absorption by the Plant Cell.—Reference has already been made to certain very simple plants each of which consists of a single cell floating in water and capable of carrying on all the essential life functions. Such a cell may be used in pointing out the relation of diffusion to absorption. A cell of this sort living immersed in the water of a river, pond, or lake is surrounded by a very dilute solution of various solutes (including carbon dioxide, oxygen, nitrogen and the nitrates, chlorides, sulphates, and phosphates of potassium, sodium, calcium, magnesium, iron, and other metals). In the vacuole is the cell sap which is a watery solution with a relatively high concentration of solutes, consisting in part (a) of substances absorbed out of the surrounding water, and in part (b) of compounds (sugars, other foods, etc.) formed within the cell from carbon dioxide, water, and other substances which have entered the cell from the surrounding water.

The cellulose wall surrounding the protoplast is a permeable membrane and can not prevent the passage through it of any substance dissolved in the cell sap or in the water surrounding the cell. The cytoplasmic membrane, however, is differentially permeable. It permits free entrance of water and of many of the substances dissolved in it. On the other hand, it restricts the passage outward of most of the substances in solution in the cell sap.

The protoplast may then be compared with a pig's bladder filled with a concentrated sugar solution and immersed in a dilute solution of salt.

The vacuole corresponds to the cavity of the bladder, the cell sap to the concentrated solution within the bladder, and the cytoplasm to the wall of the bladder.

In the single-celled plant floating in the water, somewhat as in the case of the bladder, water tends to pass from the dilute solution outside into the concentrated solution (cell sap). This tends to increase the quantity of cell sap, enlarge the vacuole, and create a pressure within the cell. There is thus created an actual hydrostatic pressure of cell contents against the wall, and this is called **turgor pressure.**

This pressure is often so great that it would burst the protoplast if it were not for the cell walls. They reinforce or " back up " the protoplast, just as the casing of an automobile tire " backs up " the inner tube, which tends to enlarge and press tightly against the cell wall so that the whole cell is distended. The same condition of " inflation " normally exists also in all the many living cells of multicellular (many-celled) plants.

In cells, such as those of the sugar beet, this pressure, due to the high concentration of sugar in the sap in the vacuoles and the entrance of water, may be as great as 20 kilograms per square centimeter.

When the wall of a living cell has been stretched to a certain extent by the pressure of entering water, the resistance of the wall to further stretching just balances the force with which the water passes into the

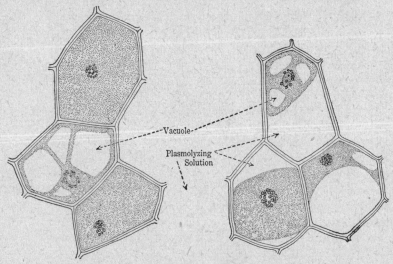

Vacuole

Plasmolyzing Solution

Fig. 43.—Plasmolysis of epidermal cells of wandering Jew (*Zebrina pendula*). *A*, cells in water. *B*, cells after brief immersion in 20 per cent solution of cane sugar. Note that the spaces between the cytoplasm and the cell wall in the plasmolyzed cells are filled with the solution in which the cells are immersed. In each drawing two cells are shown as seen in surface view and one in section.

vacuole. Consequently an equilibrium exists and there is no further entrance of water. As we shall show later, every living cell of a multicellular plant, even though it be surrounded by other cells instead of being immersed in water, is normally in a condition of distension due to turgor pressure. A cell in this condition may be compared to an inflated football. The cell wall corresponds roughly to the leather cover of the football. Although the cell wall is not " solution tight " or the cover " air tight," the strength of these outer coverings makes it possible for the relatively weak cytoplasmic sac and rubber bladder to withstand the high pressure of the solution or air within. The stretching of the cover of the football by the pressure of air within the bladder and of the cell wall by turgor pressure within the cytoplasmic sac results in the inflated ball and the turgid cell being plump and firm.

The crispness of the leaves and the rigidity of the young parts of plants are due to the turgid condition of the individual cells. If a turgid cell is placed in a solution (a) more concentrated than its cell sap, and (b) the solute of which can not pass through the cytoplasm, water will pass from the cell sap outward through the surrounding cytoplasm into the solution outside. As a result the vacuole will become smaller, the cytoplasm will shrink away from the cell wall, and the cell will no longer be plump and distended. The separation of the cytoplasm from the cell wall is called **plasmolysis.** When a lettuce leaf, crisp because of the high turgor pressure in its cells, is placed in a solution more concentrated than the cell sap, it wilts as the result of the reduction or complete loss of turgor pressure in its cells. The cell's power to grow in size is largely dependent upon the maintenance of considerable turgor in the cell.

Absorption of Dissolved Substances into Living Cells.—We have explained how water enters the living plant cell and how, as a result, the normal turgid condition of the cell is maintained. But in addition to water the plant must absorb considerable quantities of dissolved substances, such as nitrates, sulphates, and phosphates of potassium, calcium, and magnesium, the gases, carbon dioxide and oxygen, and various other solutes. Although diffusion may explain water absorption, the entrance of these solutes into living plant cells is a different matter for, whereas the water enters along a concentration gradient, solutes in many cases must be taken in against such a gradient.

It has been shown that not only simple, single-celled organisms immersed in a solution, but also the root cells of higher plants, absorb nutrients actively and build up within their vacuoles concentrations many times that of the external solution. This cannot be explained by the simple diffusion theory, and most botanists now accept the **theory of active solute absorption.** This theory asserts that living cells absorb and accumulate certain solutes by forcing the dissolved particles to move from a solution where they are less abundant, across the protoplasmic layer into the cell sap, where they reach relatively high concentrations. This is accomplished by an expenditure of energy and constitutes a considerable portion of the labor which plant cells are required to perform. Experiments have shown that high absorption rates are usually attended by high respiration rates, and it seems logical to assume that this respiration provides the energy required for absorption and accumulation.

Among the factors involved in the active absorption of solutes the following are of primary importance: concentration of solutes in the cells and in the culture medium, age and activity of the cells, the oxygen supply to the cells, the supply of organic foods, and temperature of the culture medium. Other factors affecting absorption under certain conditions of culture are: the form of ion in which the nutrient element is combined, the reaction of the culture medium, and the presence of traces of " micro-elements " including boron, manganese, zinc, and copper.

We may summarize the principal facts pertaining to absorption by the plant cell as follows:

1. All substances which enter a free floating cell or the absorbing cells of multicellular plants must be in solution in water. This applies to gases as well as other solutes. Solids or colloidal mixtures in water can not pass.

2. All substances entering must pass through the cell wall and the cytoplasm before entering the vacuoles. The cell wall is normally saturated with water and permits, in most cases, everything in true solution to pass. The cytoplasmic membranes are semipermeable (or differentially permeable), permitting some solutes to pass through them but not others.

3. Under natural conditions plant cells absorb solutes from their external medium. Usually they maintain within their vacuoles higher concentrations of solutes than occur in their external medium; that is, the total number of molecules and ions of solutes of all kinds in a given volume is greater in the cell sap than in the solution outside.

4. Since water enters the plant cell by passive diffusion, the important function by which the plant is largely able to regulate its water content is active absorption of solutes. Such absorption constitutes work and requires energy which is supplied by the respiration of foods.

5. It is apparent that an absorbing cell may at one time be (a) absorbing solutes, different ones at different rates; (b) absorbing water; (c) excluding certain solutes; and (d) giving out some solutes, for example, carbon dioxide.

Photosynthesis.—The green unicellular floating plants to which we have frequently referred in this discussion have chloroplasts and when illuminated can carry on photosynthesis, the union of water and carbon dioxide to form the sugar, glucose, and starch. This same process goes on in the green cells of multicellular plants.

The changes which appear to take place in photosynthesis may be briefly stated as follows:

6 molecules of carbon dioxide	+	6 molecules of water in an illuminated green cell	form	1 molecule of glucose	+	6 molecules of oxygen each consisting of two atoms

This process may be expressed in the following chemical equation:

$$6CO_2 + 6H_2O = C_6H_{12}O_6 + 6O_2$$

Although six molecules each of carbon dioxide and water are necessary to furnish enough hydrogen and carbon atoms for one molecule of glucose, the number of oxygen molecules is more than enough for the formation of glucose. This excess of oxygen is liberated from the plant during photosynthesis and accordingly diffuses outward into the water surrounding the cell.

Photosynthesis is a process which will not go on unless energy is constantly supplied. There are other processes of which we shall learn, which, on the contrary, do not need to be supplied with energy but which liberate energy while they are in progress. Light is the source of energy for photosynthesis. This energy is not lost but is stored in the molecule of glucose as **chemical potential energy,** and can, as we shall see, be recovered and used. It is liberated when the glucose, or related substances which the plant may produce from glucose, is broken down again, in a process called respiration, into carbon dioxide and water.

In the green unicellular plant the sugar (glucose) produced by photosynthesis may be partly utilized by being converted into another sugar (sucrose or cane sugar, $C_{12}H_{22}O_{11}$) or into the closely related carbohydrate, cellulose, and used to thicken the cell wall. Part of the sugar may be transformed into still another carbohydrate, starch, and held as reserve food in the cell. Fatty substances needed by the protoplast may be produced from the sugar. Proteins may also be formed in such a cell by union of part of the sugar with the nitrogen, sulphur, and phosphorus, derived from inorganic salts absorbed from the water of the river or lake in which the cell lives. In the formation of fats and proteins there is a rearrangement of the molecules of the sugar but there is little, if any, loss of chemical energy. Sugar dissolved in the cell sap of such a cell may be in large part responsible for the high concentration of the sap and therefore for the absorption and retention of water and the maintenance of the turgor of the cell.

During photosynthesis the carbon dioxide used is withdrawn from solution in the water of the vacuole and from the water of the cytoplasm. Thus the concentration of dissolved carbon dioxide in the cell sap becomes less than that in the water outside the cell. As a result, diffu-

sion
cont
'
in tl
As ε
libeι

T
chaɪ

E
simɪ
This
livin

Fɪɢ. ˙
n
w
t
F
r
r

outsi
The
prodι
energ
and
In th
absoι
moleι
carbc
forms
energ
direc
in th
tion.

time of each nuclear division is the same, but the chromosome number differs greatly in different species. In the reproductive cells just referred to the number of chromosomes is one-half that in the dividing nuclei of ordinary cells.

While these changes have been going on in the nucleus, there have been formed in the cytoplasm, immediately surrounding the nucleus, two groups of delicate fibers which radiate toward the nucleus from two centers on opposite sides of the nucleus.

The nucleoli and the nuclear membrane now gradually disappear and the fibers extend to the middle of the nucleus where some of them appear to become attached to the chromosomes and others join with fibers coming from the opposite side. The two cones of fibers meeting near the middle (**equator**) of the dividing cell form what is spoken of as the nuclear **spindle**.

Now the chromosomes, each consisting of two parallel strands in close contact with each other, become arranged in a plane half way between the two extremities (poles) of the spindle. Spindle fibers attached to the two strands of each chromosome appear to contract, drawing the two daughter chromosomes to opposite poles of the spindle. Thus there are formed two groups, each containing the same number of daughter chromosomes.

Soon the chromatin of each group of chromosomes begins to take on again the form of a nuclear net, one or more nucleoli make their appearance, and a nuclear membrane is formed around each of the new nuclei. Thus the process of mitosis is completed and the nuclei pass again into the resting condition.

Division of the cytoplasm begins in most cases before the daughter nuclei have fully regained the resting condition. About the time the daughter chromosomes reach the poles, the spindle begins to widen somewhat and new short fibers appear at the equator between the spindle and the cell wall. Now each fiber appears to thicken at a place half way between the two ends. These thickenings seem to increase in size and finally fuse, thus forming a continuous plate which extends across the mother cell from wall to wall. Within this plate a new cell wall is formed. After the formation of the new wall the fibers soon disappear entirely. Thus by mitosis, followed by division of the cytoplasm, two new cells are formed, and these two generally grow to the size of the original cell before a second cell division takes place.

Meiosis.—As the result of the splitting of each chromosome during mitosis the number of chromosomes in the daughter nuclei is the same as the number in the original nucleus. In meiosis the chromosomes are not split but are separated into two groups, each with half the

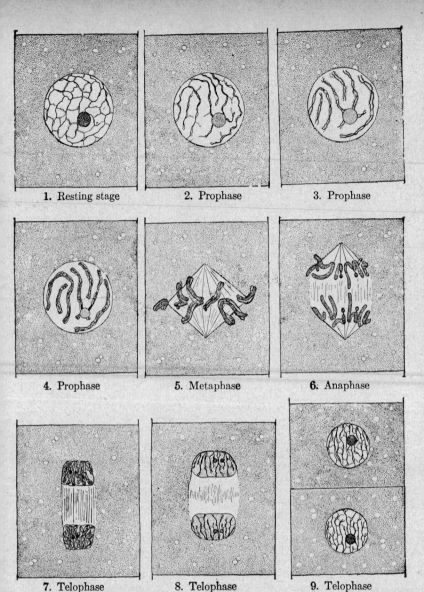

1. Resting stage   **2.** Prophase   **3.** Prophase

4. Prophase   **5.** Metaphase   **6.** Anaphase

7. Telophase   **8.** Telophase   **9.** Telophase

FIG. 45.—Semidiagrammatic representation of cell division in meristematic cells of a plant, showing nuclear division by mitosis. 1, Cell before division begins, with the nucleus in the resting condition. The chromatin threads form a net-work. 2, 3, 4, Prophase of nuclear division. In 2 and 3 the double nature of the chromatin threads is apparent. In 4 the chromosomes are distinct and their doubleness still apparent. 5, Metaphase of nuclear division; nucleolus and nuclear membrane have disappeared, the spindle has been formed, the chromosomes lie in or near the equator of the spindle, and some of the fibers are attached to the chromosomes. 6, Anaphase. Movement of daughter chromosomes away from the equator of spindle. 7, 8, 9, Telophase. In 7, daughter chromosomes form two compact masses. 8, Reorganization of resting nuclei begun, the double nuclear threads become apparent, nuclear membrane and nucleolus appear. In 9 the nuclear net is forming and the new cell wall separates the two new cells. (The nuclei redrawn from a figure in Sharp's *Introduction to Cytology*, 3rd Edition, McGraw–Hill Book Co.)

original number of chromosomes, which form the new nuclei, and accordingly meiosis is often spoken of as **reduction division** of the nucleus. We shall describe the process in detail in connection with reproduction in flowers.

Growth.—In addition to being able to absorb raw materials and light energy, to construct foods, to convert these foods into protoplasm, and to secure the necessary energy by respiration for all other processes except photosynthesis, the unicellular plant is able to grow. Growth of the cell results in part from the increase in the quantity of protoplasm, and in part from the absorption of water into the vacuole or vacuoles, increase in their volume and a stretching of the cell wall due to the resulting turgor. During growth sugar is converted into cellulose by the protoplasm lining the cell wall. Thus the thickness of the cell wall may be increased.

TISSUES

In all multicellular plants, except the very simplest ones, the plant body is made up of a number of different kinds of cells adapted to serve different functions in the life of the plant. These different kinds of cells may differ in their form, in the thickness of their walls, in the length of life of the protoplasts, or in other particulars. A group of cells, which together perform a particular function, is called a **tissue.** We shall give here the characteristics by which cells belonging to the principal tissues may be recognized. In the chapters on the stem, root, leaf, and other organs, these tissues will come up again for discussion, particularly as to their functions and their distribution in the plant. All the tissues of the plant may be classified into **meristematic tissues** and **permanent tissues.**

Meristematic Tissues

At the tips of all the roots and stems there are groups of cells which by repeated division give rise to new cells. These new cells and their subsequent enlargement are responsible for the growth in length of the stem and root, and the production of branches, stems, and of new leaves within the bud. The groups of actively dividing cells at the tips of the root and stem are spoken of as the **growing points** of stems and roots.

Just outside the cylinder of wood which forms the greater part of the stem of most shrubs and trees is a layer of cells which by their division add new cells continuously to the wood and to the inner bark. Some herbs also have such a layer of cells which causes increase in thickness of the stem. This layer is called the **cambium.** Another

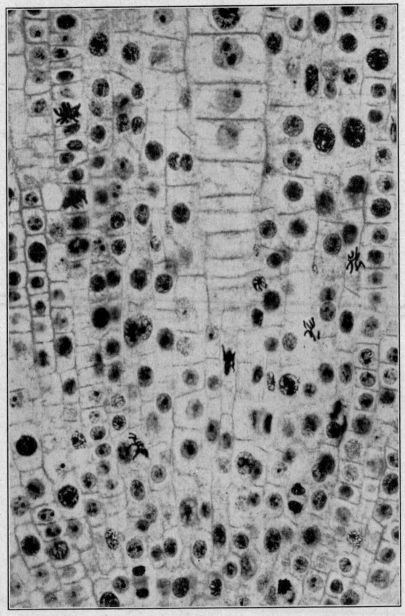

FIG. 46.—Photomicrograph of a lengthwise section of onion root tip, just back of the root cap, showing typical meristematic tissue. Observe that certain cells are in a process of mitosis.

somewhat similar layer, called the **cork cambium,** produces the outer
bark of woody plants. These cambiums and the cells of the growing
points are the principal meristematic tissues. **The meristematic tissues
are those which produce new cells and thus make possible the growth
of the roots and stems in length and in circumference.** They are
generally compact tissues, being without the intercellular spaces (spaces
between cells) which are present in most other tissues. In meristematic
cells the nucleus makes up a relatively large part of the volume of the
protoplast, the vacuoles are very small, and the cell walls are very thin.

Whereas the usual course of differentiation is progressive, that is
from meristem to adult tissues, it is not at all uncommon in plants for
differentiation to be regressive. By this we mean that tissues which
have attained the characteristics of maturity may become meristematic.
For example, in woody plants certain adult cortical cells may become
meristematic and undergo repeated divisions, producing daughter
cells, some of which become a secondary tissue known as cork, and
others become a secondary tissue known as phelloderm.

Permanent Tissues

Some or all of the new cells produced by meristematic tissues soon
become transformed into permanent tissues, of different kinds, which
make up the greater part of the plant. The permanent tissues are
made up of cells which no longer divide and which are more or less
modified by change of form, thickness of walls, composition of cell-wall
material, etc., and which are adapted to their special functions.

Epidermis.—This is the surface layer of leaves and of all parts of
the stems and roots which are not covered with bark. With rare
exceptions the epidermis is only one cell thick. The protoplasm forms
a thin layer lining the cell cavities. In the young parts of roots the
epidermal cells serve the function of absorption of water and mineral
substances from the soil. They are thin-walled and have tubular
extensions (root hairs) closed at the ends which grow out into the soil.
A further account of their structure will be found in the discussion of
the anatomy of the root. The epidermis of the parts of the plant which
are above ground serves to protect the underlying tissues from drying
out and to a certain extent from mechanical injury, the outer walls
of these epidermal cells being convex, considerably thickened, and
waterproofed. The surface layer of the outer epidermal wall of the
aerial parts of most plants consists of a waxy substance called **cutin.**
This superficial layer of cutin is called the **cuticle** and covers the entire

epidermis of the parts above the ground except where the epidermis has been replaced by cork. By means of certain stains and chemical tests the cutin can be readily distinguished from the cellulose of the rest of the wall. It is highly impermeable to water and to gases. In most plants chloroplasts are absent from the epidermal cells except in the case of the special cells (**guard cells**) which control the small openings (**stomata**) by which gases enter and pass outward from the leaves and young stems.

Simple Permanent Tissues.—It is convenient to discuss first the simple tissues, each of which consists of many cells, all of one kind. The principal simple tissues are **parenchyma, collenchyma, sclerenchyma,** and **cork.**

Parenchyma.—This tissue is widely distributed throughout the plant and makes up a large part of fruits, flowers, and leaves, and of young roots and stems which are not yet woody. Parenchyma generally consists of rounded cells with thin cellulose walls and a single large vacuole in each cell. Many intercellular spaces filled with air are found between the cells. The protoplasts remain alive for a long time, and in this respect parenchyma differs greatly from certain cells of the outer bark and of wood in which the protoplasts die almost as soon as

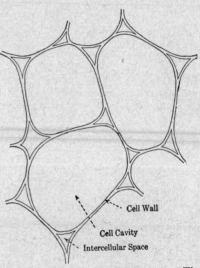

Cell Wall

Cell Cavity

Intercellular Space

FIG. 47.—Typical parenchyma tissue. The cell contents are not shown.

the cells are fully formed. Parenchyma cells are sometimes found mingled with various other kinds of cells in such mixed tissues as the xylem or wood, which we shall discuss later. Chloroplasts are present in the green parenchyma of leaves and young stems, and sometimes in the parenchyma of young fruits.

Collenchyma.—The cells of this tissue are elongated and thickened at the corners. The protoplasts are long-lived, and chloroplasts are frequently present. Collenchyma (Fig. 48) is the first of the mechanical (strengthening) tissues to be developed and is found, therefore, even in the young parts of the stem. Its cells are capable of considerable elongation after they are formed. The walls are composed of alternating layers of pectin and cellulose.

Sclerenchyma.—This includes the two most important strengthening (mechanical) tissues of plants, **fibers** and **stone cells**. **Fibers** are elongated cells, thickened all around and generally pointed at the ends. In extreme cases they may be as much as a meter in length but ordinarily they are not nearly so long as that. In some instances the thickness of the wall is so great that the cavity (lumen) of the cell almost disappears. Soon after the fibers have attained their full size and thickness

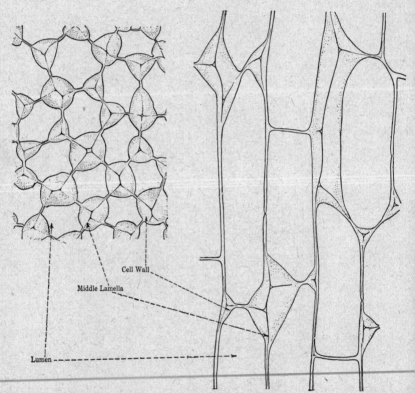

Cell Wall

Middle Lamella

Lumen

FIG. 48.—Collenchyma tissue. At left, cross section; at right, longitudinal section. The cell contents are not shown.

of wall their protoplasts die. However, before the protoplast dies, the walls frequently undergo **lignification** (impregnation of the wall with a substance called **lignin**). This change in the walls results in an increase in strength and hardness. Fibers are often very elastic and can be stretched to a remarkable degree without losing their power of returning to their original length. Linen and many other textile and cordage materials consist almost entirely of plant fibers.

Stone cells are cells which, like the fibers, have their walls lignified and greatly thickened, but which are not much elongated. From the small cell cavities of stone cells, and from the cell cavities of fibers also, minute canals extend outward through the thickened wall (Fig. 51), being separated only by the thin middle lamella from the ends of similar canals in the walls of adjoining cells. Through the middle lamella separating the ends of these canals extend plasmodesmata. Along these plasmodesmata, exchange of materials from one cell to another can go on until the thickening of the wall is completed and the protoplasts die. The gritty texture characteristic of the flesh of many varieties of pears and the hardness of the bark of many trees are due to groups of stone

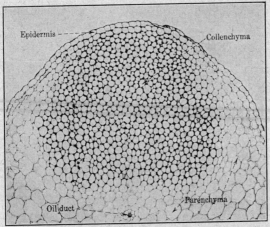

Fig. 49.—Photomicrograph showing in cross section a strand of collenchyma tissue from the petiole of celery leaf. (From Esau.)

cells. The shells of walnuts, coconuts, and many other nuts consist almost entirely of stone cells.

Cork.—The older parts of the stems and of the roots are covered with many layers of a tissue called cork (Fig. 52), which forms the outer bark. It is from this outer bark of the cork oak (*Quercus suber*) that the cork of commerce is secured. The cork cells are generally flattened and usually have relatively thin walls and no intercellular spaces. Between the middle lamella and the inner cellulose layer of each of these cell walls is a layer of a fatty substance, called suberin, which renders the cells almost impermeable to water or gases and makes this tissue an excellent protection for the stem against excessive loss of water and against mechanical injury. The protoplasts of cork cells die very soon after the cells are formed.

Complex Permanent Tissues.—In addition to simple tissues, each made up of but one kind of cell, there are also found in the plant **complex tissues** each consisting of a number of different kinds of cells. The principal complex tissues are **xylem** and **phloem,** which serve principally the function of conduction of materials lengthwise in the plant, the

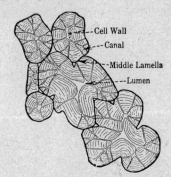

Fig. 51.—Stone cells from the shell of English walnut (*Juglans regia*).

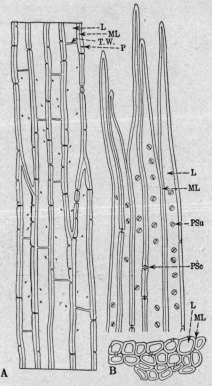

Fig. 50.—Fibers. *A,* from pericycle (*Aristolochia*); *B,* from xylem (*Liquidamber*), as seen in cross and longitudinal sections. *L,* lumen; *ML,* middle lamella; *P,* simple pit; *PSc,* pit, in cross section; *PSu,* pit, surface view; *T.W.*, transverse wall.

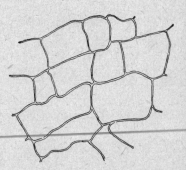

Fig. 52.—Cork cells from the stem of Dutchman's pipe (*Aristolochia*).

xylem conducting principally water and inorganic (mineral) substances which are absorbed from the soil, and the phloem transferring food from one part of the plant to another.

Xylem.—This complex tissue may include **parenchyma cells** (xylem parenchyma), **fibers, tracheids,** and **vessels.** Fibers and parenchyma cells have already been described.

Tracheids are single dead cells, always elongated, and generally pointed at the ends (Fig. 53). The walls are thin in certain places and thick in others. Sometimes the thickening is restricted to rings or spiral bands running around the cells; in other cases all the wall is thickened except for numerous small, round, or oval areas or pits. The walls of tracheids are always lignified.

A **vessel** is not a single cell but a tube made up of a series of dead

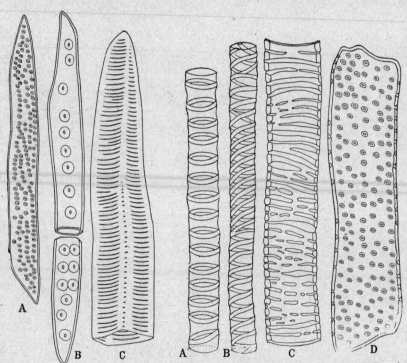

FIG. 53.—Tracheids. *A, Liquidamber; B, Pinus; C, Davallia* (a fern).

FIG. 54.—Vessels. *A*, annular (*Nicotiana glauca*); *B*, spiral (*Aesculus*); *C*, scalariform (*Cucurbita*); *D*, pitted (*Aristolochia*). *C* and *D* in longitudinal section.

cylindrical cells, most of which have the end walls dissolved away (Figs. 54 and 68). These tubes, like the tracheids, have part of the area of their walls thickened. Those which are formed in a part of the stem which has not yet finished growth in length have thickened rings or spirals. Those which are formed later have the wall much more completely thickened and the thin areas in the form of pits of various shapes. The walls of vessels, like those of tracheids, are generally lignified. Vessels are often several centimeters in length (distance between two successive cross walls), and in some trees vessels occur which exceed a meter in length.

Phloem.—This is a complex tissue which in the angiosperms consists

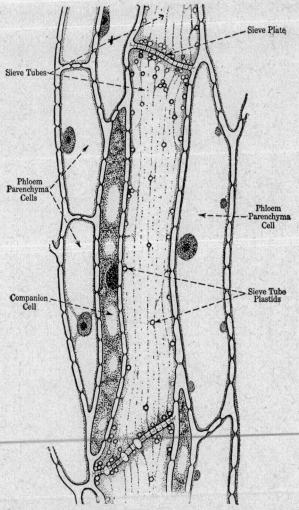

Fig. 55.—Phloem tissue from the stem of *Nicotiana tabacum*, showing sieve tubes, companion cell, and phloem parenchyma cells. (Drawing, and section from which it was made, prepared by Crafts.)

of **sieve tubes, companion cells,** and **phloem parenchyma cells** (Fig. 55). In gymnosperms, companion cells are absent. In certain groups of plants the phloem also includes **fibers.** Sieve tubes are vertical rows of elongated cells, with the end walls thickened and perforated. Through these minute perforations (whence the term sieve tube) pass cytoplasmic strands connecting the cytoplasm of adjoining sieve tubes. Nuclei are absent from mature sieve tubes, and the cytoplasm forms a thin layer surrounding a large central vacuole through which run lengthwise slender cytoplasmic strands. Adjacent to the sieve tubes there are generally found one or more parallel rows of elongated companion cells which may

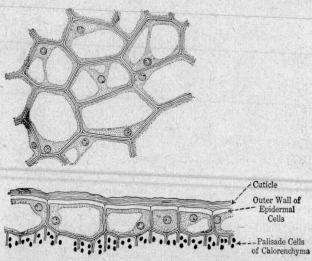

Fig. 56.—Ordinary epidermal cells from the upper side of a leaf. Above, surface view; below, as seen in section. For the stomata and guard cells see Figs. 149 and 151.

be equal in length or shorter than the cells composing the sieve tubes. They generally present a striking contrast with the sieve tubes on account of their smaller diameter, dense cytoplasm, and prominent nuclei. The walls of companion cells, sieve tubes, and phloem parenchyma cells are of cellulose. The walls separating the companion cells and sieve tubes are generally perforated. It is probable that the principal function of phloem tissue is the longitudinal transfer of organic substance synthesized in the leaves. Since the sieve-tube cells when they mature become permeable to all substances in solution, it is probably through the sieve tubes themselves rather than through other types of phloem cells that the organic substances move.

(2) **stems of herbaceous dicotyledonous plants,** and (3) **stems of mono-cotyledonous plants.** Although there is no sharp distinction between herbaceous and woody stems and although the stem of monocotyledonous plants may in some cases be woody, there are certain rather definite structural characteristics associated with each of these three types of stems but there is also much variety of structure within each of the types.

It will be necessary to distinguish here between the principal groups of the Spermatophyta in order that it may be clear of what kinds of plants the different

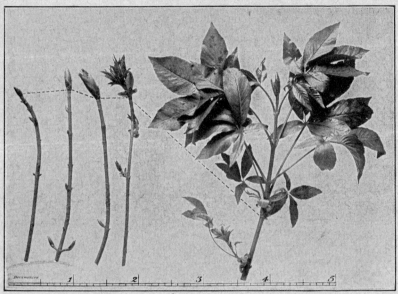

Fig. 60.—Five twigs of buckeye (*Aesculus*) showing successive stages in the opening of the terminal bud and in the growth of the internodes and leaves which, in a rudimentary condition, were contained within the bud. All the parts above the dotted line belonged to the terminal bud or were developed within a period of three weeks from a terminal bud like the one shown at the extreme left. The scale at the bottom of the figure is a decimeter scale.

stem types are characteristic. The Spermatophyta are divided into two classes, the Gymnospermae and the Angiospermae. The former, as their name, Gymnospermae (naked-seeded plants), indicates, bear their seeds not within a closed structure or fruit as the other seed-bearing plants do, but exposed, generally on the surface of a cone-scale. Almost all of the common Gymnospermae have narrow, needle-like or scale-like evergreen leaves, and bear cones. Some of the commonest plants belonging to this class are: the pines (*Pinus*), spruces (*Picea*), firs (*Abies*), hemlock (*Tsuga*), redwood and big tree (*Sequoia*), and the so-called Douglas fir (*Pseudotsuga*). Most of the common Gymnospermae are trees with excurrent branching and "soft" wood. The Angiospermae include all the other Spermatophyta. Generally they have broad leaves, and their seeds are produced in closed structures, spoken of botanically as fruits. A pea pod, an acorn, and an apple are examples of such seed-enclosing structures.

The Angiospermae consist of two subclasses, the dicotyledons and the monocotyledons. The first of these includes many more species than the second. The grasses (which include the cereals), the lilies, the palms, and the orchids are among the principal families of the monocotyledons. Most other common angiosperms are dicotyledons.

Among the most common of the more than 250 families of dicotyledons are the buttercup family, the mustard family, the rose family, the bean family, and the sunflower family. A large number of those dicotyledons which live for several years are deciduous, losing their leaves once each year and later producing new leaves. In this respect they are in striking contrast with most gymnosperms, which are evergreen. There are, however, a few deciduous gymnosperms and many evergreen dicotyledons. The dicotyledons include most agricultural plants of orchard,

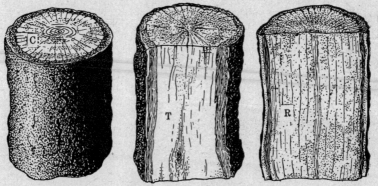

FIG. 61.—Stems showing three kinds of sections: *C*, cross or transverse. *T*, tangential. *R*, radial.

field and garden, except the cereals, asparagus, and onions, which are monocotyledons. The oak, beech, maple, ash, and other "hardwood" forest trees are also dicotyledons.

In discussing stem structure we shall have to use frequently the terms transverse, radial, and tangential as applied to sections of stems or other organs of the plant, and it is important that the meaning of these terms be explained before we proceed further. If we think of a piece of a stem as a cylinder, and if we imagine a line, which we shall call the long axis, extending lengthwise through the middle of this cylinder, we may define as follows the three kinds of sections:

A transverse, or cross, section is any section cut at right angles to the long axis. A tangential section is one cut parallel to the long axis of the stem (or other cylindrical organ) and at right angles to radii which pass through the middle line of the section. A radial section is one cut

parallel to the long axis and parallel to all the radii passing through
the section. Both tangential and radial sections are spoken of as longitudinal sections. Clearly all radial sections are at right angles to the
tangential sections and if they are cut clear through the stem from
side to side will pass through the center. Cell walls are also spoken
of as transverse, tangential, or radial if they are parallel respectively to
transverse, tangential, or radial sections.

STEMS OF WOODY PLANTS

DICOTYLEDONS AND GYMNOSPERMS

Although herbaceous stems are in general somewhat simpler in
structure than woody stems the evidence seems to show quite certainly
that this greater simplicity is not
due to the woody type of stem
having been produced by evolution from a primitive type which
was herbaceous. On the contrary, the woody type of stem
came first in evolution and from
it there later developed, by sim-
plification, the herbaceous type.
For this and other reasons we
shall discuss first the structure
and development of woody stems.

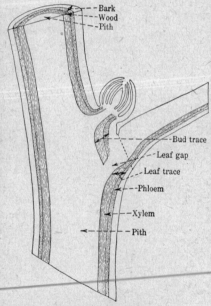

FIG. 62.—Section of stem showing the base
of a leaf which is about to fall; the
dotted line shows the approximate position of the abscission layer.

Gross Structural Features.—
If we examine with the unaided
eye or, better, with a pocket lens
of low magnification, the cut end
of a piece of a woody stem, several regions can be made out. If
the stem is one to several centimeters in diameter it will be
found to consist mostly of a
central cylinder of wood. The
bark, which includes the tissues
outside of the woody cylinder,
may be easily removed, because of the layer of thin-walled, easily broken
cells, the **vascular cambium**, lying next to the wood.

Somewhat closer examination of the woody cylinder shows at the
center, the **pith**, which consists of softer tissue. A number of circular
lines concentric with the pith and cambium are present in the wood.
The tissue between one of these lines and the next is an **annual ring**
and consists of the cells which are added to the wood by the cambium

in a single year. The radiating lines of varying length in the wood are the **wood** or **xylem rays.** They are made up of cells elongated in a radial direction which function for radial conduction of materials. In large stems (see Fig. 75) two regions can often be distinguished in the wood, an inner portion often darker in color and not active in water conduction (the **heartwood**), and the **sapwood** which lies between the heartwood and the cambium.

Two layers can often be distinguished in the bark, (1) the outer bark generally brownish in color and corky in character, and (2) the inner bark, which in young stems is generally green. All these features of the woody stem will be discussed in detail later.

The Origin and Development of the Tissues.—The development of the tissues and the structure of the stem at various ages can best be understood by examining both cross and longitudinal sections. The cross sections should be cut at various distances from the stem tip in order to show the stages in development. It should be constantly borne in mind that the greater distance any portion of the stem is from the growing point in the terminal bud, the older it is.

The meristematic cells of the growing point are all essentially alike. They form a rounded cone of tissue which is known as the **promeristem (primordial meristem)**, in which growth is chiefly by increase in the number of cells, rather than by increase in their size.

In the growing point, we note that the cells of the promeristem have differentiated somewhat in size and shape to form three main tissue groups: the **protoderm,** the **ground meristem,** and the **procambium.** These are the **primary meristems.** Their cells continue to divide, though less actively than those of the promeristem. By further differentiation they give rise to the **primary permanent tissues,** which are tissues no longer capable of active cell division but fitted to carry on the various activities of the stem.

The **protoderm** is the outermost layer of cells. It develops into the **epidermis,** a primary permanent tissue. When protoderm cells divide, the walls formed are usually radial, that is, at right angles to the surface of the stem. As a result of these radial divisions the protoderm increases in circumference and thus keeps pace with the increasing volume of the underlying tissues.

The **ground meristem** makes up the greater part of the tissue within the protoderm. It consists of relatively large thin-walled isodiametric cells, which differentiate into the following primary permanent tissue groups: the **cortex,** and **pericycle,** the **pith rays,** if these are present, and the **pith.**

When **procambium** cells first become distinguishable from the promeristem they are generally in strands, appearing therefore in a transverse section as isolated groups of cells. These strands are arranged in a circle. A little later more procambium cells may be formed between these strands until in many stems there is produced a continuous hollow cylinder (a ring when seen in transverse section) of procambium. In some stems the strands never join in this way. The procambium cells are smaller, as seen in cross section, than are those of the ground meristem. They are, however, much longer, and many of them are pointed at the ends. From the procambium three tissue groups or regions are derived as differentiation goes on.

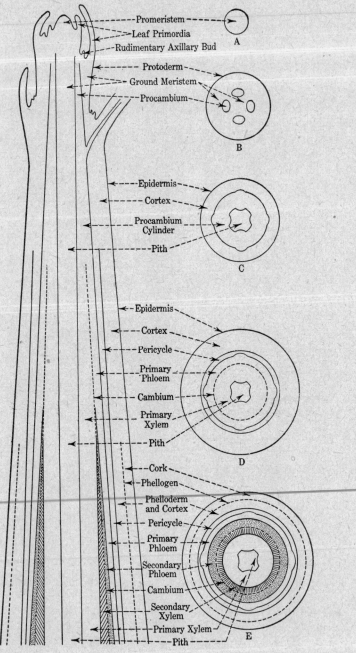

FIG. 63.—Diagram of longitudinal and cross sections of a woody dicotyledonous stem, showing primary and secondary growth.

These are the **phloem,** the **cambium,** and the **xylem.** In the cases where the procambium is in strands and these do not join to form a procambium cylinder, the phloem, xylem, and cambium from a single strand constitute a **vascular bundle.**

Primary Permanent Tissues.—Before the end of the first season's growth the differentiation of the primary meristems (protoderm, ground meristem, and procambium) into the primary permanent tissues has generally been completed. The primary permanent tissues include: (1) the epidermis, (2) the cortex, and (3) the stele, including (*a*) the pericycle, (*b*) the vascular tissue, (*c*) the pith rays, if they are present, and (*d*) the pith or medulla.

The Epidermis.—This is usually a single layer of cells generally isodiametric as seen in transverse section but somewhat elongated in the direction of the stem's length. The differentiation which takes place as the protoderm cells change over into epidermal cells consists principally of a thickening of the outer walls and to some extent of the radial walls, whereas the inner walls remain thin. While this thickening is going on, the cuticle is being formed and the cellulose wall underneath this layer is sometimes infiltrated with cutin.

The Cortex.—This tissue group is bounded externally by the epidermis and internally by the pericycle. The outer cells of the cortex, those lying just beneath the epidermis, are usually collenchyma which constitutes the first mechanical or strengthening tissue of the developing stem. Beneath the collenchyma is a zone composed chiefly of thin-walled parenchyma which makes up a large part of the cortex. In addition to collenchyma and parenchyma, sclerenchyma cells (stone cells or fibers), with lignified walls, are also sometimes found in this region. The change from ground meristem cells to collenchyma involves lengthening of the cells and thickening of the corners, whereas differentiation of the fibers is accompanied by elongation and thickening of the walls " all around." When meristem cells become parenchyma less change is involved, the cells merely growing in size in all directions, developing at the same time larger vacuoles and intercellular spaces.

The Pericycle.—Internal to the cortex there is in some plants a region called the pericycle which extends inward to the phloem. In other plants this region is not well set apart, but is confluent with the phloem. The pericycle is usually composed of two sorts of tissue, sclerenchyma and parenchyma. The sclerenchyma of the pericycle is made up of closely fitting fibers. These may form isolated groups opposite the vascular bundles or may form a continuous ring.

The Pith.—This also is formed by the transformation of ground meristem cells. It is made up of large-celled parenchyma with relatively numerous intercellular spaces, and its principal function is food storage.

FIG. 64.—Diagram showing the tissues derived from the primary meristems. (After Stevens.)

Pith Rays.—In those cases in which the procambium remains in separate strands, each strand becomes differentiated into a vascular bundle, and between these bundles wide strips of parenchyma extend from the pith to the pericycle.   Since these strips may be considered to be extensions of the pith they are spoken of as pith rays.   They may be distinguished from other rays by the fact that they always extend clear to the pith.   They also extend longitudinally from one node through an entire internode to the next node.

The Vascular Tissue.—The procambium cells of the outer portion

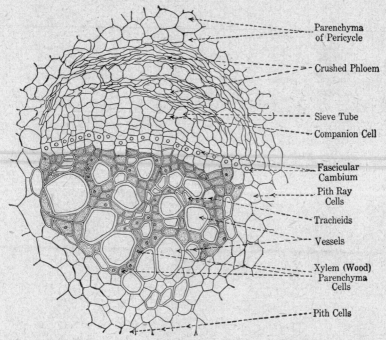

Parenchyma
of Pericycle

Crushed Phloem

Sieve Tube

Companion Cell

Fascicular
Cambium

Pith Ray
Cells

Tracheids

Vessels

Xylem (Wood)
Parenchyma
Cells

Pith Cells

Fig. 65.—Cross section of a young vascular bundle of a dicotyledonous stem.
(*Aristolochia.*)

of the procambium strand or cylinder become transformed into phloem and those of the inner portion into xylem.   Only a few of the phloem and xylem elements are differentiated at first, but their number increases with the distance from the promeristem.   A single layer of the procambium cells lying between the xylem and phloem does not differentiate at all into permanent tissue but continues to function as meristematic cells.

The Phloem.—The phloem is made up of four kinds of tissue elements: sieve tubes, companion cells, fibers, and phloem parenchyma cells, except in the gymnosperms which lack companion cells.   A description of these tissue elements of the phloem has already been given on page 90.

The Cambium.—When most of the cells of the procambium become differentiated into phloem and xylem and lose their ability to divide, a single layer of cells between the xylem and phloem retains the power of division, that is, remains meristematic. This is the *vascular cambium.* Its cells are thin-walled and rich in protoplasm, flattened tangentially, and in woody stems considerably elongated in the direction of the long axis of the stem, and pointed at the ends. In cross section, cambium cells appear brick-shaped. The cells of the cambium are capable of

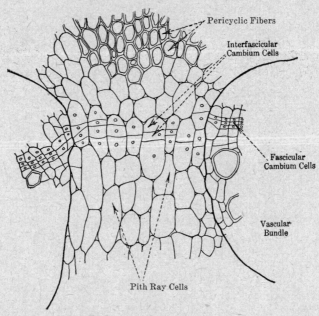

FIG. 66.—Part of a pith ray and two vascular bundles of a young Aristolochia stem, showing the origin in the stem of interfascicular cambium cells from pith ray cells.

repeated division giving rise on the inner side to new (secondary) xylem elements and on the outside to secondary phloem elements. In stems with separate vascular bundles between which are pith rays, the cambium layers of adjoining bundles are connected by strips of cambium cells formed by tangential division of the parenchyma cells of the pith ray so that a complete cambium cylinder is formed. The cambium between the bundles, by its divisions, adds new parenchyma cells to the pith rays. In stems with a continuous cylinder of xylem the cambium is from the first a continuous cylinder between the phloem and xylem.

The xylem and phloem differentiated from the procambium is called **primary xylem** and **primary phloem**; those formed by the cambium, **secondary xylem** and **secondary phloem**. The daughter cells of the cambium layer are at first very similar in appearance to the cambium cells but gradually they take on the characteristic form of the xylem and phloem elements into which they develop.

Xylem.—The principal tissue elements found in the primary xylem

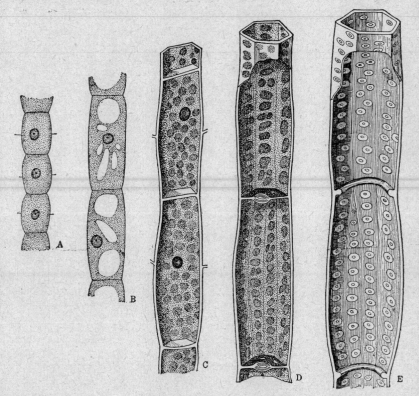

FIG. 67.—Stages in the development of a pitted vessel from procambium cells. (After Bonnier and Sablon.)

are vessels, tracheids, and xylem (wood) parenchyma cells and xylem (wood) fibers.

Vessels.—These are long tubes of considerable diameter, which have been formed by the elongation and enlargement of rows of cells of the procambium strand; in this differentiation of procambial cells, most of the end walls are totally or partially dissolved. Thus, a row of cells becomes transformed into a tube of considerable length closed at either end by walls which were not dissolved. At the time of the formation of the vessel the protoplasm of the component cells dies. Functional vessels have, therefore, no living contents (Fig. 68). Before the protoplasts disappear, the walls of vessels become thickened, and the thickening material is laid down on the walls in various patterns, such that thick and thin regions alternate. The material laid down is cellulose, but subsequently these layers of cellulose are lignified.

Depending on their sculpturing, that is, upon the distribution of the

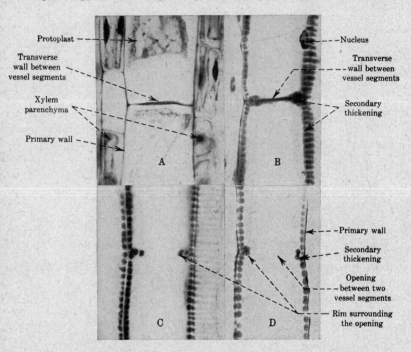

FIG. 68.—Photomicrographs showing, in longitudinal section, development of spiral vessels in celery. A, the transverse wall between two vessel segments is intact; the segments contain protoplasts and their longitudinal walls are primary throughout. B, spiral secondary thickening has been laid down over the primary walls except over the central portion of the transverse wall. C and D, the central portion of the transverse wall has been dissolved away, the protoplasts have disappeared and the vessel segments communicate with each other through a large opening. (From Esau).

thinner and thicker areas of the cell walls, vessels are spoken of as **annular** (ringed), **spiral, reticulate** (netted) or **pitted.** Annular and spiral vessels are the only kinds found in the xylem first differentiated from the procambium. They are formed before the stem has completed its elongation and can stretch owing to the thinness of the wall between the rings or spirals. In most gymnosperms vessels are lacking.

Tracheids.—A tracheid is a single elongated cell, more or less pointed at the ends.   Thus, it differs from a vessel, which is formed from a row of cells, the end walls of which have become totally or partially dissolved. Their length seldom exceeds 1 millimeter, and they have thick lignified walls which in most cases have bordered pits.   There are also spiral and annular (ringed) tracheids.

Pits may be simple or bordered, the former type occurring in vessels, tracheids, and other tissue elements of the xylem, and the latter being best exemplified in the tracheids of conifers although of common

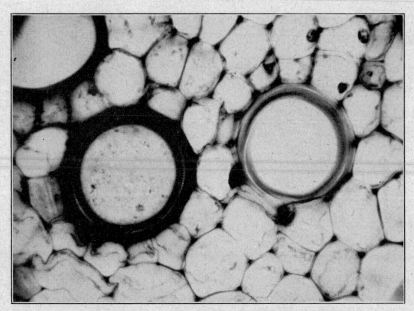

Fig. 69.—Photomicrograph showing, in cross section, two spiral vessels surrounded by xylem parenchyma from the petiole of a celery leaf. The vessel to the right is mature and empty; the one to the left is immature; it is closed by a transverse wall and contains cytoplasm. (From Esau.)

occurrence in other woody plants.   In the bordered pit (Fig. 71) the thickened portion of the wall overarches the margins of the pit.   Sometimes the original cell wall or closing membrane has a central thickened area called the **torus**.   The thinner marginal part of the closing membrane may be perforated by numerous small openings.

The tracheids, like the vessels, carry water and inorganic salts. They are also important in giving strength to the woody stem.   Like vessels, tracheids probably do not function to any extent in conduction until their protoplasts die.   It seems likely that the thin areas in the walls of vessels and tracheids make conduction of sap from one conducting element to another easier. The thick areas may, on the other hand, prevent the collapse of the walls (and resultant blocking of the cavities) when sap is being drawn up the stem by suction originating in the leaves above.

Xylem Parenchyma Cells.—These have simple pits. Their protoplasts remain alive for a long time, surviving long after those of the vessels, tracheids, and wood fibers are dead. They are found here and there among the other elements of the xylem. Their function is the

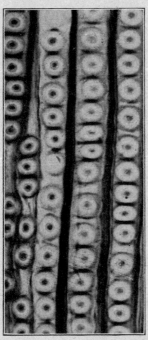

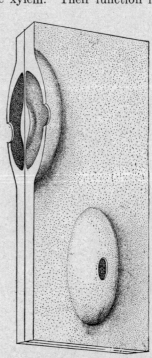

FIG. 70.—Photomicrograph of a radial section of the wood of *Sequoia sempervirens* (redwood) showing bordered pits.

FIG. 71.—Diagram showing the structure of a bordered pit. Above, the pit is shown in section.

storage of water and food, and they also conduct these substances for short distances.

A Summary of Primary Permanent Tissues.—In our study of the young woody dicotyledonous stem we have been concerned thus far only with the tissues derived from the primary meristems. At the growing point of the stem there is just one tissue—the promeristem. This meristem gives rise to three primary meristems: protoderm, ground meristem, and procambium.

These tissues further differentiate into the **primary permanent tissues.** In the following outline there is shown the relation of meristems to differentiation in the shoot of spermatophytes. The solid arrows indicate the direct, progressive origin of meristems; broken arrows indicate regressive origin of meristems.

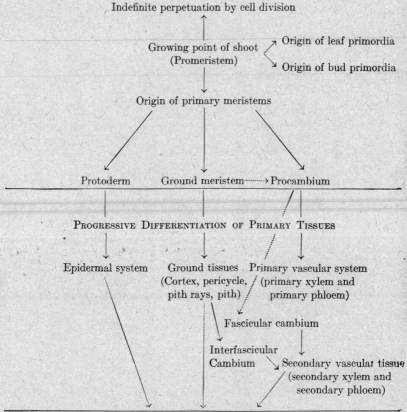

The cortex may be composed of parenchyma and collenchyma, the pericycle of parenchyma and fibers; the primary phloem of phloem parenchyma, sieve tubes, companion cells, and phloem fibers; and the primary xylem of vessels, tracheids, wood parenchyma, and wood fibers.

To the pericycle and the tissues which it encloses, whether in stem or root, the collective term, **stele,** is applied.

Secondary Growth in Woody Stems (of Dicotyledons and Gymnosperms).—The changes from the promeristem to the primary permanent tissues listed in the above outline are together spoken of as the **primary growth** of the stem. This primary growth is generally completed within a few months. Increase in length of the stem is limited to the region in which primary growth takes place. Regions of the stem which have completed length growth may increase in thickness as the result of the production of new cells by (1) the cambium (which we have already described) and by (2) the phellogen, or cork cambium (which will be discussed later). This growth in thickness of the stem is called **secondary growth** and may continue for hundreds of years, or even several thousands as in the sequoias.

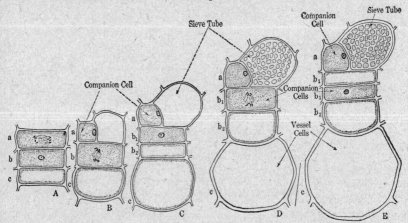

Fig. 72.—Stages showing the differentiation of cambial cells. Diagrammatic.

When a new xylem element is to be formed a cambium cell divides by a tangential wall into two daughter cells of which the inner one, next to the xylem, develops into a xylem element. The outer daughter cell, next to the phloem, remains a cambium cell and again divides. Generally it is the outer daughter cell which remains meristematic and continues to divide, but when new phloem elements are to be produced the inner daughter cell retains the power of division and the outer daughter cell is added to the phloem. The cambium cells continue thus to divide throughout the growing season, adding new (secondary) xylem on the outside of the old xylem and new (secondary) phloem on the inside of the previously formed phloem. The tissue elements of the secondary xylem may be wood parenchyma cells, vessels (formed from a series of cells), tracheids, or wood fibers. The latter differ from tracheids in having thicker walls and much-reduced pits and are thus

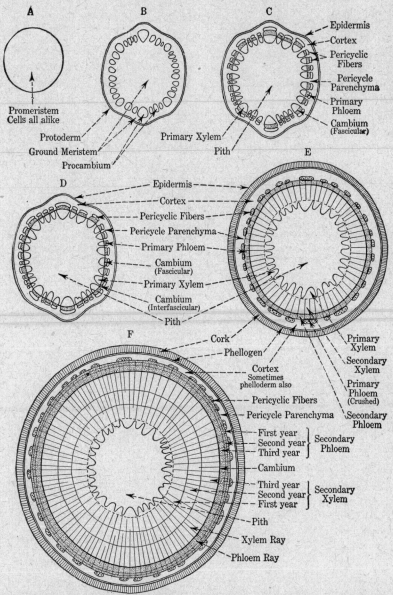

FIG. 73.—Diagrams of cross sections of a dicotyledonous stem (*Sambucus*) showing primary and secondary growth up to three years. (Drawing, and section from which it was made, prepared by Esau.)

better fitted for strengthening the stem and are not suitable for water conduction. The tissue elements of the secondary phloem may be phloem parenchyma cells, sieve tubes, companion cells, or fibers.

A daughter cell of the cambium which is to be added to the phloem may divide radially to produce a sieve tube cell and a companion cell or transversely to produce several phloem parenchyma cells.

As the radial width of the xylem increases, the distance from the phloem, which conducts food, to the innermost of the water-conducting elements of the xylem becomes greater. The resulting need for better conduction radially of water from the xylem to the phloem and cambium and of food from the phloem to the cambium and living wood parenchyma cells of the xylem seems to be met by the production of **vascular rays** by the cambium. These are formed, here and there, when a longitudinal row of cambium cells or several adjoining rows cease the pro-

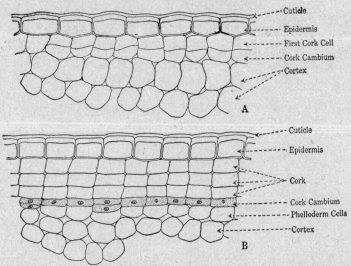

Fig. 74.—Cross sections of portions of a stem showing origin of cork cambium (*A*), and the development of cork and phelloderm from cork cambium (*B*).

duction of xylem and phloem elements and produce parenchymatous cells which are somewhat elongated radially and apparently fitted for radial conduction of materials.

The part of a vascular ray which is in the xylem is often spoken of as a **xylem** or **wood ray**; that in the phloem as a **phloem ray.** On account of their difference of origin, vascular rays should be carefully distinguished from the pith rays of stems having their vascular tissue in separate bundles.

The principal points of distinction beside the difference in origin are: (*a*) pith rays are for a given stem fixed in number; (*b*) they extend from the pith to the pericycle; (*c*) they generally extend longitudinally through an entire internode, from node to node; (d) they are primary in origin in that their tissue is formed by the differentiation of the ground meristem, though secondary tissue is added to them by the interfascicular cambium as they elongate radially. Vascular rays, on the other hand, are: (a) not fixed in number, for as the stem grows older more and more are produced; and (b) they never extend inward as far as the pith or outward to the pericycle. In a longitudinal direction a vascular ray extends for only a few cells, never throughout the length of an internode.

The term medullary ray has been so long and universally used to include both pith rays and vascular rays, and the distinction between these two kinds of rays is so fundamental, that it seems best to give up entirely the use of the older and more inclusive term rather than to restrict its use to pith rays.

Owing to the enlargement of the cylinder of tissue within the cambium ring, as a result of the addition of cells by the cambium itself, it becomes necessary for the cambium ring itself to increase in circumference. This is accomplished in certain instances by the radial division of some of the cells of the cambium to form new cambium cells. Where the cambial cells are very long, there are oblique divisions of these cells, accompanied by a slipping of the ends of the daughter cells past each other. Thus there appear two cells lying side by side where there was one cell before. These divisions result in the vascular rays becoming more distant from each other so that the tracheids, vessels, and other elements of the xylem and the elements of the phloem would come to be some distance from a vascular ray were it not for the initiation of new vascular rays by the cambium. The result is that no tissue elements of xylem and phloem are far distant from the nearest vascular ray.

The Phellogen (Cork Cambium).—The phellogen is a meristem similar in some respects to the cambium ring. Its origin is in certain cells of the cortex, or rather rarely, as in the apple, in the epidermis itself. When it arises in the cortex it is usually the cells just below the epidermis which become the phellogen. Certain of these cells become meristematic and undergo repeated tangential divisions (Fig. 74), producing daughter cells on both sides. The outer daughter cells may be transformed into **cork** cells, and thus a layer of cork is formed beneath the epidermis. The cork cells soon die and become suberized, and as a result the epidermal cells are cut off from water and food supplies and do not long remain alive. The inner daughter cells may remain alive for a long time. These cells are similar to the cells of the cortex and form a (secondary) tissue called **phelloderm.** As a rule, the phellogen produces more cork than phelloderm.

Summary of the Secondary Growth of Woody Stems.—Owing to the activities of the vascular cambium and the cork cambium there may be added to the stem each year the following:

By the vascular cambium:

1. New xylem on the outside of the old xylem.
2. New phloem on the inside of the old phloem.
3. Vascular rays in both xylem and phloem.

By the phellogen or cork cambium, or cambiums:

4. Cork on the outside of the cork cambium.
5. Phelloderm on the inside of the cork cambium.

Annual Rings.—In temperate and cold climates a season of cambial activity alternates with a period of inactivity. Each growing season the cambium produces a new layer of wood which is generally many cells thick. As seen on the end of a log these layers appear as con-

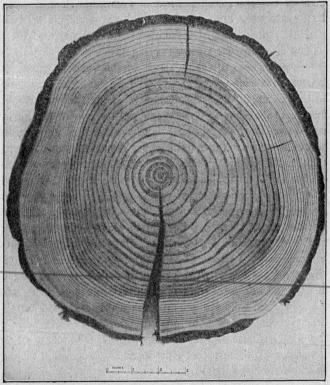

FIG. 75.—Cross section of a log of redwood (*Sequoia sempervirens*) showing annual rings, light-colored sapwood, and dark-colored heartwood. Note the radial splitting which gives evidence of greater tangential than radial shrinkage of the wood as it dries. (From Division of Forestry, College of Agriculture of the University of California.)

centric rings.   They are the **annual rings** to which reference has already
been made.

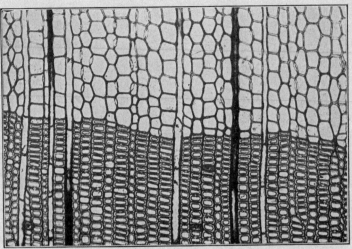

FIG. 76.—Cross section of a portion of the wood of *Sequoia*.   Portions of two adjacent
annual rings are shown.   Note the small, thick-walled tracheids of "summer
wood," and the larger, and thinner-walled tracheids of "spring wood."
(Photograph furnished by E. Artschwager.)

In woody plants growing in those parts of the world where there is

FIG. 77.—Piece of a board of Douglas fir, *Pseudotsuga taxifolia*, cut from a saw guard
in a lumber mill.   Constant pelting with sawdust from the band saw has worn
away the spring wood and left the thick-walled summer wood almost intact.
(Photograph furnished by Emanuel Fritz.)

each year a definite season of growth and a resting season or season of
inactivity, each annual ring consists of two parts which are more or

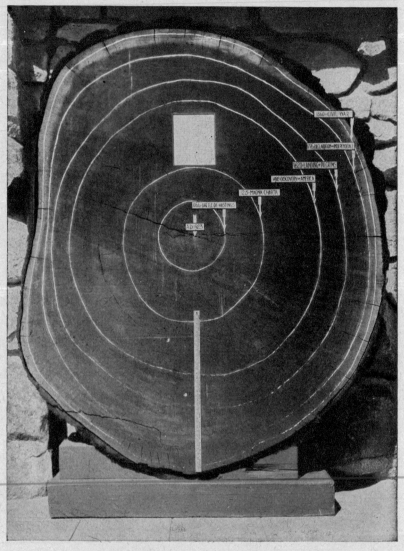

Fig. 78.—A cross section of the trunk of a relatively young tree of *Sequoia gigantea* (Big tree). The chalk lines and the arrows, except the central one, indicate approximately the annual rings formed in the years during which a number of events of great historic importance took place. The tree from which the section was cut began its growth in about A.D. 923 and was about 1000 years old when cut. There are trees now standing which are certainly twice that age and probably living trees 3000 years old exist.

less readily distinguishable. These are the inner part or spring wood and the outer part or summer wood. In the spring wood of dicotyledons, the vessels are usually large and quite numerous; in the summer wood, vessels are relatively smaller and fewer or lacking entirely. The tracheids and wood fibers of spring wood are relatively less abundant and thinner-walled than those of summer wood. The summer wood of one year (1923, for example) adjoins the spring wood of the following year (1924). Hence, small, thick-walled elements of the summer growth of one year are adjacent to the relatively large, thin-walled wood elements of the spring growth of the following year, and the sharp line of demarcation between them is thus visible even to the naked eye (Figs. 75, 76, and 84).

In most gymnosperms vessels are wholly absent and annual rings are distinguishable by reason of the differences in the tracheids of the summer and spring wood. The tracheids laid down in summer, as

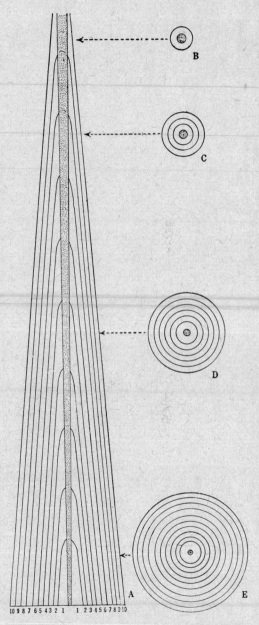

Fig. 79.—Diagram showing longitudinal and cross sections of a ten-year old tree. Note the decrease in the number of annual rings from the base of the trunk to the apex.

compared with those formed in spring, are smaller, have thicker walls, and are often radially flattened.

The width of the different annual rings in the same stem is not the same. This variation is due to differences in light, temperature, moisture, and other external conditions and also to the age of the stem.

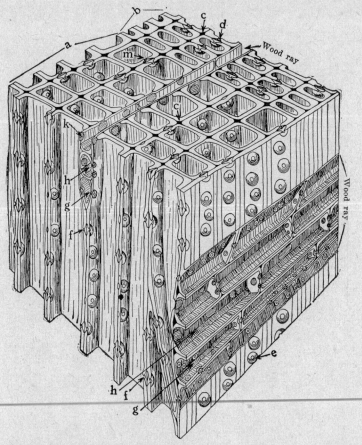

FIG. 80.—Diagram showing block of pine wood. *a*, spring wood; *b*, summer wood; *c*, intercellular space; *d*, bordered pit in tangential wall of summer wood; *m, f*, and *e*, bordered pits in radial wall of spring wood; *h* and *g*, wood ray cells; *k*, thin place in radial wall of wood ray cell. (After Stevens.)

The first few rings produced are generally wider than those formed later. If we could interpret all the variations in width of the rings we would find that much of the history of a tree is recorded in the cross section of its trunk.

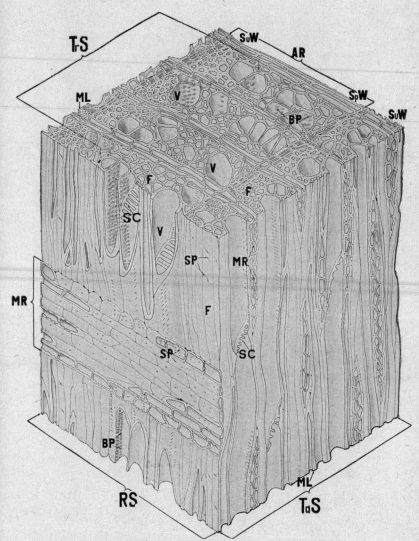

FIG. 81.—Diagram of a typical hardwood. *TrS*, cross section; *RS*, radial section; *TaS*, tangential section; *AR*, annual ring; *SuW*, summer wood; *SpW*, spring-wood; *MR*, xylem ray; *V*, vessel; *F*, wood fiber; *SP*, simple pits; *BP*, bordered pits; *SC*, scalariform perforations; *ML*, middle lamella. (After chart by U. S. Forest Products Laboratory.)

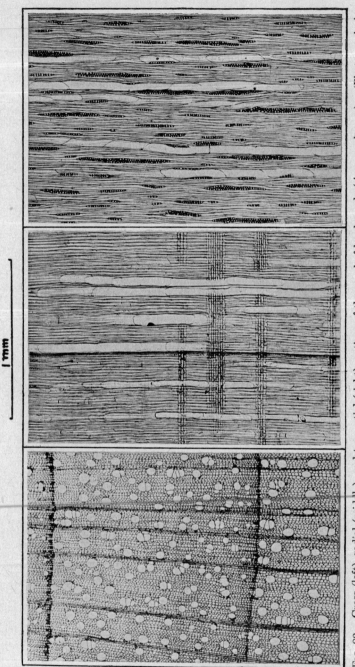

FIG. 82.—Cross (left), radial (middle), and tangential (right) sections of the wood of hard maple (*Acer saccharum*). (Photographs by United States Forest Products Laboratory, Madison, Wis.)

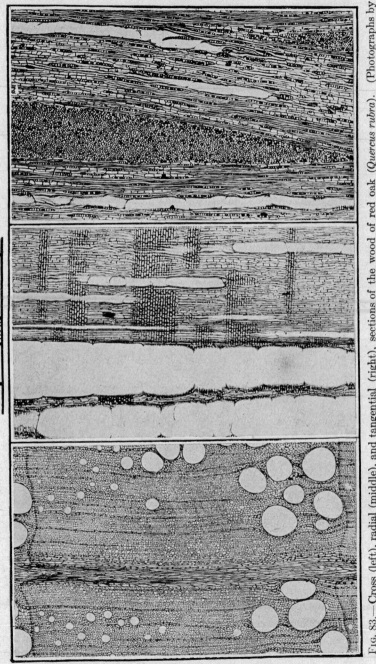

FIG. 83.—Cross (left), radial (middle), and tangential (right), sections of the wood of red oak (*Quercus rubra*). (Photographs by United Forest Products Laboratory, Madison, Wis.)

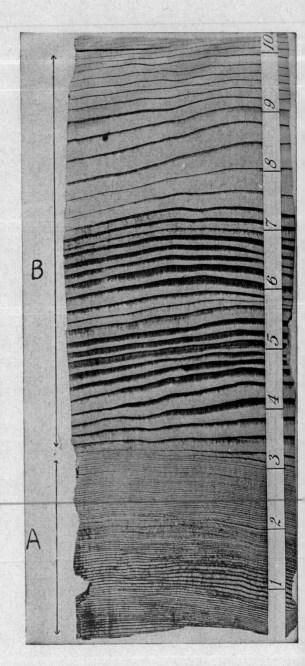

FIG. 84.—Cross section of a part of a redwood log showing the effect of external conditions on the width of growth rings. The portion of the wood marked "A" was produced during a period of about eighty years. That marked "B" was produced during a subsequent period of about forty years. Up to the time of the increase in ring width the tree grew under unfavorable conditions, crowded and shaded by larger trees which surrounded it. The surrounding trees were then felled by lumbermen and in the following forty years the increase in stem diameter was almost four times that during the preceding eighty years. (Photograph by the Forestry Division, College of Agriculture, of the University of California.)

Determining the Age of Felled Trees.—The number of annual rings seen in a cross section of a tree indicates the age of that part of the trunk. The number of annual rings decreases from the base of the trunk to its apex. For example, it is only in sections cut through at the base of a ten-year-old tree that ten annual rings will be found. Any section cut within the limits of the growth in length made by the plant during its first year will show ten annual rings. A section through that portion of the tree which was added to its length the second year will show nine annual rings; thus, in sections through the growth of the third year and each succeeding year, to the tenth, the number of annual rings will be eight, seven, six, etc., decreasing by one each year. The twig growth made the tenth year will show only one ring of wood (Fig. 79).

During the growing season, a drought or an insect attack may interrupt the activity of the cambium by destroying the foliage. Later, the tree may produce a new crop of leaves, and these will enable the cambium to become active again and to develop a new ring of wood. Thus, in a single season two rings of wood may be formed. These extra rings may lead to inaccuracies in estimating the age of a tree by counting the rings. It is not often that such extra rings are formed.

Wood.—We have used the term wood for the xylem part of the stele. Let us study the structure of the wood of an old stem (trunk) by an examination of cross, radial, and tangential sections.

Cross Section.—In cross section, the annual rings appear as more or less parallel bands, each with spring and summer wood. The wood rays are seen as narrow radial lines crossing the annual rings at right angles. The vessels, tracheids, wood fibers, and wood parenchyma have their long axes running longitudinally, and accordingly in cross section the cavities of the vessels appear as large rounded pores; the tracheids and wood fibers are seen as much smaller and thicker-walled elements which are polygonal or square in shape; the wood parenchyma cells resemble wood fibers and tracheids in cross section but have thinner walls.

Radial Section.—The annual rings appear in radial section as more or less parallel bands which impart to the wood its characteristic grain. **Coarse-grain** wood is wood with wide annual rings; **fine-grain** wood has narrow rings. Wood rays, as seen in radial section, appear as bands or bars of varying width and length, running at right angles to the vessels, tracheids, and wood fibers. Vessels appear as long, narrow grooves.

A quarter-sawed board is simply a thick radial section. The beauty of quartered oak and other woods is due to the luster of large wood rays, when cut radially.

Tangential Section.—In tangential section, the annual rings appear as wide bands, which may form various irregular figures. The wood rays are cut across and appear as lens-shaped groups of cells. Vessels, wood fibers, tracheids, and wood parenchyma appear much as they do in radial section.

Heartwood and Sapwood.—If we examine the cut end of a log, we observe that the woody cylinder consists of a light-colored outer zone, the **sapwood**, surrounding a generally darker-colored zone, the **heartwood**. Sapwood is composed of elements some of which, chiefly the wood parenchyma cells, are still alive, whereas heartwood

consists of elements all of
which are dead. The darker
color of heartwood of many
trees is largely due to the deposition in the cell walls and
cell cavities of resins, gums,
tannin, certain pigments, and
other substances. These de-
positions increase the weight,
hardness, and durability of
the heartwood, and they
also plug up the conducting
elements and thus retard or
entirely stop the movement
of sap. Transport of sap is
almost entirely confined to
the sapwood. The loss of
the conducting power of the
vessels and tracheids of the
heartwood is due in some
species to the plugging of
these elements, not only by
the substances mentioned
above, but also by **tyloses.**
These are formed while the
parenchyma cells are still
alive. Where such cells are
in contact with tracheids or
vessels, their protoplasts may
break through the thin portions (pits) of the walls of the
conducting elements and thus
form protrusions (tyloses)
into the cavities of the latter
(Fig. 85).

Bark.—All the tissue
outside of the vascular
cambium is included un-
der the term bark. The
bark is readily separated
from the woody cylinder,
because the walls of the
cambium cells are thin
and easily ruptured. The
bark is made up of the
following tissues and
tissue groups: cork, cork
cambium, phelloderm, cortex, pericycle, and phloem.

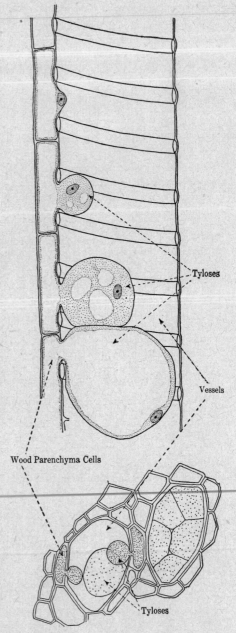

Fig. 85.—Tyloses in various stages of development in the vessels of black locust (*Robinia
pseudacacia*).

As a stem grows older, the original cork cambium may cease its activity and a new cork cambium may be formed deeper in the cortex. Subsequently, new cork cambiums may appear at successively lower levels. In a very old stem, cork cambium may be formed even as deep in the bark as the phloem. In plants in which the original cork cambium remains active for years there may frequently be seen (as in the cork of *Aristolochia*) conspicuous layers or " annual rings " corresponding to variations in the seasonal activity of the cork cambium. It will be recalled that cork is made up of dead cells with suberized walls and that this tissue is there-

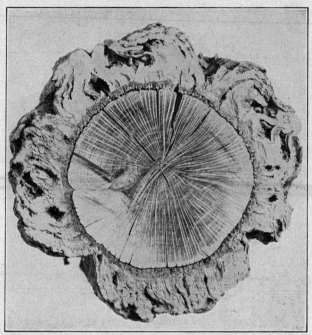

FIG. 86.—Cross section of a young tree of cork oak (*Quercus suber*), showing the unusually thick bark produced by this species, which is the source of commercial cork. Such cork as is here shown, the so-called "virgin cork," is unsuitable for "corks." It is stripped from the tree by cutting almost to the cork cambium. The subsequently formed cork tissue is more compact and homogeneous and suitable for cutting into "corks." (Photograph furnished by the Division of Forestry of the University of California.)

fore highly impermeable to water and dissolved substances. Consequently, any living cells outside the corky layer will soon die.

As a result of the increase in stem circumference through the activities of the cambium layers, the outer cork layers are stretched and may finally split. These layers may soon become detached from the stem, leaving the surface of the bark smooth, as in the sycamore (*Platanus*). In other plants, such as the oak (*Quercus*) and the elm (*Ulmus*), they may remain attached for a number of years, thus forming a thick bark which is generally broken into characteristic furrows.

The cork replaces the epidermis as a protective tissue. It shields the tissues beneath from mechanical injury, and from the entrance of insect and fungous parasites. On account of its poor conduction of heat, it may protect the underlying tissues from sudden and great changes of temperature. Most important of all, as a waterproof covering, cork is very effective. It is this property which is made use

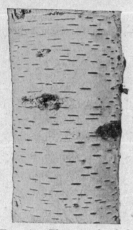

of when we utilize cork to close bottles containing liquids. The value of cork in checking water loss is also well shown in the case of the potato tuber, which is covered by a thin layer of cork. It has been determined that a peeled potato tuber may lose in twenty-four hours over sixty times as much water as it did in the same period before the layer of cork was removed.

FIG. 87.—Photograph of the stem of a white birch (*Betula alba*) showing numerous lenticels and two old leaf scars.

Lenticels.—In very young parts of stems, gases may enter and leave through the stomata of the epidermis. When cork is formed beneath the epidermis this impervious layer tends to cut off communication between the stomata and the cells of the cortex. This would prevent the access of oxygen to the cells which underlie the cork, were it not for special ventilating regions in the cork. It is always just beneath a stoma that such regions are formed. There, the cork cambium cells may give rise, not to typical cork cells, but instead to large thinwalled cells among which are intercellular spaces. These masses of

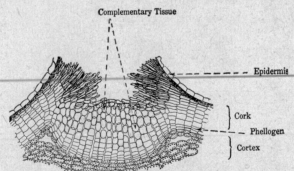

FIG. 88.—Transverse section of lenticel of two-year old stem of elder. (*Sambucus nigra.*) (After Haberlandt.)

tissue, which by enlargement finally break through the epidermis and project slightly above the surface of the stem, are known as **lenticels** (Fig. 88). They permit an exchange of gases between the atmosphere and the intercellular spaces of the tissues beneath the bark. Lenticels are especially conspicuous in such plants as plum and cherry (*Prunus*), and in birch (*Betula*).

HERBACEOUS DICOTYLEDONOUS STEMS

Herbaceous dicotyledonous stems are similar to woody stems such as we have just described in the development of their primary tissues from the promeristem and the primary permanent tissues. Most herbaceous stems like most woody stems have the vascular tissue in the form of a continuous cylinder, but sometimes there is instead a circle of distinct vascular bundles. In some cases the vascular tissue

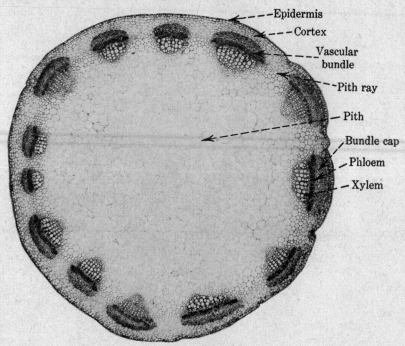

Fig. 89.—Photomicrograph of a cross-section of the stem of clover (*Trifolium repens*), an herbaceous, dicotyledonous plant.

is in distinct bundles in the upper part of the stem and in a continuous cylinder near the base. The most conspicuous difference between herbaceous stems and such woody stems as we have described is the absence of, or smaller quantity of, secondary phloem and xylem, due to the cambium being absent or its activity being limited to a single season or less. As a result the pith makes up a relatively larger part of the stem than in woody stems. Herbaceous stems thus resemble in general young woody stems. Actually, under climatic conditions which permit herbaceous dicotyledonous plants to continue their growth

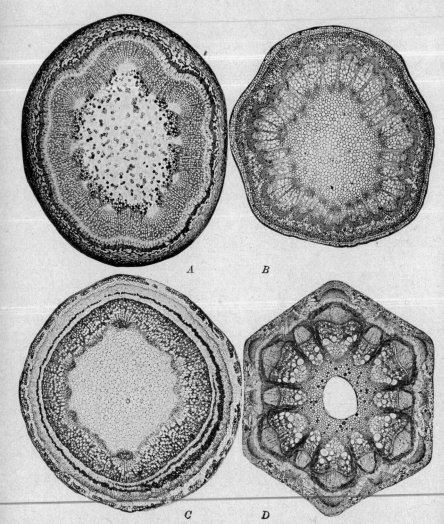

Fig. 90.—Types of dicotyledonous stems. *A, Liquidambar,* tree, stele continuous. *B, Platanus,* tree, stele dissected. *C, Lonicera,* woody vine, stele continuous. *D, Clematis,* woody vine, stele dissected. (After Sinnott and Bailey, from Eames and MacDaniels, *An Introduction to Plant Anatomy,* McGraw–Hill Book Co.)

for more than a year, they may develop relatively more secondary vascular tissue and become like typical woody stems.

THE MONOCOTYLEDON TYPE OF STEM

As in the woody dicotyledonous and gymnosperm stems and herbaceous dicotyledonous stems, the promeristem of the growing point of

monocotyledons, such as Indian corn or **Trillium,** differentiates into the
three primary meristems. The protoderm becomes a single epidermal

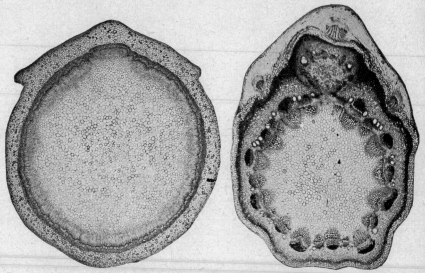

FIG. 91.—Types of herbaceous dicotyledonous stems (continued). *E, Digitalis,*
herb, stele continuous. *F, Artemisia,* herb, stele dissected. (After Sinnott and
Bailey, from Eames and MacDaniels, *An Introduction to Plant Anatomy,*
McGraw–Hill Book Co.)

layer which does not differ essentially from that of other seed plants. The
procambium always occurs in
numerous strands scattered
throughout the ground meristem or at least throughout the
outer region of it. All the
procambium cells differentiate
into xylem and phloem elements and none remain in the
meristematic condition as do
those of the vascular cambium
of gymnosperms and dicotyledons. Bundles of this sort,
which are without a cambium,
are called **closed bundles** (closed
to further growth) (Fig. 93).
Those of other seed-bearing
plants in which a cambium lies
between the xylem and the
phloem are called **open bundles.**

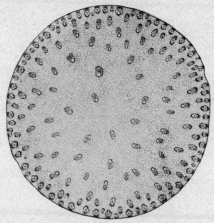

FIG. 92.—Photomicrograph of a cross section through an internode of a stem of
(*Zea mays*), an herbaceous monocotyledonous plant. Note the many separate
vascular bundles scattered through the
parenchyma.

The vascular tissue is in numerous scattered bundles, not in a single ring of bundles or in a hollow cylinder, as in dicotyledons and gymnosperms. In many grasses the center of the stem has no bundles, and as such stems grow they often develop a central pith cavity which becomes very large in the "straws" of wheat and certain other cereals.

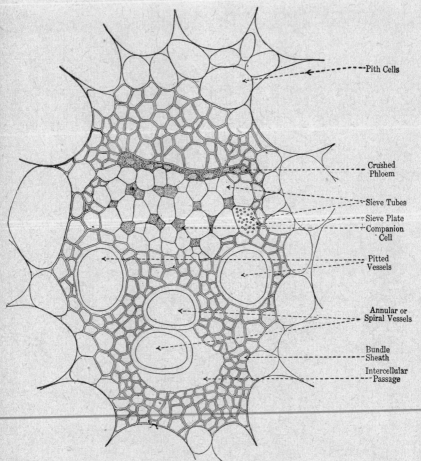

Pith Cells

Crushed Phloem

Sieve Tubes

Sieve Plate
Companion Cell

Pitted Vessels

Annular or Spiral Vessels

Bundle Sheath
Intercellular Passage

FIG. 93.—Cross section of a vascular bundle of the stem of corn (*Zea mays*)—a monocotyledon.

Between the epidermis and the outermost vascular bundles is a narrow zone corresponding to the cortex and pericycle, but these two regions are not distinctly marked off from each other in most monocotyledonous stems.

Owing to the absence of a cambium, most monocotyledonous stems are not able to add to the quantity of xylem and phloem or to increase to any considerable extent the number of cells in any of the other tissues. Most monocotyledonous stems do not increase much in thickness as they increase in age. What growth in thickness they have is due to enlargement of cells of the primary permanent tissues differentiated from the primary meristems. In a few tree-like monocotyledons, such as *Cordyline*, *Yucca*, and *Aloe*, however, there is a true secondary thickening. In these plants a cambium arises in the pericycle or in the innermost cortex and produces a limited amount of secondary tissue on its inner side. Certain groups of cells derived from this cambium develop into typical closed vascular bundles and other cells derived from it remain parenchymatous. Thus there are developed vascular

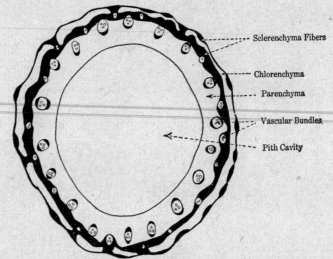

Sclerenchyma Fibers

Chlorenchyma

Parenchyma

Vascular Bundles

Pith Cavity

Fig. 94.—Cross section of the stem of rye (*Secale cereale*). Redrawn from Nathanson.

bundles which may be arranged to some extent in rows, to the outside of and between which is newly differentiated parenchyma.

The characteristic features of monocotyledonous stems are as follows:

(a) The large number of vascular bundles and their more or less scattered distribution.

(b) The absence of cambium in the vascular bundles.

(c) The slight increase in the stem circumference on account of the absence of a cambium. The increase that does occur is mostly the result of growth in the size of cells already present. Exceptions to this general statement have already been cited.

of producing marked physiological effects. In addition to their influence on root production, there is reason to believe they may affect respiration, dominance of certain parts of plants over others, flower production, fruit formation, elongation of cells, and plant movements. Their rôle in cell enlargement and certain tropisms was discussed on pages 40 and 41.

Under natural conditions, pieces of the stem may become detached and develop in the same way into new plants. Propagation by means

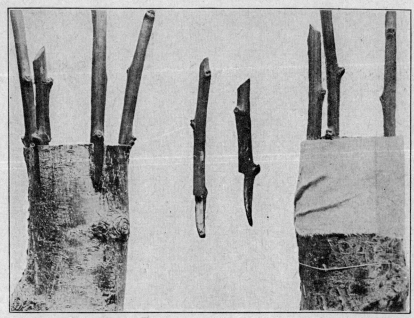

FIG. 101.—Stem grafting. Two scions are shown in center; at left, the scions are inserted in clefts of the stock, and in such a manner as to bring the cambium tissue of stock and scion in close contact; at right, the grafts have been waxed over, and covered with cloth. (From the Division of Pomology, College of Agriculture, University of California.)

of cuttings, whether of stems or of other vegetative structures, is of great importance in agriculture, because by this method new plants may be secured which are true to type. It is a matter of common knowledge that in the propagation of many economic plants by means of seeds, the offspring are often quite unlike the parent. Apples, for example, seldom come true to type when grown from seed. Hence, it is possible to secure new varieties by planting seed, but when a desirable variation appears it is propagated by means of plants which develop at the nodes of the horizontal stems (runners). These plants will have all the desirable characteristics of the plant from which they came. Propagation by means of cuttings of stems, roots, or leaves, or by grafting, often has the additional advantage that the cuttings or grafts often develop more rapidly than plants grown from seeds.

Propagation by grafting is a very old horticultural practice, and is in common use in propagating fruit trees. In grafting, a piece of one stem, called the **scion,** is attached to another stem, which is rooted and is called the **stock,** in such a way as to bring together the cambium layers of each (Fig. 101). When a stem is wounded, as in grafting, there is formed a mass of large, thin-walled cells known as **callus.** This differentiates from certain living cells of the xylem and the bark, chiefly from vascular ray cells. The cambium contributes very little to the callus. A new cambium is formed by differentiation of callus cells, and this cambium becomes continuous with the cambium of stock and scion. Phloem and xylem elements are then formed which link up phloem and xylem of scion and stock. However, there is evidence that xylem and phloem differentiate directly from callus tissue, preceding cambium formation. Thus there is a union of the stock and scion. At the same time,

FIG. 102.—A stem cutting, showing the independence of root and callus formation. (From Bioletti.)

cork cells are differentiated from outer cells of the callus, and these become continuous with old cork and thus effectively close over the point of union of scion and stock.

Budding is a horticultural practice which is essentially the same as grafting. It differs from grafting only in the character of the scion. In budding, the scion used is a single bud together with a small strip of adjoining bark. This is attached to the cut surface of the stock in such a manner as to bring the cambium of stock and scion together. The process of healing and union is similar to that which takes place in the case of a graft.

Growth Medium of Stems.—The growth medium of stems may be either air, soil, or water. Many plants produce both aerial and subterranean stems. For example, asparagus, rhubarb, and Irish potatoes have underground stems, and from these are sent up aerial stems bearing foliage, leaves and flowers. Water also is in some cases the medium of growth of stems, as in such plants as *Elodea*, *Potamogeton*, and various water lilies, etc. Such aquatic stems possess extensive systems of large connecting air spaces in the tissue of the stem in which air is stored. The entire stem system of most plants grows in air. In our common ferns the entire stem is underground, but in the tropical tree ferns there is an erect aerial stem or trunk bearing a leafy crown.

Fig. 103.—Iris plants, showing the rhizomes with leafy shoots and roots. (From Bocquillon.)

STEM MODIFICATIONS

Ordinarily we think of a stem as a cylindrical organ growing more or less erect, but there are many modifications of stems differing so much in form and in other respects from the ordinary type that they are scarcely recognizable as stems, and careful study of their origin and structure is often necessary to identify them as such. Some of the commonest types of modified stems are rhizomes, tubers, corms, and runners, all of which are vegetative reproductive structures.

Rhizomes.—These are elongated, underground, horizontal stems, generally rich in stored food. The rhizomes of *Iris* (Fig. 103), many ferns and the weeds listed in the following paragraph are good examples. Rhizomes generally bear reduced scale leaves at the nodes. Rhizomes, like typical aerial branches, possess terminal buds and produce lateral buds at the nodes in the axils of the scale leaves. The lateral buds may give rise to aerial stems which usually die back to the ground each autumn.

Many of our most pernicious weeds are rhizome-bearing perennials.

Fig. 104.—Bermuda grass (*Cynodon dactylon*) showing the underground horizontal stems (rhizomes) and the general habit of the plant.

Familiar examples are certain species of wild morning glory (*Convolvulus*), quack-grass (*Agropyron repens*), Johnson grass (*Sorghum halepense*), nutgrass (*Cyperus rotundus*), and Bermuda grass (*Cynodon dactylon*). In the eradication of weeds of this class it is not sufficient merely to prevent the maturing and spreading of seed, for the plant is capable of propagating itself readily by means of the rhizomes, as well as by means of seeds. If the aerial stems are cut to the ground

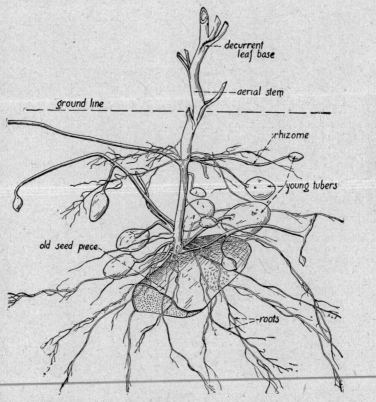

Fig. 105.—Portion of a sprouting potato tuber. (After Robbins, *Botany of Crop Plants.*)

line, new shoots are promptly sent up from the subterranean stems (rhizomes). Furthermore, if the rhizomes are broken into a number of separate pieces by cultivating implements, each piece may grow. This is simply a case of propagation by cuttings. Frequent cultivation, having as its aim the destruction of new shoots as soon as they appear, may succeed in starving out the rhizomes after a time, since food is made only in the green parts of the plant. When the food-making organs are removed, a certain amount of the stored food in the rhizomes is drawn upon to produce new aerial shoots. If these are again cut off as soon as they appear above ground, and before they have an opportunity to manufacture food, the rhizomes will finally be killed by exhaustion of their supply of stored food.

Tubers.—A tuber is a much-enlarged, short, fleshy underground stem. Tubers differ from rhizomes in their stouter form, their generally shorter internodes, and the usual absence of roots. They are commonly produced at the ends of rhizomes. The most familiar example of a tuber is the common Irish potato (*Solanum tuberosum*). When a piece of a potato tuber (really a stem cutting) is planted, "sprouts" are sent out from the "eyes." From these sprouts

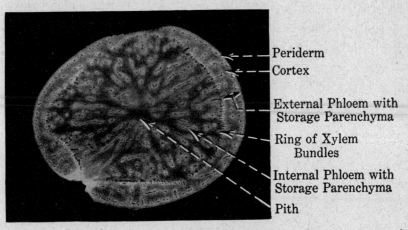

Periderm
Cortex

External Phloem with Storage Parenchyma

Ring of Xylem Bundles

Internal Phloem with Storage Parenchyma

Pith

FIG. 106.—Cross section of a potato tuber. Note the scattered bundles of external and internal phloem.

branches develop, some of which become the green, erect, leafy stems of the potato plant and some of which have no chlorophyll and grow horizontally underground. These horizontal branches have internodes and nodes with scale leaves and are quite obviously rhizomes. After the aerial part of the plant has produced a surplus of food the tips of the rhizomes become enlarged and thus form new potato tubers. Examination of a potato tuber reveals the presence of a terminal bud at the unattached "seed end" of the tuber, groups of lateral buds ("eyes") along the sides, and near each "eye" a small scale leaf. In an elongated potato, we may be able to make out the spiral arrangement of the "eyes," for there is only one "eye" at a node. The original epidermis of the tuber gradually dies and is replaced by a layer of cork cells (the "skin" of the potato) in which numerous lenticels may be observed. Careful

microscopic study of a section of a potato tuber shows the presence of
" skin " or periderm, cortex and pericycle (two narrow bands of tissue),
xylem, phloem elements (in numerous groups), a great quantity of
storage parenchyma tissue, and a central region corresponding to the
pith of typical stems.

Bulbs.—A bulb consists of a short, flattened or disc-shaped underground stem, with many fleshy scale leaves filled with stored food.
Actually a very small proportion of the tissue of a bulb is stem tissue, and
a bulb is rather a modified shoot than a modified stem. The common
onion (*Allium cepa*) is a typical example of a bulb (Fig. 107). When an
onion bulb is cut lengthwise through the center, one can see a small
disc-shaped stem upon which are borne the
numerous scale leaves which completely en-
circle the terminal bud at the tip of the
stem. Lateral buds may occasionally be
found in the axils of the scale leaves. In
the lower part of the disc-like stem there are
many rudimentary adventitious roots which

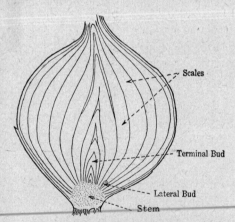

Fig. 107.—Median longitudinal section of an
onion bulb.

Fig. 108.—Corm of crocus, in
median longitudinal section.
(Redrawn from Figurier.)

develop when sufficient moisture is available. The terminal bud
develops into the aerial shoot of the plant and the axillary buds into new
bulbs. The reserve carbohydrate of most bulbs is not starch but sugars.

Corm.—A corm is a short, solid, vertical, enlarged underground
stem in which food is stored. A common example of a corm is the
underground stem of gladiolus or crocus (Fig. 108). Corms are usually
flattened from top to bottom, and bear a cluster of thick fibrous roots

at the lower side, and a tuft of leaves on the upper side. They differ from bulbs principally in being almost entirely made up of stem tissue with relatively few scale leaves whereas a bulb consists mostly of fleshy scales.

Runner.—A runner, or stolon, is a stem that grows horizontally along the surface of the ground. It resembles the rhizome in that its direction of growth is more or less horizontal, but differs from the rhizome in not being underground. The runners of the strawberry plant (Fig. 109) arise as axillary branches. The runners have long internodes, and produce leaves, flowers, and roots at certain nodes. Examination of the runners of strawberry shows that, whereas there are scale leaves at every node, new shoots and roots develop only at every other node. That is, between the parent plant and the first daughter plant there are

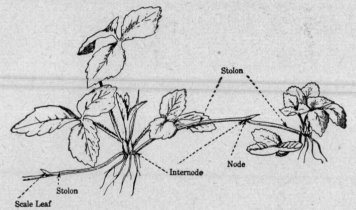

FIG. 109.—A strawberry (*Fragaria*) plant showing propagation by means of stolons.

two internodes, between the latter and the second daughter plant, two internodes, and so on. By the death of runners, daughter plants become separated from the original plants.

Stem Tendrils.—Although tendrils are generally formed from some part of the leaf, there are tendrils which are morphologically stems. This is shown by the fact that they may arise in leaf axils and bear small leaves or flowers. In the Fox grape (*Vitis*) the tendrils are stem tendrils; there is either a tendril or an inflorescence opposite each leaf.

OTHER MODIFIED STEMS

Stems may be modified to serve many other functions than those which have been mentioned above. Thus the spines of the honey locust (*Gleditsia*), *Colletia cruciata*, and a number of other plants are modified lateral branches.   Not all spines or prickles are modified stems, however.   Some are outgrowths of the epidermis (spines of roses); others are modified leaves or leaf parts, and in a few cases roots become modified into spines.

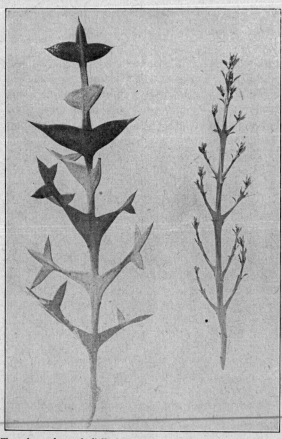

Fig. 110.—Two branches of *Colletia cruciata* a xerophytic plant in which green, flattened lateral branches serve as photosynthetic organs and also as spines. The branch to the right is taken from an actively growing branch and shows the small temporary leaves.   The branch to the left shows the characteristic spiny branches and in several places the scars of the leaves in the axils of which the branches had their origin as axillary buds.

A good many xerophytic plants (plants of very dry habitats) are leafless, or produce leaves which are shed very soon after their appearance so that the plants are leafless most of the year.   This is generally interpreted as an adaptation to the environment since the reduction of surface through loss of leaves presumably lessens the danger of excessive water loss. However that may be, such plants must carry on assimilation, and in the absence of leaves this function is performed by the stems, which are often flattened and somewhat leaf-like in form. The lateral branches of *Colletia cruciata* serve not only as spines but also

Fig. 111.—Species of *Echinocactus*, showing fleshy storage type of stem. (From Willis T. Lee in *The National Geographic Magazine*.)

are flattened and take the place of leaves in photosynthesis. Other examples are certain species of *Ruscus*, *Muehlenbeckia platyphylla*, and various species of the cactus (*Opuntia*). Such flattened, green stems of plants are called *cladodes*. They may bear flowers, fruit, and temporary leaves.

CHAPTER V

THE ROOT

It is only the fact that the roots are hidden beneath the soil which prevents it from being generally realized that the root system of a plant commonly equals or exceeds the shoot in length and extent. Often the total number of root branches is greater than the number of stem branches.

It will be recalled that roots, which may in some cases bear strong superficial resemblance to stems, are distinguished from stems by the following characteristics: **Roots rarely grow upward, they are not divided into nodes and internodes, root branches originate deep in the tissue of the root** from which they arise, and the **root growing point is covered by a special protective structure called the root cap.** In addition to these points of difference, roots and stems differ very greatly in the arrangement of their primary permanent tissues. However, those roots which develop cambium and have secondary growth in thickness come to resemble old woody stems in their structure.

Kinds of Roots.—According to their origin, roots may be classified as **primary roots, secondary roots,** and **adventitious roots.**

The primary root of a plant is the root which developed from the radicle (rudimentary root) of the embryo of the seed from which the plant grew. It is the first root of the plant and in many species remains the principal root throughout the life of the plant.

Branches of the primary root are called secondary roots. It is sometimes convenient to distinguish branch roots which arise from secondary roots, as tertiary roots, but we shall use the term secondary roots to include all branches of primary roots.

All roots which are not branches of the primary root are spoken of as adventitious roots. Adventitious roots may arise from stems and even in some cases (*Begonia, Gloxinia,* and *Bryophyllum*) from leaves. The prop roots of corn (*Zea*) (Fig. 131) which grow out from the lower nodes of the stem and, entering the soil obliquely, serve as braces for the plant, are good examples of adventitious roots. The roots which grow out from planted tubers, bulbs, and rhizomes are also adventitious roots, and when stem cuttings of such plants as pears (*Pyrus*), blackberry (*Rubus*), geranium (*Pelargonium*), and rose (*Rosa*) are placed in damp

Fig. 112.—Tap root system of the sugar beet. (**Photograph** furnished by the Great Western Sugar Company.)

sand or soil there will be produced at the lower end a number of adventitious roots.

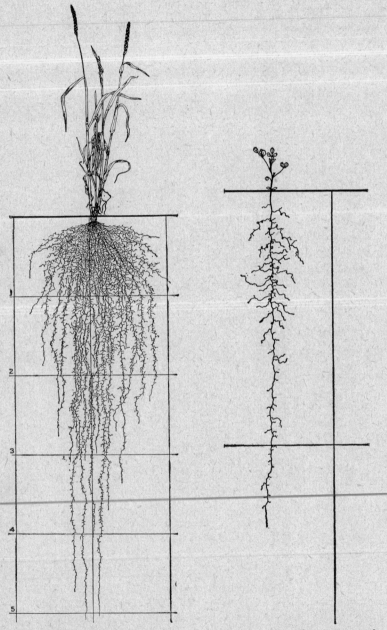

Fig. 113.—Fibrous root system of wheat. The numbers indicate depth in feet. (After Weaver, Carnegie Institution of Washington, Pub. No. 316.)

Fig. 114.—Tap root system of young sweet clover plant (*Melilotus*). (After Weaver, Carnegie Institution of Washington, Pub. No. 316.)

Kinds of Root Systems.—In many species of plants, especially among the monocotyledons, the primary root does not generally become the main root of the plant but stops growing while the plant is still young. In such cases the functions of anchorage and absorption are taken over by numerous adventitious roots which grow out at the base of the stem. There results what is spoken of as a **fibrous root system,** which is characteristic of corn (*Zea*), wheat (*Triticum*), and other grasses, the palms, and many other monocotyledons.

When the root system consists principally of an actively growing primary root with its branches (secondary roots) it is spoken of as a **tap root system** or **primary root system.** Conspicuous among the many examples of plants having such a root system are the carrot (*Daucus*), beet (*Beta*), radish (*Raphanus*), turnip (*Brassica*), and parsnips (*Pastinaca*), and other such plants in which the primary root is greatly enlarged for food storage. In most cases, as in mallow (*Malva*) and oak (*Quercus*), the primary or tap root is not so conspicuously enlarged.

The Form of the Root System.—Just as we recognize great differences in the form of the shoot systems of our common plants, so do we find conspicuous differences in the form of root systems. For obvious reasons we are much more familiar with the form of the shoot system than we are with the form of the root system.

Figures 112, 113 and 114 illustrate two types of root systems. Although soil conditions exert a marked influence on the form of the root system, it is, to a considerable degree, a specific characteristic of the plant, just as is, for example, the form of the crown of a tree. The cereals and most grasses have relatively shallow root systems which in general assume a broad, pyramidal form. The sugar beet (*Beta vulgaris*) has a deep root system.

Though shallow root systems are characteristic of certain species of plants and deep root systems of others, the depth of the root system in many cases varies greatly with soil conditions. Plants living in a dry region where they must depend for water mostly on occasional showers profit by a shallow root system with great numbers of roots in the first few inches of soil beyond which the water seldom penetrates. On the other hand, for plants growing in regions where they must depend principally on water deeper in the soil, the deep root system is more advantageous. As far as firm anchorage of the plant is concerned, the deep root system is obviously more efficient than the shallow.

STRUCTURE OF ROOTS

External Features.—The root is an almost cylindrical structure, tapering very gradually from its base, where it is attached to the stem or to a larger root, towards its free end.   By the **root tip** is meant the 4 to 6 centimeters of the free end.   It is in this part of the root that growth in length, water absorption, and most of the development of the primary tissues take place.   This part of the root may for convenience in describing it be divided into the following regions beginning at the very end:

> The root cap.
> The growing point.
> The region of elongation.
> The region of root hairs.

The **root cap** is a protective structure consisting of a thimble-shaped mass of cells covering the end of the growing point.   It will be recalled that in the stem the growing point is protected by the rudimentary leaves and bud scale, if the latter are present.   Protection of growing points may be necessary (1) because of the thinness of the walls of the promeristem cells which makes them particularly liable to mechanical injury and drying out, and (2) because these cells, upon which the growth of the organ depends, are of such great importance to the plant. In the root, protection of the growing point from injury through an excessive loss of water is generally not necessary since the root tip is seldom exposed to dry air.   Danger of mechanical injury is, however, much greater than for the growing point of the stem, as the tip is constantly being forced through the soil which is largely composed of minute pieces of rock.   By reason of the abrasion of the cap by the soil particles it is continually being worn away, but at the same time new cells are being added to it where it is in contact with the growing point. The passage of the root tip through the soil is facilitated by the fact that the outer layers of cells of the root cap become mucilaginous and thus render the cap rather slimy.

The **growing point,** as in the stem, consists of meristematic tissue (promeristem) in which active cell division is going on as long as the root is growing.   This region of the root is in most cases about a millimeter in length.   Growth in length takes place in this region but at a very much slower rate than in the region of elongation just behind it. As the result of active cell division, the number of cells in the growing point tends to increase.   Some of these cells are constantly being added to the root cap and others to the region of elongation.

In the **region of elongation** the cells produced in the growing point undergo very rapid growth in length as the result of absorption of large quantities of water and the stretching resulting from the high turgor thus developed. This region of the root is generally from 2 to 5 millimeters in length. Thus it is only a small part of the root tip—a few millimeters in length—which is actually being pushed through the soil.

In the **region of root hairs**, elongation has ceased and the surface of the root becomes clothed with a dense growth of root hairs. These structures are of great importance not only in connection with the absorptive function of the root but also in anchoring the roots firmly in the soil. In the pea (*Pisum*) there may be as many as 230 and in Indian corn (*Zea mays*) as many as 420 hairs per square millimeter of root surface. It is in this zone that the cells

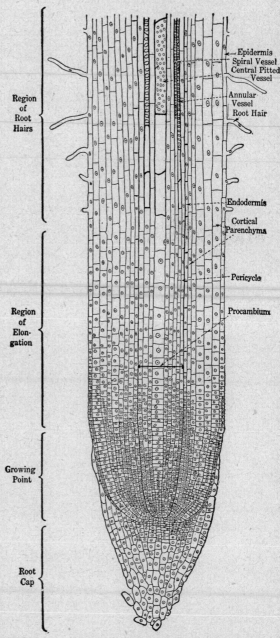

FIG. 115.—Longitudinal section of the tip of the root of barley (*Hordeum sativum*).

inside the root, which were produced in the growing point and which increased greatly in length in the region of elongation, differentiate into vessels, tracheids, sieve tubes, and the various other permanent tissues of the root. On this account it is spoken of as the **region of maturation.**

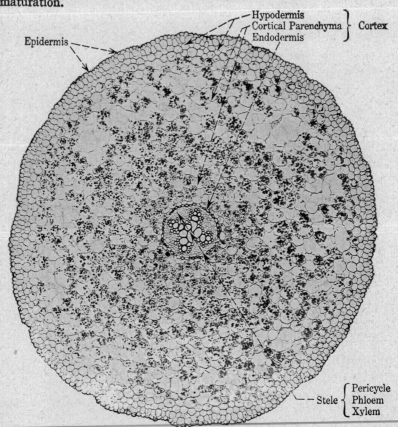

Epidermis

Hypodermis
Cortical Parenchyma } Cortex
Endodermis

Stele { Pericycle
Phloem
Xylem

FIG. 116.—Photomicrograph of a cross section of a root of buttercup (*Ranunculus*). This section was made through a region of the root above the root-hair region; accordingly there are no root hairs and the epidermis and the hypodermis are somewhat suberized.

These four regions which have been briefly described are spoken of together as the **root tip.** In the part of the root behind the tip the root hairs are withered and dead, for the life of each root hair is but a few days, the older ones dying off as new ones are produced at the lower end of the root-hair zone. In the older part of the root, growth in length never takes place but there is sometimes an actual shortening. It is in this region that secondary roots make their appearance.

Anatomy of the Root.—Roots of different kinds of flowering plants are much more uniform in their internal structure than are stems, and we shall not have to study several types as we did in the case of stems. It will be easier to gain an understanding of the anatomy of the root if we consider in order a series of cross sections from the growing point to the mature region of the root, a method similar to that used in describing the development of the tissue of the stem.

A Cross Section through the Root at the Growing Point.—A section across the root through the growing point shows that here the root

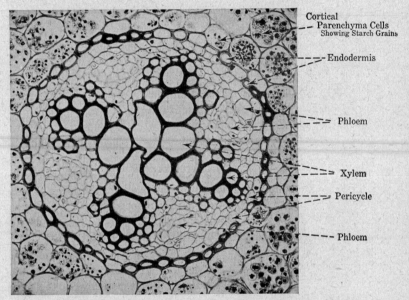

Cortical
Parenchyma Cells
Showing Starch Grains

Endodermis

Phloem

Xylem

Pericycle

Phloem

Fig. 117.—Photomicrograph showing, in cross section, the stele, endodermis and some of the cells of the cortical parenchyma, of the root of *Ranunculus* (buttercup).

is made up of typical promeristem cells, thin walled, all very much alike, and practically without intercellular spaces. If the section is made at one of those times during the day when nuclear division is most active, a great many nuclei will be in some stage of mitosis. The resting nuclei will be found to be much larger in proportion to the size of the cells than in permanent tissues. Outside of the tissues (promeristem) of the growing point there will be found in such a section a ring of cells which may be quite separated from the tissue of the growing point. These are cells of the root cap where it extends back over the growing point.

A Cross Section through the Region of Elongation.—This is also, of course, circular in outline. The cells in such a section are still meristematic but are not uniform in appearance, for some differentiation, principally in the size of the cells, has taken place. The single layer of surface cells is the **protoderm.** The circular group of cells in the center of the section is the **procambium,** and between this and the protoderm is the **ground meristem.** It will be recalled from the discussion of the anatomy of the stem that these three meristematic regions are spoken of as primary meristems.

A Cross Section through the Region of Root Hairs.—In this section the following primary permanent tissues can be seen:

1. The **epidermis** (derived from the protoderm) with its root hairs.
2. The **cortex** (derived from the ground meristem), the innermost layer of which is the **endodermis.**
3. The **stele** consisting of:

The **pericycle,** which is derived from the ground meristem, and the **xylem** and **phloem** derived from the procambium.

The epidermis consists of a single layer of cells from which the root hairs arise. The cortex is composed of numerous layers of parenchyma cells and of a single innermost layer, the endodermis, the cells of which frequently have their inner, radial, and transverse walls thickened. In other cases the endodermal cells have the walls thickened all around and in still others they are thin walled, except for a strip (the *Casparian strip*) running lengthwise through the radial and transverse wall. The thickened portions of the walls are cutinized or suberized.

The stele in most roots has no pith, whereas the stems of most seed plants have a central pith with the vascular tissue either in a continuous cylinder or in a ring of vascular bundles. The pericycle is the outermost tissue of the stele. It generally consists of one layer of parenchymatous cells forming a continuous ring of tissues.

The xylem generally consists of a central mass of xylem elements with several radiating arms, between which are groups of phloem elements. Xylem and phloem groups are separated by one or more layers of parenchyma cells. In some cases, mostly in the roots of monocotyledons, the central cells of the stele are parenchymatous and form a pith, and the xylem is in separate radial groups alternating with groups of phloem cells. For the most part the xylem and phloem elements are similar in structure and function to those of the stem. Spiral and annular vessels are relatively rare in roots. This seems to be correlated with the fact that the region of elongation in roots is very short compared with that in stems. It will be recalled that in the stem spiral and annular xylem elements are found in the part of the xylem which is first formed, that is, formed while the region in which they are produced is still elongating.

Root Hairs.—The importance of root hairs to the plant is so very great that it is desirable for us to learn more of their structure and functions. It is absolutely essential to the life of all typical land plants that they secure from the soil an amount of water at least equal to the quantity which they lose to the air by transpiration. If such plants

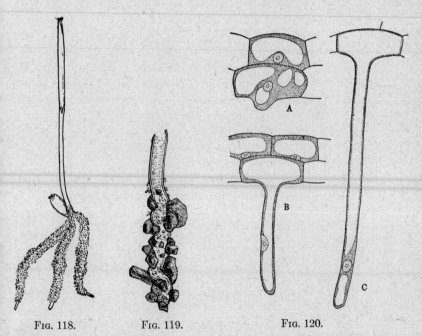

FIG. 118.   FIG. 119.   FIG. 120.

FIG. 118.—Wheat seedling showing soil particles clinging to the root hairs; note that the root tips are free of root hairs. (After Robbins, *Botany of Crop Plants.*)

FIG. 119.—The tip of a root hair showing adherent soil particles. Such particles, between and around which the root hair has grown, often become so firmly attached to the root hair that they can not be washed off or removed in any other way without injury to the root hair. (After Noll.)

FIG. 120.—Stages in the development of a root hair. (After Frank.)

are to grow and develop normally, additional water is necessary for photosynthesis and to supply that required for the formation and growth of new cells. For normal growth and development of plants, the amount of water absorbed must exceed that lost by transpiration.

The roots are the absorbing organs, but water and soil solutes are not taken in by the entire surface of the root system. The surface of old parts of roots is often covered with a layer of cork cells which is quite impermeable to water and mineral salts. Also, in old epidermal cells suberization greatly restricts the entrance of water and salts. Accordingly, absorption is carried on principally by root hairs and epidermal cells at or near the root tips. When we pull up a young herbaceous plant from loose soil, we find that it has a large number of hair-like rootlets (branch roots), which are sometimes mistaken for root hairs. If we examine these with a hand lens it will be seen that these fine rootlets and all the other roots are covered at their tips with much smaller structures, the root hairs. That root hairs are the chief water-absorbing organs of a plant is indicated by the quick wilting of plants when many of their root hairs are destroyed. The root hairs are so tender and so firmly attached to the soil particles that it is practically impossible to remove a plant from the soil without injuring or actually tearing off innumerable root hairs. Furthermore, a few seconds' exposure to dry air, when plants are transplanted, is sufficient to shrivel the root hairs and to render them unable to perform their function. Consequently, the transplanted plant generally wilts and seldom revives until new root hairs are formed.

Structure of Root Hairs.—A root hair is a lateral protuberance of an epidermal cell (Fig. 120) having the form of a slender tube closed at the free end. A root hair and the epidermal cell from which it grows are not separated by a wall. They together constitute a single branched cell with a single protoplast. Though tending to cylindrical form, root hairs may become greatly contorted in their growth between and around soil particles. They vary in length from a fraction of a millimeter to 7 or 8 millimeters. The walls are thin and composed of cellulose and pectic compounds, and are lined with a thin layer of cytoplasm. It should be specially emphasized that all the materials that enter the plant from the soil must pass through the walls and also through the cytoplasmic membranes of root hairs or epidermal cells. From the root hair, the absorbed materials pass inward to the cells of the root cortex, then to the endodermis and pericycle, and finally enter the conducting elements of the xylem. By these they are carried to various parts of the plant.

Root-hair Zone.—Functioning root hairs occur only in a definite zone, known as the **root-hair zone.** This may be well observed in young seedlings grown in moist air (Figs. 121 and 122). The root cap and growing point bear no root hairs, and the region of elongation is also devoid of root hairs. This is clearly an advantage to the plant since it is obvious that, if hairs were produced in the region of elongation, they would be broken off as this part of the root advanced through the soil. The length of the root-hair zone varies from a few millimeters to several centimeters. If the roots of a plant growing in fine sand are

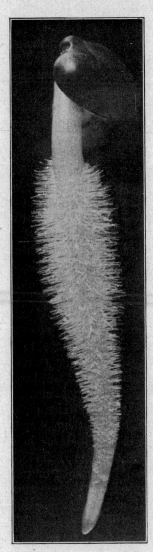

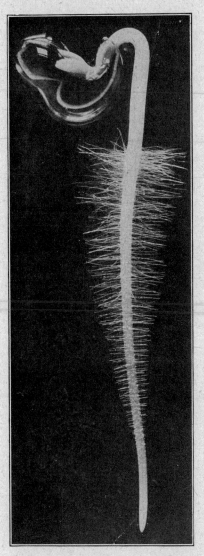

Fig. 121.—Seedling of white clover (*Trifolium*) grown in moist air. The cotyledons have not yet escaped from the seed coat but the well-developed radicle shows clearly the growing point, region of elongation and root-hair zone. Magnification 6×.

Fig. 122.—Seedling of garden cress (*Lepidium*) grown in moist air. Root hairs in various stages of development can be distinguished behind the region of elongation. Surrounding the cotyledons is the swollen gelatinous mass derived from the seed coats. Magnification 4×.

carefully removed from the sand, the root-hair zone is plainly evident because of the sand particles held by the root hairs (Fig. 119). In their growth through the soil the root hairs penetrate the small spaces

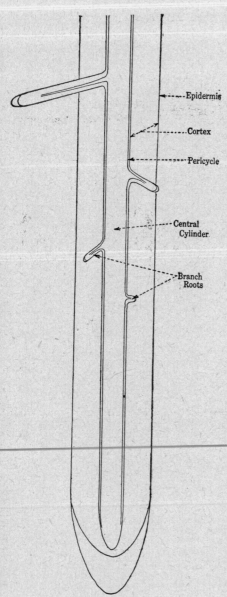

FIG. 123.—Diagram showing the manner of origin of branch roots.

between soil particles and often partly surround these particles. So close is the contact that separation of the particles of soil from the hairs is often impossible without destroying the latter. Root hairs are short-lived, functioning only for a few days or weeks. New hairs are constantly formed at the root-tip end of the root-hair zone, while the hairs at the upper end of the root-hair zone are dying. The root-hair zone advances through the soil as the root grows so that root hairs are constantly brought into contact with new soil. This is of advantage to the plant, because new stores of water and salts thus become available to the root hairs.

Many plants which produce root hairs when the root system grows in moist air or in soil develop no root hairs when the roots are grown in water. A few aquatic angiosperms and several gymnosperms such as the firs (*Abies*) and *Pinus sylvestris* produce no root hairs.

Root Branching.—It will be recalled that the outermost tissue of the stele is the pericycle. It is in this layer that branch roots have their origin. The first evidence of the formation of a branch root is the repeated tangential division of several adjacent pericycle cells (Fig. 124). Thus a group of meristematic cells is formed, and a root tip, with root cap, arises within the old root (Fig. 125). The root tip must make its way outward through the cortex and the epidermis before reaching the surface. The growing point of the branch root is said to secrete enzymes which dissolve the cell walls of the tissues through which it is passing. Such branch roots do not emerge into the soil until elongation has ceased in that part of the main root from which the branches arise.

Growth in Diameter of Root.—In most monocotyledons and many annual dicotyledons there is no secondary increase in thickness of the roots. In such plants s e c t i o n s through older parts of the root would be essentially like sections through the root-hair zone. In the region behind this zone the root hairs are withered and dead. The epidermal cells and frequently several adjacent layers of cortex cells become suberized and come to function as a protective layer.

In perennial dicotyledons and gymnosperm roots, a cam-

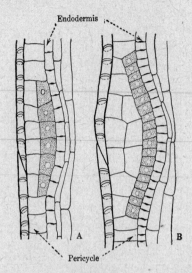

Fig. 124.—Two stages in the development of a branch root. Certain pericyclic cells (here stippled) become meristematic, first undergo tangential division, and thus initiate the process of branch root formation. (Redrawn from Van Tieghem.)

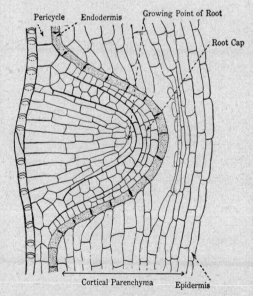

Fig. 125.—Later stage than shown in Fig. 124, showing the development of a branch root (Redrawn from Van Tieghem.)

bium arises and secondary increase in thickness normally occurs. The formation
of the cambium and the secondary growth of the root generally proceeds as follows.
First, certain parenchyma cells lying adjacent to the xylem and phloem, and those
of the pericycle lying just outside of the xylem, become meristematic and form a
cambium layer. At first, this vascular cambium, as seen in cross section, is not
circular but has the form of a wavy band, since it passes inside of each phloem
strand and outside of the xylem (Fig. 126).

Those portions of the cambium which adjoin the phloem give rise to new vascular
elements both on the outside and on the inside. The new cells formed on the outer
side become phloem elements, and are added to the phloem already present. Those
formed on the inner side become xylem elements and thus new xylem strands are
formed. There result at these points vascular bundles similar to those found in
many dicotyledonous stems. Where the cambium lies outside the original groups

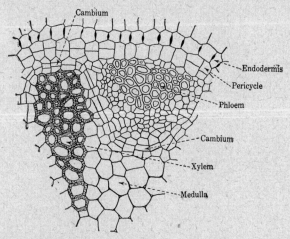

FIG. 126.—Cross section of a portion of the stele of a primary root of horse-bean
    (*Vicia faba*), showing origin of cambium.   (Redrawn from Haberlandt.)

of xylem elements it produces parenchymatous cells on both sides and thus forms
rays which lie between the vascular bundles.

Eventually the xylem produced by the cambium forms a complete
cylinder of wood with many narrow xylem rays, as in most woody
stems. Surrounding this is a narrow band of phloem and outside of
that the bark.

Soon after the vascular cambium makes its appearance, certain
cells of the pericycle undergo repeated division and thus form another
cambium. This is called the **phellogen** or **cork cambium**. The cork
cambium produces cork externally and phelloderm tissue internally.
All the tissues which originally lay outside of the pericycle die soon

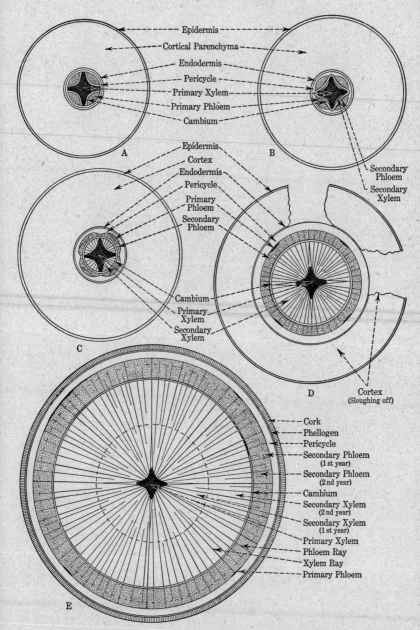

Fig. 127.—Diagrams showing stages in the secondary growth in thickness of a root. *A*, before the appearance of cambium. *B*, the formation of the cambium ring. *C, D,* and *E* stages in the development and growth of secondary phloem and xylem. Secondary increase in thickness due to the activity of phellogen is also shown. (Drawing prepared by Esau.)

after cork formation commences.   As a result of the activities of these

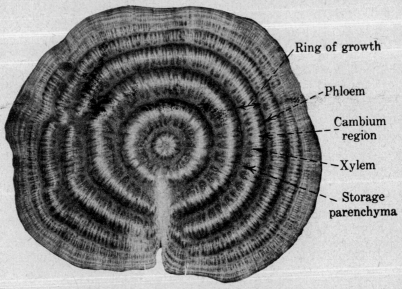

Ring of growth

Phloem

Cambium
region

Xylem

Storage
parenchyma

FIG. 128.—Cross section of sugar-beet root, a storage form of root. Observe the
rings of growth which are made in one season.   Running in from the cleft at the
bottom of the photograph is tissue of a lateral root.

two cambiums, the old root comes to resemble in structure that of an
old stem.

The Functions of Roots.

—As was pointed out in Chapter II, the functions of the root system are **absorption, conduction, anchorage,** and **storage.** We shall discuss these four processes in the order named, considering under absorption the intake, first of water, and then of solutes, primarily inorganic salts.

Importance of Water in the Life of a Plant.— Without water the plant would be unable to carry on any of its life processes.

FIG. 129.—Transverse section of an old root of
alder (*Alnus*). Note its resemblance in structure to an old stem.   (After Jeffrey.)

Water makes up 70 per cent or more of the weight of the protoplasm of all actively functioning cells. In addition the cell sap consists mostly of water, and the walls of most living cells contain a large percentage of water imbibed in the cell wall material.

In seeds and lichens and some mosses the percentage of water present may fall to as low as 10 per cent or less but growth and normal physiological activity are possible in these cases only after large quantities of water have been absorbed.

Water is needed in large quantities by the plant because:

1. It is an essential constituent of protoplasm. When the water content of the protoplasm is greatly reduced death often results or at least there is a very great reduction in protoplasmic activity.

2. It is an essential raw material for food manufacture.

3. It serves as a solvent of gases (oxygen and carbon dioxide) and of mineral nutrients and foods.

4. It serves as a medium of transportation of raw materials and foods from place to place in the plant, since their transport can take place for the most part only in solution.

5. It makes possible the maintenance of turgor in living cells; the plant functions normally only when the cells are distended with water.

In arid and semi-arid regions, scarcity of water is often the principal condition which limits the growth of plants. Under natural conditions crop plants almost always have an abundance of light and oxygen and sufficient carbon dioxide to permit normal growth during the growing season; the temperature of the air and the soil is seldom seriously unfavorable to growth; moreover, the physical and chemical nature of the soil in which crops are grown is for the most part suitable, but in many agricultural sections of the country and particularly in semi-arid and arid regions, water is the principal limiting factor in crop production. Water is a most important factor in determining both the distribution of plants over the earth's surface and the character of the individual plant. We observe marked dissimilarities in the vegetation of high mountains, dry plains, prairies, and the eastern deciduous forest belt and in the character of the plants growing in tropical rain forests, the South American pampas, the Russian steppes, deserts, and tundras. The plants of hillside, of brook bank, of gravel slope, of rock slide, of bog, of meadow, and of the margins of ponds, lakes, and rivers also differ greatly. Probably no single factor is so largely responsible for this diversity of plants in these various habitats as is the difference in supply of water.

In most plants, wild or cultivated, all water comes to the plant from the soil. As we have learned, the water enters the plant through the root hairs and passes out of the plant as water vapor, principally through small openings (stomata) in the surface of the leaves. Water entry is spoken of as water absorption, water loss as transpiration. Thus there is a stream of water through the plant, from roots to leaves. Too much transpiration and too little absorption are the principal dangers to which the plant is exposed.

Absorption of Water by Roots.—Only water and substances (including gases) dissolved in water can enter the plant from the soil and they must pass through the walls of the root hairs and also through the cytoplasmic membrane which lines the walls. The cell wall, of cellulose, is a permeable membrane through which water and all solutes present in the soil solution can pass unhindered. The cytoplasmic membrane is, however, semipermeable and prevents or greatly restricts the passage of some dissolved substances. Normally, the total concentration of the solutes in the cell sap of the root hair is greater than in the soil solution. Under this condition, the movement of water is from the soil into the root hair, and this movement of water tends to go on just as long as the concentration within the root hair exceeds that of the soil solution outside the hair. The rate of movement of water inward depends upon the relative concentration of the two solutions, and this rate tends to decrease as the concentrations of the two solutions become more nearly equal. Water is, however, constantly being withdrawn from root-hair cells to the outermost cells of the cortex and thus the concentration of the cell sap of the root hairs remains fairly constant.

Water in the Soil.—Soil is a granular material largely consisting of minute particles of rock of irregular shape together with fragments of organic material of plant or animal origin. On account of the varying size and irregular form of the soil particles there are many spaces between the particles. The size of these spaces or pores varies greatly. If the soil is very dry most of the pores are almost completely filled with air, but when there is a heavy rain the air is forced out of all the spaces, large and small, between the soil particles and they become filled with water. After the rain stops part of the water in the pores is soon carried downward by gravity and is replaced by air. (This is of advantage to plants, for most plants can not secure enough oxygen for the respiration of their roots and accordingly soon die if all of the pores of the soil are filled with water.) A considerable amount of water is still held by capillarity in the pores. It is this condition of the soil when the pores are partly filled with air which is favorable for the growth of most plants.

When roots continue to absorb water from the soil the moisture content may be reduced to a degree at which it is difficult for the plant to secure more water and, if no more water is added to the soil, the roots are finally unable to overcome the force of capillarity.

Before this point is reached the quantity of water being absorbed may have become less than that which the plant is losing by transpiration, and the plant shows evidence of wilting. The condition of such a plant is called **temporary wilting,** for absorption has not ceased entirely and the plant may recover its turgor if transpiration is reduced as it is at night when the air becomes cooler and more humid.

As transpiration continues a stage of wilting is reached at which the plant will not recover, even though placed in a saturated atmosphere, unless water is added to the soil. The plant is now in a condition of **permanent wilting.**

Thus temporary wilting is a condition from which the plant may recover if transpiration is greatly reduced whereas recovery from permanent wilting is possible only if more water is added to the soil.

A wide range of moisture content of the soil appears to be equally favorable to the growth of plants. As long as the soil is not saturated and is not so dry that it is approaching the condition which would produce permanent wilting, the

FIG. 130.—Diagram showing a root hair, h, which is an outgrowth of the epidermal cell, e, and which has grown between the soil particles. α, β water surface, δ air spaces. Water indicated by parallel curved lines, soil particles by shading with straight lines. (After Sachs.)

moisture conditions are suitable for active growth. In other words, within this range there seems to be no optimum moisture content.

Absorption of Inorganic Salts.—Land plants derive their inorganic salts from the soil. Among the inorganic salts which occur in the soil, the chief ones used by green plants are nitrates, phosphates, and sulphates. Green plants derive nitrogen principally from nitrates; phosphorus from phosphates; and sulphur from sulphates; and the essential metallic elements, potassium, calcium, magnesium, and iron, are chiefly derived from nitrates, sulphates, and phosphates of these metallic elements in the soil. These salts can enter the plant from the soil only when they are in solution. The cytoplasmic membranes are permeable to them.

It is important to keep in mind, however, that under similar conditions the **different inorganic salts move into the plant independent of the**

passage of each other and of water. A plant that absorbs twice as much water as another plant does not necessarily absorb twice as great a quantity of inorganic salts or of any particular salt. As to the conditions governing the entrance of any particular solute into the plant, see the discussion on page 73.

We may picture the process of absorption by root hairs as one in which the molecules of water and the dissolved particles of many different salts are independently diffusing through cytoplasmic membranes of the root hair at varying rates.

Whereas many soluble substances may pass from the soil through the cytoplasmic membrane into the root, it should be pointed out that water and carbon dioxide are the only substances in the cell sap of the root hairs which pass into the soil in large amounts. It should be stated that there is evidence that in the normal activity of roots significant amounts of nutrient elements are liberated into the soil or solution culture. The supposition that under certain circumstances sugar in the beet root, for example, passes from the root into the soil is not correct. The **percentage** of sugar in the root may fluctuate as a result of changes in the quantity of water present, but normally the **total quantity** of sugar in the root does not decrease appreciably except when it is drawn upon for the growth of the shoot, or used up in respiration.

On the other hand, movement of carbon dioxide (produced by respiration) from the roots into the soil can easily be demonstrated. It unites chemically with water to form carbonic acid (H_2CO_3), which aids in dissolving certain mineral inorganic compounds which are difficultly soluble in water.

Absorption and Conduction by Roots.—Water and inorganic salts absorbed by the root hair cells pass into adjoining cortex cells and thence inward through cells of the inner cortex, endodermis, and pericycle to the conducting elements of the xylem. Although water, as was mentioned on page 73, apparently moves into the xylem of absorbing roots along a gradient from a region where water molecules are abundant (the soil solution) to a region of less abundance (the xylem sap), solutes must move against a concentration gradient in entering the root. Experiments show that solutes (potassium ions, for instance) pass from a region of low concentration (the soil solution) through a region of relatively high concentration (the root hairs and cortex cells) into a solution (the xylem sap) of intermediate concentration. Energy is expended in the initial accumulation by cells of the outer region of the root.

Movement of solutes from the cortical cells containing sap of high concentration into the xylem vessels, where the sap is less concentrated, apparently takes place by diffusion accelerated by protoplasmic streaming, since the linear rate of movement is not high. The exact mechanism by which the solutes are released from living cells into the sap of the non-living xylem vessels is not known. Either a secretion of some sort or a gradient in cell activity is involved. Root structure indicates that cells outside the endodermis have readily accessible oxygen whereas cells of the stele have a restricted supply. Carbon dioxide produced by respiration in the outer cells tends to accumulate and to pass through the living regions of the stele. It seems logical that this oxygen-CO_2 relation should cause a gradient in the activity of the root cells and this, in turn, would be reflected in absorption of solutes by the cortex and release within the stele. It is interesting to note that, in the absorbing region of the root, the phloem does not lie outside the xylem but occurs in groups of cells which alternate radially with xylem masses or with the radiating arms of a single central mass of xylem. Hence, it is possible for the water and

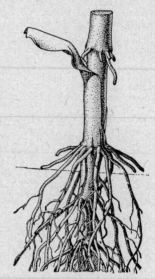

FIG. 131.—The aerial or "prop" roots of corn (*Zea mays*).

IG. 132.—Beach grass (*Ammophila arenaria*), a sand-binding plant, growing on dunes near the seashore. (From photograph by Massart.)

dissolved salts released within the stele to reach the xylem and pass upward without passing across the phloem. This dilute solution of water and salts which enters and moves upward through the

Fig. 133.—Soil erosion. In the upper photograph there is shown a slope from which the native vegetation has been removed, resulting in serious erosion of the soil. In the lower photograph a slope subject to soil erosion has been strip-planted to crops. The roots of these crop plants are effective in binding the soil and thus preventing washing from the slope.

conducting elements of the xylem to the stems and leaves is called xylem sap. If it is forced out of the cut xylem from a root system under root pressure, it is termed xylem exudate. If it passes upward through the plant under the influence of transpirational pull, it is called the transpiration stream.

Anchorage by Roots.—The roots of a plant are very effective anchorage organs. In most plants all roots perform the triple rôle of absorp-

FIG. 134.—Indian banyan (*Ficus indica*). The horizontal branches of this tree may send out aerial roots which grow downward, become attached to the soil, and serve as "props" as well as absorbing organs.

tion, conduction, and anchorage. The hold which roots have on the soil is well shown in sand dunes, where the sand is constantly shifting except where it is held in place by the roots of plants growing in the sand (Fig. 132). The erosion of hilly land, either by wind or water, or of ditch banks, levees, or other steep slopes may be effectively prevented by the roots of soil-binding plants. The efficiency of roots as soil-binders is realized when we consider the enormous area of possible soil contact. Recently, a worker made a quantitative study of the number, length, and total exposed surface area of the roots and root hairs of one rye plant. This plant had 13,815,762 roots and over 14 billion root hairs, the combined surface area of which was 6875.4 square feet. In this one rye plant, the combined length of all its roots was 387 miles.

Storage by Roots.—The roots of many plants store food and water. Such roots may become large and fleshy, familiar examples being the

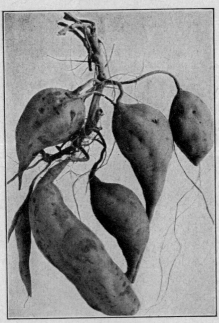

FIG. 135.—Large quantities of food are stored in the roots of the sweet potato (*Ipomoea batatas*).

sugar beet, turnip, dahlia, carrot, and sweet potato. Many plants with fleshy roots are cultivated for their roots alone and are called "root crops." Sugar and starch are the principal forms of food stored in such roots. The sugar beet, for example, contains approximately 15 to 20 per cent of cane sugar. The sweet potato, turnip, parsnip, and many other fleshy roots have considerable quantities of stored starch. Among our native plants the most striking examples of fleshy-rooted plants occur in arid regions. Such roots generally contain a large quantity of stored water which can be used by the leafy shoot during periods of drought.

The roots of perennial plants store large quantities of food even when they are not greatly enlarged and fleshy. For example, both large and small roots of fruit trees are very rich in stored food, and clover and alfalfa roots contain large quantities of starch.

Reproduction by Means of Roots.—Some plants send up stems (so-called "suckers") from adventitious buds which arise on the roots. This habit is well illustrated by the silver leaf poplar (*Populus alba*) and black locust (*Robinia pseudacacia*). It is of great agricultural importance in many weeds such as wild morning glory (*Convolvulus arvensis*), Canada thistle (*Cirsium arvense*) and spurge (*Euphorbia esula*). Plants which do not normally produce adventitious root buds may be induced to do so by injury. For example, if the shoots of such plants as red raspberry, some roses, and common barberry (*Berberis vulgaris*) are entirely cut away, the roots send forth new stems. This ability of the roots of some plants to produce adventitious buds is made use of in the propagation of certain economic plants. Roses, raspberries, some blackberries, and a number of other plants are frequently propagated by root cuttings.

CHAPTER VI

THE LEAF

Since they make the food of the plant, the leaves may be said to be the most important of the vegetative organs, the stem merely serving to support them and to conduct to them the water and salts absorbed by the root.

As to form and position, the leaf may be described as an expanded, lateral outgrowth of the stem, arising at a node, and having a bud in its axil. The principal physiological characteristic of typical leaves is their special adaptation for the function of photosynthesis and transpiration. There are, however, structures such as bud scales and the spines and tendrils of some plants which do not resemble typical leaves or perform the typical functions of leaves, but because they are found at nodes, have buds in their axils, or for other reasons, they can be recognized as foliar (leafy) in nature.

EXTERNAL MORPHOLOGY OF THE FOLIAGE LEAF

A typical leaf consists of two principal parts: the expanded **leaf blade** or **lamina** and the slender **stalk** or **petiole**. Where the petiole is attached to the stem it is often considerably broadened but in many cases this leaf base is not conspicuous. Frequently there are outgrowths, sometimes leaf-like, known as **stipules,** from either side of the leaf base. They are lacking in many plants, whereas in others they

FIG. 136.—A portion of a stem of pimpernel (*Anagallis*), showing the sessile leaves.

fall off soon after the leaves come out of the bud. Some leaves have no petioles and are said to be **sessile** (Fig. 136).

180

The Leaf Blade.—The form of the leaf blade is such as to provide a large surface for the absorption of the light energy and carbon dioxide needed in photosynthesis. On account of the thinness of the leaf blade, none of the cells lie far from the surface. This facilitates the absorption of carbon dioxide by the green cells inside the leaf. This thin

Fig: 137.—A branch of European linden, *Tilia europaea*, its leaves forming a mosaic:

sheet of leaf tissue is strengthened by the midrib and veins, which also serve to conduct raw materials throughout the leaf and to carry away the food which the green cells manufacture.

The Petiole.—The petiole connects the blade, which is the essential part of the leaf, with the stem, and conducts materials to and from the leaf blade. It is responsible for maintaining the blade in the position most favorable for the performance of its functions. The petioles of many plants are able to increase in length and to bend and twist so that the leaf blades are brought by phototropic movements into the position of most favorable illumination regardless of whether the stem to which they are attached is perpendicular, oblique, or horizontal. The resulting arrangement is often such as practically to eliminate any shading of one leaf by others of the same plant. In such cases the leaves are frequently so fitted into the spaces between one another as to form a **leaf mosaic** (Fig. 137).

In some plants the stem is partly or completely encircled by the leaf base, as in many members of the carrot family (Umbelliferae), and

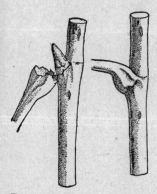

in many monocotyledons the leaf base forms a long sheath which surrounds the stem. In the grasses (Gramineae) in certain of the Musaceae, to which the banana belongs, and in some other monocotyledons, these sheaths protect the stem at the base of the internodes where its tissue long remains soft and capable of growth. In young grasses and in the banana, these sheathing leaf bases are principally responsible for the mechanical strength of the shoot.

FIG. 138.—Portion of a twig of plane-tree (*Platanus*) before (at right), and at the time of leaf fall, showing how the axillary bud is protected by the leaf base which surrounds it.

Stipules.— When these structures are present they may serve various functions. In some plants, such as fig (*Ficus*) and the tulip tree (*Liriodendron*), each bud is enclosed and protected by the stipules of the nearest leaf. Often stipules are large and closely resemble the leaf blades and share the functions of the blade. In *Lathyrus aphaca* the stipules have taken over entirely the typical functions of the blade, which itself is reduced to a branched tendril. In the black locust (*Robinia*), and in certain species of spurge (*Euphorbia*), they form spines, and in some species of smilax, tendrils.

Venation.—There are two principal types of arrangement of veins: **parallel venation** and **net venation** (Fig. 139). In parallel-veined leaves, the veins that are clearly visible to the unaided eye run parallel to each other and to the margin. This kind of venation is characteristic of the monocotyledons. The parallel veins may run lengthwise of the leaf, as in the grasses, converging somewhat at the base of the blade and at the tip; or they may be directed outward from the midrib to the margin of the leaf, as in the banana (*Musa*). When a parallel-veined leaf is examined with a lens it can be seen that small veinlets connect the

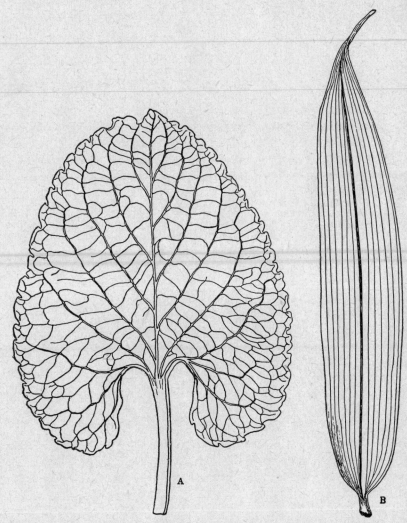

A

B

FIG. 139.—The two principal types of veining. A, Net veining as illustrated by the leaf of violet (*Viola*); B, parallel veining illustrated by the leaf of one of the bamboos. (*Arundinaria*.)

parallel veins. If the veins that are visible to the naked eye branch frequently and join again, so that they form a network, the leaf is said to be net-veined. The leaves of dicotyledons have this type of venation but it rarely occurs among monocotyledons.

Net-veined leaves that have a single primary vein or midrib from which the smaller veins branch off, somewhat like the divisions of a feather, are **pinnately veined.** Common examples of pinnately veined leaves are the willow (*Salix*), the beech (*Fagus*), the apple (*Malus*), the oak (*Quercus*), and the lilac (*Syringa*). When there are several principal veins spreading out from the upper end of the petiole the leaf is said to be **palmately veined.** Among the many plants having palmately veined leaves are the maple (*Acer*), the geranium (*Pelargonium*), grape (*Vitis*), and pumpkin (*Cucurbita*).

Form of the Leaf Blade.—Leaves are said to be **simple** when, as in most plants, the blade is all in one piece (Fig. 140). Simple leaves frequently have the blade made up of a number of lobes separated by deep

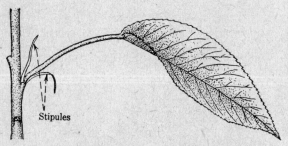

Fig. 140.—Simple leaf of pear, showing stipules.

clefts or **sinuses.** Familiar examples of simple **lobed leaves** are maple (*Acer*), sycamore (*Platanus*), and most species of the oak (*Quercus*). The sinuses of pinnately veined, lobed leaves are always directed toward the midrib. In such cases the leaves are said to be **pinnately lobed** (Fig. 141, *B*). Lobed leaves which are palmately veined are always **palmately lobed** (Fig. 141, *C*), the sinuses being directed toward the base of the blade when it is attached to the petiole. Oak leaves are pinnately lobed and maple leaves palmately lobed.

In many plants, such as most ferns, the potato (*Solanum tuberosum*), beans (*Phaseolus*), peas (*Pisum*), clover (*Trifolium*), and the horse chestnut or buckeye (*Aesculus*), the leaf blade is made up of a number of separate leaf-like parts, or **leaflets.** Such a leaf is said to be **compound** (Fig. 141, *E*). When, as in the horse chestnut and clover, the leaflets are attached directly to the end of the petiole, the leaves are said to be **palmately compound** (Fig. 141, *D*). If the petiole is extended into a long slender structure, the **rachis**, corresponding to the midrib of an entire leaf, and if the leaflets arise at intervals along this structure, the leaf is **pinnately compound** (Fig. 142).   The leaves of the pea, the black-berry (*Rubus*), most ferns, and the potato are of this type.   It is not always easy to distinguish a pinnately compound leaf from a leafy stem. The lack of a terminal bud, and the absence of lateral buds from the

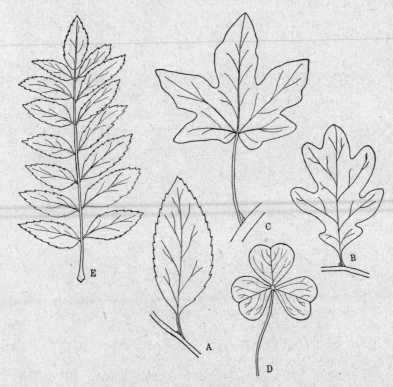

Fig. 141.—*A*, The simple, pinnately veined leaf of a plum (*Prunus*); *B*, the pinnately lobed, and pinnately veined leaf of an oak (*Quercus*); *C*, the palmately lobed and palmately veined leaf of a maple (*Acer*); *D*, the palmately compound leaf of wood-sorrel (*Oxalis*); *E*, the pinnately compound leaf of walnut (*Juglans*).

axils of the leaflets, are sufficient to prove that a structure whose nature is in question is a compound leaf and not a leafy stem.   Compound leaves are rarely met with in the monocotyledons.

The edge (**margin**) of the leaf may be smooth, as in most grasses, in onion (*Allium*), and in many other plants, or it may be variously toothed, as in the oak, rose, apple, cherry, etc.   In the latter case the teeth may vary greatly in size and form.   The systematic botanist uses many different terms to distinguish these differences in the nature of the leaf margin.

In most grasses there is an outgrowth, called the **ligule,** arising from the upper and inner side of the leaf blade where it joins the sheath

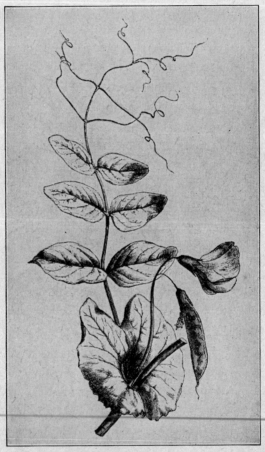

FIG. 142.—Compound leaf of garden pea (*Pisum sativum*).   Note the large, leaf-like stipules, and upper leaflets, modified as tendrils.   (From Bocquillon.)

(Fig. 143).   In some grasses, such as barley (*Hordeum*) and timothy (*Phleum pratense*), this structure is scale-like; in others, for example, Bermuda grass (*Cynodon dactylon*), it consists of a row of stiff hairs or bristles.   It is believed that the ligule serves to prevent the water which drains downward from the leaf blade from collecting inside the leaf sheath.   In some grasses such as barley (*Hordeum*), there are also two little projections called **auricles** which grow out from the opposite sides of the sheath at its upper end (Fig. 143) where it joins the blade.

DIFFERENTIATION OF THE LEAF

The development of a foliage leaf from the primordium to the adult stage involves both an increase in cell number as well as the enlargement and specialization of cells.   During the very early stages of differentiation, a leaf consists entirely of meristematic cells (Figs 46 and 144).   As growth continues, typical primordial meristem becomes restricted to certain regions, namely the apex and the margins.   At these points, new cells are rapidly produced and added to those already present.   Thus in a median longitudinal section of a young leaf, an apical region of primordial meristem is followed by a region of cell elongation and this in turn by a region of cell specialization.   True apical growth is of short duration, however, in the leaves of angiosperms and most of the growth in length is intercalary, i.e. between apex and base.   Marginal growth is often more protracted than apical growth, so that a transverse section of a young leaf may reveal a well-defined marginal band of typical primordial meristem from which a considerable portion of the tissue of the leaf blade originates (Fig. 144).   Further growth in width of the lamina is accomplished by the continued division of the cells formed from the marginal meristem.   When these cells divide, the new walls are usually formed at right angles to the surface of the lamina.   Consequently, a number of distinct layers of meristematic cells are produced (Fig. 144).   The upper and lower surface layers of cells eventually differentiate into the upper and lower epidermis, whereas from the inner layers of the young lamina the photosynthetic parenchyma (mesophyll) and veins take their origin.   It should be evident from this brief description that the **arrangement** and nature of the tissues in an adult

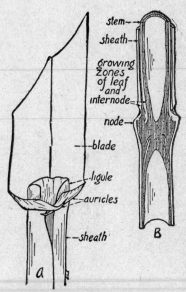

Fig. 143.—*A*, Portion of leaf of barley at the juncture of sheath and blade; *B*, stem cut in median lengthwise section.   ×2½.   (After Robbins, from *Botany of Crop Plants*.)

lamina are dependent upon the mode of growth and specialization of the cells in the original meristematic layers.

ANATOMY OF THE LEAF

A microscopic examination of a transverse section of a typical adult lamina shows three principal systems of tissues, viz.: (1) the **epidermis**, (2) the **mesophyll**, and (3) the **vascular bundles** or **veins** (Figs. 146 and 147). The epidermis covers the whole leaf surface and protects the tissues within from mechanical injury and drying out. The mesophyll is made up of parenchyma cells, most or all of which are green and able to carry on photosynthesis. The vascular bundles, or veins, consist of conducting elements for the transfer of water and inorganic salts and

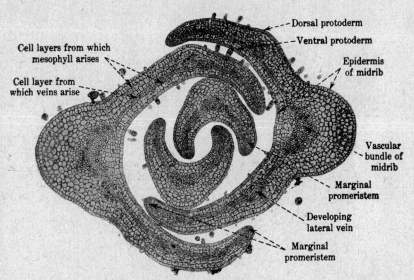

Fig. 144.—Photomicrograph of transverse section of two pairs of young foliage leaves of lilac (*Syringa vulgaris* L.), showing the marginal meristem and the general features of the meristematic cell layers of the lamina from which the epidermis, mesophyll, and veins differentiate. (After Foster.)

of foods. In the larger veins there are groups of fibers which help to give rigidity to the leaf.

The Epidermis.—The total area of the leaves makes up a very large part of the plant surface which is exposed to the air. On this account the ability of the epidermis of the leaf to retard transpiration is of the utmost importance to the plant. Plants living in a habitat where the water available for absorption by the roots is limited, and where the dryness of the atmosphere favors rapid transpiration, are prevented

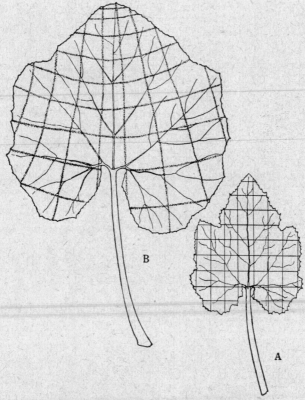

Fig. 145.—A squash leaf (*A*) young and (*B*) after it has grown to maturity. When the leaf was in the condition shown in *A*, it was marked into squares of equal size. Note in *B* that all squares have increased in size, but that certain of them have increased more than others.

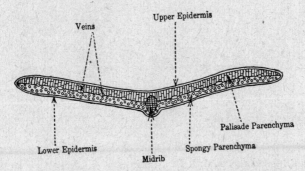

Fig. 146.—Diagram of a cross section of a typical foliage leaf.

from dying of water shortage only by the ability of the epidermis to keep the rate of water loss below that of water absorption.

The leaf epidermis of many plants may be stripped off with little difficulty. It is generally easier to remove it from the under side than from the upper side of the leaf. This is due to the fact that the mesophyll of the lower half of the leaf is a very loose parenchyma with many

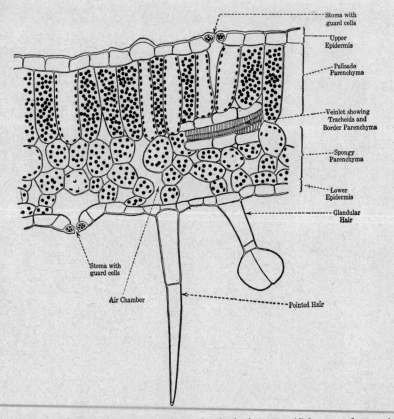

FIG. 147.—A cross section of a portion of a leaf of potato (*Solanum tuberosum*). Except for the chloroplasts none of the cell contents have been shown. Some of the cells of the palisade and spongy parenchyma have been shown in section, others in surface view.

intercellular spaces and therefore with fewer points of attachment to the epidermis than the compact parenchyma which lies below the upper epidermis.

When a piece of epidermis from the lower side of a leaf is examined under the microscope it is found to be made up of two kinds of cells, **ordinary epidermal cells** and **guard cells.** As seen in surface view, the ordinary epidermal cells of the leaves of dicotyledons generally have a wavy outline (Fig. 148). In these plants they are about as broad as they are long, but in the grasses, and many other monocotyledons having long, narrow leaves, they are elongated in the direction of the long axis of the leaf and regular in outline. In leaf cross sections it can be seen that the depth of the ordinary epidermal cells is considerably less than their breadth or length (Fig. 147). Chloroplasts are usually absent from these cells. The outer wall of ordinary epidermal cells generally averages between 0.003 and 0.004 millimeter in thickness, but it gives very effective protection against mechanical injury not only by reason of its toughness but also because of the support given it by the radial walls. It has been computed that beneath a square milli-

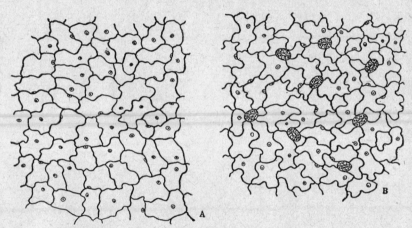

FIG. 148.—Surface view of the epidermis of a typical foliage leaf. *A*, From the upper surface of the leaf; *B*, from the lower surface. The cytoplasm of the cells has not been shown.

meter of the outer epidermal wall of the leaves of many common plants there are more than 2000 radial walls. These oppose the penetration of the epidermis by any object not having an exceedingly sharp point. The cuticle of the leaf epidermis, like that of the epidermis of the stem, is made up almost entirely of the waxy substance, **cutin,** which is very impermeable to water and to water vapor or other gases. The wall layer below the cuticle is, in many plants, made up of both cellulose and cutin and is then spoken of as the **cutinized layer.** The innermost part of the outer wall and all of the other walls of the epidermal cells are almost pure cellulose (see Fig. 150).

The protoplasts of the epidermal cells are long-lived; they do not die until just before the leaf falls. The cytoplasm forms a very thin

layer surrounding a large vacuole, and the nucleus and nucleolus are
often very conspicuous.

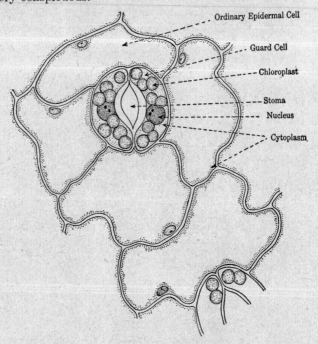

FIG. 149.—A view showing in detail a small portion of the epidermis from the lower
surface of a typical leaf.

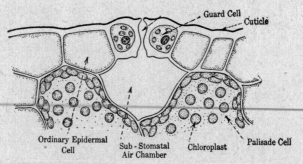

FIG. 150.—A portion of a cross section of a foliage leaf showing a stoma and a few
of the neighboring cells.   (Redrawn after Kny.)

Guard Cells and Stomata.—Scattered among the ordinary epidermal
cells of the lower epidermis, and sometimes of the upper epidermis also,
are the guard cells. These occur in pairs, and when seen in surface

view appear broadly crescent-shaped or almost semicircular in form (Fig. 149). The more or less concave sides of the guard cells are turned toward each other, and between them there is an opening or pore which leads from the outside into an air chamber in the mesophyll. This opening between the guard cells is the **stoma** (plural, **stomata**). The cuticle of the leaf is generally very impermeable to oxygen and carbon dioxide and to water vapor. The passage of these three gases into or out of the leaf takes place very largely through stomata.

By means of a very simple experiment, it is possible to show how very impermeable to water vapor the cuticle may be and with what readiness water is lost through the stomata. The tropical *Ficus elastica*, or rubber plant, which is a common house plant, has leaves which serve well for this experiment, for the cuticle is thick and the stomata are all found on the under side of the leaves. The leaves of several species of magnolia will serve equally well. If two similar leaves are removed and one is smeared with vaseline on the upper surface and the other on the lower surface, the former will begin to shrivel and dry up after a few days' exposure to the dry air of the laboratory, while the leaf whose lower surface has been smeared with vaseline will remain almost normal in appearance for weeks. This difference is due to the fact that the smearing of the under surface seals up the stomata so that little water is lost from the leaf, on account of the waterproof nature of the continuous cuticle of the upper epidermis, while covering the upper leaf surface with vaseline is almost without effect upon the already very low rate of water loss through the cuticle, but leaves the water in the leaf tissues free to pass out through the stomata of the lower epidermis.

The guard cells have numerous, conspicuous chloroplasts. In cross sections of the leaves of many kinds of plants it can be seen that the guard cell walls adjacent to the stoma are of greater average thickness than elsewhere. There may also be observed ridge-like outgrowths from the walls of the guard cells, which form a chamber, outside the stoma proper (Fig.

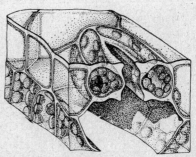

Fig. 151.—Diagram showing a typical stoma and adjoining epidermal cells as seen in surface view and in cross section.

152). Sometimes this " vestibule " has only a narrow, slit-like opening to the outside. In xerophytic plants the ordinary epidermal cells may overlap the guard cells so that the stoma and guard cells are depressed below the general surface of the epidermis. Plants growing in very moist habitats may, on the other hand, have the stomata raised above the surrounding epidermal cells (Fig. 153).

Control of Stomata by the Guard Cells.—The guard cells are able to open and close the stomata. Thus they regulate the entrance and exit of gases. The opening and closing of the stomata by the guard cells depend upon changes in the turgor of these cells. When the turgor of the guard cells becomes greater than that of the adjacent cells, the stomata are opened; when it is equal to that of the neighboring cells or when excessive water loss greatly reduces the turgor of all the living cells of the leaf, the stomata are closed. Illumination of the guard cells increases the concentration of sugar in their cell sap. This is generally assumed to be due to photosynthesis by the illuminated chloroplasts.

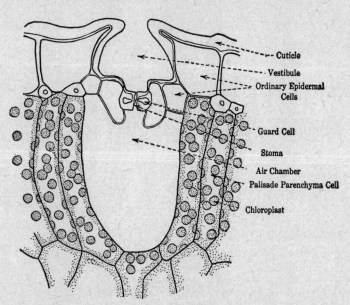

Fig. 152.—Depressed stoma of *Hakea suaveolens*. (In part after Haberlandt.)

However, in some cases at least, it seems to be caused also by a change in the acidity of the sap of these cells which in turn favors the digestion of the starch in the guard cells to sugar. In either case the sugar content of the sap of these cells increases. This sugar raises the concentration of the cell sap above that of the cell sap of the surrounding ordinary epidermal cells which are without chloroplasts or contain only a few small ones. As a result, the guard cells withdraw water from the ordinary epidermal cells and their turgor increases while the turgor of the surrounding cells decreases.

The way in which increased turgor of the guard cells brings about the opening of the stoma differs in different species, but in one of the commonest and simplest cases, the walls farthest from the stoma, having less average thickness than those next to it, stretch and bulge outward, drawing with them the walls adjacent to the stoma. The displacement of the walls bordering on the stoma is much less than that of the thin walls farthest from it but is still sufficient to leave a clear passage between the guard cells. At night or when the leaf is strongly shaded, the concentration of sugar in the guard cells

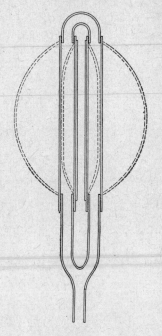

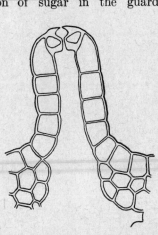

Fig. 153.   Fig. 154.

Fig. 153.—Raised stoma from the fruit stalk of pumpkin (*Curcurbita pepo*). (After Haberlandt.)

Fig. 154.—Diagram of a model illustrating the manner in which the stoma is opened when the turgor of the guard cells increases. The short, glass U-tube at the top is connected to the Y-tube, also of glass, by two pieces of rubber tubing. The inner (adjacent) walls of these two pieces of tubing are made thicker than their outer walls. The thicker portions of the walls of the rubber tubing correspond to the guard cell walls next the stoma, whereas the thinner portions of the walls of the rubber tubing correspond to the guard cell walls farthest from the stoma. If water or air are forced under pressure into the Y-tube and the rubber tubing thus subjected to internal pressure, the greater extensibility of the thin, outer walls causes them to take the position shown by the outer dotted lines in the diagram. As the result of this bulging of the outer walls of the rubber tubes the inner, thick walls are drawn apart as shown. Thus, under pressure from within the tubes, the space between the tubes is widened, corresponding to the opening of the stoma. When the pressure is reduced the inner walls tend to return to their original position, narrowing the opening between them, as when the stoma is closed by the guard cells.

becomes less, probably because part of the sugar is changed to starch. As a result the differences in concentration of the cell sap which cause the opening of the stoma no longer exist. The stretched walls of the

guard cells shorten, and the stoma is closed. If a leaf with open
stomata is placed in a solution of higher concentration than the cell
sap of the guard cells, or if it is taken suddenly from a very moist
atmosphere to a very dry one, the stomata, as a result of water being
withdrawn from the guard cells, may close even though the leaf is
brightly illuminated. The accompanying figure (Fig. 154) shows a

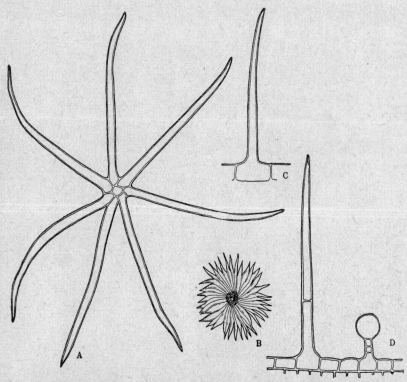

Fig. 155.—Several types of epidermal hairs. *A*, branched hair of false mallow
  (*Malvastrum*), this hair is attached to the leaf by a short stalk not shown in the
  drawing. *B*, scale-like stellate hair of *Eleagnus*, its centrally attached stalk not
  shown. *C*, pointed, unicellular hair of shepherd's purse (*Capsella*). *D*, a pointed
  multicellular and a capitate, glandular hair of geranium (*Pelargonium*).

model of a stoma and guard cells of the simple type previously
described.

We may summarize the above discussion as follows: the stomata
open when the turgor of the guard cell rises; increased turgor of the
guard cells is due to an increase in the concentration of their cell sap
which enables them to absorb water from neighboring cells; increased
concentration of the cell sap is due to an accumulation of sugar in the

guard cells; sugar accumulates when the guard cells are illuminated or when a change in the acidity of the guard cell sap favors the digestion of starch to sugar. The stomata **close when the turgor of the guard**

Fig. 156.—Leaf dimorphism in *Eucalyptus.* The branch to the left shows the sessile, dorsiventral, opposite, juvenile type of leaf, found on seedlings, very young plants, and suckers. The branch to the right shows the stalked, pendent, alternate isobilateral adult type found on older plants except where they have been cut back.

cells falls; decreased turgor of guard cells is due to a decrease in the concentration of their sap which lowers their power to absorb water from adjacent cells; decreased concentration of the sap of guard cells chiefly results from the change of sugar to starch which is insoluble.

Epidermal Hairs.—Many leaves have hairs which grow out from the epidermis. The simplest of these hairs are mere extensions of epidermal cells, the hair and the epidermal cell being in such cases a single cell. Multicellular epidermal hairs such as are found on the leaves and stems of geranium and squash plants and which consist of a single filament of cells which decrease in diameter from the base to the apex, are much more common than are unicellular hairs. Both unicellular and multicellular hairs may be branched. Glandular hairs such as occur in the Chinese primrose (*Primula sinensis*) and various plants of the Cucurbitaceae (squash family) bear at the upper end a rounded head which may consist of a single large cell or of a group of cells, and which often excretes an ethereal oil. The excretion from these glandular hairs is frequently very viscid and sticky as in the tarweeds (*Madia* and *Hemizonia*) and tobacco (*Nicotiana*).

The Mesophyll.—The upper and lower surfaces of typical foliage leaves are usually distinctly different in appearance. The upper surface is generally darker than the lower, and the larger veins which project out from the surface on the under side are, on the upper side, even with the leaf surface or depressed below it. Leaves with such differences between the two sides are called **dorsiventral leaves** or **bifacial leaves** (Fig. 147). Leaves which are held in a horizontal or oblique position by the petiole are generally of the dorsiventral type. In the adult type leaf in *Eucalyptus* and most other leaves which hang perpendicularly downward or are held erect, and are therefore equally illuminated on both sides, the two surfaces are generally similar. Such leaves are called **isobilateral leaves.**

The mesophyll of typical dorsiventral leaves is made up of two principal kinds of tissue: the **palisade parenchyma** and the **spongy parenchyma.** The palisade parenchyma consists of from one to several layers of elongated cells placed with their long axes at right angles to the leaf surface. This tissue extends downward from the upper epidermis to the spongy parenchyma. The latter tissue forms the lower portion, often somewhat more than half, of the mesophyll. The spongy parenchyma cells are not elongated like the palisade cells. Their form and arrangement are such that numerous large intercellular spaces exist between them. The cells of both palisade and spongy parenchyma contain chloroplasts and because of their green color are sometimes spoken of as chlorenchyma.

The Palisade Parenchyma.—Although this tissue is much more compact than the spongy parenchyma, intercellular spaces are by no means absent. These spaces are smaller than those of the spongy parenchyma but they are so distributed that every palisade cell is in contact with an intercellular space, and each such space communicates with the system of connecting intercellular spaces in the spongy parenchyma. Thus there is provision for the free access of carbon dioxide and oxygen to all the food-making cells of the mesophyll. On account of their position the palisade cells receive more illumination than the spongy parenchyma cells. They are more abundantly provided with chloroplasts than are the latter cells. It has been estimated that the

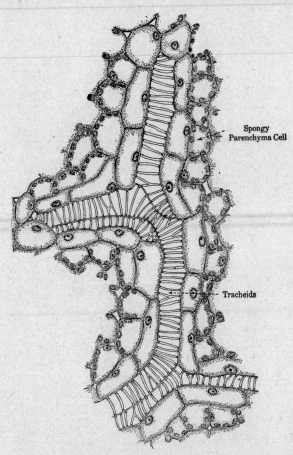

Spongy
Parenchyma Cell

Tracheids

FIG. 157.—A section cut parallel to the leaf surface and through the spongy parenchyma. The free ends of several veinlets are shown as well as the relation of parenchyma cells to the finest veins. The tracheids are the spiral type.

palisade cells of 1 square millimeter of the leaf of the castor-oil plant (*Ricinus communis*) contain over 403,000 chloroplasts, while there are only about 92,000 in the spongy parenchyma cells of the same area. The deeper green of the upper surface of most dorsiventral leaves is due to the greater number of chloroplasts and the smaller number and size of the intercellular spaces of the palisade tissue as compared with those of the spongy parenchyma.   In isobilateral leaves palisade parenchyma is generally found on both sides, there being frequently a layer of spongy parenchyma between the two layers of palisade tissue.

The Spongy Parenchyma.—In most leaves the number of stomata in a given area is greater on the lower than on the upper side, and in many plants there are no stomata whatever on the upper side.   In such leaves the supply of carbon dioxide to the palisade cells during periods of active photosynthesis would be insufficient were it not for the loose nature of the spongy parenchyma.   The light which reaches the spongy parenchyma cells is much less intense than that which falls upon the palisade tissue, for the former are shaded by the palisade parenchyma above them and the light which reaches the leaf from below is, of course, much weaker than that which falls upon the upper surface.

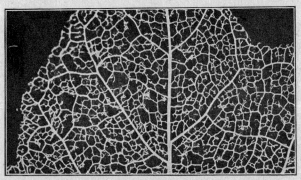

Fig. 158.—A portion of a "skeletonized leaf," all the tissues of which, except the vascular bundles, have been removed by decay, leaving the system of veins. The microscopic "endings" of the bundles and a few of the larger veinlets have been lost.

The Vascular Bundles.—It is easy to demonstrate that conduction, at least of water, is carried on by the veins of the leaf.   This can be shown by placing a leafy shoot in a water solution of some dye such as eosin.   In a relatively short time the veins will be colored deeply by the dye which was present in the water conducted by the vascular bundles of the leaf to replace that lost by transpiration from the mesophyll.

When a leaf is examined with a lens it can be seen that, in addition to the veins which can be detected by the naked eye, there are many fine branch veins, the finest of which end free, that is, are connected to other veins only at one end.   There may be as many as 6000 of these minute vein endings in a square centimeter of leaf.

Although the vascular bundles of the petiole and large veins contain vessels, tracheids, sieve tubes, and companion cells, the vein endings consist only of tracheids, the vascular bundles being reduced generally at the very end to a single tracheid which is usually of the spiral type. The vein endings are generally surrounded by one or more layers of parenchyma cells usually differing somewhat in form from the cells of the spongy palisade parenchyma. These cells, sometimes called border parenchyma, often have no chloroplasts.

Most of the cells of the palisade and spongy parenchyma are some distance from the nearest sieve tube. Clearly the tracheids which are carrying a stream of water upward to the food-making cells can not well conduct the products of photosynthesis in the opposite direction. The transfer of sugar to the nearest sieve tubes is probably carried on by the parenchyma cells surrounding the tracheids of the finest veins and the vein endings. When the sugar reaches a part of the vein where there is phloem tissue, it is conducted by this tissue to the larger veins, then to the midrib, and finally to the vascular bundles of the petiole, where it passes into the phloem of the stem.

The mechanical function of supporting the thin expanded sheet of epidermal and mesophyll tissue is performed principally by the large veins and the midrib. In the veins where phloem is present the phloem occupies the lower side of the vascular bundle and the xylem the upper side. Groups of collenchyma cells or of fibers generally accompany the large veins and increase their strength and rigidity.

The Petiole.—The petiole is sometimes cylindrical in form, but often it is flattened or grooved on the upper side. The vascular tissue of the petiole is variously arranged. Often it is not in a complete circle (as seen in transverse section) but in a semicircle or C-formed line with the opening toward the upper side of

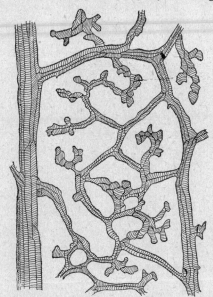

Fig. 159.—A portion of the vein system of a leaf. (Redrawn after Sachs.)

the petiole. As in the vascular bundles of the leaf blade, the phloem occupies the lower part of the petiolar bundles and the xylem the upper part. Collenchyma and fibers are often present. The form of the petiole and the arrangement of its mechanical tissues are such that it forms a relatively rigid support and yet permits the blade to yield to strong air currents.

The Abscission Layer, Leaf Fall, and Leaf Scars.—The conditions which favor leaf fall cause cells near the lower end of the leaf stalk to become meristematic and to give rise to a zone of delicate, thin-walled cells extending clear across the base of the petiole. This is called the

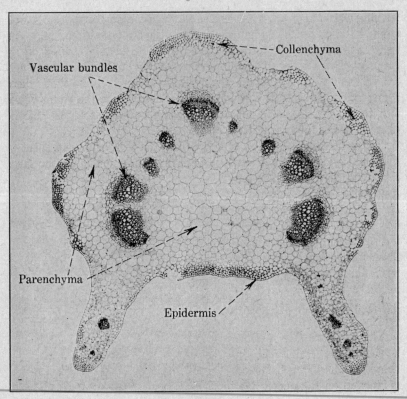

Fig. 160.—Cross section of the petiole of a sugar beet (*Beta vulgaris*) leaf.

abscission layer. The middle lamella of these cells becomes changed chemically before leaf fall and the cells separate from one another easily. When the wind, blowing against the blade of such a leaf, tends to cause the petiole to bend, the abscission layer is ruptured and the leaf becomes detached. When the abscission layer is formed the conducting elements of the vascular bundles generally remain unaffected, but they are not sufficiently strong to prevent the fall of the leaf. After the leaf

has fallen, certain cells just below the abscission layer become lignified
and suberized and form a protective coating over the part of the stem
from which the leaf has separated.   These areas, **leaf scars,** have been
referred to in an earlier chapter (Fig. 10).   Within each leaf scar the
bundle scars, or broken ends of the vascular bundles which led from the

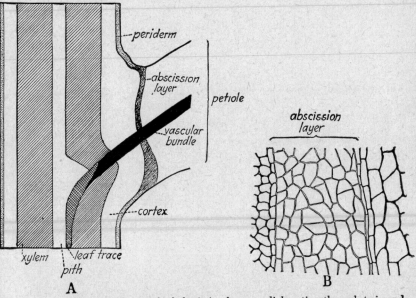

Fig. 161.—*A*, diagram showing leaf abscission layer; radial section through twig and
leaf base in *Juglans cinerea*.   *B*, detail of cellular structure of a small part of the
layer three weeks before leaf fall.   (From Eames and MacDaniels, *Introduction
to Plant Anatomy*, McGraw–Hill Book Company.)

petiole into the stem, may be seen.   The form of the leaf scar and the
number and arrangement of the bundle scars differ sufficiently in various
deciduous plants so that they may be used in distinguishing certain
genera and species in their leafless winter condition.

THE PHYSIOLOGY OF THE LEAF

The primary functions of typical leaves, for which they clearly are
specially adapted in form and structure, are photosynthesis and transpiration.   In certain cases, some of which will be discussed later in
this chapter, leaves carry on other (secondary) functions.

Photosynthesis.—The principal features of carbohydrate manufacture by green cells were briefly stated in the chapter on the cell.   Here

we shall discuss this process more fully, considering the raw materials, the energy factor, the by-product, the end-products, and finally the conditions influencing the rate of photosynthesis.

Raw Materials.—As we have learned, water and carbon dioxide are the raw materials of photosynthesis. The soil is the source of the water, and the carbon dioxide is absorbed from the atmosphere surrounding the leaves. Though the atmosphere is not absolutely constant in its composition, the percentage by volume of its principal components under natural conditions seldom varies much from the following figures:

	Per Cent
Nitrogen	78.03
Oxygen	20.99
Argon	0.94
Carbon dioxide	0.03

Traces of hydrogen, neon, helium, and other gases are present.

Each of these gases is present, therefore, in the intercellular spaces of the chlorenchyma, but carbon dioxide and oxygen are the only ones absorbed or liberated by the plant. If the concentration of either of these gases in the air within the leaf increases, some of that gas will tend to diffuse outward through the stomata. If there is a decrease in concentration of either of these gases, that gas will tend to diffuse inward through the stomata from the air outside the leaf. All the gases of the atmosphere are soluble in water, though they differ greatly in solubility. Accordingly the surface film of water on the outside of the palisade and spongy parenchyma cells, where they are in contact with an intercellular space, as well as the cell sap of these cells, contain in solution a quantity of each of the atmospheric gases. If carbon dioxide or oxygen is being produced in the cell the concentration in the cell sap increases and as a result the concentration of that gas in the surface film and in the intercellular air also increases. Increase of that gas in the air within the leaf similarly affects its concentration in the surface film and cell sap. Now, the process of photosynthesis removes carbon dioxide from solution in the cell sap. As a result there is diffusion of that gas inward from the surface film of water. The loss of carbon dioxide from this surface film is followed by its dissolving more carbon dioxide from the intercellular air, which thus has its carbon dioxide content lowered below that of the outside atmosphere. Diffusion of carbon dioxide inward through the stomata tends to make up the deficiency. Briefly stated, then, there is, during photosynthesis, a movement of carbon dioxide from the atmosphere outside the leaf to the interior of the green cells, and since oxygen is liberated within the green cells during photosynthesis it will diffuse outward, finally passing through the stomata to the atmosphere outside.

The water used by the green cells enters the root from the soil and is conducted upward through the xylem of the root and stem to the leaf. It moves through the xylem of the petiole, midrib, and veins to the finest veinlets. Water passes from the tracheids of the veinlets to the chlorenchyma cells by reason of the much greater concentration of the cell sap in those cells than of the solution in the tracheids.

The quantity of carbon dioxide and water absorbed and converted into food and tissue by the plant is surprisingly large. A tree of moderate size may have a dry weight (weight of its tissue after removal of all water) of as much as 5000 kilograms (about $5\frac{1}{2}$ tons). This is, of course, much less than the total weight of organic matter which the tree has produced, for during its life large quantities of organic material were oxidized and part of the products (for example, carbon dioxide) lost to the plant.

It has been calculated that about 2500 kilograms of the weight of such a tree consists of carbon, and to secure that quantity of carbon the tree must have taken the carbon dioxide from about $16\frac{1}{2}$ million cubic meters of air, or a volume 1 kilometer wide, 1 kilometer long, and $16\frac{1}{2}$ meters high (roughly 3300 feet square and 55 feet high).

Under conditions very favorable for photosynthesis a sunflower leaf may absorb carbon dioxide at the rate of 820 cubic centimeters per square meter of leaf surface per hour. That amount of carbon dioxide would be contained in an air column of 1 square meter cross section and somewhat more than $2\frac{1}{2}$ meters high (about 3.2 feet by 3.2 feet by 8 feet).

The Energy Factor—*Necessity of Light for Photosynthesis.*—There are several interesting methods of showing that light is essential to the union of carbon dioxide and water to form carbohydrates. One of these depends upon the measurement of the dry weight of a given area of leaf tissue before and after a period of active photosynthesis. This method was first used by the great botanist, Sachs. Early in the morning of a warm sunny day he cut a given area from one-half of each of a number of leaves. This tissue he deprived of all of its water by heating to 100° C. until it lost no more weight. In the late afternoon he cut from the intact halves of the same leaves an area of leaf tissue equal to that which had been taken in the morning. This leaf tissue he also deprived of its water. Upon comparing the dry weights he found that the tissue taken in the evening weighed more than that removed from the leaves in the morning. The difference represented part, but by no means all, of the material manufactured by the leaf tissue during the day, for some of the sugar made was conducted away from the leaf and some was lost by respiration. If this experiment is repeated with plants which are kept in the dark during the day there will be no gain in dry weight. The conclusion is inevitable that light is essential to the increase in dry weight. Furthermore, it can be clearly shown that the increase in dry weight is due to the production of sugar and starch.

If we assume that the absence of starch in the green cells of the leaf is a safe indication that photosynthesis has not taken place, we can easily show that photosynthesis will not go on unless light actually falls upon the green tissue. It is only necessary to keep a plant in the dark until its leaves have become emptied of starch, and then to place it in the light after covering one of its leaves with a mask of opaque paper or tinfoil with one or more openings cut in it. After some hours' exposure to light the leaf is removed from the plant, freed of its chlorophyll by means of alcohol, and treated with a solution of iodine. The portion of the leaf which was illuminated through the openings in the mask will take on the dark blue color which is characteristic of starch treated with iodine, while the remainder of the leaf will show no starch reaction.

A most conclusive and ingenious demonstration of the necessity for illumination, not merely of the green cells but of the chloroplasts themselves, is that devised by Engelmann. It rests upon the fact, already touched upon in the chapter on the cell, that oxygen is liberated from the cells in which photosynthesis is going on. Engelmann mounted an algal filament (one of the microscopic threads making up the green masses often seen growing in fresh-water pools or ponds) in water in which there were many motile bacteria. Then he sealed the edge of the cover glass to the slide with grease, so that no oxygen from the atmosphere might be absorbed by the water containing the bacteria and the algal filament. These motile bacteria are able to swim from place to place by reason of the rapid movements of their protoplasmic whips, or cilia. The movement of the bacteria is dependent on the supply of energy derived from their own respiration. Oxygen is necessary for respiration, and when the oxygen supply in the liquid surrounding them has been largely exhausted by their own respiration they lose their motility. Furthermore, they tend to move toward a region where that gas is more abundant; that is, they are chemotactic toward oxygen.

When Engelmann's preparation of bacteria and of the algal filament (the latter consisting of green cells placed end to end) was kept in the dark, the bacteria soon came to rest on account of oxygen shortage resulting from their respiration and that of the algal cells. However, when light was allowed to fall upon the filament of green cells, they liberated oxygen and many of the bacteria regained their motility and accumulated around the filament.   Engelmann was able to project upon the alga a spot of light so small that he would at will illuminate a portion either of the chloroplast or of the colorless cytoplasm.

The bacteria accumulated about the filament only when the chloroplast itself was lighted.   Engelmann thus showed not only that photosynthesis could not take place in the algal cells unless they were illuminated, but that it was necessary that the light actually fall upon the chloroplast itself if photosynthesis were to go on.

The experiment just described shows that chlorophyll is essential to the process of photosynthesis.   Another convincing method of demonstrating this is by the use of variegated leaves, such as those of certain varieties of geranium (*Pelargonium*)

Fig. 162.—A "starch print" on a terminal leaflet of scarlet runner bean.   The plant was placed in the dark for one day.   During this time all the starch previously produced by photosynthesis had disappeared.   The leaflet, still attached to the plant, was then covered with tinfoil, from which the letters of the word, *starch*, had been cut.   After the leaf had been exposed to moderately intense sunlight for several hours it was removed from the plant, killed by placing it in boiling water, treated with alcohol to remove the chlorophyll, immersed in a solution of iodine, and then washed.   Only where the light fell upon the leaf through the openings in the "stencil" was starch formed.   Iodine stains starch blue.   Thus the word *"starch"* appeared in dark blue upon the white leaf. A photographic negative may be used instead of a tinfoil stencil and thus portraits or other pictures can be printed upon the leaf.

and of *Coleus*, which have white bands or blotches.   If the distribution of the non-green areas of such a leaf is carefully noted or sketched, it will be found when the leaf is treated with alcohol and then with iodine solution, after being exposed for some hours to light, that starch has not been formed in the parts when chlorophyll is absent.

The Energy Factor—*Light Energy.*—In order to understand the rôle played by chlorophyll in carbohydrate manufacture it is necessary to be familiar with some of the elementary facts in regard to the physics of that form of energy called light.

There is a general agreement that the energy of an electric current is due to

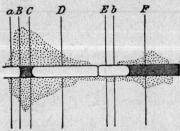

FIG. 163.—Diagram illustrating Engelmann's experiment demonstrating the regions of the spectrum most active in photosynthesis. See text for an account of this experiment. In this diagram the algal filament is shaded to show the portions which are lighted by the parts of the spectrum most strongly absorbed by chlorophyll. The dots represent the bacteria which accumulate where oxygen is relatively abundant. The lettered vertical lines show the position of certain dark lines characteristic of the solar spectrum and serve here merely to indicate different regions of the spectrum. (From Palladin, after Engelmann.)

electrons, particles of negative electricity in active movement, and that the energy of a hot body is due to rapid movement (with frequent impacts and rebounding) of its molecules; but as to the actual nature of radiant energy, including light, there are two principle theories, neither of which offers a satisfactory explanation for all the properties of light. According to one theory, visible light consists of waves or vibrations varying in amplitude (wave length) but all capable of perception by the human eye. These waves generally originate in some hot body such as the sun or other stars, the incandescent filament of an electric light bulb, or the hot carbon particles of a gas or oil flame. Since light can pass through spaces where there is no matter, there has been assumed the existence of a medium called "the ether" which is without the characteristic properties of matter but exists everywhere and is able to transmit light waves. The ether theory, though no longer accepted by many physicists, is the most easily understood of the various theories of light and makes it possible to explain certain observed facts which are not explainable by other theories. White light is made up of ether vibrations or waves of different

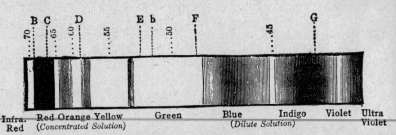

FIG. 164.—Diagram of the absorption spectrum of a chlorophyll solution. The numbers give the wave length in hundred-thousandths of a millimeter. The portion to the right is based on the absorption spectrum of a less concentrated solution of chlorophyll than the portion to the left since in a more concentrated solution the three broad absorption bands in the blue, indigo and violet appear as one band. (From Kraus.)

lengths, ranging from the relatively long waves of red light, through the successively shorter waves of orange, yellow, and green light to the very short waves of blue and violet light. The wave lengths of visible light range from about 70/100,000 of a millimeter in the extreme red through orange, yellow, green, blue and indigo to about 40/100,000 of a millimeter in the extreme violet. By means of a glass prism a shaft of white light can be resolved into its component colors. In the resulting band of color, which is called the **spectrum**, the different component colors of white light are arranged in the order of their wave length. Beyond the end of the visible spectrum at the red end, are still longer waves which our eyes are incapable of perceiving. These are spoken of as infra-red lights. Beyond the violet end are shorter waves, also invisible, which are called ultra-violet light. Such ether waves of whatever length and whether visible or not are spoken of collectively as radiant energy. The term includes the waves, up to hundreds of meters in length, by means of which wireless messages are transmitted, and the extremely short waves of the so-called X-rays as well as still shorter waves.

When white light falls upon a white object, all the different component colors are reflected to the eye. When a white object is illuminated by red light or by blue light the object appears red or blue because of the reflection to the eye of the colored light which falls upon it. Dead black material, like black velvet, absorbs practically all the light which falls upon it regardless of whether it is white light or colored light. It is black merely because it reflects no light to the eye. Colored materials absorb certain of the components of white light which falls upon them and reflect others to the eye. Thus a piece of green paper absorbs most of the light which falls upon it except the waves of green light, which it reflects. This last statement must be somewhat qualified. Strictly speaking, green light is light of a certain range of wave lengths, between about 53 and 56 hundred thousandths of a millimeter. The eye, however, perceives as green not only such monochromatic light but also mixtures of longer wave lengths (yellow light) and shorter wave lengths (blue light) even though green light is entirely absent. The light absorbed by black or other colored material is largely converted into heat energy.

The Energy Factor—*Function of Chlorophyll.*—We learned in an earlier chapter that the green color of the chloroplasts is due to a mixture of four pigments, two green ones, chlorophyll a and chlorophyll b, and two yellow ones, carotin and xanthophyll. The term chlorophyll is often used for the mixture of these four pigments found in the leaf, and it is in this sense that we shall use it in this chapter.

When a solution of chlorophyll in alcohol contained in a glass vessel is viewed by transmitted light (light which has passed through the solution before reaching the observer's eye) it appears green in color. But when the solution is viewed by reflected light it appears deep red in color. This is due to the power of chlorophyll a and b to **fluoresce** (change the wave length of some of the light which they absorb to light of longer wave length). Chlorophyll solutions and chlorophyll in the chloroplasts show red fluorescence even when the light which falls upon the chlorophyll has had all the red components removed. It is possible to determine what part of the white light is absorbed by chlorophyll by causing light which has passed through a solution of chlorophyll in alcohol to fall upon a glass prism so that it is broken up into its component colors. In place of an alcoholic solution of chlorophyll we may use a leaf the intercellular spaces within which have been filled with water to render it less opaque. The resulting spectrum will be different from the spectrum of white light which has not passed through a chlorophyll solution or a leaf. It will lack a considerable part of the red and much of the blue, indigo, and violet. Part of the red (of longest wave lengths) and most of the yellow, orange, and green are scarcely absorbed at all unless the solution is very concentrated or the leaf very thick. Thus we learn that it is a certain part of the red and some of the blue, violet, and indigo which are absorbed by chlorophyll. Part of the red (from 65 to 68 hundred-thousandths of a millimeter) is absorbed almost completely even in solutions of moderate concentration, but there is less complete absorption of the blue, violet, and indigo. Important as is the absorption of the light energy which is necessary for photosynthesis, that is not the only part played in the process by chlorophyll. It doubtless plays an important chemical rôle also in the formation of sugar from carbon dioxide and water.

The Energy Factor—*Effectiveness of Different Parts of the Spectrum.* —Photosynthesis can go on only if energy is continuously supplied from without, and light is the only form of energy which the plant can use for this purpose. Obviously light which is not absorbed can not be used for photosynthesis, but it does not follow that all the different colors of light absorbed are employed in photosynthesis. We are also not justified in assuming that the small quantity of green, yellow, and orange light which is absorbed can not be used for sugar formation. Only experiment can answer the questions as to what part of the absorbed light can be used in carbohydrate manufacture. One of the most direct methods is to project a spectrum upon a starch-free leaf which receives light from no other source, and then after a time remove the leaf from the plant and treat it with alcohol and with iodine solution. It will be found that where the orange, yellow, and green light fell upon the leaf there is little or no evidence of starch formation, but that abundant starch is present where the leaf was lighted by the blue end of the spectrum and by that portion of the red in which the absorption by chlorophyll is most complete.

By the use of his method (already described) of mounting motile bacteria together with an algal filament under a cover glass with the edges sealed to the slide, Engelmann also demonstrated that all the different components of white light which are appreciably absorbed by chlorophyll are active in photosynthesis. When he cast a small spectrum lengthwise upon the algal filament the bacteria swarmed in large numbers around the filament where it was lighted by the blue end of the spectrum and by the intensely absorbed portion at the red end (Fig. 163). The aggregation of the motile bacteria in the red part of the spectrum was greater than at the blue end, indicating that oxygen liberation and therefore photosynthesis were most active in the region of most complete absorption.

It has been shown that the greater intensity of photosynthesis in light of certain wave lengths is principally due to the chlorophyll being able to absorb a much larger proportion of such light than of light of other wave lengths. If we compare the photosynthetic activity produced by *equal quantities* of *absorbed* light energy in different parts of the spectrum we find no *very* great differences but a progressive decrease with decrease in wave length. Thus a *given quantity of absorbed light energy* in the green is slightly more effective than the same quantity in the blue. Owing, however, to the relatively small proportion of the green absorbed by the chloroplasts and the large proportion of the blue, photosynthesis is much more active in the blue part.

Efficiency of the Leaf in Utilizing the Sun's Energy.—The following table gives the principal results of one series of measurements of the efficiency of leaves in utilizing light energy. The values would vary considerably according to the species, the age of the leaf, the intensity of the light, and other factors. In these measurements variegated leaves were used. They were exposed to full sunlight and the energy quantity absorbed by the chloroplasts was determined by subtracting that absorbed by a given area of a white part of the leaf from the quantity absorbed by the same area of a green part.

	Per Cent
Total energy of sunlight falling on upper leaf surface	100
Energy absorbed by green part of a variegated leaf	80
Energy absorbed by chlorophyll-free part of such a leaf	70
Energy absorbed by the chloroplasts of the green part of the leaf	10
Energy actually utilized in photosynthesis	3.5

It is clear from this table that under the conditions of this particular experiment about 35 per cent of the energy actually absorbed by the chloroplasts or 3.5 per cent of all the light energy falling on the leaf was used in photosynthesis. A large part of the energy absorbed, but not utilized in photosynthesis, is used up in transpiration. In general the efficiency of green plants in the utilization for photosynthesis of the sunlight falling upon their leaves is probably less than the values given above, perhaps as low as 1 per cent.

The By-product.—As shown by the equation for photosynthesis ($6CO_2 + 6H_2O = C_6H_{12}O_6 + 6O_2$), oxygen is liberated during the process. We speak of the oxygen as a by-product because its formation is merely incidental to the production of sugar. It is liberated into the atmosphere which already contains sufficient of this gas for the needs of the plant.

of starch in the absence of light are milk sugar (lactose), cane sugar (sucrose), malt sugar (maltose), and grape sugar (glucose).

The Course of the Process.—It is not reasonable to suppose that the whole process of formation of glucose from carbon dioxide and water consists of a single chemical reaction. Of the several theories which have been proposed as to the successive stages in the process, most of the recent and most reasonable involve the formation from the raw materials (CO_2 and H_2O) of the compound formaldehyde (CH_2O) and the union of six such molecules to form a single molecule of glucose ($C_6H_{12}O_6$). Formaldehyde is poisonous to plants if present in high concentrations, but the continuous formation of glucose from the formaldehyde molecules would prevent the latter substance accumulating in sufficient quantities in the leaf cells to cause any injury to them. It should be stated, however, that the question of the actual course of the chemical changes involved in carbohydrate manufacture is still an open one.

Rate of Carbohydrate Production.—The amount of carbohydrate produced by a given area of leaf in a given time varies widely in different species of plants and under different external conditions particularly of temperature and light intensity. Probably under very favorable conditions a square meter of leaf surface may produce in a single day as much as 20 grams of carbohydrate, for it has been shown that the average hourly rate of photosynthesis in pumpkin plants during a ten-hour period may equal 1.8 grams per square meter.

Conditions Influencing the Rate of Photosynthesis.—Under natural conditions the rate of photosynthesis depends upon many factors, internal and external. Among the internal factors may be mentioned the structure of the leaf, the number and distribution of chloroplasts in the mesophyll cells, the quantity of chlorophyll in a given area of leaf, and the number and distribution of the stomata, which control the entrance of carbon dioxide. These factors vary greatly in different species. The principal external factors which affect the rate of photosynthesis are:

1. Temperature.
2. Intensity of illumination.
3. Carbon dioxide content of the atmosphere.
4. Water supply.

The lowest known temperature (minimum) at which it is possible for photosynthesis to go on is several degrees below the freezing-point of water. For many plants of the temperate zone the optimum (most favorable) temperature for the process is about 37° C. and the maximum (temperature above which the process ceases) from 43° to 45°. But the optimum differs somewhat in different species. It also may vary according to the other external factors. Thus the optimum temperature may be lower when the light intensity is low than when the illumination is more intense.

The amount of carbohydrate produced by a given area of leaf surface increases with increasing illumination up to a certain point (the optimum light intensity) if the temperature and the carbon dioxide supply are sufficient.

But with optimum illumination and temperature, green leaves do not, under natural conditions, produce the greatest quantity of carbohydrates which they are capable of producing. This is because the 0.03 per cent of carbon dioxide in the atmosphere is far below the optimum concentration. With conditions of temperature and illumination such as exist in nature where crop plants are developing normally, artificial increase of carbon dioxide up to a concentration of 0.25 per cent may result in increased carbohydrate production.

Under favorable natural conditions of illumination and temperature the carbon dioxide content of the atmosphere is the **limiting factor** for photosynthesis. That is to say, at the temperature of a sunny day during the active growing season, the amount of carbohydrate produced could not be increased by raising the temperature or increasing the illumination, but only by increasing the concentration of carbon dioxide above that normally present in the atmosphere. In weak light or at low temperatures the concentration of carbon dioxide may not be the limiting factor and an increased rate of photosynthesis may not be attained by increase in carbon dioxide. Which factor (light intensity or temperature) is then the limiting factor can be determined only by raising the temperature without change in illumination, and increasing the illumination without changing the temperature. The factor (light intensity or temperature) whose increase results in increase in photosynthesis can then be recognized as the limiting factor.

Over limited areas in fields adjacent to certain industrial plants which produce carbon dioxide as a by-product, and in greenhouses, artificial increase of carbon dioxide in the atmosphere has been shown to greatly increase the yield of the crops.

The Utilization of the Product of Photosynthesis.—The sugar, glucose, which is believed to be the immediate product of the photosynthetic process, constitutes the foundation material out of which many other plant substances are built up. Part of this carbohydrate is respired, liberating energy which is used by the plant in its life processes, but a very large portion is transformed chemically into substances which serve various purposes in the life of the plant. We may classify these substances as follows: (1) those which compose the cell walls of the plant, (2) reserve foods, (3) components of living protoplasm, and (4) various other substances.

Part of the sugar is converted into cellulose for the formation of the walls of new cells and for the thickening of old walls of living cells. The reserve foods of which glucose forms the basis are principally (1) **carbohydrates,** such as the **sugars** (fructose, sucrose), **starches,** and **hemicellulose,** (2) **oils,** and (3) **proteins.** The carbohydrates and oils contain the same elements, carbon, hydrogen, and oxygen, found in the glucose molecule, consequently, the chemical transformation of glucose to these substances does not involve the addition of other elements. But, in the building of proteins, the elements nitrogen, sulphur, and in some cases phosphorus are added to those of the glucose. Protein formation apparently may go on in any part of the plant. Living protoplasm is a complex mixture of a number of substances, chiefly proteinaceous in character.

Of the various other substances produced in plants the following may be mentioned: (1) the **essential oils,** such as lemon oil, cedar oil, clove oil, and other volatile oils which are capable of imparting odors to fruits and flowers and other parts of the plant; (2) the **resins,** found in many plants but particularly abundant in pines; (3) **latex,** a milky secretion; the latex of certain plants is the basis of rubber; (4) various **pigments,** such as chlorophyll, xanthophyll, carotin, and anthocyanin; (5) **alkaloids,** nitrogenous compounds, such as quinine (from the bark of *Cinchona* tree), caffein (from coffee), thein (from tea), morphine (from the poppy); (6) **glucosides,** substances which on decomposition give rise to glucose together with certain other substances; examples of glucosides are amygdalin which is found in the seeds of the bitter almond and other nuts, and sinigrin found chiefly in the seeds of mustards; (7) **enzymes,** complex protein compounds, which by their mere presence, even in very low concentration, speed up certain chemical reactions in the plant; (8) **acids,** such as malic acid (from the apple), and citric acid (from citrus fruits); (9) **tannins,** substances which impart an astringent, bitter taste to tissues in which they are present, and (10) **vitamins,** substances which occur in extremely minute quantities in plants and are detectable only through feeding experiments with animals. Animals, including man, are incapable of normal development and maintenance of health if any one of the known vitamins is lacking in their food. Little is known concerning their function in plants.

Transpiration.—The plant is constantly losing water to the atmosphere. This water comes from the soil, enters the plant through the roots, moves in the conducting tissues to the leaves, and escapes as vapor from the moist cell walls of the mesophyll into the intercellular spaces, from which it passes by diffusion through the stomata and, to a much less extent, through the cuticle to the atmosphere. There is loss of water from the young stems also and in fact from the entire surface of the plant which is exposed to air above ground.

If a bell jar be placed over a potted plant fine drops of water will soon make their appearance on the inner surface of the jar, and these will finally collect into larger drops and run down the glass walls. Evidently the air within the chamber has been receiving from some source a quantity of water, part of which has become condensed upon the glass. If the possibility of water passing into the air by evaporation from the soil or the pot is excluded by sealing the surface of the pot and the soil with paraffine, the results of the experiment are unchanged. The conclusion which can be drawn is that water passes from the aerial parts of plants into the surrounding air.

As a matter of fact, all the higher plants, except such submerged forms as water weed (*Elodea*) and water milfoil (*Myriophyllum*), are constantly losing water, which passes into the atmosphere in the form of water vapor. This process is called **transpiration.** Another method by which it may be demonstrated, and at the same time accurately measured, is by the use of a balance. If a potted plant, with the pot and soil surfaces sealed over with paraffine or completely enclosed in sheet rubber or other waterproof covering, is placed on the scales and accurately weighed, it will be found after a short interval that the plant has lost weight. Successive weighings will show that it continues to lose weight. If the plant were kept in the dark between weighings, the loss in weight would include that due to respiration as well as that resulting from transpiration, but the resulting error in transpiration measurement would not be large in an actively transpiring plant, for the loss due to transpiration would be many times the loss by respiration. The weight loss might be somewhat less than the weight of water transpired if the plant were kept in the light between weighings, for the plant might gain by photosynthesis more than it lost by respiration.

Though related to evaporation, such as takes place from a water surface or from a wet cloth, transpiration is different in that it is controlled in part by the plant itself.

Utility to the Plant.—The great surface exposed by the leaves of a typical plant is favorable to the absorption of large quantities of carbon dioxide and of light energy for photosynthesis. It subjects the plant, however, to the danger of transpiration exceeding water absorption, a condition which results in wilting, or, if long continued, in the death of the plant. The question naturally suggests itself as to whether the large water loss through transpiration is merely an unavoidable result

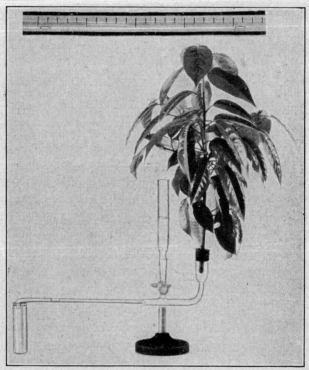

Fig. 166.—A potometer for measurement of the rate of transpiration. Withdrawal of water from the apparatus by the leafy shoot to make up for that lost by transpiration causes water to move from left to right in the horizontal capillary tube. This tube is bent downward near the end and dips under the water in the vial shown at the left, from which it draws water through its open end. If the tip of the capillary tube, which is graduated in 500ths of a cubic centimeter, is raised for a few seconds above the surface of the water in the vial an air bubble enters the tube. The distance moved by this bubble in a given time shows the rate of transpiration. By turning the stop cock at the base of the perpendicular water reservoir the bubble can be forced back to its original position after each observation. A potometer with larger receptacle for the plant so that a small plant with its entire root system can be used is preferable to the apparatus shown. Above, a portion of the capillary tube, slightly magnified, showing a bubble between the fifth and ninth graduations.

of the development of a great leaf surface by the plant or is a process which plays a useful rôle in the life of the plant. It was formerly the general belief that the inorganic salts from the soil were carried into the roots with the absorbed water, and that therefore the quantity of these salts which entered the plant depended upon the quantity of water absorbed. There is, however, no apparent reason why substances in solution in the soil should not diffuse into the root hairs even though there is no simultaneous absorption of water. It has recently been shown by experiment that reduction of the quantity of water absorbed by a plant (by reducing its transpiration) does not proportionately reduce the quantity of soil solutes absorbed.

Transpiration and the Transpiration Stream.—In the chapter on the stem, the withdrawal of water from the conducting tissues of the leaf by the mesophyll cells was given as the principal factor in maintaining the stream of water and soil solutes from the root to other parts of the plant. It is this osmotic pull upon the water in the tracheids of the veinlets which is responsible for drawing the dilute solution (the sap) upward in the vascular tissue of the veins and stem. The water drawn into the mesophyll cells tends to reduce the concentration of their cell sap. As a result, these cells would lose their power to draw water from the veinlets and the upward stream would cease or at least move much more slowly if it were not for the fact that the mesophyll cells are losing water by transpiration. Transpiration is responsible for the rise of water to the leaves but it can scarcely be said that it is on that account useful to the plant, for practically all the water raised is lost by transpiration. Bringing the mineral salts (absorbed from the soil and present in great dilution in the sap) quickly to the leaves and concentrating them there, where they are probably principally used in the manufacture of proteins, chlorophyll, and perhaps other substances, may be the single definitely useful rôle performed by transpiration.

The greater part of the energy absorbed by the leaf is already in the form of heat or is transformed into heat within the leaf. It has been suggested that the absorption of so much energy which is not used up in photosynthesis may result in the leaf being raised to so high a temperature on warm sunny days that the protoplasm would be injured or killed if it were not for the cooling effect of water evaporation (transpiration) from the leaf. Experiments with leaves which are transpiring actively and with others in which the transpiration rate is quite low do not indicate that the latter have a temperature much above the former, even on very warm sunny days. It is highly questionable whether the cooling effect of transpiration is of much importance to the plant.

Conditions Affecting Transpiration Rate.—The amount of water lost by transpiration depends upon (1) **external factors,** conditions outside the plant, and (2) **internal factors,** conditions in the plant itself.

External Factors.—In measuring the effect of external conditions upon the rate of transpiration, the balance may be used to show, by the change in weight of a plant, the quantity of water lost.

The principal external factors which affect the transpiration rate are the following:

1. Humidity of the atmosphere.
2. Light intensity.
3. Air movements.
4. Air temperature, as it affects leaf temperature.
5. Soil conditions.

Humidity of the Atmosphere.—The less moisture there is in the air surrounding the plant the greater will transpiration tend to be. Though water loss is very slight in a water-saturated atmosphere it has been shown that it does not cease entirely. When plants which have been absorbing and transpiring water actively have transpiration suddenly checked, by great increase in the humidity of the atmosphere, while intake of water continues, drops of water may come out of the tissues. This can be shown by inverting a large tumbler over a flower pot in which young oat or wheat plants are growing. If the plants have been well supplied with water and have been previously exposed to warm, dry air, drops of water will appear on the leaves and often increase in size until they fall off or run down the leaves. This exudation of water in the liquid form under the conditions described is called **guttation.** It takes place in various plants during moist, cool nights following warm summer days. Many plants possess special structures called **hydathodes** (sometimes modified stomata), through which water of guttation can easily escape.

Fig. 167.—Photograph of a rose leaf showing water of guttation adhering to the "teeth" around the margins of the leaflets.

Light Intensity.—Illumination has a marked effect on water loss by transpiration. Illumination may increase transpiration in two ways: (1) by causing the guard cells to open wide the stomata, and (2) by raising the temperature of the leaf.

Air Movements.—When the air surrounding the plant is quiet, it becomes almost saturated with water vapor because of transpiration and the slowness with which the water vapor diffuses away from the leaf. This " moist blanket " of air naturally checks transpiration. Movement of the air sweeps away this mantle of moist air and brings drier air to the surface of the leaves, and as a result transpiration increases.

Air Temperature.—In general, experiments show that, other conditions remaining constant, transpiration increases with rise and decreases with lowering of the temperature of the surrounding air, this resulting in a corresponding increase or decrease of leaf temperature.

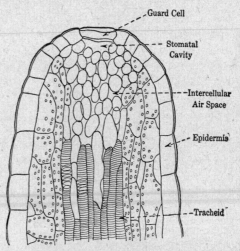

Soil Conditions.—When transpiration has been for some time more active than water absorption, the plant shows that it is suffering water shortage by beginning to wilt. Although it has been shown that the stomata may remain open for some time after wilting starts there is a large reduction in transpiration rate as soon as wilting begins. The mesophyll cells give up water vapor much less freely when they are in a condition of water shortage

Fig. 168.—Longitudinal section through a marginal tooth of a leaf of Chinese primrose (*Primula sinensis*), showing the structure of a hydathode. Not a few plants, particularly those of humid regions, possess these special structures which excrete water in the liquid form during guttation. (Redrawn after Haberlandt.)

than when they are abundantly supplied with water. This results whether the water shortage is due either to excessive transpiration or to restricted water absorption. Accordingly, any soil conditions such as a deficiency of water in the soil which affect the rate of water absorption will also change the rate of transpiration.

Internal Factors.—*Means of Limiting Transpiration.*—All flowering plants, with the exception of a few submerged aquatic ones, have provisions for regulating transpiration. If this were not so, even in the case of a plant growing in relatively moist soil, a short period of relatively low humidity, such as would result from a sudden rise in temperature, might cause serious injury or death. This would result from a failure of the roots to absorb, or of the vascular tissue to conduct, sufficient water to replace the greatly increased quantity lost by transpiration.

Through the layer of cuticle forming the surface of all mature leaves, some water does escape into the air. This loss of water through the cuticle is spoken of as **cuticular transpiration,** to distinguish it from water loss through the stomata which is called **stomatal transpiration.**

The principal means by which the plant reduces cuticular transpiration are the thickening of the outer wall of the epidermal cells, the presence of large quantities of the wax-like material, **cutin,** in this wall, and the production of close-set rods of wax (the so-called " bloom ") which occurs on many fruits, leaves, and stems and which has the appearance of a very fine powder. The leaves of tulips, pinks, or carnations, and many other plants have such a coating, or " bloom," which may easily be wiped off.

The following brief table gives the average number of stomata per square millimeter on the upper and lower surfaces of the leaves of some common plants:

Name of Plant	Average Number of Stomata per Square Millimeter	
	Upper Surface	Under Surface
Apple (*Pyrus malus*)........................	0	250
Olive (*Olea europaea*)........................	0	625
Pea (*Pisum sativum*)........................	101	216
Rubber plant (*Ficus elastica*).................	0	145
Corn (*Zea mays*)............................	94	158
Barberry (*Berberis vulgaris*)..................	0	229

Clearly the stomata on the under surface of the leaf will be less likely to endanger the plant by allowing excessive transpiration than would stomata on the upper surface. The temperature of the lower, and therefore shaded, side of the leaf will be less than that of the upper side when the sun is shining brightly, and the air adjacent to the lower surface of the leaf will not tend to be so dry as that next to the upper side of the leaf.

Leaves which hang straight down, like those of some poplars and the adult leaves of eucalyptus (Fig. 156), have about the same number of stomata on the two sides. The same is true of leaves, like those of many grasses, which stand almost or quite perpendicular. In a few plants, such as those water lilies whose leaves float on the surface of water, there are no stomata on the lower leaf surface.

Stomatal transpiration is sometimes reduced by depression of the stomata below the general surface of the leaf. In plants with such sunken stomata, gases entering the leaf have to pass through an outer chamber formed by overhanging epidermal cells before entering the stoma (Fig. 152). The transpired water vapor leaving the leaf is thus prevented from being swept away from the stoma at once by air currents, and transpiration is reduced.

Most plants are able, by opening or closing the stomata, to greatly alter the water loss due to transpiration. On page 194 a brief account was given of the mechanism by which the guard cells open and close the pore (stoma) between them. The guard cells generally react to a change from light to darkness or from darkness to light, closing the stoma in the former case and opening it in the latter. The stomata must, however, be considered primarily as serving to permit the entrance of carbon dioxide and oxygen rather than to limit transpiration, for the stomata are in general open not at the time when transpiration would tend to be the least (at night) but in the daytime when the leaf requires carbon dioxide for photosynthesis and when the open stomata will cause a relatively high rate of transpiration.

In the willows (*Salix*) the guard cells have lost their power of regulating the stomata and the latter remain permanently open. It may be largely on this account that the willows are generally restricted to habitats where there is abundant water in the soil.

Other Methods of Reducing Transpiration.—In some plants, certain grasses for example, transpiration, both stomatal and cuticular, is reduced, when water shortage begins, by rolling of the leaves. By this method the leaf surface exposed to light and to the dry atmosphere is reduced.

It is commonly assumed that the presence of epidermal hairs reduces transpiration. Of this there is some question, especially in cases where the hairs are made up of living cells. Experiments with some plants have shown that the water loss from the leaves is greater when the hairs are present than when they are lacking.

Many xerophytes (plants living in places where the water supply in the soil is small and the atmosphere very dry) have reduced both stomatal and cuticular transpiration by having very small leaves, by shedding the leaves soon after they are formed, or by producing no leaves at all. In either of the two latter cases the stems perform the typical leaf functions. Clearly such provisions for restricting water loss result in a great sacrifice of photosynthetic activity.

Respiration in Leaves.—As we have already learned, the oxidation of food into carbon dioxide and water, with the liberation of the energy which was stored in the molecules of the food substance, is a process going on in all living cells. It is particularly active in the growing parts of the plant and in the leaves and flowers. Part of the energy liberated by respiration is in the form of heat. Under natural conditions this heat does not cause any considerable rise in the temperature of the leaf, for it is quickly dissipated into the surrounding air. However, if many fresh green leaves are piled together, the center of the mass soon becomes very warm, since the heat liberated by their respiration can not readily escape. Molisch found that in the center of a large pile of fresh green pear leaves a temperature 44° C. above that of the surrounding atmosphere was attained within a little over twenty-four hours. This rise of temperature due to the respiration of the cells of the leaves is not to be confused with the heating which would take place much later due to the fermentation of the mass by bacteria and other fungi.

Special Functions Sometimes Performed by Leaves.—Besides the primary functions of photosynthesis and transpiration, the leaves of various plants may perform certain special functions in the service of the whole plant. In some cases the leaves that are adapted to carry on such special functions continue actively to transpire and to manufacture food, but in others their adaptation to perform a special rôle in the life of the plant is attended by partial or complete loss of the primary functions. Examples of such special functions are protection (bud scales and leaf spines), food storage, water storage, attachment (tendrils), and capture of insects for food.

Protection—*Bud Scales.*—We have already learned that the delicate growing point, or promeristem, within the buds is surrounded and protected by the overlapping rudimentary leaves which later develop into the foliage leaves of the plant. Except in those species which live in moist, warm habitats where there is little danger of injury from dry air or low temperature, the rudimentary foliage leaves of perennial woody plants and the other parts within the buds are protected by scale leaves called bud scales. These have already been described. They are often covered with dense hairs on the outer surface. In the poplars and many other plants they secrete a waxy or resinous substance which makes the scale covering of the buds waterproof.

Leaf Spines.—Leaves are sometimes entirely or in part transformed into spines. In cactus, for example, these spines certainly protect the plants from destruction by browsing animals. Such spines are found on many desert plants. The spines of various species of cactus and those of the barberry (*Berberis*) (Fig. 169) are formed by the transformation of the whole leaf. In the black locust (*Robinia pseudacacia*) (Fig. 170) and in various species of *Euphorbia* there are paired spines at the base of the leaves. These are transformed stipules.

Food Storage.—In the monocotyledons, particularly in the Liliaceae, such as *Tulipa* and *Allium* (the onion), there are special scale leaves, the bulb scales, which serve for food storage (Fig. 107) and make up the bulk of the bulbs which are characteristic of these and many related plants.

Water Storage.—Special water-storing leaves are borne by many plants which live in dry soil and in salt marshes where water absorption is difficult on account of the high concentration of the solutes in the soil water. Examples of plants bearing such water-storing leaves are stone-crop (*Sedum*), sea fig (*Mesembryanthemum*), and Russian thistle (*Salsola*). These leaves are generally much thickened and have a thick and very efficient cuticle. They are largely made up of water-storage tissue, consisting of large, very turgid, and swollen parenchyma cells which generally lack

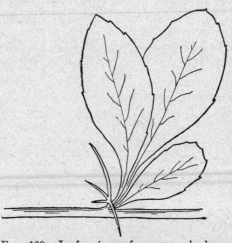

FIG. 169.—Leaf spines of common barberry (*Berberis vulgaris*). A short shoot bearing ordinary foliage leaves stands in the axil of the branched spine-like leaf.

chloroplasts and have large central vacuoles. Large quantities of water, which the plant has absorbed over a considerable period or during a short season when water was abundant, are stored in these leaves so that it may be used as needed by the plant. When the leaves of such **succulent plants** (Fig. 171) are crushed they yield an astonishing quantity of water, but under natural conditions this water is held so tenaciously that some such plants can live, and even send out new shoots, when they have been severed for weeks or months from any connection with the soil.

Leaf Tendrils.—There are many plants whose leaves are wholly or in part transformed into tendrils by which the plant may attach itself to a support. Thus, in the garden pea (*Pisum sativum*), several of the uppermost pairs of leaflets of the compound leaf have no blades, but instead form slender cylindrical tendrils (Fig. 144). In *Lathyrus* *aphaca* the whole leaf is transformed into a single tendril and the typical leaf functions are taken over by the leaf-like stipules. The petiole may serve as a tendril, as in the potato vine (*Solanum jasminoides*) and in the garden nasturtium (*Tropaeolum*); or that function may be performed by the stipules as in some species of *Smilax*, or by the rachis of the compound leaf, as in *Clematis*.

Capture of Insects by Leaves.—Without question, the most remarkable adaptation of leaves to a special function is found in the few plant species whose leaves are able, through various devices, to capture insects and secure food from their bodies. These **insectivorous** plants generally have weakly developed root systems, and are mostly found in locations where the essential minerals ordinarily secured from the soil are deficient in amount. Many of them are found in bogs where the soil is largely composed of decayed plant remains and is on that account, and because of the leaching effect of the abundant water which it contains, low in content of essential minerals. Others, like *Nepenthes*, are **epiphytes** growing attached to, but not parasitic on, other larger plants.

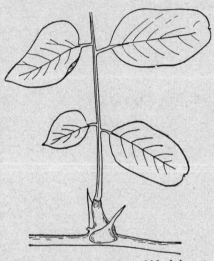

Fig. 170.—Stipular spines of black locust (*Robinia pseudacacia*).

The best-known insectivorous plants are the Venus' fly trap (*Dionaea muscipula*), sundew (*Drosera*), pitcher plants (*Nepenthes*, *Sarracenia*, and *Darlingtonia*), and bladderwort (*Utricularia*).

In the Venus' fly trap, the halves of the leaf blade each have a row of long stout teeth along the outer margin and three sensitive hairs in the center of the upper side. When an insect alights upon the leaf and touches one of these sensitive hairs the two halves fold together quickly along the midrib so that the insect is often caught. The softer parts of the captured insect are rendered soluble by a digestive juice secreted by small glandular hairs on the leaf surface.

In the sundews, the flat, more or less circular leaf blade is covered with long, radiating, glandular hairs or " tentacles " covered at the tips with a sticky secretion containing a digestive enzyme. When an insect

FIG. 171.—Various types of succulent plants including *Agave* (middle background). *Aloe* (extreme right, above), and *Cotyledon* (flowering plant in foreground). (Photograph furnished by George Stone.)

alights on a *Drosera* hair the sticky secretion holds it fast. The tentacles with which it is not in contact soon bend over until they touch the insect and so it is soon engulfed in the secretion and digested. The digested material from the insect is presumably absorbed by the plant.

In the pitcher plants, the entire leaf or a part of the leaf forms an urn or pitcher, which is partly filled with a liquid in which the captured insects drown and are subsequently digested.

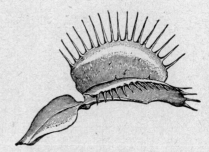

FIG. 172.—A leaf of Venus' Flytrap (*Dionaea muscipula*) an insectivorous plant. (After Darwin.)

The bladderwort (Fig. 175) is a rootless, submerged water plant, which bears numerous small bladders on the branches. Each of these

and enclose it except for a narrow pore at the end of the ovule. The two layers of tissue which thus surround the mature ovule are called the **inner integument** and the **outer integument.** In the most common type of ovule, in which the funiculus is sharply bent at its attachment to the ovule so that the ovule is directed downward toward the placenta, the outer integument generally does not develop on the side of the ovule toward the funiculus. In some species only one integument is formed. The pore leading from the outer surface of the ovule between the edges of the two integuments down to the surface of the nucellus is called the **micropyle.**

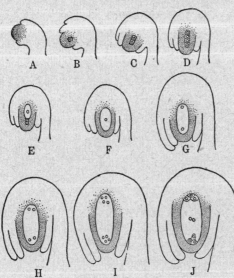

Fig. 186.—Stages in the development of an ovule, showing the origin and growth of the integuments and the formation of the embryo sac. A, inner integuments beginning to grow up about the nucellus. B, outer integuments are appearing. The continued growth of these integuments is shown in the figures which follow (C–J). B, the embryo sac mother cell which has developed from one cell of the nucellus. The nucleus of this one cell has the "2n" number of chromosomes. C, the embryo sac mother cell has undergone one division (the reduction division), to form two cells, each with "n" number of chromosomes in their nuclei. D, each of the two preceding cells has divided, resulting in a row of four cells imbedded in the nucellus. E, three of the cells (the ones nearest the micropyle), degenerate and disappear, whereas the basal cell of the four enlarges greatly. F, embryo sac with one nucleus which has "n" chromosomes. G, 2-nucleate embryo sac. H, 4-nucleate embryo sac. I, 8-nucleate embryo sac. J, mature embryo sac, with 2 synergids cells and 1 egg cell at the micropylar end, 2 polar nuclei near the center, and 3 antipodal cells.

TYPES OF FLOWERS

Thus far we have described the features common to all or most flowers, but actually flowers are very diverse in size, color, structure, and many other respects. We shall attempt to point out only a few of the most conspicuous and most important of the differences of flower structure commonly met with.

1. **Absence of Certain Parts.**—A flower which has all the usual flower parts (sepals, petals, stamens, and carpels) is called a **complete** flower. Some plants have flowers which are lacking in one or more of

the four kinds of flower parts generally present.   In many such **incomplete** flowers the perianth (sepals and petals) is absent; in others the

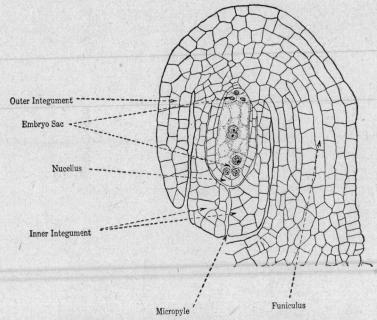

Outer Integument

Embryo Sac

Nucellus

Inner Integument

Micropyle   Funiculus

Fig. 187.—Longitudinal section of a lily (*Lilium*) ovule showing the embryo sac ready for fertilization.   At the end of the embryo sac nearest to the micropyle are the two synergids and the egg cell; at the opposite end are the antipodal cells and in the center are the polar nuclei.

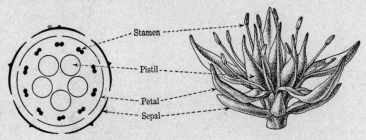

Stamen

Pistil

Petal

Sepal

Fig. 188.—A flower of *Sedum acre* (a stonecrop).   To the left of the drawing of the flower is a floral diagram showing the number and arrangement of the flower parts.

calyx is present but the corolla is lacking, and in still other incomplete flowers it is one or the other of the essential flower parts (stamens or carpels) which is not present.

Flowers without Perianth.—The absence of the perianth or its reduction to mere scales or hairs is characteristic of the flowers of such monocotyledons as the grains and grasses (*Gramineae*) (Fig. 203), the sedges (*Cyperaceae*), and the calla lily family (*Araceae*). Among the dicotyledons, the willow family (*Salicaceae*) which includes the willows and poplars, the alder (*Alnus*), the sycamore (*Platanus*), and many other plants have flowers without perianth. With very few exceptions, flowers

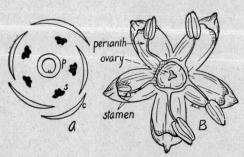

Fig. 189.—Flower of beet (*Beta vulgaris*), which has a calyx but lacks a corolla. *A*, floral diagram. *B*, face view. (After Robbins, from *Botany of Crop Plants.*)

that have no perianth are wind-pollinated and have no need for conspicuous flower parts to attract insects. Most plants whose flowers

Fig. 190.—The imperfect flowers of field pumpkin (*Cucurbita pepo*). *A*, pistillate flower; *B*, staminate flower. (After Robbins, from *Botany of Crop Plants.*)

4. D

flowers

shaped

the flow

lack a perianth and are wind-pollinated are thought to be descended from plants which were insect-pollinated and whose flowers possessed a perianth.

Flowers Having Calyx but Lacking Corolla.—Many of the flowers which have sepals but lack petals are inconspicuous and apparently not fitted to attract insects; but in others the sepals are large and conspicuously colored, and so take the place of the petals in relation to insect pollination. The nettle family (*Urticaceae*) and the goosefoot family (*Chenopodiaceae*), to which belong the beet (Fig. 189) and the pigweed, furnish examples of wind pollinated plants with flowers which lack petals and in which the sepals are not conspicuously petal-like. *Clematis*, wild ginger (*Asarum*), and Dutchman's pipe (*Aristolochia*) are plants whose flowers lack petals but whose sepals serve the usual function of petals.

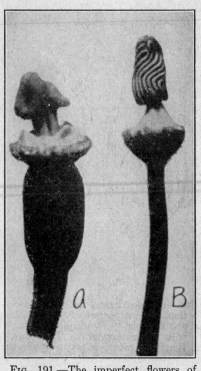

Flowers Lacking One of the Essential Parts.—Some species have incomplete flowers which lack either stamens or pistils. In these species there must obviously be two kinds of incomplete flowers if seeds are to be produced, namely, stamen-bearing or staminate flowers and pistil-bearing or pistillate flowers. Such incomplete flowers are said to be **imperfect** to distinguish them from **hermaphrodite** or **perfect** flowers (flowers with both stamens and pistils) such as are borne by

Fig. 193.—M
stamina
Plants.)

Fig. 191.—The imperfect flowers of field pumpkin (*Cucurbita pepo*) with perianth removed. *A*, pistillate flower. *B*, staminate flower. (After Robbins, from *Botany of Crop Plants*.)

arrangeme
that all the
There a
erally in th
ent form fr
familiar ex

most plants. Most species with imperfect flowers are thought to have evolved by reduction (loss of parts) from ancestors which had perfect flowers.

In some cases both staminate and pistillate flowers occur upon each individual plant of the species. This is true of Indian corn or maize (*Zea mays*) where the tassel (borne at the top of the stalk) consists of a group of staminate flowers and the young ear is a group of pistillate flowers. Other familiar examples of plants with imperfect flowers are

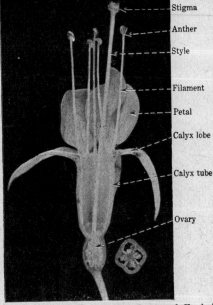

FIG. 194.—The epigynous flower of *Fuchsia*, showing united sepals (synsepaly), separate petals attached to rim of calyx tube, and united carpels (syncarpy). Right, cross-section of ovary, showing four locules, and axile placentation; left, median lengthwise section of flower.

and beans and most other plants of the Leguminosae (Fig. 195). In the peas and beans one petal (the **banner** or **standard**) is broad and conspicuous. On either side of this are two somewhat narrower petals (the **wings**), and opposite the banner two smaller petals which are loosely united along their edges to form the **keel** which encloses the stamens and pistil. In the violets the petals are not alike and one of them forms a tube or spur at its base; two of the stamens also are different from the other three and have spur-like appendages which bear nectaries. Flowers such as these do not have radial symmetry but at the most **bilateral symmetry,** which is to say that there is only one plane along which they can be cut into halves, each of which is like the mirrored image of the other.

5. Union of Flower Parts.—In most flowers, instead of all the parts being merely attached at the base to the receptacle and entirely free from each other, those of one or more whorls are to some extent united with each other or to the members of other whorls. Union of the parts of a whorl may involve carpels (**syncarpy**), stamens (**synandry**), petals (**sympetaly**), or sepals (**synsepaly**).

Syncarpy.—There are many plants whose flowers have but a single carpel, for example, all the pea or leg-

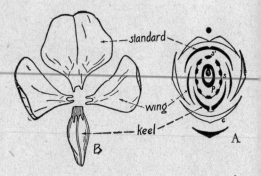

FIG. 195.—Bilaterally symmetrical flower of a legume (*Leguminosae*). *A*, floral diagram of horse bean (*Vicia faba*). *B*, corolla of a sweet pea flower (*Lathyrus odoratus*), dissected, diagrammatic. (*A*, after Eichler, *B*, after Bergen, from Robbins' *Botany of Crop Plants*.)

ume family (*Leguminosae*) (Fig. 195) and the barberry and most of the barberry family (*Berberidacae*). Most flowers which possess several carpels have the carpels more or less united into a compound pistil. In some instances, however, as in strawberry (*Fragaria*) and raspberry (Fig. 196) and blackberry (*Rubus*), the flowers have numerous carpels which are not united. In lily (*Lilium*) and azalea (*Rhododendron*), there are respectively three and five carpels united to form a single pistil. Sometimes the fusion between carpels does not extend throughout their length, so that though there may be but one ovary there are several stigmas or several styles and stigmas as in flax (*Linum*) and wood sorrel (*Oxalis*).

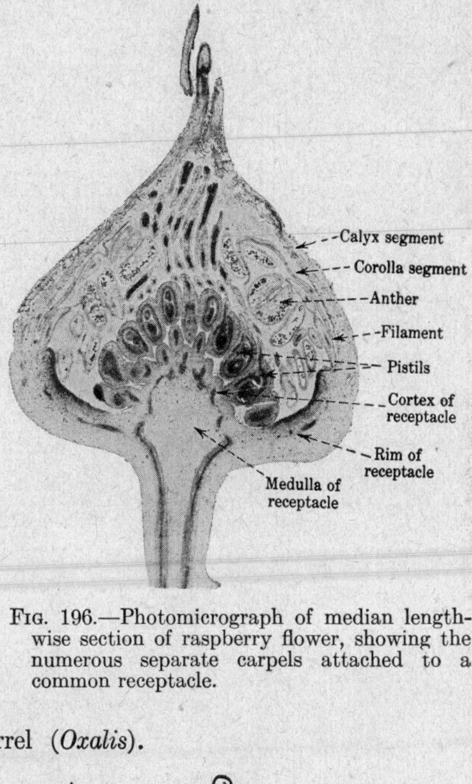

- - - Calyx segment
- - - Corolla segment
- - - Anther
- - Filament
- - Pistils
- - Cortex of receptacle
- - Rim of receptacle

Medulla of receptacle

Fig. 196.—Photomicrograph of median lengthwise section of raspberry flower, showing the numerous separate carpels attached to a common receptacle.

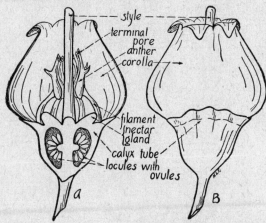

style
terminal pore
anther
corolla
filament
nectar gland
calyx tube
locules with ovules

A

B

Fig. 197.—The epigynous flower of the huckleberry (*Vaccinium*), showing united sepals (*synsepaly*), united petals (*sympetaly*), and united carpels (*syncarpy*). *A*, median lengthwise section. *B*, external view. (After Robbins, from *Botany of Crop Plants*.)

Synandry.—In the flowers of beans and peas and many related plants, nine of the ten stamens, or in some cases all ten, have their filaments united into a sheath which surrounds the pistil, but the anthers are free. In the sunflower family (*Compositae*), on the other hand, the anthers are united and form a tube around the pistil while the filaments are free. There are many other flowers in which there is a union of the stamens.

Sympetaly and Synsepaly.—In many flowers the members of one or both perianth whorls are united along the edges with other members of the same whorl. There are many familiar flowers which show distinctly a more or less complete union of the petals. Morning glory (*Ipomoea*), huckleberry (*Vaccinium*) (Fig. 197), potato (*Solanum*) (Fig. 199), and sunflower (*Helianthus*) are a few among many thousands of such sympetalous flowers. As the corolla is often sympetalous, so the calyx is often synsepalous. Examples of partial or complete union of the sepals along their edges are found in the flowers of sage (*Salvia*) and other mints (*Labiatae*), of evening primrose (*Oenothera*), of the pea or legume family (*Leguminosae*), and of several other families.

Union between Members of Different Whorls.—Union of the stamens with the carpels is not of frequent occurrence. The so-called column of the orchids is a structure resulting from the fusion of stamens and style, and in the Dutchman's pipe (*Aristolochia*) the same parts are united. In many plants, such as pimpernel (*Anagallis*), morning glory (*Ipomoea*), peppermint (*Mentha*) and potato (*Solanum*) (Fig. 199) the stamens are united at their bases to the petals.

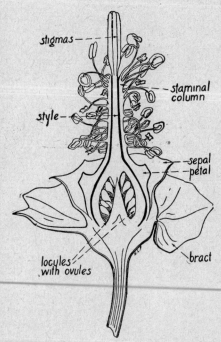

Fig. 198.—Flower of cotton (*Gossypium*) in median longitudinal section. In this, the filaments of the stamens are united (*synandry*) to form a long tube ("staminal column") enclosing the style. (After Robbins, from *Botany of Crop Plants*.)

stigmas
staminal column
style
sepal
petal
locules with ovules
bract

Hypogyny, Perigyny, and Epigyny (Fig. 198).—When the receptacle is convex or conical, the whorls of flower parts are situated one above another and in the following order, beginning with the lowest: sepals, petals, stamens, and carpels. Such a flower is said to be **hypogynous** (Fig. 201, *A*). When the receptacle spreads out into a more or less con-

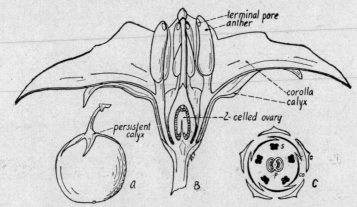

FIG. 199.—Flower and fruit of potato (*Solanum tuberosum*). *A*, mature fruit, a berry. *B*, median lengthwise section of the flower. *C*, floral diagram. Note that the stamens are attached to the sympetalous corolla. (After Robbins, from *Botany of Crop Plants*.)

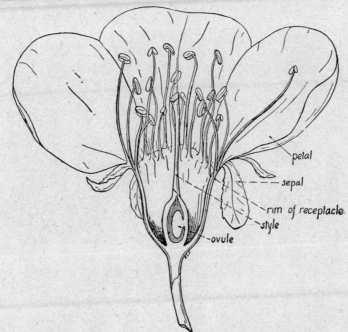

FIG. 200.—Perigynous flower of sour cherry (*Prunus cerasus*) in median lengthwise section. (After Robbins, from *Botany of Crop Plants*.)

cave structure (as in *Prunus*) (Fig. 200), at the center of which the pistil is attached, and at the margins of which the sepals, petals, and stamens have their origin, so that these parts seem to be attached around instead of below the ovary, the flower is said to be **perigynous**. The term perigynous is also applied to flowers (such as those of most saxifrages)

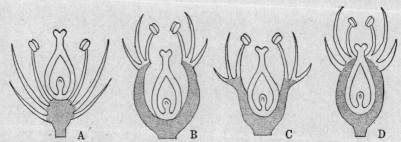

Fig. 201.—Diagrams showing the structure of (*A*) hypogynous flower, (*B* and *C*) perigynous flower, the latter being of a type in which the lower portion of the ovary is buried in the receptacle, and (*D*) epigynous flower.

in which only the lower portion of the ovary is buried in the receptacle (Fig. 202). If the concave receptacle not only surrounds the ovary but is fused with it so that the other flower parts appear to arise from the top of the ovary, the flower is spoken of as **epigynous** (Fig. 201, *D*). The fruits formed by epigynous flowers often bear at the unattached end the withered remains of the sepals and the stamens, or of other flower parts. The primrose (*Primula*) and the tomato (*Lycopersicum*) have hypogynous flowers; the cherry, peach, and plum (species of the genus *Prunus*) (Fig. 200) have perigynous flowers; and the apple (a species of *Pyrus*) and the sunflower (*Helianthus*) have epigynous flowers.

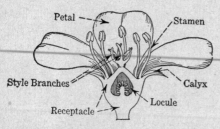

Fig. 202.—Longitudinal median section of flower of saxifrage, showing a perigynous type of flower in which only the lower portion of the ovary is buried in the receptacle. (See Fig. 201, *C*.)

Two types of flowers deserve special discussion, both because they differ so widely in structure from most flowers and because they are characteristic of two of the most important families of flowering plants—the grass family (*Gramineae*), which includes all the grains, and the sunflower or aster family (*Compositae*).

The Structure of the Grass Flower.—In the grasses the flowers occur in small groups called **spikelets** (Figs. 203 and 204). A large number of these flower groups or spikelets are produced on one flower stalk and form an inflorescence. In some instances, as for example, in wheat (*Triticum*), barley (*Hordeum*),

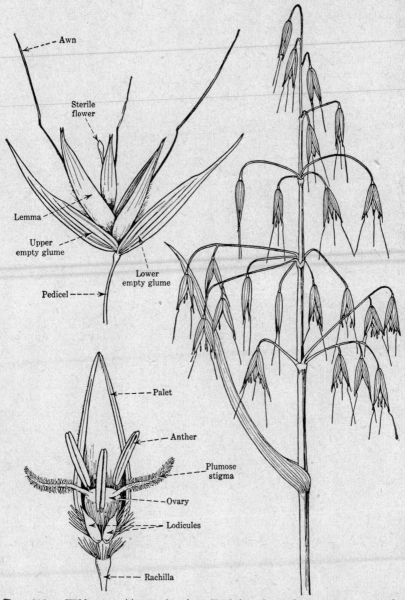

FIG. 203.—Wild oats (*Avena fatua*). (Right)—the inflorescence, a panicle (Upper left)—a single spikelet with three fertile flowers and one sterile flower (Lower left)—a single flower. (After Jepson, from *Flora of Economic Plants.*)

and timothy (*Phleum pratense*), the spikelets are attached directly
to the unbranched main stem or *rachis* of the inflorescence which latter
is then called a **spike.** In others, the spikelets grow at the ends of
branches of the rachis, forming an inflorescence which is known as a
panicle. In the panicle of the oat (*Avena*) (Fig. 203) the branches of the
rachis are long and slender.

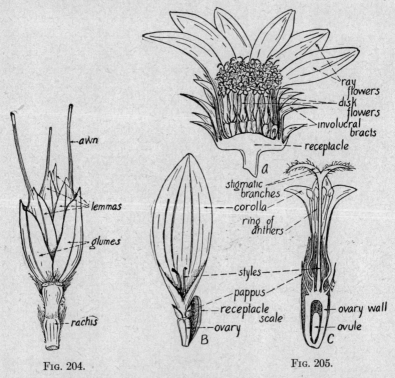

FIG. 204.

FIG. 205.

FIG. 204.—A single spikelet of wheat (*Triticum*). (After Robbins, from *Botany of
Crop Plants.*)

FIG. 205.—Jerusalem artichoke (*Helianthus tuberosus*). *A*, longitudinal section of
the head (*inflorescence*), showing the numerous separate flowers attached to a
common receptacle. *B*, a single ray flower. *C*, a single disc flower, cut lengthwise. (After Robbins, from *Botany of Crop Plants.*)

The spikelet has a shortened axis, generally spoken of as the **rachilla,**
and this axis bears a number of chaffy, two-ranked, overlapping, bract-
like structures. The two (rarely three or four) of these at the base of
the spikelet are larger than the others and enclose the rest of the spikelet.
They are called **glumes.** The number of flowers in a spikelet differs
in different species. Each flower of the spikelet is enclosed between two

bracts which usually are very similar to the glumes but smaller in size. The lower of these bracts (the one with its back turned away from the rachilla) is the **lemma**; the upper one (with its back toward the rachilla) is the **palea** or **palet**.

The flower proper consists (Fig. 203) of a single pistil with three carpels (two abortive), three stamens, and two small scale-like structures (**lodicules**) which are at the base of the ovary. The ovary contains a single ovule and has two f e a t h e r y, much-branched stigmas. The stamens at maturity have long and slender filaments and the anthers are **versatile,** that is, attached at about the middle to the end of the filament and in such a manner that they swing freely in the wind and are thus emptied of their fine, powdery pollen. The typical grass flower has no sepals or petals but the lodicules probably represent two reduced perianth segments. The f l o w e r parts remain enclosed within the lemma and palea until they are mature and ready to f u n c t i o n. Then if

Fig. 206.—Flower heads of Shasta Daisy (*Chrysanthemum leucanthemum*) and, on the left, ray flowers somewhat enlarged. Above, the familiar type with strap-shaped ray flowers, showing, in the enlarged flower, the tips of three of the five petals which together form the (strap) corolla of the ray flower. Below, a variety with tubular corolla-like ray flowers. The ray flowers of most members of the sunflower family (the Compositae) are generally incomplete, the stamens being absent.

weather conditions are favorable the lodicules swell and force the lemma and palea apart so that the plume-like stigmas and the stamens protrude. At the same time the filaments rapidly elongate. Thus the anthers can readily discharge their pollen into the air and the stigmas may receive the wind-borne pollen.

The Structure of the Composite Flower.—In such plants as the sunflower (*Helianthus*) (Fig. 205), the aster (*Aster*), dandelion (*Taraxacum*), brown-eyed Susan (*Rudbeckia*) and the globe artichoke (*Cynara*), what we ordinarily speak of as a flower is, as a matter of fact, a compact inflorescence or group of flowers called a **head.** Each of these small (true) flowers, if complete, consists of (1) a pistil made up of two carpels and having an inferior ovary and a straight style with a two-parted stigma, (2) five stamens with filaments free but with anthers united into a tube which surrounds the style, (3) a corolla of five petals, and (4) a calyx which is reduced to a mere ring of tissues or to a cluster of scales or bristles, collectively called the **pappus.** In many of the *Compositae* there are two kinds of flowers in each head, **tubular flowers** and **ligulate flowers.** The disc flowers which make up the central part of the head are tubular, whereas in the ray flowers, which are around the edge of the head, the corolla forms a strap-shaped (ligulate) structure which suggests a single petal of an ordinary flower. In some cases, as in the dandelion and lettuce (*Lactua*), the heads are entirely made up of ligulate flowers like those just described. In others, such as the globe artichoke (*Cynara*) and the burdock (*Lappa*), the flowers are all tubular. In those cases where there are both ligulate flowers and tubular flowers, the ligulate flowers are generally incomplete, being without stamens or, in some instances, lacking both pistil and stamens.

In certain plants, not belonging to the Compositae, what is ordinarily spoken of as a flower is actually a compact cluster of small flowers sur-

FIG. 207.—The so-called "flower" of mountain dogwood (*Cornus nuttallii*) which is a compact cluster of small flowers surrounded by several large, conspicuous bracts which are often mistaken for petals.

rounded by a number of large and conspicuous bracts which frequently are mistaken for petals. Examples of such plants are certain species of dogwood (*Cornus florida* and *Cornus nuttallii*) with white bracts, *Poinsettia*, which has brilliant red bracts, and *Bougainvillea*, the different varieties of which have bracts of various colors.

THE PRINCIPAL KINDS OF INFLORESCENCES

In some plants, such as *Anemone*, *Trillium*, and tulip (*Tulipa*), the flowers are borne singly at the end of a flower stalk or peduncle. In the great majority of flowering plants, however, the flowers are borne in groups or **inflorescences** resulting from the branching of the main axis or peduncle. There are many types of inflorescences depending (1) upon the manner of branching of the peduncle, (2) upon the time when different flowers in the group mature, and (3) upon the length of branches (pedicels) at the ends of which the flowers are borne. Almost all of these belong to one of two classes: (1) **racemose** inflorescences and (2) **cymose** inflorescences.

Racemose Inflorescences.—In racemose inflorescences the main axis continues to grow in length, as the result of the persistence of a primordial meristem at the tip. New floral bracts (reduced leaves in the axils of which the flowers are borne) and new buds are formed at the growing point so that there is a more or less indefinite succession of flowers, the oldest being at the base of the inflorescence and the youngest nearest to the growing point. In such flower clusters there may be flowers near the base of the inflorescence which have become mature and have given rise to fruits which are almost mature, while at the upper end minute buds containing very rudimentary flower parts may be forming. The principal types of racemose inflorescences are described below.

THE PRINCIPAL KINDS OF RACEMOSE INFLORESCENCES

I. SIMPLE RACEMOSE INFLORESCENCES.—The flowers borne on the main axis of the inflorescence, either sessile or on pedicels.

1. The *Raceme.*—The main axis of the inflorescence elongated but the flowers borne on pedicels which are about equal in length. Examples: The hyacinth (*Hyacinthus*), cabbage (*Brassica oleracea*), and currant (*Ribes*).

2. The *Spike.*—The main axis of the inflorescence elongated and the flowers sessile. Example: The common plantains (*Plantago major* and *Plantago lanceolata*).

3. The *Catkin.*—A spike which generally bears only pistillate flowers or only staminate flowers and which eventually falls off from the plant entire. Examples: The willow (*Salix*) and the hazel (*Corylus*).

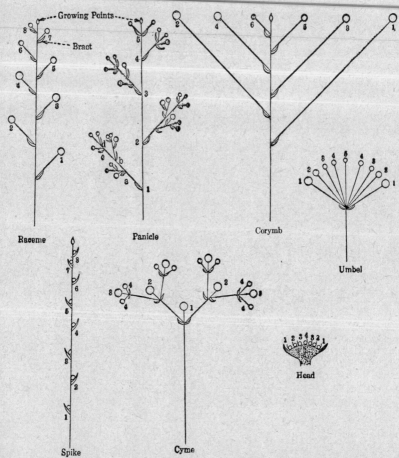

Fig. 208.—Diagrams showing the arrangement of flowers in some of the principal types of inflorescences. The flowers are represented by circles. Pedicels and subtending floral bracts are also shown. The numbers show the order in which the flowers of an inflorescence have developed, the flower marked 1 being in each case the oldest in the inflorescence. In the case of the panicle the letters *a–d* show the succession in which the flowers on the lowermost branch were formed. Note that all these inflorescences are racemose except the cyme.

4. The *Corymb.*—The main axis of the inflorescence elongated but the pedicels of the older flowers longer than those of the younger flowers so that the flowers are all in one plane, i.e., the inflorescence is flat-topped. Example: The cherry (*Prunus cerasus*).

5. The *Umbel.*—The axis of the inflorescence short and the flowers upon pedicels of nearly equal length. Example: The onion (*Allium*).

6. The *Head.*—The axis very short and the flowers sessile (without pedicels). Examples: The thistle (*Cirsium*), sunflower (*Helianthus*), and other members of the *Compositae.* (In this family each so-called flower is an inflorescence of many small true flowers.)

II. COMPOUND RACEMOSE INFLORESCENCES.—The main axis branched and each branch bearing a group of flowers.

1. The *Panicle.*—The branches of the axis bearing loose racemose flower cluster. Examples: The oat (*Avena*) and the Spanish bayonet (*Yucca*).

2. The *Compound Spike.*—The branches of the axis are spikes. Examples: Wheat (*Triticum*) and rye grass (*Lolium*).

3. The *Compound Umbel.*—The axis much shortened and its branches arranged like an umbel, each branch itself bearing an umbel. Examples: The carrot (*Daucus*), the parsnip (*Pastinaca*), and most other members of the family *Umbelliferae*.

Cymose Inflorescences.—In a cymose inflorescence the apex of the main stalk, or axis of the inflorescence, ceases to grow quite early, because the formation of a flower at the very tip involves the entire promeristem of the apex of the main stalk and thus prevents further elongation. The other flowers are produced on lateral branches farther down the axis of the inflorescence, and the youngest of the flowers in the cluster are found at the greatest distance from the tip of the main stalk. Cymose inflorescences are much less common than racemose. The flower cluster of crab apple (*Pyrus coronaria*) is an example of the simplest type of cymose inflorescence.

In addition to the inflorescences mentioned there are a number of mixed inflorescences in which cymose flower clusters are borne on racemose inflorescences, and vice versa.

REPRODUCTION BY FLOWERS

In the higher plants, the flower is the organ of reproduction. It is from flowers that seeds are produced. In our discussion of reproduction by flowers we shall consider the following processes: (1) development of the pollen grain, (2) development of the ovule, (3) pollination, (4) growth of the pollen tube, (5) fertilization, (6) formation of the embryo and endosperm, and (7) development of the seed tissues outside the embryo and endosperm.

Although we have already briefly described the fully developed stamens and ovules, an account of the principal features of the development of the pollen grain and embryo sac is also necessary to an understanding of reproduction by flowers.

Development of Pollen Grain.—In an early stage in the growth of the anther there are produced in the young pollen sac, rounded cells, called **pollen mother cells,** each of which by two successive divisions forms four pollen grains. In the first of these divisions the nucleus divides by meiosis or reduction division, and as a result the number of chromosomes is reduced to n, that is one-half the number ($2n$) which are present in the nuclei of most of the cells of the plant. The second division does not involve reduction, and accordingly the nuclei of the four pollen grains produced from each pollen mother cell have n chromosomes. About the time the pollen grains are shed from the anther the single nucleus contained in each divides by mitosis into two, the **generative nucleus** and the **tube nucleus**. These are not separated by a cell wall, but the cytoplasm surrounding the generative nucleus is often distinctly differentiated from the rest of the cytoplasm of the pollen grain.

Development of the Ovule.—(See Fig. 186). The ovules first make their appearance in the ovary of very young flowers as small protuberances from the surface of the placenta. At first the ovule consists entirely of young nucellus tissue and shows no indication of the development of integuments, but as the ovule grows, the integuments, originating as two collars of tissue around the base of the ovule, grow up round the nucellus. In the very young ovule all the cells of the nucellus are essentially alike and the nuclei have the $2n$ chromosome number. As the ovule grows, one cell within the nucellus becomes conspicuously larger than the other cells, and this cell, which is called the **embryo sac mother cell,** soon undergoes two successive divisions, giving rise to a row of four cells. In the first of these two cell divisions the nucleus divides by meiosis, and accordingly each of the four cells has n chromosomes.

Now the basal cell of the four (the one farthest from the micropyle end of the nucellus) grows rapidly in size whereas the other three soon degenerate and disappear. This single surviving cell, the nucleus of which has the n chromosome number, continues to increase in size until it makes up a large part of the volume of the nucellus. Its nucleus divides and the two daughter nuclei move to opposite ends of the large cell. Each of the daughter nuclei now undergoes two successive nuclear divisions so that there is a group of four nuclei at the micropylar end and a group of four at the opposite (basal) end of the embryo sac. One nucleus from each group of four now moves toward the center of the embryo sac where they come to lie near each other or in actual contact. These are the **polar nuclei.**

Of the three remaining nuclei near the micropylar end of the embryo sac, two are the so-called **synergid nuclei** and the third is the **egg nucleus.** Each of these three nuclei, together with some of the surrounding cytoplasm, is now separated from the others and from the rest of the embryo sac by a very thin membrane so that there are three cells at the micropylar end of the sac, namely, two synergids or **synergid cells** and the **egg cell,** which is usually spoken of merely as the **egg.** The three nuclei at the opposite end of the embryo sac are called the **antipodal**

nuclei. Each of these nuclei, together with some cytoplasm, generally becomes surrounded by a cell membrane, so that they can now be spoken of as **antipodal cells.**

Pollination.—The transfer of pollen from the anther to the stigma is called **pollination.** The anthers of the stamens open when the pollen is mature and the pollen grains escape. In grass flowers and other flowers whose pollen is carried by the wind, the anthers are attached to the filaments in such a manner that air movements easily swing them back and forth. As a result, the pollen falls from the anthers and is launched into the air. The pollen grains, being small and light, may be carried considerable distances by a slight breeze. Some of the pollen grains, although relatively few compared to the great number which are lost and never function, thus reach the stigmas of flowers of the same species. The stigmas of such species are generally much branched and plume-like so that the chance of pollen coming into contact with them is greater than would otherwise be the case. In such plants pollen is often produced in great quantities. Thus in Indian corn each group of staminate flowers (tassel) may produce from 20,000,000 to 50,-000,000 grains of pollen. **Wind-pollination** is characteristic of most plants with relatively inconspicuous flowers, such as the grasses, poplars, alders, birches, oaks, and hops. In a few cases water and birds are the agencies of pollination. In the majority of flowering plants, however, pollen transfer is accomplished by bees (which visit the open flowers and secure nectar for the making of honey or to get pollen for the feeding of the young bees in the hive), or by other insects. Such plants are said to be **insect-pollinated.** In insect-pollinated plants, the pollen does not fall from the opened anthers but sticks to the outside of the shrunken anthers until, through contact with the body of an insect, some of it is swept off and adheres to the insect. When the insect visits another flower some of this pollen may be rubbed off on the stigmas. Except in the case of certain nut trees, insects are necessary for the pollination of most orchard trees.

FIG. 209.—The hind legs of the honey bee are well constructed for the collection of pollen. (From California Agricultural Experiment Station Bul. 517.)

Pollen may be transferred from an anther to the stigma of the same flower or to the stigma of another flower on the same plant, in both of which cases **self-pollination** is said to have taken place. If pollen is transferred from an anther to the stigma of a flower on another individual plant, it is spoken of as **cross-pollination.**

Some plants are normally self-pollinated. This is true of most cereals (except rye and corn), of garden peas, tobacco, cotton, and some other plants. In a great many species, however, cross-pollination is the rule. Self-pollination, in some species, may be attended by a reduction in vigor and productivity. Darwin in 1876 concluded from

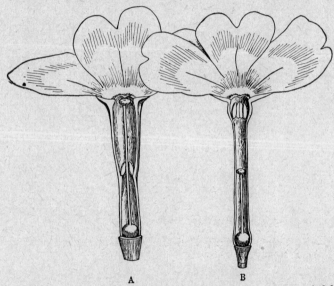

A   B

FIG. 210.—Flowers of a primrose showing heterostyly. *A*, long-styled form.
B, short-styled form. (After Darwin.)

his rather extensive experiments in many plant families, that, in general, the plants resulting from cross-pollination excelled in vigor, weight, height, and other characters those plants resulting from self-pollination. However, there are reasons for believing that the advantages of cross-pollination and disadvantages of self-pollination have been overstated.

In many flowers conditions exist which make self-pollination difficult or impossible and which aid or insure cross-pollination. Among such conditions are the following:

1. The anthers of a flower shed their pollen before the stigma of that flower is receptive (beet, *Beta*, and red clover, *Trifolium pratense*).

2. The stigmas mature and become incapable of pollination before the anthers open (common plantain, *Plantago*, and avocado, *Persea*).

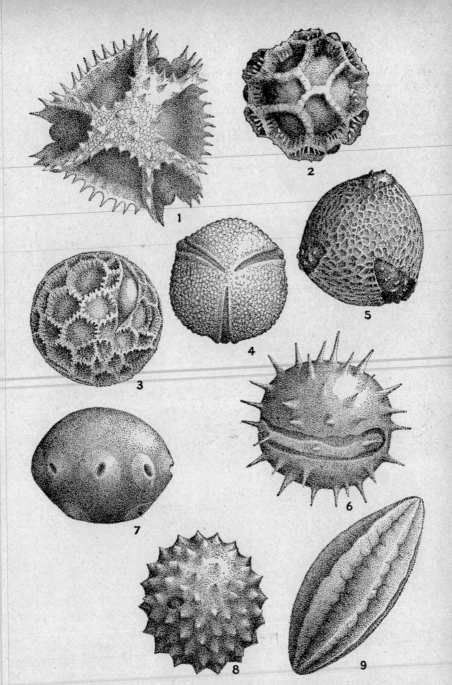

FIG. 211.—Pollen grains of various forms and markings. 1. *Tragopogon pratensis* (Oyster plant); 2. *Stokesi laevis* (Stokes aster); 3. *Polygonum chinense* (Knotweed); 4. *Fagus grandifolia* (Beech); 5. *Salix fragilis* (Willow); 6. *Nymphaea advena* (Water lily); 7. *Juglans nigra* (Black walnut); 8. *Ambrosia trifida* (Great ragweed); 9. *Ephedra glauca* (Joint pine). (After Wodehouse, from McGraw-Hill Book Company, Inc.)

centrations from 1 : 1000 to 1 : 1,000,000; of these naphtheleneacetic acid was the most potent, causing all the flowers to set fruit used in 0.006 per cent concentration.

Structurally, the wall of the ovary, before its development into a fruit begins, is relatively simple, being largely made up of parenchyma cells. The structure of the fruit wall or **pericarp,** into which the ovary wall develops, is, however, sometimes quite complex. Three distinct layers are generally present in the pericarp. Named in order, beginning with the outermost, these are the **exocarp, mesocarp,** and **endocarp.**

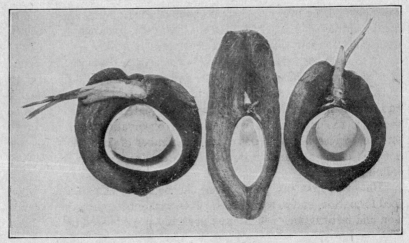

Fig. 214.—Fruits of three varieties of coconut (*Cocos nucifera*), split lengthwise and showing the structure of the fruits, and stages in the germination of the seed. The smooth, surface layer of the fruit is the exocarp, the thick, fibrous layer (husk) making up most of the volume of the fruit is the mesocarp, and the horny inner layer (shell of the coconut) is the endocarp. The "meat" (showing as a white layer) is the endosperm within which is buried the embryo which lies below one of the "eyes" of the shell (not shown in the figure). The coconut in the middle of the figure shows an early stage, and the other two later stages in germination. The large rounded structure within the cavity of each coconut is the single cotyledon which grows rapidly during the early stages of germination and absorbs food from the endosperm for the growth of the embryo. (From Otto Wilson in *Nature Magazine.*)

The exocarp of the mature fruit varies widely in structure in different types of fruit. It usually consists of a single layer of epidermal cells. Hairs are often present, as are also stomata.

The mesocarp in some fruits forms a very thin layer, whereas in others it may be as much as several centimeters thick.

The endocarp may be a single cell layer, as in the fruit of buckwheat (*Fagopyrum esculentum*), or it may be composed of a number of cell layers variously modified, as in the fruit of the plum, cherry, and other stone fruits.

KINDS OF FRUITS

Though most fruits consist of only a single ovary there are some, including a number of the most important cultivated ones, which consist of or include several ovaries. In some of these cases the several ovaries are from a single flower and in others they are from several very closely clustered flowers.

All fruits may be classified on the basis of the number of ovaries involved in their formation into the following three groups:

Simple Fruits—consisting of a single enlarged ovary, with which some other flower parts may be incorporated. Most common fruits are simple fruits except those listed below as examples of aggregate and multiple fruits.

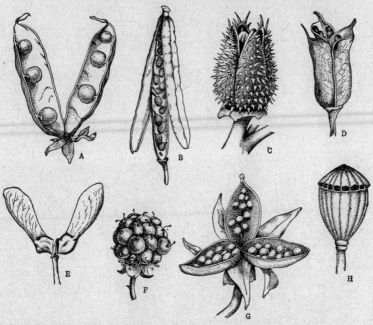

FIG. 215.—Fruits of common plants, illustrating, with the exception of *E* and *F*, the principal methods of dehiscence. *A*, pod of pea (*Pisum sativum*). *B*, silique of mustard (*Brassica*). *C*, capsule of Jimson weed (*Datura*), septicidal dehiscence. *D*, three follicles of larkspur (*Delphinium*). *E*, samara of maple (*Acer*). *F*, aggregate fruit of raspberry (*Rubus*). *G*, capsule of violet (*Viola*), loculicidal dehiscence. *H*, capsule of poppy (*Papaver*), poricidal dehiscence.

Aggregate Fruits—consisting of a number of enlarged ovaries belonging to a *single flower* and massed on or scattered over the surface of a *single receptacle*. The separate ovaries are spoken of as fruitlets. Examples: raspberry, blackberry, and strawberry.

Multiple Fruits—consisting of the enlarged ovaries of *several flowers* more or less coalesced into one mass. Examples: mulberry, fig, and pineapple.

Simple fruits, on the basis of their consistence, structure, and dehiscence (manner of opening), include the following principal kinds:

I. **Fleshy Fruits** (pericarp fleshy).

    A. Berry—the ovary wall fleshy and enclosing one or more carpels and seeds. Examples: grape, pepper, tomato, and date.

        (*a*) *Pepo*, a type of berry with hard rind. Examples: squash or cucumber.

        (*b*) *Hesperidium*, a type of berry with a leathery rind. Examples: orange and lemon.

    B. Drupe or stone fruit—derived from a single carpel and one-seeded; exocarp thin, forming the skin; mesocarp fleshy; endocarp stony. Examples: cherry, peach, almond, plum, and olive.

    C. Pome—derived from several carpels; receptacle fleshy; outer portion of pericarp fleshy; inner portion papery, forming " core." Examples: pear, apple, and quince.

II. **Dry fruits** (pericarp dry).

    A. Dehiscent fruits (splitting open when ripe).[1]

        (*a*) Legume or true pod—carpel one; splitting along two sutures. Examples: pea, bean, vetch.

        (*b*) Follicle—carpel one; splitting along one suture. Examples: milkweed, larkspur, columbine, peony.

        (*c*) Capsule—carpels two or more; dehiscing in one of four different ways:

            1. Along the line of union of carpels (septicidal dehiscence)—azalea.

            2. Along the middle of each carpel (loculicidal dehiscence)—iris, lily.

            3. By pores at the apices of carpels (poricidal dehiscence)—poppy.

            4. Along a circular horizontal line (circumscissile dehiscence)—purslane and plantain.

        (*d*) Silique—carpels two; separating at maturity, leaving a partition wall persistent—crucifers.

    B. Indehiscent (not splitting open when ripe).

        (*a*) Achene—one-seeded; seed attached to ovary wall at one point only. Examples: buckwheat, sunflower, buttercup.

        (*b*) Caryopsis (grain)—one-seeded; pericarp firmly united all around to testa or seed coat. Examples: wheat, corn, rice, barley, broom corn, oats, and all other grasses.

        (*c*) Samara or " key " fruit—one- or two-seeded; pericarp, bearing a wing-like outgrowth. Examples: ash, elm, maple.

        (*d*) Schizocarp—carpels two or more; united, splitting apart at maturity. Examples: carrot, parsnip, parsley, celery, mallow.

        (*e*) Nut—a hard, one-seeded fruit, generally produced from a compound ovary.

Simple Fruits.—The fruits of the great majority of flowering plants are simple fruits, each arising from a single ovary. The principal types

---

[1] Exceptions in this group are fairly numerous, examples being the fruits of *Rhaphanus, Neslia; Cakile* in Cruciferae, *Glycyrrhiza lepidota* and *Psoralea* in Leguminosae, and *Gaura* and *Stenosiphon* in Onagraceae.

of simple fruits have been mentioned in the classification given and will be discussed later in this chapter.

Aggregate Fruits.—An aggregate fruit is one composed of a single receptacle upon which are massed many similar fruitlets. It is derived from a single flower having many pistils. The various kinds of aggregate fruits differ in the type of their individual fruitlets. For example, in the dewberry, raspberry, blackberry (Fig. 216), and other species of *Rubus*, the individual fruits of the aggregate are drupes and constitute the pleasant-flavored portion of the fruit; in the dewberry and black-berries, the drupelets adhere firmly to the receptable, whereas in rasp-berries the drupelets easily separate from the receptable when the fruit is picked and cling together in the form of a cup. In the strawberry (*Fragaria*) the individual fruitlets are achenes, and it is the flesh of the enlarged receptacle which gives the characteristic flavor. As shown in the diagram of a longitudinal section (Fig. 219) of the ripe aggregate "fruit" of strawberry, the receptacle consists of a fleshy pith and cortex with vascular bundles between them. The persistent calyx and withered stamens at the base of the strawberry con-stitute the "hull." The achenes are commonly spoken of as "seeds."

Fig. 216.—The aggregate fruit of blackberry (*Rubus* sp.). Each so-called "fruit" is an aggregate of drupelets. (From Division of Pomology, College of Agriculture, University of California.)

Multiple Fruits.— Whereas an aggregate fruit, as we have just learned, is derived from a single flower having many pistils, the multiple fruit is developed from the ovaries of many separate and yet closely clustered flowers. Among the most familiar examples of plants bearing multiple fruits are the mulberry (*Morus*), pineapple (*Ananassa sativa*), and fig (*Ficus*). In the mulberry there are staminate and pistillate flowers, which occur in separate inflorescences. The pistillate flowers are crowded together to form a small, dense inflorescence. Each flower possesses a single, one-celled ovary. Each ovary develops into a nutlet which is enclosed by the thickened, juicy calyx lobes. The separate fruitlets, as they grow, become crowded together and somewhat coalesced to form a multiple fruit, the mulberry.

In the fig the flowers line the inner wall of an enlarged, fleshy hollow receptacle. Staminate and pistillate flowers may be borne in the same or in different receptacles. Each pistillate flower has a single one-celled ovary, which develops into a nutlet. These nutlets are embedded in the wall of the fleshy receptacle. The succulent receptacle, together with the enclosed nutlets derived from many flowers, is the "fig."

FIG. 217.—The multiple fruit of the pineapple, in surface view and in longitudinal section.

This type of multiple fruit is sometimes called a **syconium**. In the common edible fig (Mission fig) the receptacle comes to maturity without fertilization of the enclosed pistillate flowers. However, in the Smyrna fig and several other varieties, the figs do not ripen properly unless fertilization and seed formation have taken place.

In the pineapple (*Ananassa*) there is a central axis which is the axis of the inflorescence from which the multiple fruit develops. Growing out from this elongated central portion are numerous sessile flowers, the fleshy bases and ovaries of which are fused to form the outer edible part of the pineapple.

Simple Fleshy Fruits.—*Berry.*—This is a kind of fruit possessing one to many seeds embedded in the fleshy endocarp and mesocarp. The tomato is a common example of a berry. Whereas the wild form of our common garden tomato (*Lycopersicum esculentum*) has a two-celled fruit, cultivated forms of the common garden tomato have a large number of locules in the fruit, in which the placentae are exceedingly fleshy.

Another familiar berry is the grape (*Vitis*). It has a smooth epidermis, often covered with a waxy secretion ("bloom"). In Old World grapes (*Vitis vinifera*), including such varieties as Muscat and Malaga, the exocarp ("skin") of the mature berry does not separate easily

known from the mesocarp (" pulp "). In American grapes, such as the Con-
a drup cord variety, on the other hand, the exocarp separates readily from the
fruit is mesocarp.
splits
the cla The date is a berry, for its " stone " is actually the seed and not
norma the stony endocarp as in the drupes of peaches, plums, etc.

In the orange, lemon, lime, and grapefruit the fruit is a type of

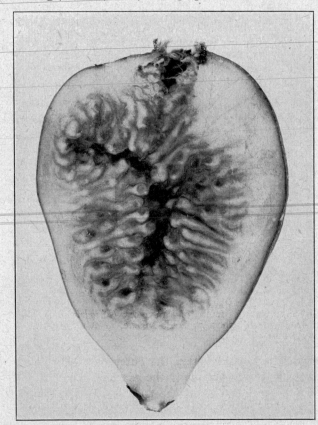

FIG. 218.—Multiple fruit of fig (syconium) in median lengthwise section. Note the thick wall of the hollow receptacle, lined on the inside with numerous flowers. The opening at the top of the receptacle permits the entrance of the fig wasp, essential for pollination.

flower, berry called a **hesperidium**. It is made up of a thick, leathery rind
into a (exocarp and mesocarp) with numerous oil glands, and a thick juicy
single portion, the endocarp. The juice is in " pulp sacs," which are long,
thick-w glandular hairs, being outgrowths from the endocarp walls. In the
Por common sweet orange (*Citrus sinensis*) there are normally ten two-seeded
forms locules, each representing a carpel. However, the number of locules and

(plumule), (3) the hypocotyl, terminating in the (4) rudimentary root or radicle. The two cotyledons are large and fleshy and contain stored food, chiefly starch. Although the young foliage leaves are small, their veins can be easily seen with a lens.

The endosperm is lacking in the bean seed, having been absorbed by the developing embryo.

Castor-oil Plant.—*Dicotyledonous Seed with Endosperm.*—At one end of the castor-oil seed is a spongy structure, the **caruncle,** which is an outgrowth of the testa or outer seed coat. It covers and obscures the micropyle. Adjacent to the caruncle is the hilum, and running approximately the full length of the seed is the raphe. Sections of the

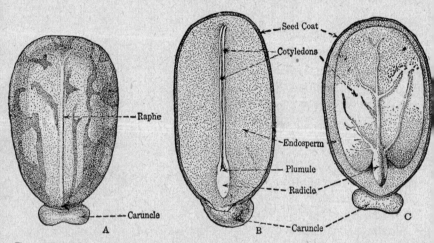

FIG. 233.—The seed of castor-oil plant (*Ricinus communis*). *A*, external view. *B*, median longitudinal section cut at right angles to the broad surface of the cotyledons. *C*, median longitudinal section, cut parallel with the broad surface of the cotyledons.

seed show the embryo embedded in a massive endosperm which makes up most of the bulk of the seed.

The embryo of the castor-oil seed consists of two cotyledons, with conspicuous veins, a very short hypocotyl, a diminutive plumule, and a short radicle. The relatively slight development of the plumule and radicle in the castor-oil seed is characteristic of many dicotyledonous seeds having endosperm. In dicotyledonous seeds in which the endosperm is used up by the embryo before the seed ripens, the plumule and radicle are generally (as in the bean) larger and more differentiated.

The Grass Seed.—*Monocotyledonous Seed with Endosperm.*—The grains (fruits) of cereals are of such great economic importance that it will be worth while to give a rather detailed discussion of a typical one (wheat). The grain consists of a single-seeded fruit with the pericarp (ovary wall) closely adherent to the seed.

In the mature grain there is a tuft of hairs, the **brush**, at the small (stigmatic) end of the grain. Along one side of the grain is a groove or furrow. The position of the embryo may be easily made out at the base of the grain.

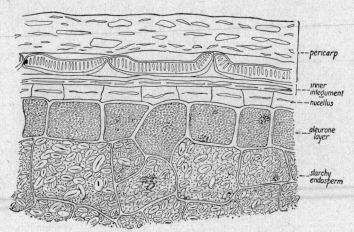

Fig. 234.—Cross section of a portion of a mature wheat fruit (grain.). (After Robbins, from *Botany of Crop Plants*.)

In a cross section of a mature wheat grain, cut at right angles to its length and so as not to include any part of the embryo, the following layers may be recognized (Fig. 234).

1. Ovary wall or pericarp, of several cell layers.
2. Seed coat, two layers of inner integument cells.
3. Nucellus, one layer of cells.
4. Aleurone layer, outermost layer of endosperm.
5. Starchy endosperm.

The pericarp of the mature grain is composed of several layers of much compressed cells, the original lumina or cell cavities of many of which can scarcely be distinguished. Their walls are thickened, cuticularized, and lignified.

In the young wheat grain, the seed coat is composed of two integuments of two layers each. In the ripening process, the outer integument is entirely absorbed, so that in the mature grain the seed coat consists of two rows of cells, belonging to the inner integument. The walls of these cells are slightly lignified. The coloring matter of the grain is found in the inner layer of the seed coat. The epidermis of the nucellus which surrounds the aleurone layer is the only portion of the nucellar tissue which is present in the grain.

The endosperm consists of two portions, (1) the aleurone layer and (2) the starchy or floury endosperm. The aleurone layer is a single layer of large cells immediately inside the nucellus. These cells are generally packed with aleurone grains, which are small protein bodies. The starchy endosperm is made up of large, somewhat elongated, thin-walled cells. They are filled for the most part with starch grains. Granules of protein including gluten occur among the starch grains.

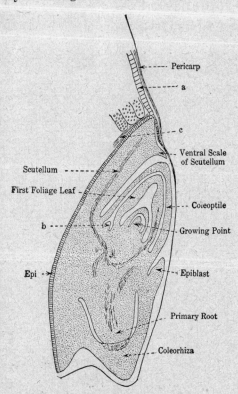

Scutellum

First Foliage Leaf

b

Epi

Pericarp

a

c

Ventral Scale of Scutellum

Coleoptile

Growing Point

Epiblast

Primary Root

Coleorhiza

Fig. 235.—Longitudinal section of the embryo of wheat; *a*, aleurone layer; *b*, bud in axil of coleoptile; *c*, crushed empty cells of the endosperm; Epi, epithelial layer of the scutellum (Redrawn from Percival.)

The structure of the embryo of the wheat grain is shown in the lengthwise section reproduced in Fig. 235. The radicle is surrounded by the root sheath or **coleorhiza**. Between the radicle and the point of attachment of the cotyledon is the very short hypocotyl. The stem growing point is surrounded by several rudimentary foliage leaves. The growing point and foliage leaves (together forming the plumule) are surrounded by the leaf sheath, or **coleoptile**.

In wheat, as in all members of the grass family, there is a single cotyledon. It is a structure which lies in contact with the endosperm and digests and absorbs food from the endosperm which it passes on to the growing parts of the embryo. This cotyledon remains within the seed during germination and never develops, as do the cotyledons of the castor-oil seed and some beans, into a green leaf-like structure. It is called the **scutellum**. On the opposite side of the hypocotyl from the scutellum is a small projection called the **epiblast**. It has been suggested that this latter structure represents a suppressed second cotyledon. The surface of the scutellum where it is in contact with the endosperm is made of a layer of cells—the columnar epithelium

—which secrete the enzymes by which the starches and proteins in the endosperm are digested (rendered soluble).

The embryo is rich in fat, mineral matter, and protein, and contains

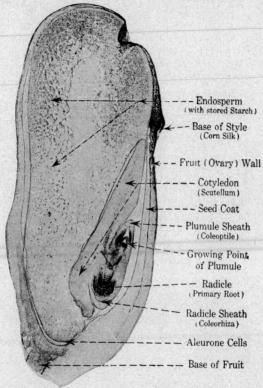

Endosperm
(with stored Starch)

Base of Style
(Corn Silk)

Fruit (Ovary) Wall

Cotyledon
(Scutellum)

Seed Coat

Plumule Sheath
(Coleoptile)

Growing Point
of Plumule

Radicle
(Primary Root)

Radicle Sheath
(Coleorhiza)

Aleurone Cells

Base of Fruit

Fig. 236.—Photomicrograph of a lengthwise section of a grain of corn (*Zea mays*):

considerable quantities of soluble carbohydrates (sugar), but little or no starch. About one-sixth of the dry weight of the embryo is fat and one-third protein.

DISSEMINATION OF SEEDS AND FRUITS

The migration of plants over the surface of the earth is accomplished in many different ways. We have seen that some plants, such as strawberries, Canada thistle, and others, migrate by means of runners, or rhizomes; this method is very slow. In others, such as the tumbleweeds (Russian thistle, witch grass, tumbling pigweed, and others), the whole plant is carried by the wind, rolling for many miles over treeless areas, scattering seed as it travels. In most plants the seeds or fruits alone are the chief means of plant migration.

There are many structural modifications by which dissemination (wide distribution from the place of their origin), of seeds and fruits is

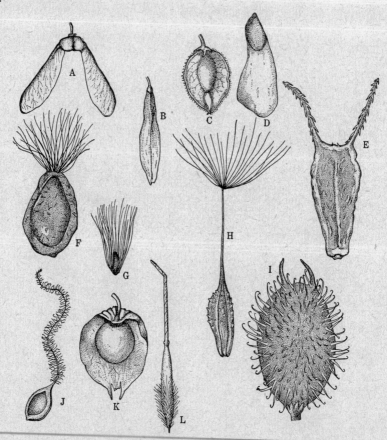

Fig. 237.—Various seeds and fruits showing devices for dissemination. *A*, winged fruit of maple (*Acer*). *B*, winged fruit of ash (*Fraxinus*). *C*, winged fruit of elm (*Ulmus*). *D*, winged seed of pine (*Pinus*). *E*, barbed fruit of Spanish needles (*Bidens*). *F*, milkweed (*Asclepias*) seed with tuft of hair. *G*, hairy seed of cottonwood (*Populus*). *H*, fruit of dandelion (*Taraxacum*) with parachute-like tuft of hairs. *I*, hooked fruit of cockle-bur (*Xanthium*). *J*, fruit of *Clematis* with long plume-like style. *K*, fruit of ground cherry (*Physalis*), with membranous envelope. *L*, bearded fruit of porcupine grass (*Stipa*).

secured. Some of these adapt the seed or fruit for dispersal by wind, others for dispersal by water, and others for dispersal by animals. **Wind, water,** and **animals,** including man, are the chief agencies in seed and fruit dissemination.

The following outline gives the chief adaptations favoring dispersal and cites examples of each kind of adaptation:

1. Adaptations Favoring Dispersal by Wind.

(a) Winged seeds and fruits. Examples: Fruits of maple (*Acer*), ash (*Fraxinus*), and elm (*Ulmus*), and the seeds of pines (*Pinus*), Catalpa, and firs (*Abies*).

(b) Seeds with long, silky hairs which are epidermal outgrowths. Examples: Cotton (*Gossypium*), milkweed (*Asclepias*), and willow (*Salix*).

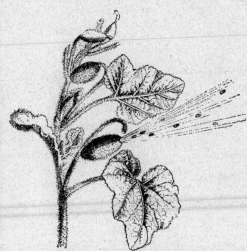

(c) Fruits with parachute-like tufts of hairs. Examples: Dandelion (*Taraxacum*), lettuce (*Lactuca*) and oyster plant (*Tragopogon*).

(d) Fruits with long, plumed styles which are persistent. Examples: Wind flower (*Anemone*), and *Clematis*.

(e) Fruits with membranous envelope containing air. Examples: Ground cherry (*Physalis*), and hop hornbean (*Ostrya*).

2. Adaptations Favoring Dispersal by Water.

(a) Fruits with membranous envelope containing air. Example: Sedges (*Carex*).

FIG. 238.—The squirting cucumber, *Ecballium elaterium*. (From Bocquillon.)

(b) Fruits with coarse, loose, fibrous exocarp, as in the coconut (*Cocos nucifera*). In the irrigated districts, irrigation water is a most important factor in the dissemination of weed seeds.

Ditch banks generally are densely overgrown with weeds, which may shed their seeds in the water. These seeds are carried by the stream, given a good soaking in transit, and planted on a well-soaked soil—all conditions being ideal for germination. It has been found that a great variety of seeds will float even though lacking special adaptations to insure buoyancy. Among such seeds are those of pigweed (*Amaranthus*), lamb's quarters (*Chenopodium album*), tall marsh elder (*Iva xanthifolia*), curled dock (*Rumex*), and dandelion (*Taraxacum*).

3. Adaptations Favoring Dispersal by Animals.

(a) Fruits with beards or awns which adhere to the hair of animals, or to the clothing of man. Examples: Chiefly grasses, including porcupine grass (*Stipa*), wild barley (*Hordeum*).

(b) Fruits with spines. Examples: Ground bur-nut (*Tribulus*), and sandbur (*Cenchrus*).

(c) Fruits and seeds with hooks or barbs. Examples: Spanish needles (*Bidens*), cockle-bur (*Xanthium*), and bed straw (*Galium*).

(d) Fleshy, edible fruits which are eaten by birds and carried varying distances by them, and the seeds of which are then regurgitated or discharged with the excrement. Many seeds are resistant to the digestive fluids.

(e) Nuts which are carried away and hidden by animals, chiefly squirrels. Here are included hickory nuts (*Hicoria*), walnuts (*Juglans*), etc.

(f) Fruits and seeds covered with viscid materials. Examples: Fruits of Sage (*Salvia*), and seeds of garden cress (*Lepidium*) and mistletoe (*Viscum*).

4. **Explosive Fruits.**—In a considerable number of species the seeds are scattered to some distance from the plant by the sudden and forcible rupture of the fruit. Among the most familiar examples are touch-me-not (*Impatiens*), castor-oil plant (*Ricinus*), and the squirting cucumber (*Ecballium*) (Fig. 238).

Seeds and Fruits Distributed by Man.—Man in his various industrial pursuits is a most important agent in the dissemination of fruits and seeds. Probably no other means of introducing weeds, for example, is so important as the sale and distribution of farm and garden seed, containing the seeds of various weeds. Many European plants are now " at home " in this country, their seeds having been brought here as " impurities," in shipments of commercial seed. Weed seeds are also carried in screenings, in baled hay, in the packing about trees, in feedstuffs, and in manure.

SEED GERMINATION

As we have already learned, **a seed is essentially a young plant (embryo) arrested in its development.** It will be recalled that an individual plant does not begin its life as a seed, but instead as a single cell, called a **zygote.** The new individual plant comes into existence at the time of fertilization—when a sperm (male) nucleus from the pollen tube fuses with the egg (female) cell in the embryo sac of the ovule, thus forming a zygote. The zygote undergoes repeated division, and by growth and differentiation there results a young plant which, with its surrounding protecting coats and its stored food, is called the seed. After the seed has matured there is normally a period during which growth and development of the embryo are at a standstill. **Resumption of these activities is called germination.** The cells of the young embryo are very much alike and there is no or little indication of different organs which compose the mature plant. These cells divide and redivide, increase in size, and, after a time, there is the appearance of rudimentary organs, such as roots, stems, and leaves. In other words, there is growth, which includes increase in the number and size of cells and differentiation. All the complex tissues and organs which compose the seedling, and later the mature plant, have as their parent the fertilized egg cell.

Conditions Necessary for Germination.—For this resumption of growth and development the following external conditions are essential: (1) a sufficient supply of water, (2) favorable temperature, and (3) a supply of oxygen. If any one of these is lacking the seed will not germinate.

In a few cases, for example, certain varieties of tobacco (*Nicotiana*), mistletoe (*Phoradendron*), and certain other plants, the percentage of germination is increased by exposure of the seeds to light, after they have absorbed water.

Water.—Water plays a most important rôle in the germination of seeds. The significance of water in the life of the plant has already been discussed (see page 170) but it is well, at this point, to give special attention to the functions which water performs in seed germination.

(1) *Water softens the seed coats, and thus enables the embryo to break through them more easily.*

(2) *The water absorbed by embryo and endosperm causes the seed to swell and this results in the bursting of the seed coats.*

(3) *Water facilitates the entrance of oxygen into the seed.* Dry cell walls are almost impermeable to gases, but if the walls have imbibed considerable water, gases can diffuse quite readily through them. As the walls of the cells of the seed coats and embryo take up water, an increased oxygen supply to the living cells results and more active respiration is made possible. On the same account, the carbon dioxide produced by respiration is able to diffuse outward.

(4) *Water dilutes the protoplasm and permits its various functions to go on actively.*—Since the protoplasm of the cells of the embryo and other living parts of the seed loses most of its water before the seeds are shed, its activities are almost completely suspended from that time until germination. Living cells can not actively carry on any of their normal processes, digestion, respiration, assimilation, or growth, unless their protoplasm contains much water.

(5) *Water makes possible the transfer of soluble food from the endosperm or cotyledons to the growing points of the embryo, where they are necessary for the building up of new protoplasm.*

Favorable Temperature.—For the seeds of any kind of plant there is a temperature, called the **minimum temperature,** below which germination will not take place. There is also a **maximum temperature** above which the seeds will not germinate, and a temperature at which germination goes on most rapidly, that is, the **optimum temperature.** These cardinal temperatures vary in different varieties of the same species. The seeds of many "cold season crops" such as peas, lettuce, radish, barley, wheat, and other small cereals will germinate readily at temperatures as low as 10° to 16° C. while the seeds of corn, pumpkin, cucumber, egg plant, and many other "warm season crops" require a much higher temperature (about 21° to 27°) for good germination.

Oxygen.—Oxygen is essential for germination, because without it respiration can not go on in the seed. Respiration is very active in germinating seeds, as it is in all tissues where growth and other cell activities are proceeding at a high rate. On that account large quantities of oxygen must be available to the seed if germination is to proceed normally.

THE GERMINATION PROCESSES

The principal processes going on in the seed during germination are:

1. Absorption of water by imbibition and osmosis.
2. Digestion.
3. Food transfer.
4. Assimilation.
5. Respiration.
6. Growth.

Water Absorption.—The initial process in seed germination is the absorption of water, and the consequent softening of the seed coats and swelling of the seed. The seed coats are largely made of material which readily takes up water by imbibition, and, as frequently is true, imbibition is here attended by a decrease in the mechanical strength of the imbibing material, in this case the cell wall material of the seed coats. The imbibition of water by the embryo and endosperm causes a swelling of these structures, and as a result a rupturing of the softened seed coats. The functions of the absorbed water have been discussed.

Digestion.—It was pointed out on page 286 that the principal foods stored in seeds are starch, hemi-cellulose, fats, and proteins, all of which are insoluble or colloidal substances. In the seed, these stored foods can not be transported from cell to cell and utilized in building up protoplasm and cell walls until they are changed into a soluble and diffusible form. **The process of rendering foods soluble and diffusible is termed digestion.** In this process certain digestive agents, which belong to the class of substances called **enzymes,** are required.

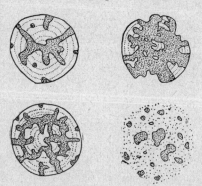

Enzymes are substances, produced in living cells and probably of the nature of proteins, which resemble inorganic catalysts such as platinum in that certain chemical changes go on very rapidly in their presence but very slowly or scarcely at all when they are not present.

FIG. 239.—Digestion of starch grains by diastase. The four figures show successive stages of digestion by the enzyme, diastase. (Redrawn from Strasburger.)

When fuel gas is allowed to escape into the air there is no appreciable oxidation of the gas by the oxygen of the air. If a fragment of asbestos covered with finely divided platinum is held in the mixture of gas and oxygen the oxidation of the gas will go on at a rapid rate and produce so much heat that a flame will be produced, and the gas will be lighted. Beside platinum a number of substances not produced in living cells have a similar power of "speeding up" chemical changes without their being used up themselves during the process. Some of these inorganic catalysts are of very great utility in the chemical industry.

It is impossible to exaggerate the importance of the organic catalysts, or enzymes, which are produced in the living cells of plants and animals.

They greatly accelerate the rate of many important changes in cells which otherwise would practically not go on at all. Also, owing to the presence of the proper enzymes, changes may go on in living cells at relatively low temperatures (below 40° C.) which would otherwise go on at the same rate only at such high temperatures as would be fatal to all living protoplasm. No enzyme has been secured in sufficient purity to determine its exact composition. The principal characteristics of enzymes may be summarized as follows:

1. They are produced by living protoplasm.

2. They may be separated from protoplasm and still retain their activity for years if stored under proper conditions.

3. They are effective in small quantities.

4. They are sensitive to heat. Most enzymes are rendered permanently inactive by heating to 60° C.

5. They are generally specific, one enzyme being effective in one chemical change only. Thus diastase changes starch to certain sugars and zymase converts glucose into alcohol and carbon dioxide, but neither is able to bring about any chemical change other than the characteristic one mentioned.

Digestion, rendering insoluble substances soluble and diffusible, is only one of a great many different kinds of chemical changes which are brought about by enzymes.

The principal classes of digestive enzymes found in seeds and the products of the digestion which they carry on are:

Enzyme	Substance Digested	Products
Diastase	starch	maltose (a sugar)
Cytase	hemi-celluloses	mannose and galactose (sugars)
Lipase	fats	glycerine and fatty acids
Proteases	proteins	peptones
Peptases	peptones	amino acids

Food Transfer.—Absorption of water, the secretion of enzymes, and digestion are but preliminary to the transfer of food from the storage cells to the growing parts of the germinating seed. Conductive tissue is poorly developed in the rudimentary plant or embryo seed. Hence, transfer of material from one part to another must be almost entirely by diffusion from one living cell to another. In the germinating seed a concentration gradient is established between the part of the seed where soluble food is being produced by digestion of stored food and the parts (radicle and plumule) where food is being used up. From our discussion of diffusion in Chapter II, we understand that any substance tends to diffuse from a region where there are more dissolved particles of that substance per unit volume of solution to a region where there are fewer particles of that same substance per unit volume. At the growing points of the embryo, soluble foods are being transformed into cellulose walls and into protoplasm, and are thus being removed from solution. Hence a constant reduction in the concentration of soluble foods is going on at the growing points. The direction of movement of soluble foods is toward these points of relatively low concentration of such substances, and away from the parts of the seed (storage regions) where soluble foods are being produced by the action of enzymes upon the insoluble stored food.

Assimilation.—This is the final step in the utilization of the stored food. It is the transformation of the digested foods into the living substances (protoplasm) and of certain of these foods by the protoplasm into cell walls. We know almost nothing about the process, however, for an understanding of it would necessitate our first learning much more than is now known of the actual nature of protoplasm.

Respiration.—Respiration goes on more actively in germinating seeds than in almost any organ or tissue of the flowering plants. It will be recalled that respiration is an energy-releasing process in which part of the food is broken down into very much simpler compounds, such as carbon dioxide and water, and the energy stored in the food is released. This released energy is in part used by the seedling plant in the work of building up the complex compounds of which the plant is composed. Much of it, however, is dissipated as heat.

Consideration of the equation for the respiration of glucose, $C_6H_{12}O_6 + 6O_2 = 6CO_2 + 6H_2O$, would lead us to expect that respiration would be accompanied by a loss of weight, if no other process went on at the same time which added to the weight. If seeds are germinated in distilled water and in the absence of light, water absorption would be the only process which could increase their weight. It is possible therefore, by comparing the *dry weight* of the two lots of seeds (originally of the same weight) one lot of which has remained ungerminated while the others have grown into seedlings under the conditions mentioned above, to demonstrate that respiration causes loss of material from the plant. Under the conditions of such an experiment no photosynthesis or intake of mineral salts could take place. The loss in dry weight is due to respiration.

That germinating seeds respire very actively is shown by the large quantity of carbon dioxide which they give off. Germinating lettuce seeds may produce as much as 82 cc. of carbon dioxide per gram of dry weight in twenty-four hours at 16° C., and poppy seeds as much as 122 cc. per gram in the same time and at the same temperature. Fig. 240 illustrates an experiment to demonstrate the evolution of carbon dioxide during the germination of seeds. Similar apparatus might be used to measure the quantity produced.

Part of the energy liberated in respiring seeds is in the form of heat. If rapid loss of heat is prevented, a mass of germinating seeds may actually become warm to the hand. If the seeds are kept in Dewar flasks

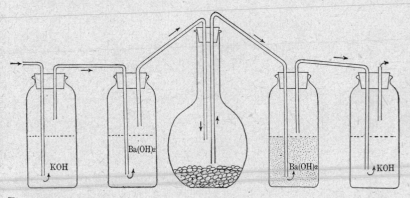

FIG. 240.—Diagram of apparatus used to demonstrate the evolution of carbon dioxide from actively respiring seeds. Air enters the apparatus by the tube at the left and passes throug.. in the direction shown by the arrows. As the air bubbles through the tion of pota: ium hydroxide (KOH) in the first bottle the carbon dioxide gas in the air is absorbed by the solution, potassium carbonate being formed and remaining in the solution. The air is next passed through a solution of barium hydroxide Ba(OH)₂ to show whether all the carbon dioxide has been absorbed by the KOH solution. If the carbon dioxide had not been completely removed a white precipitate of barium carbonate would be formed. The absence of any such precipitate shows that the air passing into the flask containing germinating seeds is free of carbon dioxide. The evolution of carbon dioxide by the seeds is shown by the formation of the white precipitate of barium carbonate ($BaCO_3$) as the air from the flask is drawn through the next bottle. The KOH bottle at the right serves to prevent any carbon dioxide from passing in the reverse direction.

(similar to " thermos " bottles) after their surfaces have been sterilized (to kill bacteria and fungi) and they have been soaked in water, they may, as they germinate, reach a temperature as much as 35° C. above that of soaked dead seeds.

Growth.—The swelling of the seed, due to imbibition of water and to growth, is followed by the bursting of the seed coats. Freed from the seed coats, supplied with water and dissolved foods and with oxygen for respiration, the embryo now grows actively. Its growth is due (1) to the enlargement (largely by the absorption of water into the

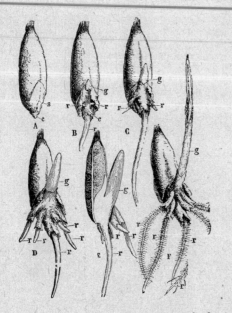

vacuoles, and the stretching of the walls) of cells already formed, and (2) to the production of new cells at the growing point of the radicle and the plumule. The growth of the radicle and the plumule into root system and shoot system differs in no important particular from the development and differentiation of tissue from the growing points of the root and terminal bud as described earlier in this book.

The radicle is usually the first embryo structure to protrude from the seed. It grows downward, sends out branches, develops root hairs, and thus enlarges its absorbing surface and attaches the seedling plant to the soil.

FIG. 241.—Stages in the germination of wheat. *c*, coleorhiza; *g*, coleoptile; *r*, roots; *s*, embryo. (After Bocquillon.)

In many plants, such as the common bean, sunflower, and squash, the cotyledons and plumule are brought up to the light by the growth of the hypocotyl, the seed coats generally remaining in the soil. In oaks and in other plants, such as garden pea and scarlet runner bean, the cotyledons remain below the ground. In the cereals, the one cotyledon (scutellum) does not come to the surface. After the young plant reaches the light and develops chlorophyll-bearing tissue, it is no longer dependent upon the store of reserve food within the seed, but is now able to carry on photosynthesis.

CONDITIONS AFFECTING THE VITALITY OF SEEDS

By the vitality of seed is meant its capacity to germinate and produce seedlings capable of developing into an adult plant. Among the chief factors which determine the vitality of seeds are the following:

1. Vigor of the parent plant.
2. Conditions to which the seeds are exposed while developing.

3. Maturity of the seeds.

4. Conditions, such as temperature and atmospheric humidity, under which the seeds are stored.

5. Age of the seeds.

(1) **Vigor of the Parent Plant.**—Weakly parent plants often produce seeds which are deficient in stored food material and the embryos of which are abnormally small. The plants grown from such seeds are often less vigorous than those produced from normal seeds.

(2) **Conditions to Which the Seeds are Exposed while Developing.**—The amount of moisture in the atmosphere and its temperature during the period of seed maturing may influence the vitality of the seeds. Most seeds mature best under dry atmospheric conditions. Low temperatures early in the autumn may injure the partly mature seed. Corn, for example, suffers from freezing if the grain is not thoroughly dry. Corn containing 13 per cent moisture, however, may be stored with safety in bins exposed to temperatures much below freezing.

(3) **Maturity of Seeds.**—Although seeds will often germinate before they have reached full maturity, the plants grown from such seeds are usually weak, as is evidenced by the fact that they can not withstand such unfavorable conditions as can those from fully matured seeds. Moreover, the yield from immature seeds is lower than from properly matured seeds. Immature seeds lose their vitality much more quickly than do mature seeds.

(4) **Conditions under which Seeds are Stored.**—In a ripe seed, the essential part of the seed, the living embryo, is in a relatively inactive state. The conditions under which seeds are stored should be such as to keep the embryo in this inactive state. That is to say, the temperature should be kept fairly low and uniform, and the atmospheric humidity relatively low. If seeds are not stored in a dry place, the moisture present may be sufficient, provided there is the proper temperature and oxygen supply, to start germination. If germination processes are started, it follows that the respiration rate increases, that there is a loss of dry weight, and a consequent decrease in the amount of stored food and therefore of stored energy in the seeds. Seeds stored in bulk under such conditions may " heat." This may be due in part to heat liberated by the respiration of the seeds themselves and in part to the heat of respiration of fungi and bacteria growing on the seeds. The heat thus developed may become so intense as to actually kill the embryos.

If they have been thoroughly dried and are not allowed to absorb moisture, many seeds can withstand a short exposure to temperatures as high as 100° C, the boiling-point of water, or a month at —194° C., the temperature of liquid air.

(5) **Age of Seeds.**—All seeds gradually lose their vitality with the lapse of time. The rate at which they lose their vitality depends upon the kind of seed and upon the condition of storage. The seeds of willow (*Salix*), for example, die unless they germinate within a few days after they are shed. On the other hand, the seeds of some legumes have been known to retain their vitality for fifty to eighty years. Recent studies of Indian lotus (*Nelumbo nucifera*) fruits which had lain buried in a peat bed probably for more than 200 years showed a very large percentage of the seeds to be still capable of germination. However, there is no reason for believing any of the frequent reports that the seeds placed in Egyptian tombs thousands of years ago are still capable of germination.

Seed Testing.—Although there is often a correlation between size or weight of a seed and its vitality, it is impossible to distinguish from external appearance living from dead seeds without making germination tests.

It is the practice of many growers to determine the percentage of germination of seed intended for planting. This is done by taking several hundred of the seeds and placing them in moist soil, sand, or sawdust, or between folds of cloth or blotting paper, and keeping them at a proper temperature. After a period, the length of which will depend upon the kind of seed; a count may be made of the seeds which have germinated, and the percentage of viable seeds may be determined.

DORMANCY OF SEEDS

Many seeds, though viable, are incapable of germination immediately after they become mature, even when placed under favorable conditions. This characteristic of certain seeds is called **dormancy** or **delayed germination.** The dormancy of cells is a well-known phenomenon. In dormant seeds, for example, are groups of meristematic cells in a resting stage. Such cells may remain in this condition of inactivity for many years. Resting cells capable of growth under suitable conditions also occur in stem buds, in root tips, and in vascular cambium. They occur in all sorts of special resting structures such as bulbs, tubers, rootstocks, and corms. There are various ways of breaking the " rest period," that is, of breaking dormancy. Whenever this is done, and by whatever methods, it means that inactive meristem is stimulated to activity, and this may also involve renewed activity of storage cells far removed from meristematic zones. In a wheat grain, for example, germinating is a renewed activity of certain meristematic cells—their multiplication and differentiation. But in order to grow there must be a movement of food to these cells. Consequently, activity of storage cells in the endosperm of the wheat grain remote from the growing points is initiated. First, renewed activity in storage cells results in a secretion of enzymes, among these being diastase, which digests starch, changing it to sugar. Coincident is an increased permeability of cell walls, and then follows the diffusion of sugar from cell to cell, its entrance into conducting tissue, and its movement to the growing points. Then the cells of these regions multiply and differentiate. Growth has begun.

Causes of Seed Dormancy.—Delayed germination in seeds may be due to several causes, such as:

1. Rudimentary embryos.
2. Seed coats which prevent the intake of water.
3. Embryos incapable of rupturing the seed coats.
4. Retardation of gaseous exchange.
5. Necessity for after-ripening.

(1) *Rudimentary Embryos.*—Some seeds, such as those of *Gingko*, buttercup (*Ranunculus ficaria*), corydalis (*Corydalis cava*), herb-Paris (*Paris quadrifolia*), and others, have immature embryos at ripening time. They must complete their development before germination, and the process of maturing may require weeks and sometimes months even under favorable conditions.

(2) *Seed Coats which Prevent the Intake of Water.*—The so-called "hard seeds" of alfalfa, sweet clover, and other legumes often fail to grow readily even when placed under excellent conditions for germination because their seed coats are highly impermeable to water. The permeability of their seed coats can be increased by "scarifying," that is, by scratching the surface by various means. As a result, water can enter the seed more readily and germination soon takes place. Otherwise it may be years before sufficient water enters to make germination possible.

(3) *Embryos Incapable of Rupturing the Seed Coats.* In this case the embryos are mature and seed coats do not inhibit the intake of water but the seed coats are so tough that the pressure of the growing embryo is not sufficient to break them. Common pigweed (*Amaranthus*) seeds fall in this class. The exposure of such seeds to freezing and thawing and to the action of soil organisms gradually softens the coats and makes germination possible.

(4) *Retardation of Gaseous Exchange.*—The tissues surrounding the embryo may prevent the ready intake of oxygen by the embryo and perhaps also the giving off of carbon dioxide. This inhibition of gaseous exchange not infrequently retards or prevents the growth of the embryo. The seeds of cocklebur (*Xanthium*) are delayed in germination on this account.

(5) *Necessity for After-ripening.*—The embryos of some seeds, such as those of hawthorn (*Crataegus*), appear to be incapable of germination even when the seed coats are removed and all external conditions are favorable for germination. Experiments show that the delay is not due to any of the four causes already mentioned. Such seeds must go through a series of changes known as "after-ripening." In the hawthorn it has been found that the principal change associated with after-ripening is an increase in the acidity of the cell sap in certain portions of the embryo. It is believed that this acidity produces conditions which favor the absorption of water and the formation and activity of enzymes, and thus stimulates growth. In the hawthorn, the after-ripening process may be hastened by treating the seeds with dilute acids. This process may also be hastened in some instances by exposure of the seeds to low temperatures, particularly to freezing or to successive freezing and thawing.

SEEDLINGS

We have seen that in the germination of the seed the embryo grows, the seed coats burst, and the young plant emerges. For a time, the young plant is wholly dependent upon food stored within itself or within the endosperm, with which it may maintain contact for a time. Not until the shoot reaches the light and is thus able to manufacture its own food and until it develops a root system does it become independent. **From the time when the young emerges from the seed to the time when it becomes entirely dependent upon food manufactured by itself, it is called a seedling.** Seedlings may be divided into two quite distinct types, as follows: (1) *Those in which the cotyledon or cotyledons are raised* *above the ground* (where they may function for a time as photosynthetic organs by the lengthening of the hypocotyl); and (2) *those in which the cotyledon or cotyledons remain beneath the ground*. In this type of seedling, the hypocotyl undergoes little or no elongation.

The first type of seedling is illustrated by the onion (*Allium*) among monocotyledons, and among dicotyledons by such well-known plants as the common bean (*Phaseolus vulgaris*), squash (*Cucurbita*), sunflower (*Helianthus*), and apple (*Pyrus*).

The second type of seedling occurs in all grasses and in many other

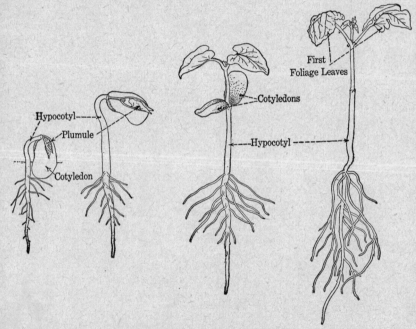

FIG. 242.—Stages in the germination of the seed of common bean (*Phaseolus vulgaris*).

monocotyledons, and in such dicotyledons as peas (*Pisum*) and scarlet runner bean (*Phaseolus multiflorus*).

Several stages in the germination of the common bean (*Phaseolus vulgaris*) are shown in Fig. 242. Some of the stored food in the cotyledons is used by the developing root, but a considerable quantity still remains even after the cotyledons are raised above ground. Even before this food is exhausted, the cotyledons, which are now in the light, become green and carry on photosynthesis to some extent. However, the reserve food in them is gradually used up by the developing plant, and they shrivel until finally their epidermis alone remains. As soon as the cotyledons unfold, the plumule begins to grow more actively, and very soon true foliage leaves are exposed to the light and begin their functions of carbohydrate synthesis and transpiration.

In some plants, such as the castor-oil plant and buckwheat, the cotyledons are thin, and contain little stored food. They absorb food for the embryo from the endosperm and later serve temporarily as

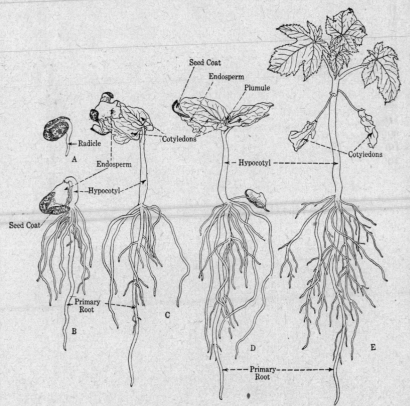

Fig. 243.—Stages in the germination of a seed of castor-oil plant (*Ricinus communis*).

photosynthetic organs. They remain attached to the seedling much longer than in the bean and carry on photosynthesis for some time.

In the germination of the wheat grain, the primary root is the first embryo structure to emerge. The coleorhiza is ruptured but remains as a collar about the root where it breaks through seed coats and pericarp. Very soon several branches of the primary root appear, which, together with the primary root itself, constitute the primary root system. It will be recalled that the growing point of the plumule and the young leaves are enclosed by the leaf sheath or coleoptile. In the growth of the plumule, the end of the coleoptile is broken open and the first foliage leaf emerges. It is from the first leaf node that the first adventitious roots arise. Other whorls of adventitious roots arise from the nodes above. Thus there are formed clusters of adventitious roots at the basal nodes, which are separated by very short internodes,

The germination of wheat illustrates a type occurring in all grasses. In this group, as has been seen, there is one cotyledon (scutellum), which remains within the seed. It serves as a food-absorbing and food-transporting organ. The primary root system usually is temporary and soon dies. However, in some cereals it may remain alive and active for several months. It is followed by successive whorls of adventitious roots which constitute the permanent root system of the plant.

CHAPTER IX

RELATION OF THE PLANT TO ITS ENVIRONMENT

In the preceding chapters of this book, reference has frequently been made to the effect of various external conditions or factors upon the development, structure, and activities of the various organs of the seed plant. It will be well to bring together here a statement of these various factors and their effects upon the plant. Collectively, these external factors are spoken of as the **environment**, and their effect upon plants and animals in nature is the special field of that branch of biology which is called **ecology**. It is well known that two individuals of a given plant species may differ very greatly if grown in different environments. Thus, most plants of a given species differ greatly in size, form, foliage, and other particulars, when grown in dry hard soil by a roadside where they are exposed to strong sunlight, from other plants of the same species grown in a cool, moist, and shaded ravine. Trees of a given species grown near timber line are strikingly different from individuals grown at lower altitudes. Environmental factors may be classified as follows.

1. *Climatic factors*, those which act upon the plant through the atmosphere.

2. *Edaphic factors*, those which operate through the soil.

3. *Biotic factors*, those arising from the presence of other plants and animals.

Some of the principal factors under each of these three groups are:

Climatic factors:
  Heat.
  Temperature.
  Light.
  Carbon dioxide concentration.
  Atmospheric humidity and precipitation.
  Wind.

Edaphic factors:
  Available water in the soil.
  Air in the soil.
  Temperature of the soil.
  Quantity and nature of the soil solutes.

309

Biotic factors:
  Competition among different species.
  Grazing by animals.
  Soil bacteria, algae, and protozoa.
  Parasitic fungi.
  Insects that injure plants.
  Insects that carry pollen.

TEMPERATURE

Each of the physiological processes which go on during the life of any particular plant has certain temperature limits (maximum and minimum) between which it can take place, and a characteristic temperature (optimum) at which it goes on most actively.

The minimum, optimum, and maximum temperatures for one process may differ considerably from those of another process taking place in the same plant at the same time. Moreover, in the case of a given process, such as photosynthesis, the cardinal temperatures may vary rather widely in different species. The minima seldom are lower than one or two degrees above 0° C., and the maxima are generally below 45°. Even in those parts of the world where the temperature for a period is below the minimum for vital activities plants may exist. In such cases the plants remain dormant except for the relatively short periods during which the temperature rises above the minimum. It is a familiar fact that some plants not only can not carry on their vital functions at low temperatures but are actually killed even by short exposure to temperatures at or slightly below the freezing-point of water. It is also recognized that different tissues of the same plant vary in their resistance to low temperatures.

When plant tissue freezes, water is withdrawn from the cells into the intercellular spaces where ice crystals are formed. Injury resulting from freezing temperature appears to be due, in part at least, to this withdrawal of water from the protoplasm with the resulting high concentration of salts which may cause precipitation of the proteins of the protoplasm. If this precipitation is extreme or persists for some time the cells are killed.

In some of these cases the resistance to low temperatures seems to be due to peculiarities, as yet unexplained, of the protoplasm, which make it immune to the injurious effects attending ice formation. In others, resistance is due to certain substances, sugar, for example, which are present in the cell sap in such quantities as to prevent freezing of the water in the protoplasm except at very low temperatures. At 0° C. pure water freezes, but any non-volatile solutes in solution in water lower the freezing-point. The greater the concentration of solutes in the solution the lower will be the freezing-point. The change of stored starch into sugar, which takes place at low temperatures in some plants, protects them from being killed by low temperatures.

Gardeners commonly practice the process of "hardening" their transplants. If a tomato plant, for instance, is removed suddenly from a warm greenhouse in the spring to the garden out-of-doors, it has little resistance to low temperatures, and the death point, temperature at which it will be killed by cold, is relatively high. The usual procedure is to move the plants from the greenhouse to a cold frame where, after remaining for a time where the temperatures are intermediate between those of the greenhouse and out-of-doors, the plants may be planted with safety in the open.

Differences in temperature in different parts of the world and at different altitudes constitute what is probably the most important factor in determining what plants shall or shall not grow in a given region.

LIGHT

We shall mention only a few of the effects which differences in intensity of light produce in the structure and activities of plants. By the term light we mean to include all the energy (radiant energy) which reaches the plant from the sun. Light may affect the plant and its activities in the following ways:

1. By reason of the dependence of the process of photosynthesis on the intensity of illumination.

2. By heating effect.

3. By furthering transpiration through heating of the leaf.

4. By its effect upon the direction of growth of certain plant organs and upon orientation of leaves.

5. By its effect upon the distribution of plants.

6. By the effect not only of light intensity but of duration of illumination upon the rate of growth and development of plants and particularly upon flower production.

7. By its effect upon the form and internal structure (anatomy) of leaves.

8. By its effect upon the form of the shoot system of plants.

As we have already learned, the rate of growth of green plants past the seedling stage will be determined largely by the surplus of food produced above that respired. The amount of this surplus will depend, within certain limits, upon the intensity and duration of illumination. Very intense direct sunlight, however, may be detrimental to plants.

Plants growing in habitats where they are exposed much of the time to very strong sunlight generally have smaller leaves and shorter internodes than shade plants and are accordingly of more compact form. The difference between the form of trees which have developed as isolated individuals and that of others of the same species which have grown in a forest, closely surrounded and accordingly largely shaded by other trees, is principally due to differences in illumination. Many other examples of the effect of illumination upon the form of the shoot system could be cited if space permitted. The leaves of shade plants, in addition to being in general larger than those of sun plants, are almost always more or less horizontal so that the light falls upon them at right angles to their surface. Those of sun plants, such as eucalyptus and the various so-called compass plants (such as *Silphium laciniatum*), hang down or are held perpendicular, and as a result the sun's rays strike the leaf surface at an acute angle and less radiant energy is absorbed by the leaves than if the leaf surfaces were horizontal. Since the various species of sun plants and of shade plants are adapted to differences in illumination, so that they can develop best in habitats which are respectively intensely and weakly illuminated, it follows that the distribution of these plants in nature will be determined by the intensity of illumination of different locations.

FIG. 244.— Two potato plants, *A*, grown in the light, and *B*, grown in the dark. The two plants have the same number of internodes. A plant such as *B*, which has been grown in darkness, is white or yellow in color, has much longer internodes than a normal plant and has very much reduced leaves. Such a plant is said to be *etiolated*. Etiolated plants cannot continue to grow after the food in the tuber, bulb or seed from which they have developed has been exhausted. (After Pfeffer.)

One of the most striking examples of the relation between illumination and the development of certain species is furnished by the spring-flowering plants of the floor of dense deciduous forests. In the early spring before the trees have developed their leaves, the floor of such a forest is well lighted, but, later, owing to the growth of foliage of the trees, little light reaches the ground. Many small plants, such as Dutchman's breeches and squirrel corn (species of *Dicentra*) and *Clintonia*, growing in such locations, develop their leafy shoots very early in the spring from underground storage structures. These leafy shoots utilize the light available, before they are shaded by the foliage of the

FIG. 245. — Timothy plants grown under different lengths of day, as indicated by number of hours on the containers. The control plant (*C*) was grown under natural length of day. Photographed July 1, 1931. Heads were first found on a length of day of $13\frac{1}{2}$ hours, this being the shortest which was favorable to heading. (Photograph furnished from Journal of Agricultural Research, Vol. 48, No. 7, 1934, article by Evans and Allard.)

tree above them, and after a short period of very active food manufacture the leafy shoots flower and soon die. During this short period these plants accumulate enough food in their underground storage organs to make possible the rapid development of another crop of leafy stems early in the next spring. In the case of many plants the development of flowers is dependent not so much upon the intensity of light as upon the relative length of day and night. Thus, some plants which flower only during the long days of June can be made to bloom in midwinter if the length of daily illumination is increased by artificial lighting. And other plants which normally bloom and fruit in the autumn, when the days are short, can be made to bloom and fruit in midsummer, if the length of day is shortened by placing them in the dark for a part of each day.

Differences in illumination are largely responsible for the very great differences in the internal structure of the leaves of those species which are known as sun plants and those known as shade plants. The following are the principal anatomical characteristics of the leaves of sun plants and shade plants:

SUN PLANTS	SHADE PLANTS
Thick palisade parenchyma, the cells being longer or the number of layers of palisade cells being greater.	Thin layer of palisade cells or none at all.
Spongy parenchyma not well developed.	Well-developed spongy parenchyma.
Thick leaves.	Thin leaves.
Small intercellular spaces.	Large intercellular spaces.
Thick and heavily cutinized epidermis.	Thin and slightly cutinized epidermis.
Stomata confined to lower side or more abundant on the lower side.	Stomata on both sides, the number on the two sides nearly or quite the same.
Frequently smooth and shiny surface, capable of reflecting much of the light falling upon them.	Generally dull surfaces.
Often densely hairy.	Seldom very hairy.

Similar differences are frequently found between different individuals of the same species which are growing respectively in sunny and in shaded habitats.

CARBON DIOXIDE CONCENTRATION

Carbon dioxide is a raw material used in photosynthesis; consequently, as a factor of the environment it is of very great importance. However, under natural conditions concentration of carbon dioxide in the atmosphere varies only within narrow limits. Accordingly, there are no recognizable effects upon plants growing naturally which can be attributed to differences in carbon dioxide supply.

ATMOSPHERIC HUMIDITY AND PRECIPITATION

The significance of water for the life of the plant and the different indispensable rôles which it plays in the various vital processes have already been discussed (Chapter V, page 170.) In this chapter we shall merely call attention to the ways in which variations in the water of the atmosphere may affect the plant.

Atmospheric Humidity.[1]—There is always, even in the driest regions, some water present in the air in the form of gas (water vapor). The water vapor in the atmosphere is spoken of as atmospheric humidity. When the air contains all the water vapor it can hold it is said to be **saturated,** but the percentage of water in a saturated atmosphere varies widely with the temperature.

Precipitation.—Precipitation, that is, water in the liquid form (rain) or the solid form (snow), is a factor second in importance only to temperature in determining the distribution of different plants in the various regions of the earth. It is not so much the total amount of precipitation falling throughout the year as its distribution throughout the year which determines what kind of plants will grow in a given region. For example, in the tropics where the rainfall is heavy and rather uniformly distributed throughout the year, the dominant vegetation is evergreen forest; on the other hand, in those parts of the tropics where the total rainfall for the year is equally heavy, but is restricted to a few months of the year, the forests are chiefly of the deciduous type.

Of the total precipitation, a part is absorbed by the soil, a part runs off and enters streams, and hence does not become available to plants, and a small portion is absorbed directly by such plants as certain algae, lichens, mosses, and by a few seed plants which have special aerial absorbing organs. Examples of the latter are the aerial roots of certain orchids.

[1] The amount of moisture in the air may be expressed in several different ways. One of the most used and most convenient methods is to express it in terms of relative humidity. By relative humidity is meant the amount (weight) of water vapor in any quantity of air, compared with the total amount of water vapor which the air is capable of holding at the temperature in question. Thus air which is water saturated has a relative humidity of 100 per cent. If only half the amount of water vapor necessary to saturate it is present the relative humidity is 50 per cent. Thus if air is in contact with a free water surface it is able at 0° C. to absorb water until in one kilogram of this saturated air there are 3.78 grams of water vapor. If this quantity of air, now having a relative humidity of 100 per cent, were warmed to 10° C., without its having opportunity for the absorption of more water, its relative humidity would be almost exactly 50 per cent because the quantity of water present in a kilogram of saturated air at 10° is 7.53 grams or almost twice 3.78 grams. In the above statement it is assumed that atmospheric pressure remains constant at 76 cm. of mercury. The humidity of the air surrounding the plant is the most important single factor in determining the rate of transpiration. Low humidity is often assumed to be principally responsible for the various devices which plants employ to reduce transpiration. (See discussion of transpiration, Chapter VI, pages 216–224). It is not, however, the percentage of water vapor in the atmosphere which determines, other things being equal, how rapid transpiration shall be. It is, instead, the percentage of water which the air can still absorb before saturation is reached. With a given percentage of water in the atmosphere, this quantity increases with increase in temperature.

WIND

One of the principal effects of wind on plants is that of increasing the rate of transpiration. In a still atmosphere, the water vapor transpired from the leaf accumulates about the transpiring leaf surface, retarding the further diffusion of water vapor out of the leaf. If, however, this layer of very humid air is carried away by wind as fast as it accumulates, water vapor diffuses at a greater rate from the leaf, that is to say, transpiration is more rapid. If the winds which blow over the surface of plants are cool and humid, as when they have crossed large bodies of water, they are less effective in

Fig. 246.—"Wind timber" on the slopes of Long's Peak, Colorado. (Photograph furnished by R. J. Pool.)

Fig. 247.—"Wind timber" on the slopes of Arapahoe Peak, Colorado, at an altitude of 11,500 feet.

increasing the rate of transpiration than are dry warm winds, such as have crossed dry, hot land areas.

The trees are generally smaller in locations where there are strong prevailing winds than in other localities, the trunks are frequently bent away from the wind, and the branches on the windward side are often almost entirely suppressed so that the tree has a one-sided form. To what extent these results are due to the mechanical effect of the wind is not altogether clear. Certainly strong winds are often responsible for the deformations of exposed trees on sea coasts and on mountain tops

(Figs. 246 and 247), although in the latter case the weight of the winter snow which bends or breaks the branches is also an important factor in causing the deformations. The main stems of trees which grow in places where they are exposed to strong prevailing winds do not grow in thickness equally on all sides. The stems have longer diameters in the direction of the wind than at right angles to it.

Along the sea coast and in deserts where there are large areas covered with loose sand, wind may cause the formation of dunes. The vegetation of dunes must be adapted to change in the form of the dunes, brought about by the shifting of the sand. The most successful dune plants are perennials with long, branched rhizomes, and very long roots. These enable the plants to adjust themselves to changes in the depth of sand covering them, as a result of dune movement.

AVAILABLE WATER IN THE SOIL

By far the most important of the environmental factors which have to do with the soil (edaphic factors) is the supply in the soil of water available to the roots of plants. This depends upon a great many other factors: climatic, edaphic, and biotic. In the chapter on the Root, pages 153–175, the absorption of water from the soil was discussed and something was said of the conditions affecting the available water in the soil. The principal factors determining the quantity of available water are given below.

Principal Factors Influencing the Available Water in the Soil.

1. The amount of annual precipitation.
2. The distribution of precipitation over the year.
3. The humidity of the atmosphere, since it affects the rate of water loss from the soil by evaporation.
4. The distance of the water table (level of standing water in the soil) below the surface of the soil. The fluctuations in the height of the water table from one season to another depend chiefly upon the precipitation and evaporation.
5. Rate at which water percolates downward into the soil. This is most rapid in sandy soil, and progressively slower in clay and humus.
6. The power of the soil to raise water from the water table by capillarity. Water is raised much higher by capillarity in clay soil than in sandy soil, but it rises at a more rapid rate in sandy soils than in clay soils.

7. **Vegetation.** The plants growing in a soil may greatly decrease the amount of water in the soil. On account of the water absorbed by the roots of plants and lost by transpiration from them, the soil may lose water much more rapidly than if it were bare.

FIG. 248.   FIG. 249.

FIG. 248.—Spanish bayonet (*Yucca whipplei*), a xerophytic plant of the chaparral belt in the mountains of southwestern United States. (Photograph by H. P. Chandler.)

FIG. 249.—A giant cactus (*Carnegia gigantea*), an extreme xerophyte, growing in the desert region of southwestern United States.

The importance of the available water in the soil is so great in its effect upon plants that botanists are accustomed to classify plants, as regards their relations to environment, largely on the basis of their water requirements, recognizing the following principal types of plants:

1. **Xerophytes.**—Plants which are very resistant to drought, or live in very dry places: Russian thistle (*Salsola*), millet (*Setaria italica*), sorghum (*Andropogon*), cactus (*Opuntia* and other genera), sagebrush (*Artemisia tridentata*), etc.

2. **Hydrophytes.**—Plants which live in water or in very wet soil: Cat-tail (*Typha*), water lilies (*Castalia, Nelumbo*), sedges (*Carex*), etc.

3. **Mesophytes.**—Plants growing best with moderate water supply: The common plants of meadow and forest.

4. **Halophytes.**—Plants able to grow in salt marshes and on alkali soils where there may be an abundance of water in the soil, but where, on account of the high concentration of the soil solution, water is absorbed with difficulty: Greasewood (*Sarcobatus*), salt brush (*Atriplex*), glasswort (*Salicornia*), etc.

AIR IN THE SOIL

The quantity of air in the soil is of considerable importance to plants growing in it. The living cells of the root, particularly those of the growing points and the adjacent, actively growing regions, must have oxygen to support respiration. Normally the roots secure the necessary

FIG. 250.—A water lily (*Nymphaea*), a typical hydrophytic plant. The rhizome and roots are in the soil beneath the water. The leaves and flowers are brought to the surface of the water by the elongation of their stalks.

oxygen for respiration by its diffusion into the roots through the root hairs and ordinary epidermal cells. This inward diffusion of oxygen from the soil atmosphere ordinarily goes on readily because of the thinness of the walls of these cells and the absence of a cuticle. A moderately dry soil, not excessively fine in texture, contains a large quantity of air in the pores between the soil particles. A very wet soil contains less air than would the same soil in a drier condition, for part of the space (larger pores) which would be occupied by water in the wet soil is occupied by air in the drier soil. In a water-soaked soil there is practically no air save that which is dissolved in water. As a rule, the larger the soil particles and the looser and more porous the soil the better is the supply of oxygen to the roots. If the soil about their roots is continuously water-soaked, most plants die on account of insufficient oxygen supply.

There are some plants which can thrive although the root system is submerged in water or surrounded by a soil which is water-soaked. Almost all such plants contain in the stem and root large communicating air spaces. Thus, air absorbed into the leaves and stems may reach the living cells of the root in sufficient quantity. Some plants (which thrive even though their roots are surrounded by water or water-saturated soil), like the bald cypress (*Taxodium distichum*) and various species in tropical mangrove swamps, produce special root branches which grow upward until their ends are above the water level. These special root branches have a central core of loose parenchymatous tissue through which air passes downward to the submerged parts.

The composition of the soil air differs somewhat from that of the atmosphere. The air of the soil is considerably richer in carbon dioxide than that of the atmosphere; this is due to the respiration of soil bacteria and other fungi and of the roots themselves.

SOIL TEMPERATURE

The temperature of a soil may very greatly affect the plants which grow in it. One of the principal effects of low soil temperature is the reduction of the rate of water absorption by the root. Actively transpiring plants may undergo serious water shortage even when their roots are in a soil containing abundant water if the temperature of the soil is very low. Evergreen trees, growing, as many of them do, in regions where the winters are cold, are in considerable danger of water shortage during cold weather; although their roots are unable to absorb much water from a cold soil, their foliage, which is retained throughout the winter, may, on sunny days, transpire considerably. It is probably on this account, and also perhaps because the absence of vessels from their wood makes it less efficient in water conduction, that there is necessity for reduced transpiration and that these coniferous trees have linear leaves with relatively little surface, a very thick cuticle, and stomata depressed below the leaf surface. These are characteristics of xerophytic plants and, actually, even though they may grow in regions of relatively high humidity and soil moisture, these gymnosperms, such as the pine (*Pinus*), fir (*Abies*), and hemlock (*Tsuga*) are xerophytic plants.

The soil temperature depends upon a great many factors, chiefly (1) the air temperature, (2) the intensity of the sunlight, (3) the period during which the sun shines upon the soil, (4) the angle at which the sunlight strikes the soil, (5) the color of the soil (dark soils absorb heat more readily than light-colored soils), (6) the physical nature of the soil, (7) the amount of water in the soil (a wet soil is usually cooler than a dry one), and (8) the presence or absence of a layer of leaves or other soil cover.

QUANTITY AND NATURE OF THE SOIL SOLUTES

Water absorption by the roots can take place only if the concentration of the cell sap of the root hairs is greater than that of the soil water. The adaptations of plants growing in salt marshes or in so-called alkali soils are similar to those of plants growing where the soil is very dry or the humidity of the atmosphere is very low, and such halophytic plants have been shown to have cell sap in the absorbing cells of the root the concentration of which is higher than that in most other plants. If the root systems of most plants were exposed to such concentrations as exists in salt, swampy, and strongly "alkali" soils, they would not be able to absorb sufficient water to replace that lost by transpiration and would soon die.

Sometimes the soil water is deficient in one or more of the essential elements which the plant must secure from the soil. It will be recalled that these elements are potassium, calcium, magnesium, iron, nitrogen, sulphur, and phosphorus, and certain others needed only in very minute quantity. Plants growing in such soils may have their growth much reduced or show other abnormalities.

There is a wide variation in the tolerance of different plants for acid and alkaline soils. Certain plants, such as sour dock (*Rumex acetosella*), heather (various *Erica* species), and the moss (*Sphagnum*), growing normally on quite acid soils, do not thrive in soils which are rich in lime. Other plants, such as salt bush (*Atriplex*), grow normally on alkaline soils, but do not flourish in acid soils.

THE INFLUENCE OF CERTAIN BIOTIC FACTORS UPON PLANTS

Other species of organisms, both plants and animals, are as much a part of the environment of a given plant as are the various climatic and edaphic factors which we have mentioned above. Though in general these biotic factors are second in importance to the factors which have to do directly with soil and atmospheric conditions, they are of great importance, and sometimes (for example, in certain dangerous plant parasites) of greater importance than any other factor in determining whether given individuals or species shall survive in a certain locality.

In nature, plants compete for space, light, water, and inorganic salts. Ordinarily water is lost more rapidly from soil covered with plants than from bare soil. As the result of the competition of plants for the water in a soil, certain species may die off because of excessive drying of the soil by other species which absorb water more rapidly. In a similar manner, there is competition in a forest for light, and the dense shade of the larger plants may prevent the growth of smaller plants which would grow in the locality if it were not for the shading. On the other hand, certain plants which grow well beneath the trees of the forest because the temperature there is relatively low and the humidity high would not be able to grow in that locality if the trees were removed.

Grazing by animals may greatly affect the plants growing in a certain habitat. Most species are unable to survive frequent removal of leaves and parts of the stem by grazing animals. As a result, those plants (principally certain grasses) which are able to withstand cropping and to spread without seed formation (that is by rhizomes) tend to take full possession of a closely grazed piece of land.

The soil itself contains many simple organisms, such as algae, bacteria and other fungi, and protozoa. Some of these, particularly certain of the bacteria, add to the fertility of the soil by increasing the amount of nitrogen available for the seed plants growing in it. Other organisms in the soil may be injurious to seed-bearing plants either because they lessen soil fertility (some of them greatly reduce the available nitrogen) or because they are the cause of root diseases.

Parasitic organisms, bacteria and other fungi, nematode worms, and insects are biotic factors of very great importance. The insect parasite, *Phylloxera*, which at one time destroyed most of the French vineyards, the fungus parasite causing chestnut blight, which has killed many of the chestnut trees of the United States, and the parasitic fungus responsible for the white pine blister rust, a plant disease which has caused great losses of the white pines of the eastern United States, are particularly striking illustrations of the importance of parasitic plants and animals as living factors in the environment surrounding plants.

TRANSFORMATION OF MATERIALS AND ENERGY BY THE PLANT

If it were possible to take moving pictures of the whole plant, showing in a few minutes all the movements of the plant over a period of one to several weeks, we could observe the roots twisting and turning and making their way around and between soil particles, the young shoots of germinating seeds forcing their way through the soil, and the movements of the parts of opening buds. In short, we could see that various organs of the plant are in almost constant motion. The protoplasm of many cells, probably most living cells, moves from one part of the cell to another. These movements and various other activities of the plant involve the expenditure of energy, and the only source of energy for any of the activities of the plant, except photosynthesis and transpiration, is the process of respiration.

Mention has been made of the fact that if it were not for green plants none of the animals or chlorophyll-free plants in the world could exist. This is true because the heterophytic plants (plants which lack chlorophyll and are accordingly unable to make their own food) and the animals are incapable of building up from the simple inorganic compounds in the soil and atmosphere the complex organic substances of which their bodies are constructed. The formation of these complex compounds, or foods, constitutes the great rôle of green plants in organic nature. The making of foods by plants is of very great significance for two reasons:

1. Because these foods furnish the material out of which the bodies of plants and animals are constructed.

2. Because, in the making of these foods, energy from the sun, which is the world's great source of energy, is stored, and this stored energy can be released within the bodies of the living organisms by respiration. Since green plants are responsible for important transformation (1) of materials and (2) of energy, it will be fitting to summarize these changes in material and energy.

The Materials Which Green Plants Absorb and the Changes Which These Materials Undergo.—The principal substances which are taken into green seed plants in considerable quantity and which are essential to their proper development are as follows:

From the soil:

Water.

Salts, containing the following essential elements and certain others in minute quantity:

Nitrogen—principally as nitrates but in some cases as compounds of ammonia.

Phosphorus—as phosphates.

Sulphur—as sulphates.

Potassium ⎫
Calcium   ⎪
Magnesium ⎬ In combination with one of the three preceding elements.
Iron   ⎭

From the atmosphere:

Carbon dioxide.

Oxygen.

The principal changes which these substances undergo in the plant will be briefly stated.

Water.—In Chapter V, page 170, there will be found a statement of the various functions which water performs in the living plant. Most of these functions do not involve, however, a transformation of water into any other substance, and it is with such changes that we are now concerned. The water used in photosynthesis is so transformed, that is, it ceases to be water and becomes part of the sugar, presumably glucose, which may later be changed into some other sugar or into starch, cellulose, or various other substances. The water which passes from the plant during transpiration in the form of water vapor is changed only in its physical form and not (chemically) into any other compound. During the process of respiration, organic compounds, presumably sugars, are broken down and water is formed again.

Nitrogen, Phosphorus, and Sulphur.—These elements are particularly important as the raw materials, together with soluble carbohydrates, of the amino acids from which proteins are built up. Proteins contain from 15 to 19 per cent of nitrogen and from $\frac{1}{2}$ to $1\frac{1}{2}$ per cent sulphur. The formation of proteins and related substances probably takes place principally in the leaves. Phosphorus is found in some proteins, particularly the nucleo-proteins of the nucleus, which contain from 0.3 to 3 per cent of that element. Inorganic phosphates are changed to organic phosphorus compounds principally in the leaves. There is no evidence that animals are able to use nitrates, sulphates, and phosphates to build up their own amino acids or proteins. These latter substances are just as essential to them as to plants, but they are all secured directly or indirectly from plants. The nitrogen, sulphur, and phosphorus which are absorbed by the plant (and the same is true of potassium, calcium, magnesium, and iron) never leave the plant except when parts of the plant (leaves, fruits, flowers, or broken branches) are separated from it.   If proteins containing these elements are broken down in the plant, the simple compounds resulting are not excreted as is nitrogen in the form of urea by the higher animals. Instead, they are again used for the building up of proteins and amino acids.

Potassium, Calcium, Magnesium, and Iron.—Though all the higher plants must be supplied with these elements, we have little knowledge

Fig. 251.—Tomato leaves showing, on the right, a leaf from a plant supplied with a sufficient quantity of all the necessary minerals and, on the left, a leaf showing spotting and other abnormalities characteristic of plants grown under conditions which were the same except that the supply of potassium was deficient.   (After Johnston and Hoagland.)

of the changes which the simple inorganic compounds of these elements undergo within the plant.   Part at least of the magnesium is used in the making of chlorophyll a and chlorophyll b.   Iron is also essential to chlorophyll formation, although the chlorophyll molecule contains no iron.   Iron is also believed to be concerned, perhaps as a catalyst, in oxidation processes in the plant.   It may be that potassium, calcium, and iron perform their essential function without change from the simple inorganic form in which they exist in the soil solution.

Carbon Dioxide.—Carbon makes up from 40 to 50 per cent of the dry weight of all plants, and the gas carbon dioxide is the source of all this carbon. The carbohydrates are utilized in the making of proteins and fats. When sugars, which are the principal directly respirable materials in the plant, are respired, carbon dioxide is again formed and liberated into the atmosphere. When plant parts die, the sugars, starch, cellulose, fats, and all other organic compounds are broken down by bacteria and other fungi and the carbon is finally set free from these compounds in the form of carbon dioxide. Thus there exists in nature a carbon cycle in which the carbon of carbon dioxide is continuously being built up into complex foods, which are again broken down with the formation of carbon dioxide. The autophytic plants (those which possess chlorophyll and can make their own food), animals, bacteria and other fungi, both of the land and sea, may all play a part in this carbon cycle. In Chapter XII will be found a brief account of this cycle and a diagram illustrating the part played by different organisms.

Oxygen.—Carbohydrates, protein—in fact all essential substances in the plant—contain oxygen in combination with other elements. This oxygen is derived for the most part from water or from carbon dioxide used in photosynthesis. But the plant also absorbs the free oxygen of the atmosphere. This is utilized solely for respiration and becomes part of the compounds produced by respiration.

Nitrogen.—A few simple green plants, such as some algae, and certain bacteria are able to use as nitrogen for protein manufacture the free nitrogen gas of the atmosphere. Under natural conditions most of the nitrogen is secured from the soil in the form of compounds of nitrogen with other elements.

In addition to the ten elements—carbon, hydrogen, oxygen, nitrogen, sulphur, phosphorus, potassium, magnesium, calcium, and iron—long recognized as essential to the continued growth and development of green plants, there are certain other elements, which are known to be beneficial or indispensable. For example, it has been found that **manganese, boron, copper,** and **zinc** are essential to the growth of a number of different kinds of green plants, but that very small amounts suffice. Our failure to recognize earlier that certain of these elements are essential is due to two facts. First, that they are needed only in very small quantities, and second, that the "chemically pure" compounds used in preparing culture solutions in the past have generally, or at least frequently, contained unsuspected traces of these elements quite sufficient in quantity to supply the needs of the plant's growth in culture.

Other elements concerning which there is some evidence indicating their importance to particular plants are: **silicon, sodium, chlorine, aluminum, bromine,** and **iodine.**

Energy Changes Brought About by the Plant.—We have already learned that certain chemical changes, for example, burning and respiration, are attended by liberation of energy.

It is one of the principal rôles of green plants to take certain of the simple compounds (carbon dioxide and water) in which no available energy is stored and build them up into much more complex substances in which there is stored or potential energy. It is the energy of sunlight which is thus stored by green plants. These substances produced by plants are the source of all the energy which is used by animals within their bodies, and by heterophytic plants. Moreover, if we except the energy of falling water and wind, and that of the tides and waves which we may sometime be able to utilize, **all the energy which is used by man for any purpose is secured from the energy stored in the substances made by plants.** Our principal fuels, wood and coal, are unmistakably plant products. Petroleum is also, in all probability, a direct or indirect product of green plants. The energy set free in the form of heat when these fuels are burned can be changed into mechanical energy by the steam engine or gasoline motor. This in turn may be transformed into electrical energy by the dynamo, and this again into light energy by the electric lamp or into heat again by the electric stove. But whatever form it may take, the energy secured by the combustion of coal, wood, or petroleum is but the energy of sunlight which perhaps hundreds of centuries ago was absorbed by green leaves when carbon dioxide gas and water were being united in the leaves to produce the energy-storing substances from which these fuels were formed. Green plants are then preëminent not only as makers of substances essential for the building and repair of the bodies of all organisms but also as the storers of the sun's energy for use within the bodies of organisms, and for use in the industries. The amount of energy which can be secured from other sources than the combustion of the products of photosynthesis is only a small fraction of that used in industry. Man is accordingly, and may always be, dependent upon green plants for much of the energy used in the industries, as he is also for all the energy used within his own body. The following is a brief summary of the energy changes involved in the life of a green plant:

I. Radiant energy of sunlight falls upon green leaves.

II. A large part of this is absorbed by the leaves (in some cases at least as much as 80 per cent).

   1. Part of this is changed to heat, raises the temperature of the leaf, and is lost to the air if the air is cooler than the leaf.

   2. Part of it, after being changed into heat, is used in changing water into water vapor during transpiration.

3. Part of the radiant energy absorbed (under natural conditions a very small part) is used in photosynthesis and stored in the carbohydrate molecules.

III. The energy stored in that part of the carbohydrate which is transformed into cellulose is not liberated until the cellulose is burned or decays.

IV. The sugars in the plant are in part respired, and their stored or potential energy is liberated.

1. Of this energy, a large part is in the form of heat and is lost to the surrounding air.
2. The remainder of the energy freed by the respiration of sugar is used for various physical and chemical activities taking place within the plant.

V. Sugars, or compounds formed from sugars, are used as food by animals or by those plants which can not make food. These are in part respired by these organisms and furnish heat and other forms of energy necessary for the life processes. In the case of the higher animals, the heat produced is in part used to maintain the temperature essential to the health of the animal.

VI. Dead plant tissue or plant products may decay. In that case carbohydrates or other energy-storing substances are broken down by bacteria and other fungi which cause decay, that is to say, these substances are respired by the organisms of decay and liberate energy, partly as heat and partly in other forms used by the bacteria and other fungi.

VII. When dead plant tissues or plant products are burned as fuel, the compounds of which they consist are broken down into carbon dioxide, water, and other simple compounds, and energy is liberated as light and heat.

PLANT ASSOCIATIONS

Rarely in nature do individual plants grow isolated from other individuals of the same species. On the contrary, plants, like human beings and other animals, generally live in associations, groups or communities, such as forest and meadow. This community life among plants, as among animals, is largely a response of individual plants to a given set of environmental conditions. We may speak of a black spruce community, a maple-birch community, a water-lily community, and so on. Those communities are very seldom made up of individuals of a single species. Even though the community is designated by the name or names of one or a few of the most prominent (dominant) species, a considerable number of species is almost always present. Plant communities or associations, such as a yellow pine forest or a sphagnum swamp, generally owe their origin largely to the existence in a given location of environmental conditions particularly favorable to the species which they include or at least unfavorable to species with which they would be forced to compete in other locations. At the same time a plant association once established may have a marked influence upon its surroundings. It may modify the texture and water content of the soils and the amount of soil salts; and to a certain degree it may alter light, humidity, temperature, and air movement in the vicinity. This is true not only of natural plant associations but also of those artificial plant associations established and maintained by man. Thus windbreaks may greatly reduce water loss from the soil on their leeward side, and a heavy crop of corn will change considerably the quantities of various mineral salts in the soil. So it is that just as the environment affects the character of vegetation, the vegetation may to some extent react upon the environment. Although it is important to know what influence certain soil conditions have upon the growth of our crop plants, it is often as important to understand what effect a given crop is going to have upon the soil and thus upon crops which follow it. Our orchards, fields, and gardens are cultivated communities of plants. Many problems arise as to the best methods of handling these communities, and these problems may be quite different from those which arise in connection with the individual plant.

Plant Invasion.—There is a tendency for plant individuals and plant communities or associations to extend their areas of distribution; this implies the invasion of new territory. For example, the seeds from an individual plant may be carried by various agencies such as wind, or birds, to places more or less remote from the parent plant. If the seeds find in these new areas conditions suitable for their germination, and if the plants can grow to maturity in the new habitat, reproduce, and finally become established there, then invasion is complete. Striking examples of the invasion of a species are furnished by certain weeds. Seeds of the Russian thistle found their way into the United States in 1873 in flaxseed brought from Russia and sown near Scotland, South Dakota. As a result of its very efficient means of seed dispersal and its ability to become established in a variety of soil and climatic conditions, the Russian thistle has invaded a large part of western United States.

A plant association such as a forest may also invade territory and displace another association. For example, a burnt-over mountain slope, temporarily occupied by an herbaceous growth, may be invaded by the dominant tree species of the region, together with their plant associates, and as a result a characteristic forest growth comes to occupy the area.

There are in nature various barriers, which prevent species or plant communities from extending their geographical range. These may be either physical or biological. Deserts, mountain ranges, and large bodies of water are physical barriers. For example, hydrophytic and mesophytic species can not successfully invade a desert and spread to suitable habitats beyond. Vegetation may be a biological barrier. A

Fig. 252.—Invasion of bad-land slopes by Russian thistle (*Salsola kali var. tenuifolia*). (Photograph furnished by F. E. Clements.)

dense forest, for example, is a barrier to the invasion of light-demanding species, which are prevented by the forest from extending their distribution in that direction.

Plant Succession.—A plant association existing in a given location does not necessarily remain permanently in possession of the area in question. Thus if we observe over a period of years the vegetation of an area, small or large, we may note that its character changes; that there may be a succession of plant communities, one replacing the other, and successively occupying the same area. In some cases such succession goes on at too slow a rate to be observed within a single lifetime. The following three types of succession of associations have been recognized:

1. *Regional successions*, due to widespread climatic changes.
2. *Topographic successions*, due to changes in topography resulting from erosion or deposition of material, as at the base of cliffs or at the mouths of streams.
3. *Biotic successions*, due to plant and animal factors, such as the accumulation of humus in the soil or the destruction of some species by insect parasites or plant diseases.

An example of an extensive regional succession is the invasion, following the glacial period, of southern species into those regions which

Fig. 253.—Invasion of sandy plains by evening primrose, Colorado Desert. (Photograph furnished by F. E. Clements.)

experienced marked climatic changes due to the recession of the continental ice sheet.

Topographic successions are more rapid than regional successions. They are well illustrated in the development of flood plains along rivers, where erosion and deposition of sediment bring about progressive changes in the habitat which result in corresponding progressive changes in the vegetation.

Biotic successions are seen to advantage in the filling of ponds and lakes, where there is an accumulation of humus, resulting from the death of the plants. The original aquatic vegetation is displaced by swamp vegetation, and this in turn by a mesophytic type.

The Climax.[1]—Wherever bare areas arise, as the result of the

[1] This section on the climax was prepared by Dr. F. E. Clements of the Carnegie Institution of Washington.

destruction or removal of the plants by fire, landslide, climatic changes, or other cause, development of a new plant cover is initiated by **invasion** and carried forward by **succession** through a series of communities. The successional process terminates in a final stable vegetation that persists until again removed by some disturbing agency or displaced by a major change of climate. This ultimate or adult community of plants is termed the **climax,** not merely because of its position at the end of the series of successions, but also by reason of its close dependence upon the corresponding climate. The most familiar climaxes are the deciduous forest of the East and the prairie of the West, which before the coming of white men were more or less continuous over vast regions.

Fig. 254.—Initial community of lichens on petrified logs, Petrified Forest, Arizona
(Photograph furnished by F. E. Clements.)

Even then, however, these extensive climax communities were interrupted here and there by lakes and streams, by rocky ridges and cliffs, sand dunes and bad-lands in which succession was slowly but steadily at work, building up or stabilizing soils and thus extending the climax community. With the entrance of white settlers, the destruction of the climaxes by fire, lumbering, and clearing kept pace with the westward movement, and each climax became a mosaic of remnants of forest or prairie with innumerable successional stages in a general pattern of cultivated fields.

Here and there where the reaction of the plant community upon its environment was especially slow, a certain stage in succession would persist for centuries and thus simulate a climax. Familiar examples are to be found in the peat bogs or muskeags of the Northeast, the coastal swamps of the Gulf region, and the tule marshes of California.

FIG. 255.—Climax of deciduous forest along the upper Delaware River. (Photograph furnished by F. E. Clements.)

Where forest fires have been frequent, the succession is unable to proceed to the climax proper, but is halted usually in the preceding pine

FIG. 256.—Climax of mixed prairie composed chiefly of *Stipa* and *Agropyrum* species. Scottsbluff, Nebraska. (Photograph furnished by F. E. Clements.)

community. This is then termed a subclimax and is well illustrated by the pine-barrens of the Atlantic Coast, the jack-pine woods of the

Lake region, and the lodgepole-pine forests of the Rocky Mountains. Overgrazing may often produce somewhat similar consequences, such as the short or buffalo grass subclimax of the Great Plains or the tall-grass prairie of the Mississippi Valley.

Quite apart from the modifications due to succession and disturbance, each climax exhibits a more or less definite structure. This is due in part to variations in climate over such a great area as that occupied by the prairie or hardwood forest, and in part to the differences in the requirements of the controlling species or dominants. For example, the prairie climax or formation is subdivided into some six communities or associations on the basis of various groupings of the dominant grasses. These are (1) the true prairie of the Missouri Valley, (2) the coastal prairie of the western Gulf region, (3) the mixed prairie over the Great Plains from Saskatchewan to Texas, (4) the desert plains in the Southwest, and (5) the bunch-grass prairies in the Northwest, and (6) California respectively. The deciduous forest exhibits three associations, the more northerly maple-beech, the oak-chestnut of the Appalachian region, and the wide extent of oak-hickory that encloses these on the east, south, and west. The great transcontinental band of the spruce-fir climax is divided into an eastern and western association, while the coniferous climaxes of the great Cordilleras are represented by different groupings in the Rocky Mountains and the Sierra-Cascade system. Other climaxes are constituted by the giant trees of the northwest coast, by the elfin-wood or chaparral of California, the sagebrush of the Great Basin, and the desert scrub of the Mohave, Colorado, and Sonora deserts.

This chapter and the preceding ones have dealt largely with those features which are common to all or at least most of the seed-bearing plants. In Part II, attention will be directed more particularly to the structural (morphological) and functional (physiological) differences existing between different plants. Instead of limiting ourselves to the Spermatophyta, as in Part I, we shall discuss representatives of each of the five great divisions of the plant kingdom. In addition, an attempt will be made to indicate the general course of evolution by which, from very simple and primitive plants, the complex and highly differentiated Spermatophyta have arisen.

PART II

A Survey of the Plant Kingdom with Particular Emphasis upon Development, Reproduction, and Relationships, Including also a Chapter on Evolution and Heredity

CHAPTER X

INTRODUCTION

Point of View.—In the first part of this volume we have discussed the form and anatomy of the various organs of the plants belonging to the Spermatophyta, and have given an account of the physiological processes going on in these plants.

In the second part we shall be mostly concerned with the groups, Algae and Fungi, which make up the subkingdom Thallophyta, and with the Bryophyta and the Pteridophyta which with the Spermatophyta constitute the subkingdom Embryophyta. In our study of these plants and of a few representatives of the Spermatophyta, we shall attempt to emphasize the following considerations:

1. The probable course of evolution from the simplest plants through forms of increasing complexity to the seed plants, which are the most highly organized of living plants.

2. The great variety in form and structure of the organisms making up the plant kingdom.

3. The peculiarities in structure, and particularly in function, by which many of the simpler plants manage to live successfully under conditions very different from those surrounding typical seed plants.

4. The importance of certain simpler plants, particularly the bacteria and other fungi, in relation to health, and to agriculture and other industries.

5. The function of reproduction in plants and particularly the mechanism of inheritance.

6. The principal laws of heredity and of evolution as illustrated by plants.

THE MEANING OF PLANT RELATIONSHIPS

There exist in the world today about a quarter of a million different kinds of plants which have been described and named, and the number of named species of animals is much greater, nearly a million. New species are constantly being discovered by the systematic botanist and zoologist.

Among this great variety of different kinds of organisms there are many groups of species which obviously resemble each other more than they do any other kinds of organisms. Familiar examples of groups of similar species are the oaks, all of which bear acorns and most of which have pinnately lobed leaves; the mints, which generally have square stems and whose foliage often has an aromatic odor; the beans, peas, and similar plants, whose fruits are pods or legumes and whose flowers are of a form which suggests a butterfly; and the toadstools and mushrooms with their stalked, umbrella-shaped caps. A careful comparison of the organisms about us would reveal, even to one without special knowledge, many more such groups of strikingly similar plants.

Both the existence of so many different kinds of organisms and the striking similarity between the members of such groups as have just been mentioned demand an explanation.

We have already referred to the two explanations which have been offered in the introductory chapter at the beginning of this volume. The first is the **theory of special creation**, which assumes that each species that exists or ever existed was separately created, and that each of the specially created individuals of a species was endowed with the power of producing other individuals like itself, but was without ability to give rise to individuals differing from it. This theory does not furnish any explanation of the close resemblances which exist between certain kinds of organisms.

The second explanation is the **theory of organic evolution**. So closely is the name of Charles Darwin associated with this theory that many persons without biological training believe that the theory originated with him. Actually it had its beginning as early as the time of the Greek philosophers, long before the beginning of the Christian era, and it was clearly and comprehensively stated by Lamarck, who was born more than sixty years before Darwin. Darwin was one among many scientists of his time who accepted the theory of organic evolution. His special service lay in his attempt to work out the factors in nature by which organic evolution has been brought about and his masterly presentation of the evidence in support of the truth of organic evolution. In a subsequent chapter we shall give an account of his work and of later attempts to discover how the evolution of plants and animals goes on.

Evolution is a process in which great differences arise through a succession of relatively slight changes. It is clear that such a process is constantly going on among other things besides plants and animals. History teaches us that present-day governments, methods of education, agriculture, medicine, manufacturing processes, dress, machinery, weapons, methods of warfare, means of communication, and everything else in our modern civilization have come about through evolution. History is indeed merely an account of the evolution of human institutions, arts, and practices. Inorganic evolution (the evolution of other things than organisms) is illustrated by the collections, which may be found in many great museums, showing the history of development in human apparel, implements of various sorts, optical instruments, etc. Within our own life many of us have witnessed practically the whole course of the evolution of the aeroplane and methods of wireless communication. The geologist can inform us very fully in regard to the evolution of the hills, valleys, streams, and other features of the regions in which we live, and the astronomer knows much of the evolution of our earth and other planets and of the sun and stars.

It is, however, with the evolution of organisms (organic evolution) that we are here concerned. The now generally accepted explanation of the great number of plants and animal species, and of the close similarity existing between some of these, is called the **theory of organic evolution.**

The principal features of this theory are briefly these:

1. The existing kinds of plants and animals and all the kinds that are now extinct, with the exception of one or a few original and very simple forms, have arisen from preëxisting kinds by relatively slow changes.

2. If the preceding proposition is true, it follows that all the different kinds of plants and animals are related.

3. Those species which are similar in many particulars are **closely related**, that is, they are not separated by many forms from a common ancestor (species) from which they have all descended.

4. Although it is natural to look upon evolution as **progressive**, that is, as such that it results in an increase in complexity and differentiation, it may often be **retrogressive** and result in a development of forms having less complexity and differentiation than their ancestors.

If we could secure specimens of all the kinds of plants and animals which now exist or which ever have existed, it should be possible by comparison of their structure to work out the whole course of evolution. Many species of plants and animals have become extinct. In the case of a few species extinction has actually taken place since man has been studying plants and animals, and thousands of kinds of organisms died out before the animal species we call man was himself evolved. In the rocks we find the remains of some of these extinct plants and animals as fossils. These remains are in many cases mere fragments of the bodies of these organisms, and it is probable that fossil remains of many of these extinct plants and animals, particularly of the simpler and more primitive forms, will never be found, and we shall never have direct knowledge that such plants or animals ever existed.

CLASSIFICATION OF PLANTS

In spite of the fact that our knowledge of the extinct species, and of living species too, is very incomplete, it is possible for us to trace with considerable certainty the course of evolution within certain groups of related plants. Thus we arrive at a natural classification of such groups. Our conclusions in such cases are largely based upon a comparison of the structure and development of the plants or animals in question. Experience teaches us, however, that certain resemblances between different species are not to be considered as evidence of their close relationship. Thus the fact that a fly and a sparrow both have wings is no basis for the conclusion that these two winged animals are more closely related to each other than they are to any wingless animals. Though the wings of these two kinds of animals are superficially alike, since they are organs adapted to the same function, a study of their structure and development shows that in most respects they are dissimilar organs. The wing of the fly is in a reality a flap of skin, while the wing of a bird corresponds to the fore limbs of the quadrupeds. Organs which are superficially similar merely because adapted to the same function, but which have not been evolved from the same structure possessed by some common ancestor are said to be **analogous**. Organs such as the wing of a bird and the fore limb of one of the higher animals, which, though perhaps differing in function, have had a common origin in evolution are spoken of as **homologous**. Thus, as we shall later show, the leaves of a moss plant and of a tree are analogous but not homologous, whereas the scales of a pine cone and the leaves of a maple are presumably homologous.

Characteristics Used as Bases for Plant Classification.—Since we shall be concerned to some extent, in the following chapters, with the relationship of the various plants discussed, we may well mention a few of the characteristics of plants which are used to determine relationship. These vary in their value in different groups of plants.

1. *Cell Structure.*

One of the simplest groups of plants (the blue-green algae or *Myxophyceae*) is made up of individuals, the cells of which, with few exceptions, have no nuclei. There is considerable reason to believe that they are rather closely related to the Bacteria, which are also without definite nuclei. Other examples might be cited in which similarities of cell structure seem to indicate relationship.

2. *Arrangement of Cells.*

In some of the very simple plants, each cell division is followed by a separation of the daughter cells, so that an individual plant consists of a single cell; in other simple plants the cells remain together in pairs; in others they form filaments, sheets of cells, or cell groups of various shapes. Although all these different types of cell arrangement may occur in different groups of plants, they often do indicate the relationship of species within one of these groups.

3. *Presence or Absence of Certain Vegetative Organs and Tissues.*

The possession of roots by all the Pteridophyta is probably an indication that these plants are more closely related among themselves than are any of them to the mosses or other rootless plants. The absence of vessels from the wood of most gymnosperms indicates that these plants are more closely related among themselves than they are to the angiosperms, in most of which vessels occur.

4. *Similarity of Reproductive Structures.*

Comparison of the flower parts or of other structures connected with sexual reproduction is one of the most used and most dependable bases for judgment as to the relationship of plants. The vegetative structures of closely related plants, such as the leaves, may be adapted to very different environmental conditions and so may be dissimilar. Their reproductive structures, on the other hand, being shorter-lived, are subjected for shorter periods to environmental influences. In general, their relation to the environment is not so close and they are therefore less likely to change in response to differences in the environment. Reproductive structures are more conservative than vegetative organs and are therefore more dependable as indicators of relationship.

A decision as to the relationship of two species or plant groups is generally based upon several similar characteristics. A single characteristic, especially if it relate to vegetative structure, is in many cases not considered a safe basis for judging relationship, for similarity or difference in respect to this characteristic may be due to the influence of environment.

Our knowledge of plants is too incomplete for us to work out a
natural classification which will show the real relationships of all plants.
Accordingly, the classifications of plants which we use are in part
natural and in part artificial. Systematic botanists are constantly
endeavoring to increase our knowledge of the evolution of the plants
with which we are acquainted and thus to approach more nearly to the
ideal of a complete natural classification. The following classification
gives the principal groups of plants of which the plant kingdom is
made up.

A Classification of the Plant Kingdom

Scientific Names of the Groups	Common Names
THALLOPHYTA	
Algae	
Myxophyceae	Blue-green Algae
Chlorophyceae	Green Algae
Phaeophyceae	Brown Algae
Rhodophyceae	Red Algae
Fungi	
Schizomycetes	Bacteria
Myxomycetes	Slime Fungi
Phycomycetes	Algal Fungi
Ascomycetes	Sac Fungi
Basidiomycetes	Club Fungi
EMBRYOPHYTA	
Bryophyta	
Hepaticae	Liverworts
Musci	Mosses
Pteridophyta	
Lycopodineae	Club mosses and related plants
Equisetineae	Horse-tails
Filicineae	Ferns
Spermatophyta	
Gymnospermae	Conifers and related plants
Angiospermae	Flowering plants
Dicotyledones	Dicotyledons
Monocotyledones	Monocotyledons

The two divisions (Algae and Fungi) into which the subkingdom
Thallophyta is subdivided are artificial groups based upon the manner
in which these plants secure their food. The algae, with few excep-

tions, are able to carry on photosynthesis and are therefore independent of any other organisms. The fungi, on the other hand, must, like animals, secure their food ready made. That is, the algae are **autophytic** and the fungi **heterophytic.** Actually, however, some of the fungi are no doubt more closely related to some of the algae than they are to certain other species of the fungi, and certain algae are more closely related to certain fungi than they are to certain algae.

A classification which is in many respects preferable to the classification given above places all plants in two large groups, one including the **Thallophyta** and **Bryophyta,** which are non-vascular plants, the other including the **Tracheophyta,** or vascular plants. Within the **Tracheophyta** are the following four sub-groups:

1. **Psilopsida**—most primitive vascular plants, represented chiefly by fossil forms, although a few living forms are in existence.

2. **Lycopsida**—represented by *Lycopodium, Selaginella, Lepidodendron,* and *Isoetes.*

3. **Sphenopsida**—represented by *Equisetum,* and other closely related forms, living and fossil.

4. **Pteropsida**—represented by the ferns, the gymnosperms, and the angiosperms.

CHAPTER XI

THALLOPHYTA—ALGAE

CHARACTERISTICS OF THE THALLOPHYTA

The name Thallophyta means **thallus** plants, a thallus being a plant body without true roots, stems, or leaves. There are, however, thallus plants in other groups besides the Thallophyta, and in some plants belonging to the Thallophyta there are structures which resemble superficially the roots, stems, and leaves of the flowering plants and which perform the same functions, at least in part.

The Thallophyta include plants of great diversity, many of which have little in common save the small size and simplicity of most of them. In size they vary from bacteria, many of which have a diameter of less than 1/2000 millimeter, to the giant brown seaweeds of the California coast, which may be several hundred feet long. Typically, the Thallophyta are aquatic plants, but most of the fungi, though preferring moist locations, do not thrive if submerged in water.

The multiplication and distribution of thallophytes are generally accomplished by means of spores. These are single protoplasts, naked or surrounded with a cell wall, which, after becoming separated from the plants producing them, can develop into new individuals.

Methods of Reproduction.—Within each of the three divisions of the Embryophyta (Bryophyta, Pteridophyta, and Spermatophyta) there is a general similarity in methods of reproduction, but among the motley assemblage making up the Thallophyta there is great variety in this respect. Reproduction in the Thallophyta may be either by the **asexual** or the **sexual** method. In the former method each new individual is the product of a single parent plant, whereas in the sexual method each new individual develops from a cell (the zygote) which is the product of the fusion of two protoplasts generally originating in different parent individuals.

Asexual Reproduction.—Fission.—The simplest form of asexual reproduction is called **fission**. It is restricted to unicellular organisms and is the sole method of reproduction employed by the most primitive plants. It consists merely in the division of a single-celled individual into two new single-celled individuals of equal size. These two new individuals, produced by fission, together contain all the materials of the single parent cell. Organisms which reproduce solely by this method, therefore, never die except as the result of shortage of food or water or other unfavorable external conditions. Natural death (death from old age), such as most plants and animals experience, does not take place among these forms. This is the method by which bacteria and many blue-green algae reproduce.

Asexual Reproduction—by Spores.—Asexual spores may be **non-motile**, or **motile** by means of whip-like filaments of protoplasm called **cilia**.

(*A*) The motile asexual spores are called **zoospores**. There are other motile cells produced by plants, but zoospores are the **only motile protoplasts that are able to develop directly into new individuals**. Zoospores do not have any cell walls but simply consist of a naked mass of protoplasm. In some cases the entire protoplast of a vegetative cell escapes as a single zoospore; in others the protoplast of a vegetative cell divides into two or more protoplasts, each of which develops one or more cilia and becomes a zoospore.

(*B*) Non-motile asexual spores often consist of a vegetative cell which has a thickened wall and may or may not be larger than the vegetative cell. Such spores are produced by *Nostoc, Cylindrospermum,* and other algae. In other cases, especially among the fungi, the non-motile asexual spores are special cells and are produced within an organ called a **sporangium**.

Sexual Reproduction.—The protoplasts which fuse to form the zygote in the process of sexual reproduction are called **gametes** (Fig. 264, *E*). They are almost always naked protoplasts, having no cell wall. In the blue-green algae, in many other simple algae, and in the bacteria there is no sexual reproduction. In the most primitive cases of sexual reproduction in plants, the gametes are all alike in size and structure. Such gametes are called **isogametes**. They are generally motile, having cilia, as do the zoospores. The gametes are, however, usually unable to produce new individuals until they have fused in pairs. It is customary to speak of the fusion of isogametes as **conjugation**, and of the resulting zygote as a **zygospore**. The protoplast of the zygospore forms around itself a cell wall which soon becomes much thickened and protects the protoplast within. The zygospore generally remains in a resting condition for some time before it germinates.

Most Thallophyta and other plants having sexual reproduction do not have isogametes but produce two kinds of gametes (**heterogametes**). These heterogametes may differ merely in size, the smaller ordinarily being more active than the larger. Generally, however, the larger gametes are without cilia and therefore incapable of locomotion. The smaller, active gametes, which are called **male gametes** (**sperms**), are produced in much greater numbers than the larger **female gametes** (**egg cells**) (Figs. 272 and 276). The term **gametangium** is applied to the organ in which gametes are produced, regardless of whether they are male or female. A male **gametangium** is known as an **antheridium** and a female gametangium as a **oogonium**. In plants which produce heterogametes the zygote is formed by the fusion of a **sperm** with an **egg cell,** and not by fusion of two gametes of the same sort. The zygote resulting from the fusion of heterogametes is generally called an **oospore.** The actual fusion is called **fertilization.** In general, we shall use the term zygote for the protoplast formed by the union of gametes whether the fusing gametes be alike or unlike.

The zygotes resulting from the union of unlike gametes generally become surrounded by a thick wall, as do those resulting from the union of like gametes, and in most cases they do not germinate and develop into new plants until after a period of dormancy. Such zygotes, generally germinate in much the same manner as asexual spores. If they are resting spores, capable of remaining dormant for some time, their protoplasm generally contains much less water than does active protoplasm. When the conditions for germination are favorable, water is absorbed through the spore wall by the enclosed protoplast. The resulting swelling of the protoplast ruptures the spore walls, and a part of the protoplasm extrudes through the opening. The protoplasmic projection soon forms an enclosing cell wall which, with the contained protoplasm, is called the **germ tube.** This tube continues to grow, and in most cases its contents divide to form a number of cells from which the new plant develops.

The following is a summary of methods of reproduction in Thallophyta:

Asexual Reproduction (without union of protoplasts).
  (a) Fission—division of a single-celled individual into two new individuals of equal size (Fig. 257).
  (b) Asexual spore formation—motile asexual spores or zoospores (Figs. 264, *G*, and 270) and non-motile asexual spores (Fig. 313).

Sexual Reproduction (with union of protoplasts).
  (a) Conjugation—the fusion of similar gametes (isogametes) to form a zygote (sometimes called a zygospore).

(b) Fertilization—the fusion of dissimilar gametes (heterogametes, sperms and egg cells) to form a zygote (sometimes known as an oospore).

The Thallophyta consist of two groups, the **Algae** and the **Fungi.** The algae are the **autophytic** thallophytes, that is, they are able to build up their own foods out of inorganic materials, such as carbon dioxide, water, and simple mineral substances. The fungi are **heterophytic** thallophytes, that is, they must secure food directly or indirectly from other organisms. Among the algae there are a few species which have lost the ability to make their own food but which show in their structure such unmistakable evidence of close relationship to typical algae that we include them among the algae in spite of their heterophytic habit.

ALGAE

(AUTOPHYTIC THALLOPHYTA)

Characteristics of the Algae.—With very few exceptions, the algae possess chlorophyll, although many of them, particularly the red algae and the brown algae, are not green in color because of other pigments which are associated with the chlorophyll and mask its green color.

The great majority of algae are aquatic, though some grow on soil and a few others on the stems of trees or upon other objects exposed to the air. Algae make up the greater part of the vegetation of the ocean. The free-floating marine plants are generally unicellular forms and are spoken of collectively as the **phytoplankton** of the sea, **plankton** being a collective name for free-floating aquatic animals and plants. Many of those growing near the shore line or in shallow parts of the sea constitute the **phytobenthon** of the sea. (**Benthon** is a collective term for attached aquatic plants and animals.) These plants are mostly algae (" kelps " and other " seaweeds "). Algae are also common in bodies of fresh water, both as plankton and benthon plants. There is a great range of size and complexity among the algae. The smallest are microscopic, unicellular plants and the largest are made up of millions of cells and may be several hundred feet in length. The plant body of these large forms is made up of various organs within which there is considerable differentiation of tissues.

The names of the four classes of the algae are based upon the characteristic differences in color. However, the color differences are not the sole or the most important ones. The members of each class have certain characteristics in common, such as cell structure, reproductive processes, etc., which in general are much more dependable as indicators of relationship than is color. There are in fact some Myxophyceae which are brown, some Chlorophyceae which are red, and some Phaeophyceae and Rhodophyceae which are green.

THE MYXOPHYCEAE—BLUE-GREEN ALGAE

Characteristics of the Myxophyceae.—The plants of this group, which is often spoken of as the **blue-green algae,** are made up of cells which are without definite nuclei or chloroplasts. The pigments of the cells are generally restricted to the outer region of the protoplast, but this colored part is not sharply marked off from the colorless protoplasm within, which is called the **central body.** The central body has been called an " incipient nucleus," and may represent a stage in the evolution of a true nucleus. It contains in all cases granules of chromatin or a similar substance which probably plays the same rôle as the chromatin of the nuclei of most plants. In addition to a mixture of chlorophylls a and b, carotin and xanthophyll, the plants of this group generally contain other pigments (accessory pigments) the commonest of which is a blue pigment called **phycocyanin.** It is soluble in water and can easily be separated from the green pigment, which is not water-soluble and can readily be extracted with alcohol. A red accessory pigment also is present in some forms, so that there are " blue-green " algae which are red. One such form, *Trichodesmium erythraeum,* is a floating marine plant which gives a bright red color to the water when present in large quantities. The Red Sea owes its name to the occasional coloring of its waters by this organism. Almost all Myxophyceae secrete considerable quantities of a gelatinous substance which forms a sheath or matrix around the cells or cell groups. Sexual reproduction does not occur in the Myxophyceae. It has been definitely shown that certain species of this group of plants are able to fix atmospheric nitrogen, that is to say, to force the element, nitrogen, into union with other elements and thus utilize it in their own metabolism. Certain bacteria also have this power of fixing nitrogen, but most plants are unable to make any use of the free (uncombined) nitrogen of the air.

Distribution of the Myxophyceae.—These plants are abundant in fresh and in brackish water and many forms are found in the sea. They are important elements in the plankton and benthon. A number of forms are abundant in moist soil. They form the principal vegetation of hot springs, where they have been found living in water at a temperature as high as 87° C. A few plankton forms are exceedingly troublesome in reservoirs, giving a disagreeable flavor to the water.

Certain of the Myxophyceae are associated with fungi in the formation of lichens, although most lichens are associations of green algae (Chlorophyceae) and fungi. This association of autophytic and heterophytic organisms in the lichens is believed to be of mutual benefit. Such a relation between two organisms involving benefit to both is called **symbiosis**. The food of lichens must clearly be supplied by the algal component, but the fungus is believed to assist the alga by reason of its ability to absorb moisture from the air and retain it tenaciously. Colonies of certain blue-green algae grow within the thallus of *Anthoceros*, one of the Bryophyta, and in the roots of a spermatophyte, *Cycas*. It is doubtful whether the relation in these two cases is one of mutual benefit.

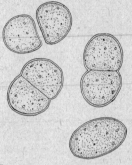

Fig. 257.—*Synechocystis*. A blue-green alga the cells of which are solitary except during fission. Several stages of fission are shown as well as a single cell about ready for division.

In moist regions Myxophyceae are abundant on the trunks and branches of trees and on rocks, and their presence is an important factor in the coloration of the landscape. In waters which are contaminated by sewage or which contain large quantities of organic matter from other sources, the blue-green algae are often abundant.

Habits and Life History of Representatives of the Myxophyceae.—The simplest members of this group consist of single cells which are generally spherical or oval. Such a form is *Synechocystis* (Fig. 257). When a single *Synechocystis* individual has grown to a certain size, it divides into two cells of equal size and these soon become separated from each other. Thus one individual gives rise to two. The two new individuals grow in size until they in turn undergo division, and thus four new *Synechocystis* plants are formed. This is a form of asexual reproduction called **fission** which is the simplest form of reproduction. Each of the new unicellular *Synechocystis* plants is able to carry on all the essential life processes.

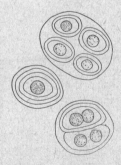

Fig. 258.—*Gloeocapsa*, blue-green alga the cells of which occur generally in groups, the cells formed by the fission of a single cell being held together by the gelatinous coating of the cell from which they came.

They generally live either immersed in water or in very moist habitats where they are wet most of the time. Through the surface of the cell the protoplast within absorbs water, inorganic salts, and the gases carbon dioxide and oxygen. By photosynthesis the protoplast forms carbohydrates which, as in the higher plants, are used in part for respiration and in part for the formation of substances from which new protoplasm can be built up. As we have seen, reproduction also is carried on by each of these solitary unicellular plants.

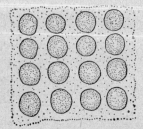

FIG. 259.—*Merismopedia*, a blue-green alga the cells of which are held together by a gelatinous matrix. The cells divide in two planes only and as a result the groups of cells have the form of flat plates. These may grow to considerable size and consist of scores of cells.

In some forms, such as *Gloeocapsa*, which are otherwise not much different from *Synechocystis*, the cell wall is thick and gelatinous but of such consistency that after fission the daughter cells are held within the wall of the parent cell. Each of these cells produces in turn a gelatinous coating of its own. Even after the fission of these daughter cells the jelly-like layer derived from the single cell from which they have arisen may remain intact. Thus we find in a mass of *Gloeocapsa* (Fig. 258), groups of two, four, eight, or even more cells, together with single cells which have been released by the disorganization of the mucilaginous matrix. The cells of a group are entirely independent of the other cells of the same group and are able to carry on all the necessary life processes if freed from any connection with the other cells. *Merismopedia* (Fig. 259) is another blue-green alga the cells of which are held together by a gelatinous matrix. In this form, cell divisions take place alternately in two planes which are at right angles to each other. There results a plate or sheet of cells, one cell thick, and these groups, in which the cells are very regularly arranged, may attain considerable size.

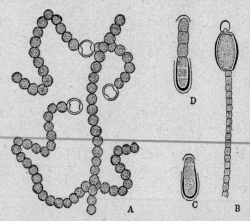

FIG. 260.—*A*, *Nostoc*, filament with heterocysts; *B*, *Cylindrospermum* filament showing terminal heterocyst and thick-walled resting spore; *C* and *D*, germinating resting spores.

In *Nostoc* and *Oscillatoria* the divisions are all in parallel planes, so that from one cell by a succession of divisions a chain or filament of cells arises. In *Nostoc* many hundreds of these filaments are united within a mass of jelly produced by the cells. In some species of *Nostoc* these gelatinous colonies may reach a diameter of 10 or 12 cm. Here and there in *Nostoc* filaments there are enlarged and colorless spherical or barrel-shaped cells called **heterocysts** (Fig. 260). The filaments seem to break apart easily where there is heterocyst, and the resulting short filaments, which are called **hormogonia** (singular, hormogonium), may grow into long filaments by fission of their cells. In *Nostoc* and some other genera the heterocysts appear to facilitate the formation of hormogonia, but there are several genera in which the heterocysts are terminal (borne at the ends of the filaments), and there are a number of genera which have no heterocysts and yet form hormogonia freely. The hormogonia of some species are capable of locomotion and can creep out of the gelatinous matrix and give rise to new colonies. Besides the ordinary oval or spherical vegetative cells, and the heterocysts, a third kind of cell is sometimes found in *Nostoc* filaments (Fig. 260). These are the resting cells, or spores, which are formed from ordinary cells by increase in size, accumulation of reserve food, and thickening of the wall. These spores are probably much more resistant to water shortage and unfavorable temperatures than are the ordinary cells. When conditions favorable to the growth of *Nostoc* return, the thick-walled resting cells, or asexual spores, germinate and a new filament is formed.

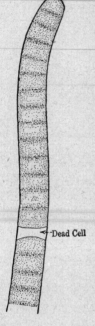

←—Dead Cell

FIG. 261.—A portion of a filament of *Oscillatoria*, one of the commonest blue-green algae. The divisions of the cells take place in parallel planes so that the cell groups are filamentous and unbranched. As the result of the death of a cell here and there, the filament breaks up into short pieces called hormogonia.

Another filamentous blue-green alga, which is exceedingly common is *Oscillatoria* (Fig. 261). The cells, with the exception of those at the ends of the filament, have the form of short cylinders, which may even be much shorter than they are wide. The terminal cells are generally rounded at the free end, because the turgor of these cells is not balanced by the turgor of an adjacent cell as it is in the case of cells within the filament. The most striking characteristic of *Oscillatoria* is the fact that the filaments are capable of a swaying or oscillating movement, to which the plant owes its name, and of a twisting or rotating motion. In addition, the filaments can move from place to place, so that if a mass of *Oscillatoria* is placed upon a wet surface the threads soon spread out into a uniform film. Neither spores nor heterocysts are formed in *Oscillatoria*. Hormogonia are formed by the death of a cell or of a group of cells here and there in the filament.

Although in *Nostoc* and *Oscillatoria*, the cells are arranged in groups or colonies of definite and characteristic form, and although there may be some differentiation of cells (ordinary vegetative cells, spores, heterocysts), the ordinary cells, if separated from each other without mechanical injury, could doubtless live just as well as isolated cells as they do in the groups. These plants are probably to be considered rather as colonies of unicellular plants than as multicellular individuals.

THE CHLOROPHYCEAE—GREEN ALGAE

Characteristics of the Chlorophyceae.—All the plants included in this group have chloroplasts and definite nuclei. These two characteristics distinguish the Chlorophyceae from the blue-green algae but not from the red or brown algae.

Most of the green algae have only those pigments which are typically present in green cells—**chlorophyll a** and **chlorophyll b**, **carotin**, and **xanthophyll** (see pages 55 and 209). In most of them starch is the first visible product of photosynthesis, although some produce no starch and have oil as their principal reserve food.

Distribution of Chlorophyceae.—Members of this group are found in every conceivable moist place where the temperature is not very high and where light can penetrate. The larger number are fresh-water plankton or benthon plants, but many are marine. There are a number of green algae which are commonly found in soil, but they can live, of course, only very near the surface. A few green algae, such as the common *Protococcus* and *Trentepohlia*, are epiphytes on the bark of trees or attached to fence posts or other objects.

A green alga resembling *Protococcus* is the autophytic component of most lichens, growing in symbiosis with a fungus. There are a few simple green algae which are regularly found in the bodies of certain primitive animals such as the sponges. Some actually live within the cells of animals, as does the alga *Chlorella* in the cells which line the body cavity of the hydra (*Hydra viridis*).

Habits and Life Histories of Representatives of the Chlorophyceae.—We shall not attempt to discuss the various groups which are included in the Chlorophyceae but shall instead give a brief account of the structure and reproduction of the few forms listed below:

1. Forms which, as far as is known, are without sexual reproduction or zoospore formation—*Protococcus* and *Scenedesmus*.

2. Forms which produce isogametes and zoospores—*Ulothrix*.

3. Forms which produce isogametes but no zoospores—*Spirogyra* and the Desmids.

4. Forms which produce heterogametes and zoospores—*Oedogonium* and *Vaucheria*.

Protococcus.—*Protococcus viridis* is probably the commonest green alga in the world. It is found everywhere in the temperate parts of both hemispheres except where the climate is very dry. It forms a green coating on rocks, fence posts, and the trunks and branches of

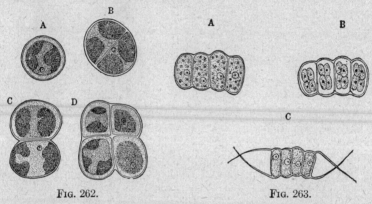

FIG. 262.   FIG. 263.

FIG. 262.—*Protococcus*, a simple green alga, in which the cells remain united for some time after fission, forming groups of varying size and cell number.

FIG. 263.—*Scenedesmus*, a simple green alga without zoospores or gametes, the cells of which form colonies of four (less commonly eight) cells attached side by side. *A* and *C*, two common species. *B*, the first of these giving rise to four new colonies.

trees. This coating is generally restricted to the most shaded and therefore the most moist side of trunks, branches, and fence posts, which in the north temperate zone is frequently the north side. In many locations the direction of the prevailing winds is such that the north side is not the most moist and the growth of *Protococcus* is not principally on the north side.

The cells of this plant have walls which are quite thick. The protoplast has a definite nucleus with nuclear membrane and a single large distinct chloroplast. This is a lobed structure which partly lines the inside of the cell wall. The large lobes are easily mistaken for separate chloroplasts.

Among *Protococcus* individuals examined under the microscope there will be found solitary cells which are generally spherical in form, groups of two cells, or four cells, and, rarely, of more than four. Where the cells of a group are in contact with one another they are flattened. The groups of two and of four cells arise by successive divisions of one of the solitary spherical cells. The divisions may take place in three planes.

The different cells of the groups eventually become separated from one another, round off, and then undergo division again and form other groups. Reproduction in *Protococcus* is then by fission, and each cell is to be considered as an individual plant, though the separation of the cells of a group is often long delayed.

The cells of *Protococcus* are remarkably resistant to drought, and are able to absorb water from moist air. When the air is dry the life processes go on at a very low rate, but when the cells are wet by rain or heavy dew or are exposed to moist air, they are able to resume photosynthesis and other vital processes.

Ulothrix.—The genus *Ulothrix* is an example of a form having sexual reproduction by isogametes and also asexual reproduction by means of zoospores. It is an unbranched filamentous alga. Some species of the genus grow in fresh water and others in the sea. It is of particular interest because it illustrates how sexual reproduction may have originated. The filaments of *Ulothrix* are made up of short cells, each with a single nucleus and with the single chloroplast in the form of a band around the middle of the cell.

In *Ulothrix* the basal cell of the filament is colorless, elongated and narrowed at the base and forms a **holdfast** (Fig. 264, *A*). Here is a simple case of specialization of one cell of a cell group for a function not performed by other cells of the group. In this we have what seems to be the beginning of the development of the multicellular type of plant.

Under certain conditions, not yet well understood, some or all of the cells of the *Ulothrix* filament except the holdfast cell may give rise to zoospores. The whole protoplast of a cell of a filament may form a single zoospore or it may divide into two, four, or eight protoplasts, or sometimes as many as sixteen or thirty-two protoplasts, each of which becomes a zoospore. In any case there is a contraction and rounding up of the protoplasts and development of four cilia by each zoospore (Fig. 264, *C*). Soon after their formation the zoospores generally escape from the filament by an opening which is formed in the lateral wall, and start to swim about in the water. They may continue in active motion for from one to several days and may travel a considerable distance during that time. Finally they cease their movement and attach themselves at the ciliated end to some other alga, to a stone, or to some other object in the water. Following this the cilia are lost and a cell wall is formed, and then by elongation and division the zoospore develops into a new filament (Fig. 264).

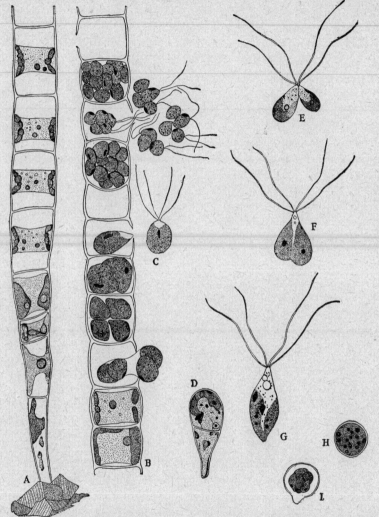

FIG. 264.—*Ulothrix zonata.* *A,* a portion of a filament showing the holdfast cell at the base, and the ordinary vegetative cells. *B,* a portion of a filament which has formed gametes in three cells (above) and zoospores in four cells (below). The gametes are generally smaller than the zoospores and always bear two cilia each, the zoospores each have four cilia. *C,* a zoospore which has just escaped. *D,* a germinating zoospore. *E, F* and *G,* stages in the fusion of gametes. *H,* a zygote in the resting condition. *I,* germinating zygote showing the division of its protoplast into a number of zoospores. (*A–D* after Dodel *E–H* after Oltmanns.)

Ulothrix reproduces not only asexually by means of zoospores, but sexually by the fusion of gametes in pairs to form zygotes. The formation of the gametes in *Ulothrix* is very similar to the process of zoospore formation. The gametes arise from divisions of the protoplasts of the cells of the filament, but are generally smaller than the zoospores. They escape from the cell in the same manner as the zoospores and like them are without a cell wall.

The gametes swim about for a time and then fuse (conjugate) in pairs, but fusion takes place only between gametes produced in different filaments. The resulting fusion cell, or zygote, remains motile for a short time but soon comes to rest and secretes a thick wall about itself (Fig. 264).

The zygotes of *Ulothrix* generally remain in a resting condition during the period of the year unfavorable to vegetative activity and later germinate, each producing a number (four to sixteen) of zoospores, or in some cases non-motile spores, which then develop into new individuals.

The nuclei of the zoospores of *Ulothrix*, and also those of the gametes, have n chromosomes. The zygote nucleus has $2n$ chromosomes, but the first division of the zygote nucleus is a reduction division. The zygote nucleus is therefore the only nucleus produced in the life cycle which has the $2n$ chromosome number.

The following points in the reproduction of *Ulothrix* are of special significance:

1. Zoospores and gametes are similar in origin and both are naked, motile protoplasts.
2. Zoospores and gametes differ only in size, in the number of cilia, and in the fact that the latter must fuse before a new plant can be produced. The gametes are isogametes.
3. Zoospores produce new plants at once; the zygotes are resistant spores which can withstand unfavorable conditions and normally germinate only after a period of rest. The zygote nucleus has $2n$ chromosomes.
4. Zygotes do not give rise to new filaments directly, but when they germinate they divide repeatedly and form a number of zoospores or non-motile spores which then produce new filaments. The first division of the zygote nucleus is a reduction division.

Sea lettuce, or *Ulva*, is a rather close relative of *Ulothrix*. It is common along the coast in many parts of the world. Its plant body is not filamentous but has the form of a thin sheet of cells attached at one end. *Ulva* resembles *Ulothrix* in the relatively slight differentiation between zoospores and gametes.

Spirogyra.—In the common alga, *Spirogyra*, one of the free-floating, fresh water algae known as " pond scum " (Fig. 265), we have a representative of a group of algae which produces no zoospores and whose sexual reproduction is isogamous, that is, by the union of similar gametes.

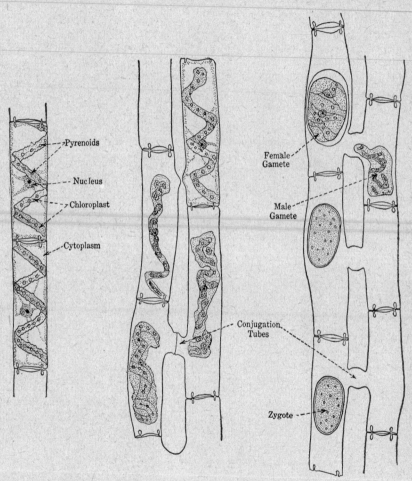

Fig. 265.—*Spirogyra.*   To the left two cells from a filament in the vegetative condition.   The other two figures show successive stages in scalariform conjugation.

The filaments of *Spirogyra* are surrounded by a layer of mucilage which can sometimes be seen under favorable illumination and which gives a characteristic slimy feel to the plant by which it and closely related forms can be easily recognized in the field.

The most characteristic feature of *Spirogyra* is the spirally arranged ribbon-like chloroplast.   Certain species have but one chloroplast in a cell while others have several chloroplasts and some may have as many as fourteen.   The chloroplast commonly has a lobed or toothed margin. Here and there along the middle of the chloroplasts are conspicuous pyrenoids (nodule-like protein bodies around which starch is deposited) which are connected by a ridge on the inner side of the chlorophyll band.

The *Spirogyra* cell is cylindrical in form and is lined by a thin layer of cytoplasm in which the chloroplast or chloroplasts are embedded. The nucleus with the cytoplasm which surrounds it is suspended in the center of the single large vacuole, either by fine strands, or by a narrow band, of cytoplasm.

The *Spirogyra* filament grows by the elongation and division of all the cells in the filament.   Division generally takes place at night.   The nucleus divides by mitosis, and then the two-nucleate protoplast is cut in two by a ring of cellulose which grows inward from the outer wall and which finally becomes a disc separating the two new cells.

Reproduction.—No zoospores or other non-sexual spores are produced by *Spirogyra*.   However, in some species of *Spirogyra* the cells of the filaments may become separated from one another by softening of the middle lamella of the end walls and each may then grow into a new filament.

In *Spirogyra* the gametes are the protoplasts of ordinary vegetative cells, and are not ciliated.   In most cases conjugation takes place between the cells of two *different* filaments.   This is called **scalariform** (ladder-like) **conjugation** (Fig. 265).   Conjugation may also take place between adjoining cells of the *same* filament.   This is known as **lateral conjugation** (Fig. 266).   In scalariform conjugation, short papillae are produced on the adjacent sides of the cells of filaments where they are in contact with each other.   These papillae or short outgrowths from cells which lie opposite one another in the two filaments become attached at their ends and elongate, pushing the filaments apart. Finally the end walls of the outgrowths of the conjugating cells are dissolved away and the cell cavities then communicate with each other through the open tube (**conjugation tube**) which connects them.   Meanwhile, the protoplasts which are to fuse contract somewhat.   Then the protoplasts (gametes) from one filament pass over into the cells of the other filament and fusion of gametes takes place.   Though the gametes are morphologically alike and therefore are considered to be isogametes, the fact that the gametes in one filament remain passive and those in the other are capable of movement indicates a slight physiological differentiation of gametes.   In certain species of the genus *Zygnema*, which is closely related to *Spirogyra*, both gametes pass into the conjugating tube and join there. In this case, the gametes show no trace of sexual differentiation.

In *lateral conjugation* of *Spirogyra*, a passage is formed between adjoining cells of a filament, either by a conjugating tube developed near the adjoining ends of the conjugating cells or by an opening through the end wall separating these cells. Through this passage alternate protoplasts move into their neighboring cells. If all the cells of a filament have conjugated by the lateral method, alternate cells of the filament are empty after conjugation and alternate cells contain zygotes. However, when all the cells of two filaments conjugate by the *scalariform method*, one filament becomes empty and every cell of the other filament contains a zygote except in cases in which, because of difference in length of the cells of the two conjugating filaments or for other reasons, an occasional gamete fails to conjugate. A gamete which fails to unite with another gamete generally develops into a thick-walled spore, just as do the zygotes, and may upon germination give rise to a new filament. The thick wall of the zygote consists of three cellulose layers, of which the middle one contains some chitin. The zygote when first formed contains abundant starch

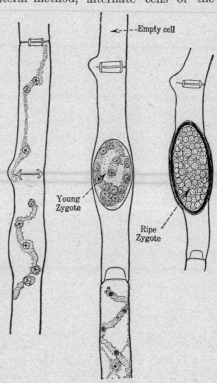

FIG. 266.—*Spirogyra*, showing three stages in lateral conjugation.

which is soon converted into oil. This serves as the food reserve of the spore. The zygote does not generally germinate very soon after it matures. It is probably resistant to conditions of drought and low temperature which would kill the vegetative cells. It generally falls to the bottom of the pond or stream where it is formed, and after a period of rest (generally until the following spring) it germinates. Germination is probably dependent upon conditions favorable for the vegetative activities of *Spirogyra*, that is, abundance of water, mode-

rate temperature, and sufficient illumination.   When the zygote germinates (Fig. 267) it absorbs water, and the protoplast within increases
in size and bursts the outer and middle walls of the
spore; the inner cellulose wall becomes extended (as
the protoplast pushes out) to form a tube which
elongates into a new filament.

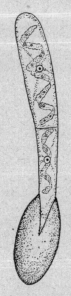

The nuclear changes involved in the fusion of
gametes, the germination of the zygote, and the
early stages of growth into a new filament are interesting and significant.   The nucleus of the zygote
contains chromatin derived from the gametes and
has $2n$ chromosomes.   It soon undergoes division
and the resulting nuclei again divide, so that
the zygote has four nuclei.   One of these two
nuclear divisions is a reduction division, in which
the chromosome number is reduced to the normal number for ordinary cells of the species (Fig.
268).   Three of these nuclei disintegrate, so that
the mature zygote has but a single nucleus, with
" n " chromosomes.

Fig. 267.—Germi-
nation of a zygote
of *Spirogyra*.

The significant points in the reproduction of
Spirogyra are as follows:

1. No zoospores are produced and no other
non-sexual spores are formed except that a gamete
which is prevented from fusing with another gamete may function
as a spore.

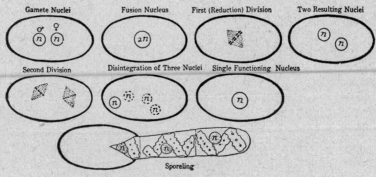

Fig. 268.—Diagrams showing nuclear changes in the zygote of *Spirogyra* from conjugation to germination.

2. The gametes are the protoplasts of ordinary vegetative cells.
3. Characteristic conjugating tubes connect pairing cells.

4. The gametes are morphologically alike (isogametes) but show a beginning of differentiation since half of them are capable of movement, the other half being non-motile.

5. The chromosome number ($2n$ in the fusion nucleus of the zygote) is reduced to n by one of two divisions of the fusion nucleus which take place in the zygote before germination. Three of the four n nuclei thus formed in the zygote disintegrate.

6. Zygotes give rise to new filaments directly.

Desmids.—Belonging to the same order as *Spirogyra* is a group of beautiful unicellular plants, called *desmids*. For the most part these grow solitary, but sometimes they remain attached after division, and thus form filamentous colonies. Some species are common in the fresh-water plankton. One of the most familiar is the crescent-shaped *Closterium*, which is frequently found among filamentous green algae. The most striking feature of this genus is the presence of a small spherical vacuole at each of the extremities of the cells. Within each of these vacuoles is a group of minute crystals of calcium sulphate or gypsum which are in constant vibration. The movement of these crystals is not a vital phenomenon but is the so-called Brownian movement, which can be observed when any very finely divided insoluble substance suspended in water is examined under the microscope. It results from the vibration of the molecules of the surrounding liquid. These molecules are constantly moving and when they strike against one another they rebound. Some of them strike against the suspended particles and tend to displace them, but since the molecular bombardment is from all sides, suspended particles are not caused to move except when they are of very small size. Then, as in the case of these gypsum crystals, a larger number of impacts on one side than on the other will cause a small particle to be displaced, only to be pushed in another direction in the next instant. These vibrating crystals are, however, not found in most desmids.

With the exception of a few species the cells of desmids consist of two similar halves, **semi-cells,** in each of which there is a single chloroplast consisting of radiating plates. Most desmids have a constriction, called the **isthmus,** between the two semi-cells. Many species are capable of locomotion. Multiplication results from the division of the desmid into two cells, each consisting of one of the previous semi-cells. Then each of these halves develops another semi-cell and thus two complete desmids are formed.

Desmids may also reproduce sexually. Generally the desmids come together in pairs, the cells break at the isthmus, the protoplasts of each pair of desmids fuse and then a thick wall is formed about the resulting zygote, which, after a resting period, germinates generally to form two new desmids. This is clearly not a method of multiplication, for from two desmids one zygote is produced and this in turn gives rise to only two desmids. The formation of a resistant zygote may be of advantage in tiding the plant over a period unfavorable

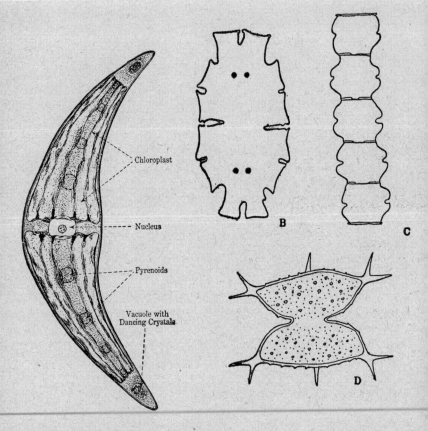

Fig. 269.—Desmids. *A, Closterium*, showing the cell contents. *B*, and *D*, two other forms showing the two semi-cells and the constriction (the isthmus) between the semi-cells, two features which are characteristic of most desmids. *C*, desmids united in a filament or chain.

to the existence of the vegetative cells. It is also not unlikely that the mingling of protoplasm from two plants may result in increased vigor. In the case of those few desmids whose nuclear changes during zygote formation and germination have been studied, the nuclear behavior is similar to that described for *Spirogyra*.

Oedogonium.—*Oedogonium* is a common unbranched, filamentous green alga which reproduces by means of zoospores and also by unlike gametes. It is a plant with more differentiation among its cells than any form thus far discussed. The young plants grow attached to other immersed water plants or to other objects in the water. They may become detached and free-floating when older. The basal cell of an attached filament forms an organ of attachment, or **holdfast**. Gametes are not produced in ordinary vegetative cells, as in *Ulothrix* and *Spirogyra*, but in special cells called gametangia, much different in form from the vegetative cells although developed from them. On

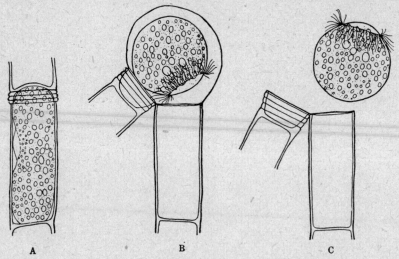

Fig. 270.—Formation and escape of a zoospore in a species of *Oedogonium*. (Redrawn from Hirn.)

account of this physiological division of labor, *Oedogonium* may well be considered a truly multicellular plant.

The vegetative cells of *Oedogonium* contain a single nucleus and a chloroplast. The chloroplast differs somewhat in form in different species but it is generally reticulate (in the form of a net). The zoospores produced by *Oedogonium* are green in color and consist of the entire protoplast of a vegetative cell. They are provided with a ring or collar of cilia around the colorless forward end. Generally only a few cells of a filament produce these motile spores. Following its escape from the cell in which it is formed (Fig. 270), the zoospore swims about for some time and finally comes to rest in contact with some solid object, attaches itself by the ciliated end, loses its cilia, and forms a cellulose wall. It then elongates somewhat and by repeated cell division and growth of the resulting cells develops into a new filament. The basal cell remains colorless and develops at the lower end a disc-like or branched holdfast.

Sexual Reproduction.—The male gametes, or sperms, of *Oedogonium* are much smaller than the female gametes, or eggs. The latter are without cilia and remain within the female gametangium (oogonium) until after fertilization. The sperms are like miniature zoospores in form and are produced in much larger numbers than are the egg cells. In some (**homothallic**) species of *Oedogonium* the male gametangia (also called antheridia) are produced in the same filament as the female gametangia, and in other (**heterothallic**) species the two kinds of gametangia are borne on different filaments. In either case the female gametangia are spherical or oval cells. After the development of the female gamete or egg, a pore or a slit is formed, by the dissolution of a small area of the oogonium wall, through which the sperm may enter. The female gametangia develop from cells which are at first similar in their appearance to the ordinary vegetative cells. When the female gametangium has been formed, the protoplast within shrinks away from the wall and a portion of the egg cell near the pore becomes clear and free from chlorophyll. This is the receptive spot where fusion with the sperm takes place. The sperms are liberated from the male gametangia, where they are produced singly or in pairs.

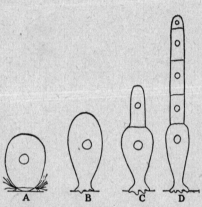

FIG. 271.—Germination of a zoospore of *Oedogonium* diagrammatically represented.

Fertilization.—Some time after the entrance of the sperm into the egg cell, a thick wall is formed about the zygote. The contents lose their chlorophyll, and the starch in the zygote is converted into oil. Decay of the oogonium wall releases the zygote, which is resistant to conditions unfavorable to the vegetative cells. It should be borne in mind that the zygote nucleus contains the chromatin from the nuclei of both the sperm and egg and that when it undergoes mitosis, twice as many chromosomes will appear as are characteristic of the nuclei of the vegetative cells.

Germination of the Zygote.—After a period of rest the zygote will germinate if conditions of moisture, temperature, etc., are favorable

(Fig. 271). The zygote absorbs water, its wall softens, and the proto-plast within increases in size. Then the nucleus divides twice in succession and four protoplasts are formed. Each of these produces a ring of cilia and becomes a zoospore. Thus from each zygote four new individuals may arise. One of the two divisions of the $2n$ nucleus of the zygote which result in the formation of the four zoospores is a reduction division, and the resulting nuclei have half the number of chromosomes which appear at the beginning of the first division of the zygote nucleus.

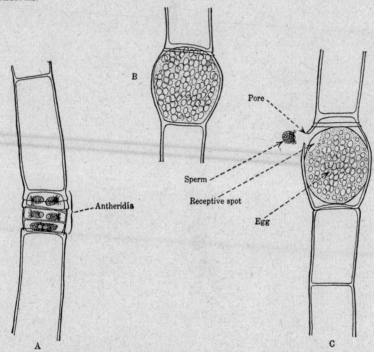

Fig. 272.—*Oedogonium.* *A*, portion of a male filament showing several antheridia. *B*, an immature oogonium. *C*, part of a female filament showing a ripe oogonium, the egg cell of which is about to be fertilized. For the ripe oospore and the structure of a vegetative cell, see Fig. 274, *A*. *C* somewhat diagrammatic.

Production of Dwarf Males.—In certain species of *Oedogonium* the individuals that produce the male gametangia consist of very short and narrow filaments, generally of only two to four cells. These are called **dwarf males.** They are attached to the female plants and thus grow epiphytically. They arise from special zoospores which are smaller than those which give rise to the female filaments, and are formed in special sporangia, called **androsporangia** (Fig. 274, *C*), which are similar in form to the antheridia. These drawf males are generally found in considerable numbers attached to the outside of the female gametangia or to adjacent cells of the female filament.

Significant Facts Relative to the Structure and Life History of Oedogonium:

1. The gametes are heterogametes (sperms and eggs). The female gametes are large, non-motile, well stored with food, relatively few in numbers as compared with the sperms, and are retained within the female gametangium until after fertilization.

2. The cells of the filaments are not alike as in *Oscillatoria* or *Spirogyra*, but in addition to the or-

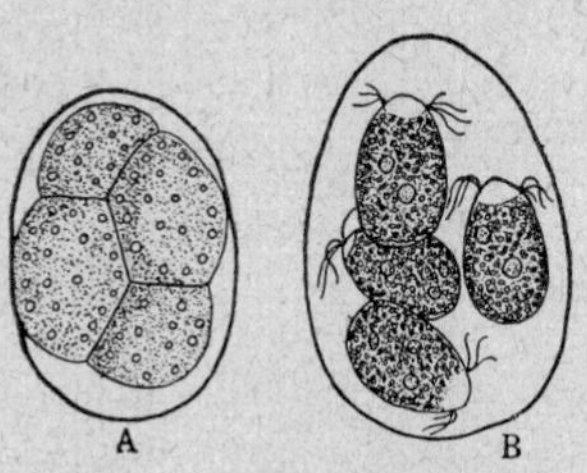

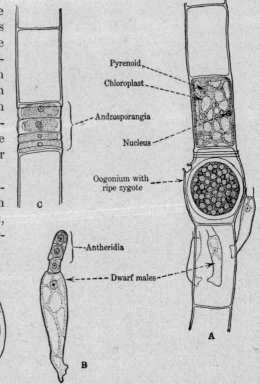

FIG. 273.   FIG. 274.

FIG. 273.—Germination of zygote of *Oedogonium.* A, the protoplast of the zygote which has divided into four protoplasts. B, the four zoospores formed from the four protoplasts. The zygote has a nucleus with "2n" chromosomes, the zoospores having nuclei with "n" chromosomes.

FIG. 274.—A species of *Oedogonium* which produces dwarf males. A, portion of an oogonial filament showing the structure of a vegetative cell, an oogonium containing a ripe zygote and three dwarf males which have discharged their sperms. B, a single dwarf male showing the holdfast cell at the base and the antheridia. C, a portion of a filament with androsporangia within which are developing androspores (zoospores which germinate and give rise to dwarf males).

dinary vegetative cells there are special cells which serve as organs of attachment, in some species special cells to which the function of producing new cells is restricted and cells which develop into the gametangia.

3. The zoospores and sperms are multiciliate and are very similar

except that the sperms are much smaller than the zoospores. This resemblance is in accord with the hypothesis that gametes originated from zoospores.

4. As usual, the zoospores germinate at once and serve as a means of multiplication and distribution, while the zygotes, like those of *Ulothrix* and *Spirogyra*, are resting cells which can resist conditions unfavorable to the vegetative cells and which can remain inactive for long periods. They are to be considered a means of tiding the plant over periods unfavorable to growth and food-making, rather than as a means of multiplication and dispersal.

5. The zygote at germination produces four zoospores, each of which may develop into a new *Oedogonium* plant. One of the two nuclear divisions which result in the formation of the nuclei of these four zoospores is a reduction division so that the $2n$ chromosome number of the zygote nucleus is reduced to half that number in the nuclei of the zoospores and the cells of the filaments which develop from them.

Vaucheria.—Another very common alga, which like *Oedogonium* produces heterogametes and reproduces asexually by zoospores, is the so-called " water felt," *Vaucheria*. In the structure of the plant body and of the gametangia and zoospores it is very different from *Oedogonium*.

Most of the species of *Vaucheria* grow in fresh water or on moist soil, although there are a few marine species. It generally grows attached, often forming dense mats of branched filaments. The plant body consists of a branched tube having no cross walls except those which cut off the parts (zoosporangia and gametangia) within which the zoospores and gametes are produced.

The tubular filament is lined with a continuous layer of cytoplasm in which there are embedded many ellipsoidal chloroplasts and numerous minute nuclei. A large central vacuole occupies the center of the filament. Plants like *Vaucheria*, whose protoplasm is continuous and multinucleate and without any division by walls into separate protoplasts, are called **coenocytes**. Starch is lacking in *Vaucheria*, but small drops of oil are abundant in the cytoplasm. The filaments of *Vaucheria* are relatively weak and easily crushed on account of the absence of cross walls.

Zoospore Formation.—The zoospores of *Vaucheria*, which are multinucleate, are produced singly at the tips of the filaments, in zoosporangia (Fig. 275) which are cut off by transverse walls from the rest of the filament. The protoplasm of the zoosporangium contracts from the wall and produces a great number of cilia which arise in pairs. There is a nucleus near the base of each pair of cilia and not far below the surface of the zoospore. The center of the zoospore is occupied by a single large vacuole. *Vaucheria* is unusual in that it produces a coenocytic zoospore. The zoospores of all other genera closely related to it are relatively small, biciliate protoplasts with a single nucleus and are produced in large numbers in a single sporangium. It seems likely that the zoospore of *Vaucheria* is to be considered as the undivided contents of a single sporangium.

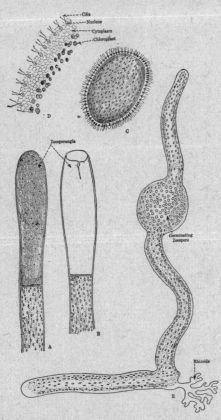

This compound zoospore is large enough to be visible to the naked eye. It escapes by the rupture of the wall at the end of the sporangium, and after swimming about for a relatively short time it comes to rest, withdraws its cilia, forms a cell wall and germinates by sending out one or more tubes which develop into typical *Vaucheria* filaments. A much-branched, colorless organ of attachment may be developed by the filament where it comes in contact with some solid object.

Sexual Reproduction.—All the fresh-water species of *Vaucheria* are homothallic, that is, male and female gametangia (antheridia and oogonia) are produced on the same filament. The gametangia are produced from short side branches of a vegetative filament. The male gametangium is an elongated curved structure. Its multinucleate protoplasm is cut off by a transverse wall from the protoplasm of the vegetative part of the plant. The protoplasm of the male gametangia divides into a number of uninucleate protoplasts, each of which develops into a pear-shaped sperm with two

Fig. 275.—Asexual reproduction of *Vaucheria sessile*. *A*, zoosporangium the contents of which will develop into a zoospore. *B*, zoosporangium from which the zoospore has escaped. *C*, a zoospore. *D*, a portion of the peripheral zone of a zoospore. *E*, young plant developing from germinating zoospore. (Redrawn, *A*, *B*, after Gotz; *C*, after Strasburger; *D*, after Sachs; *E*, after Oltmanns.)

cilia on the side (laterally), not at the end.   The sperms escape by
the dissolution of the end wall of the gametangium.

The protoplasm of the oval oogonial branch is at first multinucleate,
but before the female gametangium is cut off from the rest of the plant,
all the nuclei except
one return to the fila-
ment.   After the for-
mation of the wall
which separates it
from the main fila-
ment, the contents of
the female gametan-
gium contract.   A
"beak" is formed at
the end of the oogo-
nium, and through
this an opening is
formed by which the
sperm may enter to
fertilize the egg cell.

After fertilization
the zygote forms a
thick wall and under-
goes a resting period
of several months.   A
large amount of oil is
present in the resting
zygote.   Upon ger-
mination it produces
a new filament di-
rectly.   Reduction di-
vision has not yet been
observed.

The following
points in the reproduc-
tion of *Vaucheria* are
of special importance:

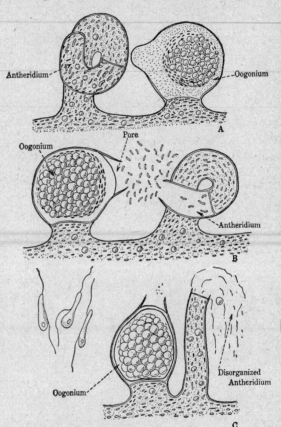

Fig. 276.—Sexual reproduction in *Vaucheria sessilis*.   *A*,
gametangia before fertilization.   The antheridium not
yet mature, the oogonium mature and ready for
fertilization.   Note the cytoplasm of the egg protruding through the pore.   *B*, just after the escape
of the sperms and the fertilization of the egg.   *C*, some
time after fertilization, showing the thick-walled
zygote within the oogonium and the disorganized
antheridium.   To the left of *C*, several sperms.   (Redrawn after Sachs.)

1. The zoospores
are produced in spo-
rangia at the tips of the filaments.

2. The zoospores are coenocytic and multiciliate.

3. The zoospores develop directly into typical *Vaucheria* filaments.

4. Male and female gametangia are produced on short side branches of vegetative filaments and are separated from the rest of the plant by cross walls.

5. A single uninucleate egg is produced in each female gametangium, and numerous uninucleate, biciliate sperms in each male gametangium.

6. The zygote becomes surrounded with a thick wall and, after a resting period, germinates and produces a new filament directly, without zoospore formation.

Other Green Algae.—Systematic botanists have divided the Chlorophyceae into a number of smaller groups, each of which seems to have evolved independently from some ancestors which were probably unicellular motile plants. Within several of these smaller groups it is possible to find series of genera which indicate the development from very simple forms without sexual reproduction, through forms of more complexity and with isogamous sexual reproduction, to forms in which the gametes are differentiated into

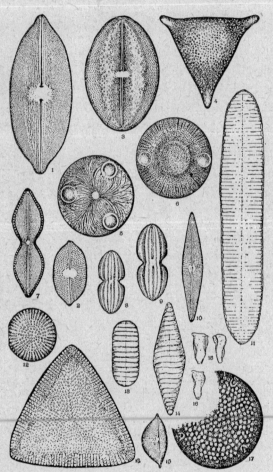

Fig. 277.—Diatoms (all highly magnified) showing various forms and markings. (From Wolle's *Diatomaceae of North America*.)

sperms and eggs. It appears that there has been, at least in several of the groups, a parallel development from very simple to more complex plant bodies, and that sexual reproduction and the development of heterogamy have developed independently in several such groups.

There are many beautiful and interesting groups of green algae which it has not been possible even to mention here. One group of unicellular plants which is probably related to the green algae deserves inclusion in our discussion. These plants are the **diatoms** (Fig. 277). Their most striking characteristics are the large quantity of silica with which the cell wall is impregnated, and the fact that walls consist of two halves, called **valves** (Fig. 278), which fit together like the two parts of a pill box. These minute plants some-times form colonies, but most species are truly unicellular and are found either attached to larger water plants or other objects, or floating free in the water. They are components of the plankton of the sea and of lakes and ponds. Some two thousand species of diatoms have been described.

The protoplast enclosed within the valves of the cell wall contains a single nucleus and generally two chloroplasts. In addition to chlorophyll, an accessory pigment, brown in color, is present in most cases. When floating marine or fresh-water diatoms die, and the cellulose of the wall is decomposed, the form of the valves and the delicate sculpturing characteristic of the valves of many species remain intact because of the large quantity of silica present. These dead diatoms sink to the bottom and accumulate in great quantities. In some regions which were once below the level of the sea, great deposits of these remains (called *diato-maceous earth*) have been found. Exposed deposits of a depth of over 200 meters

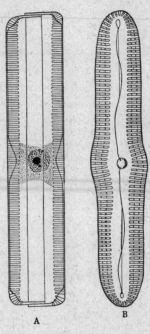

Fig. 278.—Diagrams showing the structure of a diatom (*Navicula*) as seen in two views. The two longitudi-nally placed ribbon-like chlo-roplasts are not shown. (Re-drawn from Ehrenburg.)

exist in California, and certain subterranean deposits are known to have a thickness of nearly 1000 meters (Fig. 279). In a cubic centi-meter of this material there may be over two and a half million diatom shells. Diatomaceous earth is extensively used in industry where it is employed for filtering liquids and for insulation to prevent loss of heat from boilers and furnaces.

Though most diatoms are autophytic (able to manufacture their own food by photosynthesis) there are a few species, living in water

containing much organic matter, which are colorless and live as saprophytes by absorbing their food from the water instead of making it.
Many diatoms are capable of rather active locomotion.   They multiply
by the division of the protoplast into two, each of the protoplasts
receiving one of the original valves and forming one new valve.   As a
result, one of the new diatoms is smaller than the parent cell.   Sometimes the protoplasts of two small diatoms escape from the valves and

Fig. 279.—Quarry of diatomaceous earth in the Lompoc Valley, California.   (Photograph furnished by Johns-Manville Company.)

fuse to form a zygote, called an auxospore, from which a full-sized
diatom develops.   Auxospores are also produced asexually in some
diatoms.

THE PHAEOPHYCEAE—BROWN ALGAE

The third group of the algae, Phaeophyceae, or brown algae, includes
the largest and the most highly differentiated of the thallophytes as well
as many forms of small size and very simple structure.   The range of
size is from species which are microscopic to such genera as *Macrocystis*
which probably may become as much as 100 meters in length, although
that figure has never been definitely authenticated.

Characteristics of the Phaeophyceae.—No unicellular organisms are found in this group. All the Phaeophyceae have cells with definite nuclei and distinct plastids. These latter contain, in addition to chlorophyll a, chlorophyll b, carotin, and xanthophyll, a brown accessory pigment called **fucoxanthin,** which usually entirely hides the green color of the chlorophyll. All of the brown algae normally grow attached, but

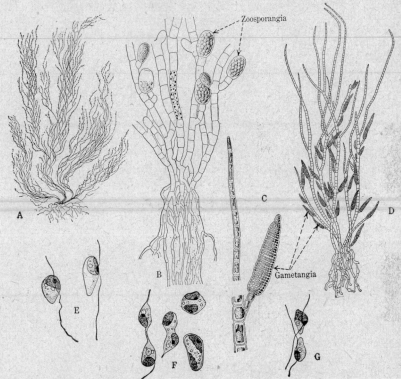

Fig. 280.—Structure and reproduction of a species of *Ectocarpus.* *A*, habit drawing. *B*, portion of a plant showing sporangia. *C*, a single gametangium and vegetative cells. *D*, portion of a plant showing gametangia. *E*, two zoospores. *F*, several stages in conjugation, including a zygote, to the right of the letter. *G*, two gametes about to conjugate. (*A* to *D* after Setchell and Gardner.)

plants may become detached and still survive. Floating masses of the brown alga, *Sargassum* (Fig. 284), make up the greater part of the flora of the "Sargasso Sea." In the Phaeophyceae no resting spores are produced. The motile cells, whether zoospores or gametes, have in most cases two cilia which are laterally attached.

Distribution of Phaeophyceae.—These plants are marine and much more common and better developed in the cool ocean waters of the temperate zones than in warm tropical seas.

Representatives of the Class.—Among the best-known representatives of this class are the simple filamentous species of the genus *Ectocarpus;* the large forms which are called "kelps" and which include the common genera *Laminaria, Nereocystis, Macrocystis,* and *Postelsia* (sea palm); and the rock weeds (*Fucus*).

Fig. 281.—Three young plants of one of the largest kelps (*Nereocystis lüetkeana*). (After Postels and Ruprecht.)

Structure and Life History of Ectocarpus.—*Ectocarpus* is a form which, like *Ulothrix*, illustrates the way in which sexual reproduction may have arisen and heterogamy developed. The plant body consists of attached tufts of branched filaments consisting of one or several rows of cells. The sporangia in which the zoospores are produced are generally single cells borne at the end of a special short lateral branch, although they may be within the main filament. Numerous zoospores are produced within each sporangium. They escape by the dissolution of the wall at one place and swim about for some time by means of their two unequal, laterally inserted cilia. When they come to rest they develop directly into new individuals.

The gametangia are multicellular structures, larger than the sporangia and generally on a special lateral branch. They are made up of cubical cells, the protoplast of each of which becomes a gamete. The gametes are similar to zoospores in structure but normally do not

FIG. 282.—A large kelp (*Pelagophycus*) from the Californian coast. (Photograph furnished by W. A. Setchell.)

develop new plants without fusion to form a zygote. Fusion occurs only between gametes from different plants. When the zygotes germinate they give rise to new plants directly.

Among the different species of *Ectocarpus*, there are apparently the beginnings of a differentiation of gametes. In some forms there is a slight difference in size, and it is said that in such cases only gametes differing in size are able to fuse. In short, little distinction seems to exist in the genus *Ectocarpus* as a whole, between zoospores and gametes, and there occur various gradations between isogametes and heterogametes.

The Kelps.—These are the plants which form the extensive kelp beds off the Pacific coast. The largest of the kelps, *Macrocystis*, is said to reach a length of 100 meters; and the stalk of *Nereocystis* (Fig. 281) has been known to grow to a length of 30 or 40 meters. These plants possess a **holdfast,** or organ of attachment, a stalk or **stipe,** and expanded blade-like portions. There is a considerable differentiation of tissues also.

Fig. 283.—The sea palm (*Postelsia palmae-formis*), a remarkable kelp found on some of the most exposed rocky shores of the California coast, where it is almost constantly subjected to the battering of the waves. This plant has a very effective system of holdfasts and a stout stipe surmounted by flattened blades. (From a photograph furnished by Gardner and Setchell.)

The kelps were formerly believed to be isogamous plants. It has been recently shown, however, in the case of several species, that the structures formerly thought to be isogametes are really zoospores, and that these upon germination give rise to very small plants quite unlike the typical kelp plants. These minute plants, which have previously escaped discovery, are of two sorts (antheridial and oogonial), producing respectively sperms and eggs. From the zygotes resulting from the fusion of sperms and eggs develop typical kelp plants. Thus there is in these plants and probably in most of the Phaeophyceae an alternation, in the life cycle, of gamete-producing plants with plants which produce asexual spores. Such an alternation also exists in certain Rhodophyceae and in all the plants belonging to the Bryophyta, Pteridophyta, and Spermatophyta.

Fucus.—*Fucus* (Fig. 286) is the so-called bladder wrack, which is generally abundant on the rocks between the high and low tide levels on the shores of most temperate seas. It is related to *Sargassum* (Fig. 284), which is found mostly in tropical seas. Off the southeast coast of the United States is the great area, about a quarter of a million square miles in extent, of floating seaweed called the Sargasso Sea. The principal plants found there are two species of *Sargassum*. Pieces of these plants probably were brought by ocean currents from the coasts of the West Indies or of tropical America where they grew attached. For ages they have multiplied vegetatively in the Sargasso Sea.

Life History of Fucus.—Since there is no asexual method of reproduction in *Fucus*, it is convenient to begin the life history with the zygote. This is produced outside of the plant in the open sea by the fusion of one of the very great number of biciliate sperms with a very

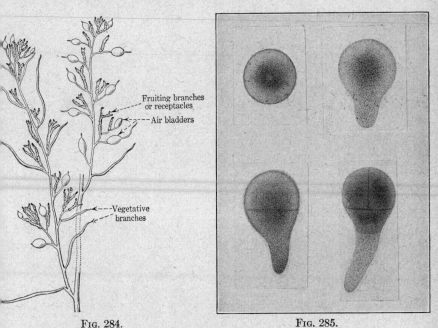

Fruiting branches
or receptacles

Air bladders

Vegetative
branches

Fig. 284.   Fig. 285.

Fig. 284.—Part of a plant of *Sargassum*.   (After Gardner and Setchell.)

Fig. 285.—Fertilization of the egg and germination of the zygote of a species of *Fucus*. Upper left, an egg surrounded by many sperms. Upper right, a zygote germinating. The tubular outgrowth, which later forms a holdfast at the tip, arises always on the side of the zygote away from the light. Lower left, the young plant has divided into two cells by a transverse wall. Lower right, a wall at right angles to the first divides the upper of the cells shown in the left-hand figure into two cells.   (After Thuret.)

large egg cell, which may have a volume as much as thirty thousand times as great as that of a sperm.

Germination of Zygote.—This zygote does not become a resting spore, as in the fresh-water algae, but almost at once forms a thin cellulose wall about itself and then germinates and grows into a new plant. When it germinates it forms, on the side away from the light, a short tube (Fig. 285). By this tubular outgrowth, which may branch, the new plant attaches itself to some solid object. Then many cell divisions take place, so that soon the plant is made up of many cells. One of these, at the extreme tip, is the **apical cell.** It is in a constant state of division and corresponds to the promeristem of the seed-bearing plants. After the formation of the apical cell all subsequent growth of the plant results from the division and enlargement of

Fig. 286.—A frond of a species of *Fucus*, showing the dichotomous method of branching, and the fruiting branches with numerous conspicuous swellings (openings of the conceptacles). (Photograph furnished by Gardner and Setchell.)

cells cut off from this cell. We shall find that such growth from an apical cell is characteristic of most of the plants belonging to Bryophyta and Pteridophyta, as well as of *Fucus* and many other large marine algae. As cell division and enlargement of the new cells continue in *Fucus*, the new plant develops a body consisting of (1) a disc-like holdfast, (2) a stalk called the **stipe,** and (3) a broad, flattened part, the **frond.**

By this time it is possible to see at the extreme end of the flattened portions an elongated pit. The apical cell lies at the bottom of this pit. Before the new *Fucus* plant has attained any considerable size, the apical

cell divides lengthwise into two
equal halves, each of which now
functions independently as an
apical cell. As a result, a
forking of the frond takes place
and after a time each of the
branches will again fork as a
result of the division of each
of the apical cells into two.
This method of branching by
forking is called **dichotomy**. It
is relatively rare among plants.
Much more common is the mo-
nopodial type of branching in
which numerous small branches
are formed on the sides of a
main axis or stem which is continuous. As the plant grows
the fronds fork repeatedly.

*Structure of the Mature
Plant.*—A cross-section of a
vegetative branch of *Fucus*
shows some differentiation of
tissues. There is a compact,
dark brown, outer region called
the **cortex,** and an almost colorless central portion made up
of a loose mass of elongated
cells which is called the **medulla** (Figs. 287*A* and 288*A*).

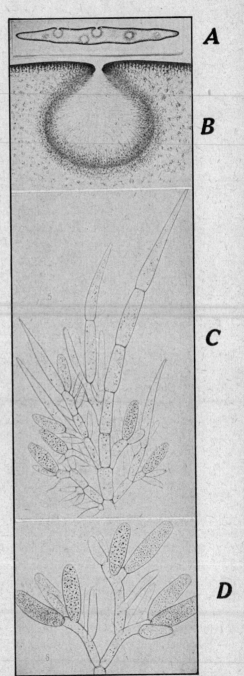

A

B

C

D

FIG. 287.—A species of *Fucus* in
  which the antheridia and oogonia
  are borne on different individuals.
  A, cross section of a fruiting tip
  of a male plant, showing the compact outer region (the cortex),
  the loose tissue within (the medulla), and several antheridial
  conceptacles. *B*, a single antheridial conceptacle in section showing the opening to the surface
  (the ostiole) and the antheridial-
  bearing hairs which arise from
  the inner surface. *C* and *D*,
  antheridia and the branched
  hairs upon which they are borne.
  (After Thuret.)

In certain species of *Fucus* (notably *Fucus vesiculosus* of the Atlantic coast) air bladders, which arise by the accumulation of gas in large intercellular spaces, are borne some distance from the tips of the flattened branches.

Reproduction.—The gametangia are borne within nearly spherical chambers in the swollen tips of the branches. These cavities are called **conceptacles** (Fig. 287, *B*). Each conceptacle opens to the surface of the branch, by a small pore, the **ostiole.** From the inner surface of the conceptacle, slender, multicellular, unbranched hairs (**paraphyses**) grow out. They are all directed toward the ostiole, and in certain species of *Fucus* some of them actually grow out through the ostiole, and protrude as cottony tufts. Directed as they are toward the opening (ostiole) of the conceptacle, the paraphyses probably facilitate the escape of the gametes when the latter become mature, for fertilization in *Fucus* takes place outside the conceptacles.

In some species such as the common eastern species, *Fucus vesiculosus,* the male and female gametangia are produced in different conceptacles which are borne on different plants. In that species the male plants, when the gametangia are mature, can be easily distinguished from the female plants because of the yellow or orange color imparted to the former by the immense number of sperms, each of which has an orange pigment spot. In other species the male and female gametangia (antheridia and oogonia) are produced within the same conceptacle.

Development of Sperms.—Antheridia are produced among the paraphyses of the antheridial conceptacles or the mixed conceptacles of species producing both kinds of gametangia in the same conceptacle (Fig. 287). They are ovoid cells which are borne on much-branched hairs. Each of the cells which is to become an antheridium contains at first a single nucleus. This nucleus divides into two, and these into four and so on until in most species sixty-four nuclei are produced. Finally each nucleus, with a small amount of cytoplasm, becomes a sperm. The sperms are more or less pear-shaped and have two laterally attached cilia of unequal length and a pigment spot or eye spot. When the sperms are mature the whole mass within one antheridium escapes by a rupture of the outer layer of the antheridium. The paraphyses secrete considerable mucilage. When the *Fucus* plants are exposed to the air at low tide, there is some drying out of the fronds and some shrinkage. The contraction of the outer tissue of the fruiting frond results in the mucilage within the conceptacle, together with masses of sperms or eggs, being extruded from the ostiole. The rising tide washes off the extruded mucilage and liberates the gametes which are then free to fuse.

Development of Eggs.—The oogonia are also borne among the para-

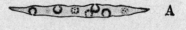

A

physes. In the development of these gametangia a short outgrowth arises from the cells which form the wall of the conceptacle. This outgrowth divides transversely into two cells of which the outer becomes the oogonium and the inner a **stalk cell.** The oogonial cell enlarges and becomes filled with dense protoplasm. Its single nucleus then undergoes three successive divisions, giving rise to eight nuclei. There follows a division of the cytoplasm into eight masses, each of which with a nucleus becomes an egg (Fig. 288). These eggs become rounded within the oogonium but are without any cell wall.

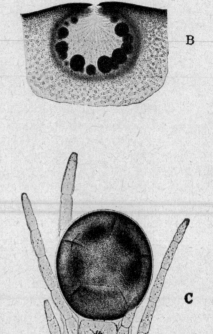

B

C

The oogonium wall is made up of several layers. At maturity of the eggs the outermost layer is ruptured and the eight eggs escape from the oogonium but remain within the two inner layers of the wall. In succession the outer and the inner of these layers ruptures and the eggs are finally allowed to escape into the sea water (Fig. 285) where fertilization takes place. The fertilization of many of the eggs is made certain by reason of the great numbers and motility of the sperms and the characteristic substance given out by the egg, which attracts the sperm.

FIG. 288.—A species of *Fucus* in which antheridia and oogonia are produced on different individuals. *A*, a cross section through a fruiting branch of a female plant showing the cortex, medulla, and several oogonial conceptacles. *B*, a single oogonial conceptacle in section, showing the ostiole and the oogonia and paraphyses which line the conceptacle. *C*, a portion of the floor of the conceptacle showing an oogonium attached by its stalk cell and surrounded by a number of paraphyses. Note that the protoplasm of the oogonium has undergone cleavage to form the eight eggs which have not yet rounded up. (After Thuret.)

In *Fucus* the reduction of chromosomes, from the double or $2n$

number characteristic of " the plant " to the half or n number found in the egg and sperm, takes place at the first division of the antheridial and the oogonial cells, that is, not long before the time of gamete formation. At fertilization the chromosome number is doubled, so that the oospore and the plant into which it develops have nuclei with $2n$ chromosomes.

Among the most important features of the structure and life history of *Fucus* are the following:

1. The great size and complexity of the plant body compared with the Myxophyceae and the Chlorophyceae, and the considerable differentiation of tissues. These are even more marked in some of the kelps.

2. The terminal growth from a single apical cell.

3. The habit of dichotomous branching.

4. The absence of zoospores or other means of asexual reproduction.

5. The extreme differentiation of the gametes, the sperms being very small in size, highly motile, and produced in very great numbers, and the eggs being large, relatively few in number, and without power of locomotion.

6. The production of eight egg cells within a single female gametangium.

7. The fact that the eggs, instead of being retained and protected within the female gametangia until after fertilization, as in *Oedogonium* and *Vaucheria*, and in the Bryophyta and the Pteridophyta, are expelled before fertilization.

8. The fact that the reduction division takes place when the gametes are produced (at the first divisions of the antheridial and oogonial cells) and not, as in *Spirogyra* and *Oedogonium*, at the germination of the zygote.

9. The almost immediate germination of the zygote, in contrast with the delayed germination of the zygotes of *Spirogyra, Oedogonium, Ulothrix,* and *Vaucheria.*

THE RHODOPHYCEAE—RED ALGAE

The fourth class of algae is made up of plants which are mostly marine, although a few species live in fresh water. All the members of this class are multicellular. In general they are clearly more differentiated than the green algae, but as a group are characterized by simpler structure than the kelps and the Fucales. Most of the vegetative cells have a single nucleus, though in some of the red algae large vegetative cells with several nuclei occur. The plastids, which may occur in large numbers in each cell, contain in addition to chlorophyll a, chlorophyll b, carotin, and xanthophyll, a red accessory pigment called **phycoerythrin.**

In many red algae the cell walls are very thick, so that the protoplasts appear to be embedded in an extensive gelatinous matrix. In these forms there are often pits in the cell walls through which extend protoplasmic connections between the protoplasts of adjoining cells.

Some of these plants, which have a finely branched plant body, are certainly to be considered the most delicate and beautiful of all marine plants. In one group of red algae, the coralline algae, the cell walls become impregnated and encrusted with large quantities of carbonate of lime and are strongly suggestive of corals. Certain related red algae similarly encrusted with lime have played an important part in the building up of coral reefs. Sexual reproduction is always heterogamous.

Distribution.—The Rhodophyceae are abundant in the seas of the temperate zones. They are generally found below low-tide level and may grow at depths as great as 200 meters.

Reproduction.—None of the red algae produce ciliated cells of any kind. Sexual reproduction, when it occurs, is in all cases heterogamous. The male gametes are spherical, nonmotile sperms produced singly in structures called antheridia, and are carried by the movements of the

Fig. 289.—A portion of a plant of *Pterosiphonia*, a genus closely related to *Polysiphonia*. The tetrasporic plants, the male plants and the female plants can not be distinguished from one another by the naked eye. (Photograph furnished by N. L. Gardner.)

water to the female gametangia, known in this group as **carpogonia.** Each carpogonium is a cell enlarged at the base and elongated at the unattached end into a relatively long filament, the **trichogyne,** and when a sperm comes into contact with a trichogyne it adheres to it. Then the wall of the trichogyne dissolves at the point of contact and the nucleus of the male gamete passes down through the trichogyne and fuses with the nucleus of the female gamete at the base of the trichogyne.

The zygote in some of the simplest species gives rise to numerous short branches on the ends of which are borne spores called **carpospores**. In many species the formation of these carpospores from the zygote is a process of great complexity.

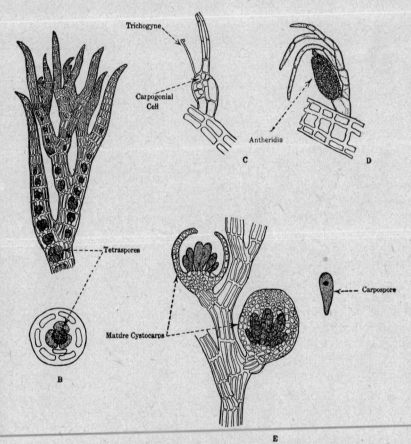

Fig. 290.—Structure and life history of a species of *Polysiphonia*. Upper left, a fragment of a tetrasporic plant, showing the form and arrangement of the vegetative cells (this feature is the same in the sexual plants), and groups of tetraspores. *B*, cross section of a branch showing the arrangement of the tetraspores and vegetative cells. *C*, branch bearing a procarp which consists of a carpogonium (carpogonial cell) and adjacent cells. *D*, branch bearing antheridia. *E*, branch showing the cystocarps whose formation from the procarps is initiated by fertilization. To the right is a single carpospore. These are produced in the cystocarps.

Alternation of Generations in the Rhodophyceae.

—In some of the red algae the carpospores germinate and produce new plants upon which are borne carpogonia and antheridia. These are, however, the exceptional cases. Usually, for instance in the genus *Polysiphonia*, the life history is more complicated. In these forms, when the carpospores germinate they give rise to plants which resemble superficially the plants that produce the carpogonia and antheridia, but which never form gametes. Instead of gametes, these plants which develop from the carpospores form asexual spores, in groups of four and are called **tetraspores** in the case of *Polysiphonia* and many other genera. These spores are usually produced in groups of four, each group resulting from two successive divisions of certain cells of the asexual or tetrasporic plants. The tetraspores upon germination generally do not give rise to tetrasporic plants but instead to sexual plants bearing antheridia and carpogonia. Thus the life cycle consists of two phases which alternate with each other.

It has been shown that, in *Polysiphonia* and in several other genera in which this alternation of asexual and sexual phases or generations takes place, the sexual and asexual plants are characterized by a difference in the number of chromosomes in their nuclei. The nuclei of the gamete-bearing plants have n chromosomes. The gametes also have n chromosomes, but as the result of the fusion of the nuclei of the two gametes the zygote has $2n$ chromosomes, and so do the carpospores and the tetrasporic plants which develop from them. One of the two nuclear divisions which occurs when the tetraspores are formed is a reduction division, and accordingly the tetraspores have n chromosomes, as do the nuclei of the gamete-bearing plants which are produced when the tetraspores germinate. The life cycle of these plants is shown in somewhat greater detail by the following diagram, in which is also indicated the chromosome number of the various stages in the life cycle.

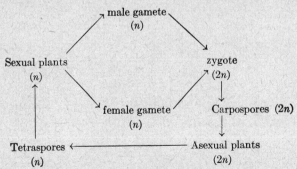

In each cycle the chromosome number is doubled when the gametes fuse and halved again at the reduction division just before tetraspore formation.

This alternate doubling and halving of the chromosome number is not, however, the characteristic thing about the life cycle of the red algae;

it has been shown to occur in the life cycle of *Spirogyra, Oedogonium,* other green algae, and some of the kelps and it is clear that it must take place in the life cycle of even the simplest algae having sexual reproduction, since the zygote nucleus contains the chromosomes from the two gamete nuclei. The remarkable thing about the life cycle of such plants as *Polysiphonia* is that, instead of the chromosome number being halved almost immediately as in *Spirogyra* (at the germination of the zygote), the reduction division is delayed until after the zygote has given rise to another plant morphologically indistinguishable from the sexual plant until near maturity when tetraspores are produced.

SUMMARY

Origin and Evolution of Sex in the Algae.—In the most primitive algae, reproduction is by fission. When the cells of such plants are united in colonies, the colonies eventually break up into groups of a few cells, each group growing by the fission of its different cells until larger colonies are formed (hormogonia production in *Oscillatoria*). Such plants may produce resistant spores (thick-walled cells with much reserve food) which can carry the organism over periods of drought or unfavorable temperature.

In several groups of algae, zoospores (motile, asexual spores) were probably produced before sexual reproduction originated. The zoospores serve for multiplication and for wider distribution of the species. These zoospores appear to have been the structures from which gametes originated in the evolution of sex in plants. In the more primitive of plants having sexual reproduction, the gametes are alike in structure (isogametes). In less primitive forms they are structurally of two kinds (heterogametes, i.e., sperms and eggs).

In some of the forms which produce both zoospores and gametes, as in *Oedogonium,* the gametes, or at least the male gametes, are essentially the same in structure as the zoospores, though smaller in size.

In several distinct algal groups there are slight differences in the size of the gametes of a given species, or in the duration or degree of their motility. Such species exhibit the beginnings of differentiation of the sex cells into male and female gametes.

In forms in which the gametes are further differentiated there may exist great differences in the size of the two kinds, complete loss of motility of the female gamete, and great increase in the number of male gametes produced by a single plant, together with corresponding decrease in the number of female gametes. In some of the algae in which there is a very marked differentiation of the gametes, the female gamete is retained within the gametangium (oogonium) until after fertilization.

Conditions Favoring Zoospore and Gamete Production in the Algae. —In general, zoospores are not produced except during periods favorable to the vegetative activity of the plant. Sexual reproduction seems frequently to be brought on by conditions not favorable to vegetative activity. The zygote in many algae is a thick-walled, resistant spore, capable of withstanding conditions which would be fatal to the vegetative cells. Upon the return of favorable conditions it germinates and produces a new plant.

Relative Complexity of Algae and Typical Land Plants.—Such complexity as is characteristic of typical land plants is not found in the algae, not even in the great kelps. The relatively small number of organs and slight differentiation of tissues in the algae are sufficient for successful existence in the comparatively uniform environment of the water habitat. The plants, being largely supported in the water by their buoyancy, have less need for mechanical tissues than plants which grow erect in the air. Special tissues for absorption and conduction are less needed than in the case of land plants, since the immersed algae are entirely bathed in water, which supplies the necessary mineral salts, carbon dioxide for photosynthesis, and oxygen for respiration. Tissues for the regulation of water loss are obviously entirely unnecessary.

CHAPTER XII

THALLOPHYTA—FUNGI

INTRODUCTION

The fungi do not constitute a natural group. Among them are included plants which are certainly more distantly related to each other than they are to certain plants outside the fungi. The single definite basis of distinction between the algae and the fungi is the fact that the algae can make their own food from simple inorganic food material, whereas the fungi, lacking chlorophyll, must secure their food ready-made from some other living organisms or from the dead remains or products of some organism.

An organism deriving its food from the *living* body of another plant or an animal is termed a **parasite.** The rusts and smuts of cereals are good examples of parasitic fungi. An organism obtaining its food from the *dead* body or the non-living products of another plant or animal is called a **saprophyte.** Common saprophytic fungi are the molds and mushrooms. Plant pathologists are primarily concerned with **parasitic fungi,** for these are the organisms that attack many useful living plants, derive nourishment from them and seriously injure them. Plant diseases, which result from the attacks of parasitic organisms, cause tremendous losses.

There is not always a sharp distinction between parasites and saprophytes, and it is quite difficult in some cases to tell to which of these classes a given plant should be assigned. There are some fungi, for example, certain species of *Fusarium*, which may attain their best development as parasites, but which may be able to exist for a time as saprophytes. Such organisms are called **facultative saprophytes.** Also there are some fungi, such as certain of the black molds, which normally are saprophytes in their habits, but which may now and then become parasitic, and therefore are called **facultative parasites.** These two groups are in contrast to those which are obliged to live strictly as saprophytes or parasites, as the case may be, and which are called **obligate saprophytes** or **obligate parasites.**

In the condition called parasitism, one organism, the **parasite,** secures its food entirely or in part from the tissue of another organism. The organism at the expense of which the parasite lives is called the **host.** The parasite contributes nothing to the advantage of the host.

We shall include in our discussion of the fungi an account of two groups of Thallophytes which are by many authors excluded from the fungi proper, but which are unable to make their own food. These are the first two of the groups listed below.

We shall consider the fungi as consisting of the following five groups:

> The Schizomycetes or Bacteria (Fission Fungi).
> The Myxomycetes (Slime Fungi).
> The Phycomycetes (Algal Fungi).
> The Ascomycetes (Ascus Fungi).
> The Basidiomycetes (Basidium Fungi).

These five groups include a large proportion of the parasitic or saprophytic plants in the Plant Kingdom except a relatively small number which show by their structure and development that their closest relatives belong to one of the great groups of autophytic plants; and except a considerable number of fungi of great economic importance whose complete life histories have not been worked out. Because of this incompleteness they have been placed in a group known as Fungi Imperfecti. However, the life histories of many have been completed and thus they have been placed in their proper classification.

BACTERIA

General Characteristics.—The bacteria are strictly unincellular organisms. Sometimes the individuals remain more or less united and thus form irregular masses or filaments, but in such cases each cell is self-sufficient and there is no evidence of division of labor among such cells. Bacterial cells, like the cells of the Myxophyceae, are without definite nuclei. Multiplication is entirely by fission, although the whole protoplast in some bacteria may become surrounded by a thick wall and thus form a resistant spore. The bacteria are either parasitic or saprophytic, with the exception of a very few forms which can make their own food.

Distribution of Bacteria.—These tiny organisms are all about us. They are found floating in the atmosphere, mostly as "passengers" on dust particles, up to a height of several thousand feet, except just after heavy rains or snow storms when the air is practically free of them. They are present in rain water and in freshly fallen snow, as well as in all natural bodies of water and in all drinking water which has not been boiled. They are abundant upon the surface of the human body and are present in large numbers in the intestinal tract and on all the mucous membranes. Bacteria are found in soil down to a depth of six feet and more, many millions often being present in a gram of soil. They are, of course, particularly abundant in sewage. It has

been shown that there may be as many as six billion in a cubic inch
of sewage.   Living bacteria are present on the surface of all the objects
about us except those which have recently been heated to a high temperature or otherwise sterilized.   They are seldom found within the
tissues of plants and animals except when the organisms are suffering
from one of the numerous diseases which bacteria may cause.

Size of Bacteria.—These organisms are very small but they vary
in size within rather wide limits.   Among the smallest known bacteria
is a rod-shaped form which is $\frac{1}{2}$ micron long and $\frac{1}{5}$ micron wide, but
the average dimensions of the rod-shaped forms are probably about
2 microns by $\frac{1}{2}$ micron.   (A micron, the unit of microscopic measurement, is $\frac{1}{1000}$ of a millimeter or about $\frac{1}{25000}$ of an inch.)

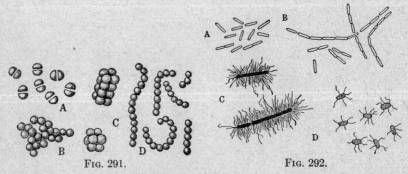

FIG. 291.   FIG. 292.

FIG. 291.—Coccus forms of bacteria. *A, Diplococcus. B, Staphylococcus. C, Sarcina.
D, Streptococcus.*

FIG. 292.—Bacillus forms of bacteria. *A, Bacillus sporogenes. B, Bacillus subtilis*
(young stage). *C, Bacillus proteus. D, Bacillus typhosus.* All magnified
about 750×.

Multiplication of Bacteria.—A bacterium which is abundantly
supplied with food and surrounded by conditions favorable to it will
grow to a certain maximum size and then divide by fission into two bacteria of equal size.   Under favorable conditions the organisms increase
in number by this method very rapidly, so that the descendants of a
single bacterium may be, within a few hours, literally countless.   Some
bacteria may divide as often as once in twenty minutes.   It has been
estimated that if the cholera organism maintained its maximum rate
of fission for twenty-four hours, the bacteria which would thus be
produced from one bacterium would number 47×10^{20} or 4,700,000,000,-
000,000,000,000 and would weigh about two thousand tons.   This
number is, of course, quite beyond our conception, but we gain some
idea of its immensity when we learn that it is over seventy billion
times the number of seconds since the birth of Christ.   As a matter

of fact, long before any such number of bacteria could be produced by fission, the processes of growth and division would have been slowed down or entirely interrupted by the exhaustion of the food supply or by the accumulation of poisonous waste products of metabolism (chemical changes in the living organism).

Form Types of Bacteria.—There are three principal morphological types of bacteria: spheres, rods, and spirals. These are spoken of respectively as **cocci** (singular coccus), **bacilli** (singular bacillus), and **spirilla** (singular spirillum).

Structure of the Bacterial Cell.—Many bacteria have the cell wall surrounded by a capsule or envelope of gelatinous material. In some forms this gelatinous mantle holds the bacteria together after division, so that they form filaments or irregular masses. This is the case with the bacteria which are responsible for the production of vinegar. The gelatinous mass with embedded bacteria is the so-called "mother of vinegar." The cell wall proper differs from that of typical plants in that it contains no cellulose. It is very similar chemically to the protoplasm itself. The protoplast consists of cytoplasm, through which

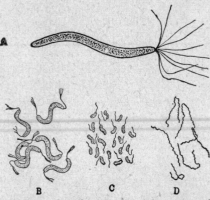

Fig. 293.—Spirillum forms of bacteria. *A*, a species of *Thiospirillum* (a sulphur oxidizing organism). *B*, *Spirillum undulum*. *C*, *Vibrio cholerae*. *D*, a species of *Spirochaete*. All magnified about 1000×.

are scattered particles of chromatin. That the protoplast is bounded by a semi-permeable membrane is clear from the fact that the bacterial cell may be plasmolyzed. This fact is the basis of the commonly used methods of preserving food from spoiling by bacteria and similar plants through the use of salt and sugar. When foods are preserved in sugar, sugar syrup, dry salt, or brine, the bacteria are unable to grow because of the withdrawal of most of their water by osmosis.

Spore Formation.—Some bacteria are capable of producing resistant spores which can withstand high temperatures, the presence of poisonous substances, and other unfavorable conditions which are fatal to the ordinary vegetative cells. Fortunately, only a few disease-producing bacteria form spores. With few exceptions, the spores are produced singly within the vegetative cells. The protoplast contracts and becomes surrounded by a relatively thick wall. Generally, the wall of the cell

fermented by the enzyme zymase, but many yeasts produce another enzyme, called **sucrase**, which brings about the hydrolysis of cane sugar with the formation of the two hexoses, fructose and glucose. The fermentation of hexose sugars is really an incomplete respiration carried on by the yeast cells. If there is an abundant supply of oxygen they can carry on ordinary and complete respiration of this sugar with the production of carbon dioxide and water.

Starch is a carbohydrate which yeasts are generally unable to ferment. In the brewing industry the starch of barley and other grains must be changed to sugar by the process of malting before fermentation can take place. In malting, the grain is allowed to germinate and the **diastase** produced by the seed during germination changes the starch of the seed into sugar.

Yeast is used in baking because the carbon dioxide liberated by the fermentation of a small part of the sugar contained in the dough forms bubbles and thus renders the bread " light."

Acetic Acid Fermentation.—After alcoholic fermentation has progressed to a certain point, the concentration of alcohol becomes so great as to kill off the yeast organisms or at least prevent their further activity. Then, if the solution contains not more than about 14 per cent of alcohol and if it is exposed to the air, acetic acid bacteria, which were already present or which have entered from the air, increase rapidly in number and bring about acetic acid fermentation. In this process alcohol is converted into acetic acid and water. This change is an oxidation and will therefore not go on unless considerable quantities of oxygen are available. The following equation represents this change:

$$C_2H_5OH + O_2 = CH_3COOH + H_2O$$

$$\text{(alcohol)} \quad \text{(oxygen)} \quad \text{(acetic acid)} \quad \text{(water)}$$

The enzyme that brings about this change has not been isolated but it is probably an intracellular one. After practically all the alcohol has been converted into acetic acid and water, the acid may be decomposed with the formation of carbon dioxide and water. The bacteria of acetic acid fermentation utilize the alcohol as a source of food and secure from its fermentation (an exothermic process) energy for their own use.

Lactic Acid Fermentation.—Another carbohydrate fermentation, and one carried on principally by bacteria, is lactic acid fermentation. It is the production of this acid which causes the souring of milk, and the coagulation of the protein (casein), which is ordinarily called curdling.[1]

---

[1] Lactose, the principal sugar present in milk, can not be directly fermented, but when it is hydrolyzed by the enzyme *lactase* (produced by milk-souring bacteria) into the simple sugars, glucose and galactose, fermentation of these sugars can be accomplished by lactic acid bacteria.

When the acid has reached a certain concentration, which differs according to the type of lactic acid bacteria which are principally involved, the fermentative activity of the bacteria ceases. Although the lactic acid bacteria are a source of serious loss because of the quantities of milk which they make useless for ordinary consumption and because of the effort and expense which are necessary to prevent the souring of milk before use, their activities are not entirely harmful. The lactic acid bacteria are useful to the producer of butter because the presence of lactic acid in the cream increases the yield of butter and improves the flavor as well. They are also necessary to the production of sour-milk cheeses. The curd used for sweet-milk cheeses, however, is produced by the coagulating enzyme, rennet, which is introduced by the cheesemaker.

Bacteria in Relation to Soil Fertility.—Of the essential materials for food manufacture secured by the green plant from the soil, nitrogen is, next to hydrogen and oxygen, the one which is needed in largest quantities. This element makes up a large part of the molecule of the different proteins of which protoplasm largely consists. Because nitrogen is needed in such quantities by the plant and for other reasons, soil nitrogen is the element more likely to become insufficient in quantity, after repeated cropping of the soil, than any of other essential elements. Large quantities of the nitrogen from the soil which has been built into plant proteins are removed in the form of stored food in the grain or other useful parts. Although the waste products from domestic animals, containing much of the nitrogen of the food which they have eaten and utilized in their metabolism, is in part returned to the soil as fertilizer, much of the nitrogen of the crops removed from the soil is never returned to it, but is altogether wasted or even discharged into and allowed to pollute our rivers. As a result, maintenance of the supply of soil nitrogen is one of the principal problems of soil fertility.

Nitrogen Fixation.—The atmosphere contains about 80 per cent of gaseous nitrogen. It has recently been reported that certain cereals are able to secure a very small part of their nitrogen from the gaseous or free nitrogen of the air, but it is certainly true that they must secure most of their nitrogen in some other form. In the absence of all nitrogen except free nitrogen, the higher plants do not thrive. Nitrogen in the form of nitrates (salts in which nitrogen and oxygen, in the proportion of one atom to three, are united with some metal, as in $NaNO_3$, KNO_3, and $Ca(NO_3)_2$), is the most favorable for the use of crop plants. Nitrogen in the form of ammonium salts (salts in which nitrogen and hydrogen are united, in the proportion of one atom to four, as $(NH_4)_2CO_3$ and NH_4NO_3), can also be used but is less favorable. A number of agencies can cause the free or gaseous nitrogen of the atmosphere to unite with other elements and thus make it available for the use of green plants. The union of free (gaseous) nitrogen with some other element or elements to form a compound is called **nitrogen fixation**. The common methods by which nitrogen fixation takes place in nature are (1) electrical discharges in the atmosphere, (2) activity of bacteria living free in the soil, and (3) activity of bacteria living symbiotically.

Electrical discharges in the atmosphere, both in the form of lightning and in the form of silent discharges, which are constantly taking place between the atmosphere and the earth, bring about the union of small quantities of atmospheric nitrogen and oxygen. The resulting oxides of nitrogen are washed from the air by rain and thus reach the soil, where they combine with other substances to form nitrates. The quantity of fixed nitrogen which thus reaches the soil is, however, exceedingly small.

Nitrogen Fixation by Bacteria Living Free in the Soil.—It can be shown that bare soil, even when it is prevented from receiving any nitrogen compound from the atmosphere, may increase in the amount of combined nitrogen which it contains. It is not difficult to demonstrate that this is due to bacteria present in the soil, for in sterilized soil no such increase in combined nitrogen takes place. These non-symbiotic nitrogen-fixing bacteria have the power of combining the nitrogen of the air in the soil with other elements and thus building up complex organic nitrogen compounds. These complex compounds are later broken down in the soil and form nitrates. The best-known nitrogen-fixing bacteria living free in the soil are *Clostridium pasteurianum* and several species of *Azotobacter*. This bringing of the free nitrogen into combination with other elements is an energy-absorbing process, and the necessary energy for it is secured by the bacteria from the oxidation (respiration) of organic carbon compounds in the soil.

Nitrogen Fixation by Symbiotic Bacteria.—In addition to the nitrogen-fixing bacteria which live free in the soil, there are others which live in the roots of certain flowering plants, particularly members of the Leguminosae (bean family). The nitrogen-fixing bacterium which is commonly found in the roots of various beans, peas, lupines, clovers, and other leguminous plants is called *Pseudomonas radicicola*. When grown in culture as a free-living organism it does not have the power of fixing nitrogen. There are several strains of this organism, each of which seems to prefer association with certain species of leguminous plants. The bacteria gain entrance to the roots when the latter are young, and by their presence cause the formation of swellings or tubercles upon the root. The cells of these tubercles are largely filled with the bacteria.

The atmospheric nitrogen is probably fixed by these organisms in the form of organic nitrogen compounds. The seed plant bearing the tubercles is able to absorb and to use this organic nitrogen, or some simpler nitrogen compound arising from its partial decomposition. The relation between *Pseudomonas radicicola* and the leguminous plant is certainly one of **symbiosis** (living together of two kinds of organisms with mutual

Fig. 295.—Base of a plant of scarlet runner bean (*Phaseolus multiflorus*) showing root tubercles which contain symbiotic nitrogen-fixing bacteria.

benefit). The bacteria secure food from the protoplasm of the leguminous plants in whose roots they live, and the legume secures nitrogen from the bacteria. Seedlings of leguminous plants, grown in sterilized sand and provided with all the essential substances except combined nitrogen, develop no tubercles and soon show evidence of nitrogen shortage. If plants grown under such conditions and showing evidence of lack of nitrogen are watered with a soil extract from unsterilized soil in which legumes have grown, *Pseudomonas radicicola* is introduced, tubercles are formed, and the plants thrive. Even though the plants are cut and removed from the field, there is an increase in the amount of combined nitrogen in the soil in which a legume crop has grown. The roots left in the soil and the tubercles which they bear undergo decay, and the combined nitrogen within them finds its way into the soil. There it is converted into nitrates. A number of plants, among others the common alder (*Alnus*), usually have nitrogen-fixing bacteria growing in symbiosis with them, and stimulating the roots to tubercle formation.

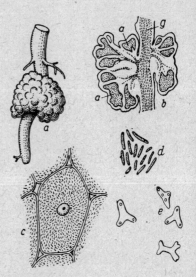

Nitrification.—As a result of the breakdown in the soil of proteins from dead organisms or their organic products, considerable ammonia is liberated into the soil. If this remained in the form of ammonia gas it would diffuse into the atmosphere and thus be lost to the soil in which it was produced. Actually most of it is combined in the soil with other substances to form salts, such, for instance, as ammonium carbonate, $(NH_4)_2CO_3$. It has been observed that, even in bare soils, the quantity of nitrogen in the form of ammonium compounds tends to decrease, and that the quantity of nitrogen in the form of nitrates tends to increase proportionally. This conversion of ammonium nitrogen into nitrate nitrogen was formerly believed to be a simple chemical

FIG. 296.—Root tubercles from a lupine plant (*Lupinus*). *a*, exterior view 5 times natural size. *b*, longitudinal section showing at *a* the tissue filled with bacteria. *c*, a cell from *a* filled with nitrogen-fixing bacteria but still containing the nucleus of the root cell (magnified 200 times). *d*, nitrogen-fixing bacteria from a root tubercle. *e*, bacterioids (modified forms of bacteria in old tubercles). *d* and *e*, enlarged 1000 times. (After Fischer.)

change with which organisms had nothing to do. It has been shown, however, that the **change of ammonium salts into nitrates which is called nitrification** does not take place if the soil has been sterilized, an indication that organisms of some sort are concerned in the process. The transformation is known to take place in two stages: (1) the conversion of ammonium nitrogen into the nitrogen of nitrites, such as KNO_2 and $Ca(NO_2)_2$; and (2) the conversion of nitrites into nitrates. The two stages are carried on by different bacteria. The first step is performed by several species of the genus *Nitrosomonas*, and the second by bacteria belonging to the genus *Nitrobacter*. These two kinds of organisms always occur together and are common in soils, manure heaps, river water, and sewage. As rapidly as nitrite is formed by *Nitrosomonas* it is converted into nitrate by *Nitrobacter*, so that in some cases it is not possible to detect nitrites in soils in which nitrification is going on. Neither of these organisms can thrive in the presence of large quantities of carbohydrates or of other easily oxidized organic compounds. Accordingly, the nitrification is not active in very heavily manured soil until other bacteria have fermented most of the organic material.

Favorable soil conditions for active nitrification are sufficient lime and good tillage and drainage. Tillage and drainage are important in order that the soil may be well aerated and that thus sufficient oxygen may be available for the oxidation of ammonium nitrogen to nitrate nitrogen.

Nitrosomonas and *Nitrobacter* are autophytic plants. They are like green plants in that they are able to manufacture their own food from water and the carbon dioxide of the air or that easily secured from bicarbonates in the soil. They differ from green plants, however, in that they can carry on this synthesis of food in the dark. They secure the energy for this endothermic process not from light but from the oxidation of ammonium-nitrogen to nitrite and of nitrite to nitrate, these two latter processes being themselves exothermic. Thus these organisms are as truly autophytic as green plants. Supplied with ammonia or nitrites by the oxidation of which they secure the energy necessary for food manufacture they could live in a world containing no other kind of organisms. Similarly certain other bacteria live autophytically, securing their energy for food synthesis by the oxidation of hydrogen sulphide (H_2S) to sulphur and finally to sulphuric acid sulphur (H_2SO_4). There are several other kinds of autophytic bacteria. Such food manufacture by use of energy secured from a chemical reaction (oxidation of ammonia, nitrite, hydrogen, sulphide, etc.) is called **chemosynthesis** in contrast with photosynthesis which utilizes the energy of light.

Denitrification.—There have been found in soil and in manures, as well as in the air and in natural bodies of water, bacteria which, instead of increasing the quantity of nitrate nitrogen, carry on the **reverse process and convert nitrates into nitrites, into gaseous oxides of nitrogen, or even into free nitrogen,** a process which is called **denitrification.** If this process of denitrification results in the formation of free nitrogen, the nitrogen passes into the air and is lost from the soil. Some of these harmful denitrifying bacteria are most active in soil which is poorly drained and therefore not well aerated. Large quantities of unfermented organic matter encourage the denitrification process. Accordingly, very heavy dressing of soil with unrotted manure is in general to be avoided.

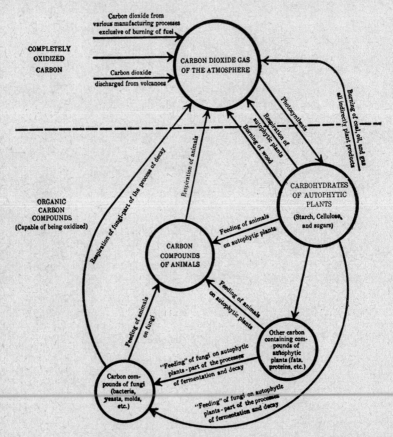

FIG. 297.—Carbon cycle diagram, showing the principal sources of the carbon dioxide of the atmosphere and the principal changes which it may undergo in organisms.

The Carbon Cycle and the Nitrogen Cycle.—We have repeatedly referred to the fact that autophytic plants build up the simple inorganic substances, water, carbon dioxide, and salts containing calcium, potassium, magnesium, iron, sulphur, nitrogen, and phosphorus, into relatively complex organic substances which constitute the food not only of these green plants but also of all animals and heterophytic plants

These organic substances are broken down again in the destructive processes (notably respiration) which go on in all living organisms. In the dead bodies of plants and animals and in the excretions of animals there are large quantities of carbon, nitrogen, and the other essential

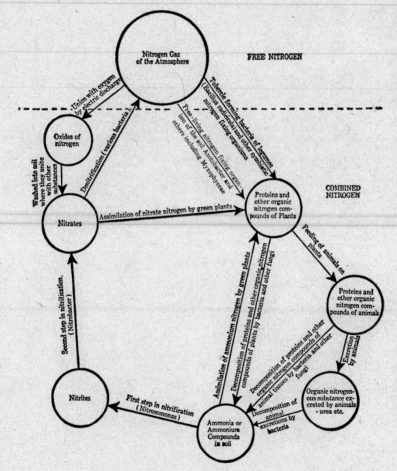

Fig. 298.—Nitrogen cycle diagram, showing the principal changes in form which nitrogen may undergo in organisms.

elements (in the form of organic compounds), which are not available for the use of green plants. If it were not for the bacteria and other fungi which bring about the fermentation of proteins, carbohydrates, and fats, these essential elements would remain permanently locked up in dead organisms and animal excretions. In time so much carbon and nitrogen would be removed from " circulation " as the result of this " hoarding " of the natural supply, that autophytic plants could no longer live and therefore all other organisms would soon succumb.

Fortunately for the continuance of life on the globe, various bacteria and other fungi can " unlock " the organic compounds of dead plants and animals and of the excretions of animals and convert the essential elements into forms in which they can be used again as raw material for food manufacture by autophytic plants. Thus it is that these elements pass repeatedly through a cycle in which they are first converted from simple to complex compounds and then returned to the simple form by respiration, or by fermentation by bacteria and other fungi. If we could trace the history of any nitrogen or carbon atom, for instance, we might find that it had been part of hundreds of different organisms in succession; that it had literally " transmigrated " from an oak, to a bacterium, to a wheat plant, to a man, and thus through innumerable changes throughout the ages since life first appeared upon the earth. The principal changes which carbon and nitrogen may undergo in the course of the carbon and nitrogen cycles are graphically shown in the accompanying diagrams (Figs. 297 and 298).

MYXOMYCETES OR SLIME FUNGI

Characteristics of the Myxomycetes.—In the Myxomycetes there seems to be a combination of animal and plant characteristics, and on this account these organisms have engaged the interest of both botanists and zoologists. During the vegetative part of their existence these plants consist of multinucleate masses of naked protoplasm, and are capable of amoeboid movement (movement by flowing of living substance), and of engulfing solid food particles. These characteristics —absence of cell walls, locomotion by streaming of protoplasm, and ability to take solid food particles into the protoplasm—are generally considered to be animal characteristics. In their reproduction, however, the Myxomycetes are more like certain plants (some kinds of fungi) than they are like any animals, and their spores have cellulose walls, another plant characteristic. With the exception of two or three parasitic genera, they are all saprophytes, securing their food from the decaying leaves and twigs and rotting wood of moist habitats, mostly in the forests. Because of their delicate structure and occasionally brilliant coloring, many of the Myxomycetes are of remarkable beauty.

Life History of Typical Myxomycetes.—One of the most widespread and common genera of Myxomycetes is *Stemonitis*, which we shall use as a type of the class. In the ordinary vegetative condition the plant consists of a slimy mass of protoplasm, termed a **plasmodium** (plural, **plasmodia**). There are no walls surrounding the plasmodium, and the numerous nuclei are distributed throughout the general cytoplasm without separating walls. The protoplasm exhibits a streaming motion and creeps about over the surface of the substratum by extending and withdrawing portions of its body. These arm-like processes are called **pseudopodia** (singular, **pseudopodium**). The plasmodium is sensitive, to light and, while in its vegetative state, avoids strong light, creeping about on the surface of logs and among decaying leaves and sticks in

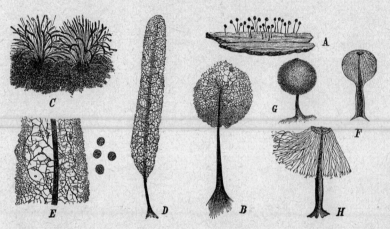

FIG. 299.—Myxomycetes. *A–B. Comatricha nigra; A*, group of sporangia, natural size; *B*, a single sporangium enlarged showing the stalk and the net-like capillitium. *C–E, Stemonitis fusca: C*, sporangia, natural size; *D*, a single sporangium enlarged showing the stalk and capillitium; *E*, portion of capillitium and spores. *F–H, Enerthema papillatum; F*, unripe sporangium; *G*, mature sporangium; *H*, capillitium. (*C, D*, after Harshberger. *A, F, G, H*, after Rostafinski; *B, E*, after de Bary; all from Harshberger's *Mycology and Plant Pathology*.)

moist and shady places. Just before the reproductive stage begins it moves from the shade and into drier, more elevated and more highly lighted places.

After a while locomotion ceases, and then spore-containing structures (sporangia) are developed either singly or in groups. A typical sporangium, such as occurs in *Stemonitis* and *Arcyria*, consists of an enlarged upper portion in which the spores are formed and a slender stalk which is attached to the substratum. The sporangium is covered with a hardened envelop, termed the **peridium.** The internal protoplasm of the sporangium usually differentiates into the following: (1) **spores,** each of which is uninucleate and surrounded by a cellulose wall, and

(2) **capillitium,** consisting of simple or branching tubes or threads. The spores are enmeshed in the network of the capillitium, which is hygroscopic and by its movement discharges the spores after the drying and breaking of the peridium. The spores are then dispersed by the wind. In the germination of the spore, for which abundant water is essential, the wall is ruptured and the contents escape as a naked amoeboid protoplast. Later it develops a single **flagellum** or **cilium,** by the motion of which the body is propelled about in the water. These ciliated motile protoplasts multiply rapidly by division. After a time each loses its cilium, becomes amoeboid and may multiply by fission to form more ciliated cells. Presently these uninucleate cells come together in pairs and fuse to form zygotes. Nuclear fusions occur in the zygote. These zygotes then coalesce in large numbers to form a plasmodium.

FIG. 300.—A myxomycete plasmodium in the active, vegetative condition, creeping over the end of a log. (From a photograph by William Crowder in the *National Geographic Magazine.* Reproduced by permission.)

The stages in the life history of a typical myxomycete may be summarized as follows: plasmodium—sporangium—spores—amoeboid uninucleate protoplasts—ciliated stage multiplying by fission—fusion of gametes to form zygotes—coalescence—plasmodium.

PHYCOMYCETES

Characteristics.—To this group belong such common fungi as the water molds, the mold which causes the well-known "white rust of mustards," common bread mold, and the downy mildews. This group of fungi is called the Phycomycetes (alga-like fungi) because of the close resemblance which they show to certain algae (1) in the structure of the filaments (hyphae) which make up the plant body, and (2) in their method of reproduction. The hyphae are, like the filaments of *Vaucheria,* coenocytic, that is filaments without cross walls except where the reproductive organs are cut off. The absence of cross walls in the hyphae is characteristic, and by this vegetative feature they can usually be distinguished from the sac-fungi (Ascomycetes), and the basidium-fungi (Basidiomycetes), both of which groups have **septate hyphae.**

Two main groups of Phycomycetes are recognized, the **Oomycetes** and the **Zygomycetes.** The principal orders of each are given below, together with a few representative genera.

I. **Oomycetes.**—Heterogamous; zoospores produced by most forms; generally aquatic. The principal groups are:

(a) *Saprolegniales.*—The members of this group are commonly called water molds. Many of these occur in ponds and streams on the dead bodies of insects, and on other organic matter. Several species attack fish, producing a serious disease. A representative group in this order is the genus *Saprolegnia*, which contains many species.

(b) *Peronosporales.*—This is a large group of parasitic forms which includes *Albugo* and the downy mildews (*Plasmopara, Peronospora, Phytophthora,* and other genera). One species, *Pythium de Baryanum*, is one of many fungi which may cause the common disease of seedlings known as **damping off.**

II. **Zygomycetes.**—Isogamous; no zoospores; mostly aerial forms. The principal groups are:

(a) *Mucorales.*—Some of these are the black molds, and are mostly saprophytic. Common bread mold, *Rhizopus nigricans*, is the best-known representative.

(b) *Entomophthorales.*—The members of this group are parasitic on insects.

SAPROLEGNIA (WATER MOLD)

Most of the species of *Saprolegnia* are saprophytes. These saprophytic species are common in streams and ponds on the bodies of dead insects and crustaceans and other decaying organic matter. A few species are parasitic and attack living fish or fish eggs, being particularly destructive when they infest the eggs and young fish in the hatcheries. Water molds may easily be obtained for study by placing dead flies in stagnant water. Within a few days, the insects generally become surrounded by a whitish growth of *Saprolegnia* or some other member of the family to which it belongs.

The Plant Body.—The plant body consists of numerous branched filaments or hyphae which are coenocytic in structure. These nonseptate, multinucleate hyphae penetrate the substratum (material upon which they live) and absorb organic substances which are used as food and which make possible the growth of hyphae.

Asexual Reproduction.—After a period of vegetative activity, hyphae grow out to the surface of the substratum and protrude into the surrounding medium. Some of these filaments become swollen at the tip, and cross walls are formed, separating the swollen portions from

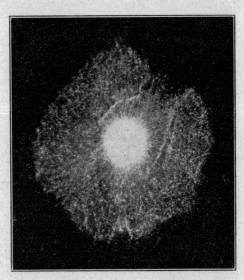

Fig. 301.—Growth of *Saprolegnia* on a bit of dead organic matter.

the rest of the hyphae. This terminal structure becomes a **sporangium,** its contents dividing up into a large number of **zoospores,** each having a single nucleus and two cilia borne at one end. After escaping through a terminal pore, they swim about in the water for a time, come to rest, withdraw their cilia, and form a wall. Later, each one of these produces a single zoospore with two cilia attached laterally, which swims about in the water and, if it comes to rest on suitable material, sends out tubular outgrowths which penetrate and infect this new material. It is not clear what is the significance of the formation of the two different zoospore stages in the life history of *Saprolegnia*. The asexual method of reproduction in *Saprolegnia* resembles somewhat that in *Vaucheria*. In both genera, the sporangia develop as terminal cells. It will be recalled that in *Vaucheria* a single multinucleate and multi-ciliate zoospore is produced in each spor-angium and that the cilia occur in pairs, with a single nucleus near the base of each pair. In *Vaucheria*, however, the protoplasm of the sporangium does not break up into numerous separate zoo-spores, as it does in *Saprolegnia*, nor is there a second formation of zoospores.

Sexual Reproduction.—The gametangia of *Saprolegnia* also resemble those of *Vaucheria*. The female gametangia (oogonia) may be borne either at the ends or on the sides of hyphal branches. Each female game-tangium is a spherical structure, the contents of which form one or more eggs. Male game-tangia (antheridia) arise on branches near the oogonia. They are tubular in form and curve so that they come in contact with the female gametangia. A slender tube is then sent out which penetrates the wall of the fe-male gametangium. A tube may be sent out to each egg. The contents of the male gametangium consist of several non-motile male gametes. These are discharged into the egg, and fertilization takes place, after which the eggs form thick-walled zygotes which upon germination form new hyphae directly.

In many cases, the eggs develop into new hyphae without fusion with the male gam-ete. It will be recalled that such develop-ment of a gamete without fertilization (par-thenogenesis) sometimes occurs in *Ulothrix* and it is not infrequent in *Spirogyra*. This

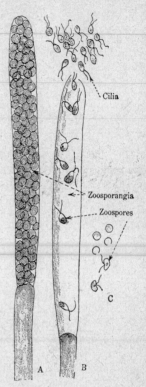

FIG. 302.—*Saprolegnia* show-ing asexual reproduction. *A*, a mature zoosporangium a short time before the liberation of the spores. *B*, a zoosporangium dis-charging zoospores which have terminal cilia. *C*, several of these zoospores which have become en-cysted; also two of the laterally biciliate zoospores which develop from the encysted zoospores.

phenomenon is occasionally met with in all the great groups of plants in which sexual reproduction takes place.

ALBUGO CANDIDA

Another representative of the Oomycetes is *Albugo candida,* which belongs to the order Peronosporales. It is a parasite, attacking members of the mustard family (Cruciferae) and causing a disease known as **white rust.** The principal symptoms of the disease are distortions and enlargements of the flower clusters and fruits, and the development of porcelain-white blotches or blisters on the leaves and stems.

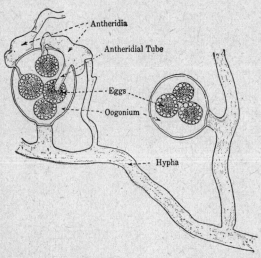

FIG. 303.—Sexual reproduction in *Saprolegnia.* (Redrawn from Sinnott in *Botany,* McGraw-Hill Book Co., Inc.)

The Plant Body.—The mycelium is composed of non-septate hypha which penetrate the tissues of the host, occupying intercellular spaces. The hyphae send out small, slender, lateral projections called **haustoria,** which penetrate the cell walls, enter the cells, become swollen at the tip, and act as absorbing organs.

Asexual Reproduction.—(See Figs. 305 and 306, *A.*) At certain points on the stem or leaves of the host, hyphae develop in great abundance just below the epidermis. They give rise to numerous, erect, spore bearing branches (**sporangiophores**) at the tips of which chains of sporangia are cut off. The growth of the sporangiophores and sporangia finally ruptures the epidermis, the sporangia breaking off easily and being dispersed by the wind. Each sporangium is multinucleate. In the film of water which may occur on the surface of the host, the protoplasmic contents of the sporangium divide into numerous laterally biciliate zoospores. These escape, swim about for a while, and then come to rest and develop a germ tube which is capable of penetrating the host and starting a new mycelium.

Sexual Reproduction.—(See Fig. 306.) The female gametangia and male gametangia develop on separate hyphae within the intercellular spaces of the host tissue. Within the female gametangium there are numerous nuclei, but one of these occupies the center of the female gametangium and is surrounded by a broad zone of cytoplasm which is somewhat differentiated from the multinucleate protoplasm lying outside of it. The central nucleus and the zone of cytoplasm around it constitute the female gamete.

The male gametangium is an elongated cell and, like the female gametangium, is multinucleate. It comes in contact with the oogonial walls, and sends out a fertilizing tube which penetrates the wall and the

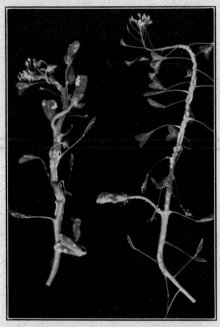

Fig. 304.—White rust (*Albugo candida*) on shepherd's purse. Note the porcelain-white blotches on the stems and fruits, and the distortions and enlargements of these parts.

outer multinucleate layer of the protoplasm of the female gametangium. Through this tube, one or more male nuclei pass, one of which unites with the egg nucleus. The fertilized egg nucleus, together with the surrounding cytoplasm, constitutes the zygote, which develops a heavy wall about itself and is later set free by the decay of the host tissue in which it is embedded. These zygotes are resting bodies, and a period of rest is necessary before they are capable of germination. On germination, the zygote gives rise to many zoospores.

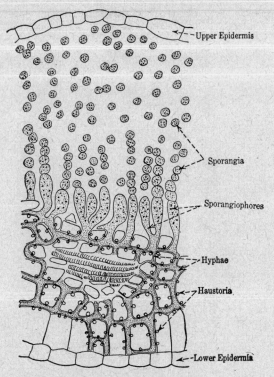

Fig. 305.—Cross section of leaf of shepherd's purse (*Capsella*) parasitized by "white rust" of crucifers (*Albugo candida*) and showing the hyphae with their knob-like haustoria, the erect sporangiophores, and multinucleate sporangia. Note that by growth of the sporangiophores and sporangia the epidermis is being torn from the underlying mesophyll. (Redrawn from Chamberlain.)

THE DOWNY MILDEWS

The downy mildews are characterized by the development of sporangiophores on the surface of the host rather than beneath the epidermis as in *Albugo*, and by the fact that the sporangia are borne singly, rather than in chains. Female and male gametangia are often produced, and the zygote, when it germinates, may form a germ tube directly, or give rise to zoospores. There are three common genera in the family, which cause diseases known popularly as "downy mildews." These are *Phytophthora*, *Plasmopara*, and *Peronospora*. *Phytophthora infestans* is the cause of the well-known potato disease known as "late blight." It is of interest to note that the serious famine in Ireland in 1845 was largely due to the failure of the potato crop resulting from the attacks of this fungus. The mycelium is found in the tissue of leaves, stems,

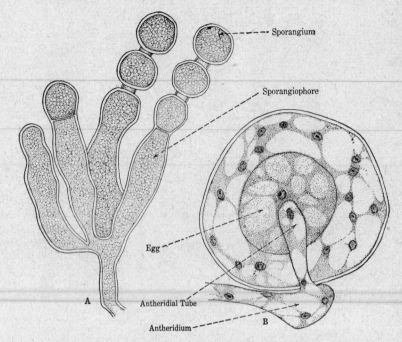

FIG. 306.—"White rust of crucifers" (*Albugo candida*). *A*, showing development of sporangia. *B*, fertilization.

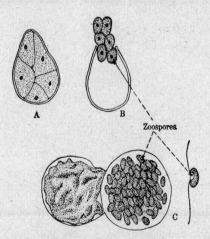

FIG. 307.—"White rust" of crucifers (*Albugo candida*). *A*, sporangium, the proto-plasmic contents of which have divided preparatory to zoospore formation. *B*, zoospores, with cilia not yet extended, escaping from sporangium. *C*, ger-minating zygote discharging the numerous zoopores which for a time are sur-rounded by a membrane. (*C*, redrawn from de Bary.)

Fig. 308.—Downy mildew (*Plasmopara viticola*) of the grape. (After Dept. of Plant Pathology, Cornell University, from Owens' *Principles of Plant Pathology*.)

and tubers and causes a wilting or blighting of the leaves and a rot of the tubers. The sporangiophores which emerge through the stomata are branched, and at the tip of each branch a single sporangium is borne. The sporangium generally germinates directly, but under certain conditions its protoplasmic contents break up into zoospores. The disease spreads rapidly from plant to plant by means of the sporangia, which are carried by the wind, and its progress may be so rapid as to devastate extended areas within a few days.

Plasmopara species are responsible for downy mildews of the grape (*Plasmopara viticola*) (Fig. 308) and of the cucumber (*Plasmopara cubensis*). As in *Phytophthora*, the sporangiophores issue from the stomata and bear singly at the branch tips sporangia, each of which give rise to several laterally biciliate zoospores. However, in this genus the contents of a sporangium may develop a germ tube directly.

FIG. 309.—Downy mildew of the grape (*Plasmopara viticola*). At the left a young cluster of Concord grapes affected with the disease. At the right a healthy cluster. (From Hein, in Circular of the *Insect Pest and Plant Disease Bureau* of Nebraska.)

In the genus *Peronospora*, the sporangium does not produce zoospores but upon germination develops a mycelium directly. Onion mildew, caused by *Peronospora schleideniana*, is a disease of considerable consequence in this country.

RHIZOPUS NIGRICANS (BREAD MOLD)

This is the best-known representative of the Zygomycetes. It is very commonly found growing on stale bread, decaying fruit and vegetables, and other organic materials left exposed to the air in moist places. *Rhizopus* spores are almost always present in the atmosphere except just after a heavy rain or snow storm when the air is almost free of bacteria and fungus spores.

If a piece of bread which has been moistened and exposed to the air is kept at a moderate temperature for a day or two in a closed dish or under a bell jar there generally develops upon it a mass of whitish mycelium. The hyphae of which this mycelium is made up develop from spores which settled from the air upon the bread and, finding there a suitable substratum, germinated.

The Plant Body.—The mycelium of bread mold consists of profusely branching coenocytic hyphae. These grow upon and within the sub-

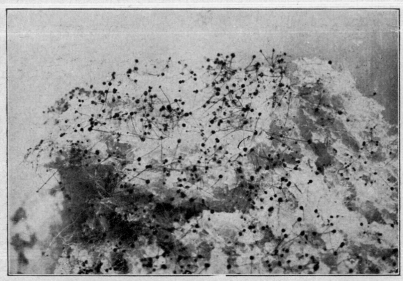

Fig. 310.—Photograph of *Rhizopus nigricans* growing on bread, showing mycelium and sporangiophores bearing sporangia. From a photograph by C. T. Gregory in *The Nature Magazine*.

stratum which supplies the necessary food. Certain hyphae, called stolons, of larger diameter than those which are formed within the

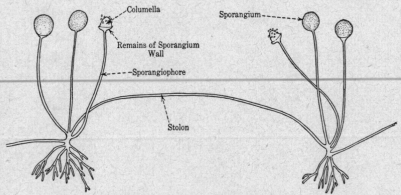

Fig. 311.—Bread mold (*Rhizopus nigricans*), showing groups of sporangiophores, rhizoid-like branches, and stolons.

substratum, grow just above its surface for a short distance, and then come into contact again with the substratum. At the point of contact there is produced a cluster of branches which penetrate the material upon which the fungus is growing and constitute a holdfast. Later there arise at this point a number of erect branches upon which the sporangia are produced. From the base of these another stolon grows out, and this in turn comes into contact with the substratum and

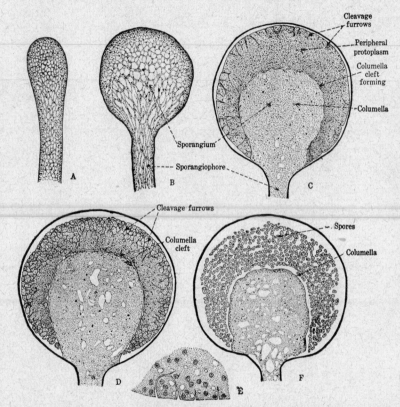

Fig. 312.—Stages in the development of the sporangia and in the formation of the spores of *Rhizopus nigricans* (black bread mold) as seen in longitudinal sections. *A* and *B* show the enlargement of the free end of a sporangiophore to form the sporangium. *C, D* and *F* show the formation of the columella, and of the spores by furrowing of the cytoplasm between the columella and the sporangium wall. *E* shows in greater detail a small portion of the protoplasm of the sporangium represented in *C*. (Redrawn from D. B. Swingle's paper, Bureau of Plant Industry, Bulletin No. 37.)

another holdfast and group of erect hyphae are formed. This may be repeated many times. The behavior of these horizontal hyphae suggests somewhat the formation and rooting of the runners or stolons of strawberries and other stolon-bearing plants, and on that account this fungus once bore the specific name *stolonifer* (stolon bearing).

Asexual Reproduction.—The erect hyphae arising at the points of attachment of the stolons grow away from the substratum and the tip of each of these develops into a globular **sporangium.** Hence such hyphae are called **sporangiophores** (sporangium-bearers). Several stages in the development of a sporangium are shown in Fig. 312.

As the sporangium commences its development, the tip of the sporangiophore begins to swell and in this region the protoplasm becomes more dense and the nuclei more numerous than toward the base. Gradually the protoplasmic contents of the swollen tip increase in density toward the periphery, whereas the central portion remains less dense and vacuolate. Finally a cleft is formed between the denser, peripheral protoplasm and the central protoplasm, and at this cleft a wall is constructed which separates the two regions. This dome-shaped wall is called the **columella.**

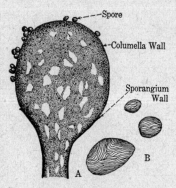

Fig. 313. — *Rhizopus nigricans* (common black mold). *A*, Columella of sporangium after the breaking of the sporangium wall. *B*, mature spores (highly magnified and showing characteristic sculpturing of wall).

During the development of the columella, the dense peripheral protoplasm breaks up into numerous angular masses, each containing several nuclei and surrounded by a cytoplasmic membrane. Each one of these multinucleate masses becomes rounded off and surrounded by a thick, black, cellulose wall, and develops into a spore. The sporangium wall finally becomes mucilaginous, so that it readily dissolves in the presence of water, and the numerous spores are set free. It is known that these spores will retain their vitality for many years in a dry state. On the other hand, they are capable of immediate germination, if they fall upon a suitable substratum.

Sexual Reproduction.—Sexual reproduction occurs under certain conditions, later to be described. In this process, pairs of club-shaped hyphal branches are formed which come into contact at their tips. (See Fig. 314.) The mass of dense protoplasm in the tip of each of these branches is cut off by a cross wall. The enclosed compartments thus formed are the **gametangia** and the multinucleate protoplasm enclosed in each is a **coenogamete.** Following a dissolution of the walls of the gametangia at the point of contact, the two adjoining coenogametes fuse. The zygote thus formed develops a thick black wall about itself, and after a resting period may germinate and send out an erect hypha, at the tip of which a sporangium containing asexual spores is formed.

It very often happens that no zygotes make their appearance in *Rhizopus* cultures even though the growth of mycelium is luxuriant, the production of asexual spores abundant, and the cultures apparently normal in every respect except for the absence of any indications of sexual reproduction. In such cases no change in the substratum, or in the conditions under which the fungus grows, will induce zygote formation. In certain localities zygotes may not be found in *Rhizopus* cultures prepared over a period of many years, while in other localities they are formed in every culture.

The reason for this peculiar condition has been made clear by the investigations of the American botanist, Blakeslee. He has shown that there are two strains or races of *Rhizopus nigricans*, the only conspicuous difference between the two being that

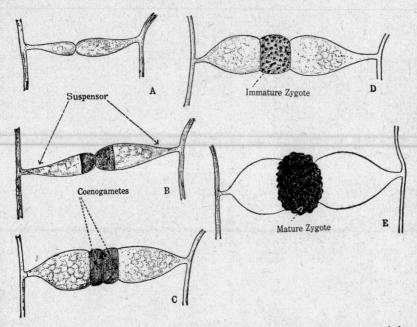

Fig. 314.—Bread mold (*Rhizopus nigricans*), showing stages in the formation of the zygospore.

one strain (which he calls the " + strain ") grows somewhat more vigorously than the other (the " − strain "). Sexual reproduction never takes place unless these two strains grow together in the same culture, for hyphae of the " minus " strain can not conjugate with other hyphae of the same strain, nor can hyphae of the " plus " strain conjugate with other " plus " hyphae. In some localities only one of the strains seems to be present and persists by reason of the production of asexual spores, but in such localities, zygotes will never be formed unless the strain which is lacking is introduced from some other place.

We have to do here with a slight sexual differentiation, scarcely recognizable externally but clearly apparent from the behavior of the two strains. There are some other molds which resemble *Rhizopus* in this respect. All such species are said to be **heterothallic.** In the case of such molds, opposite strains of different species may conjugate incompletely but without zygote formation (Fig. 315).

The zygotes of heterothallic species contain nuclear material from both strains. However, it has been found in certain heterothallic species that the two strains are segregated sometime before the formation of the asexual spores in the sporangium to which each zygote gives rise when it germinates. Accordingly there are two

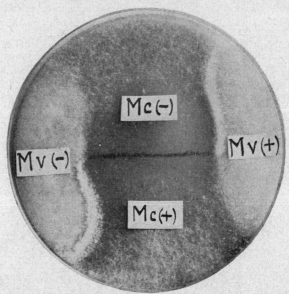

Fig. 315.—Petri dish culture of two species of mold (*Mc* and *Mv*), showing their behavior when two different strains of the same species grow together and when strains of two different species grow together. When a favorable substratum (such as nutrient agar-agar jelly or moist bread) is inoculated at one place with spores of the minus strain *Mc*(−) of a mold and at another place with spores of the plus strain *Mc*(+) of the same mold the mycelia of the two strains will grow outward from the points of inoculation over the surface of the substratum and will finally come into contact. Soon a black line will appear where the growths of the two strains have come into contact, this line resulting from formation of zygotes where the hyphae of the two strains have conjugated. If the two inoculations had been made, not with plus and minus strains of the species, but with one strain *Mc*(−) or *Mc*(+) of one species and with the opposite strain *Mv*(+) or *Mc*(−), respectively, of some other mold there generally appears a distinct white line resulting from incomplete conjugation (without zygospore formation) between the opposite strains of the two different molds. Clearly in the case of a heterothallic mold of which only one strain is known, it is possible by growing it with both strains of another mold to determine whether it is the "plus" or "minus" strain. (After Blakeslee from Gager.)

kinds of asexual spores, those which, when they germinate, will give rise to plants of the minus strain and those which on germination give rise to the plus strain. In the case of *Rhizopus* none of these spores develop into plants combining the characters of two strains. There are many molds related to *Rhizopus* which form zygotes by the conjugation of hyphae of the same mycelium. These are spoken of as **homothallic.**

PHYCOMYCETES—A SUMMARY

1. The group includes both parasitic and saprophytic forms. There are parasitic species which attack animals and others which attack plants. Various kinds of organic matter furnish a suitable food supply for the saprophytic forms.

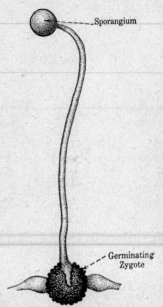

2. The hyphae are characteristically coenocytic and non-septate.

3. Asexual reproduction (a) by means of sporangia which produce motile spores (*Albugo* and usually the downy mildews); (b) by non-motile spores (as in *Rhizopus*); or (c) by zoospores (in *Saprolegnia*). Sporangia arise by abstriction and either occur in chains as in *Albugo* or singly at the tip of hyphal branches as in the downy mildews.

4. The gametes may be structurally similar, as in the Zygomycetes; or unlike as in the Oomycetes.

5. In the Phycomycetes a transition is noted from the aquatic to the terrestrial habit. The Oomycetes are chiefly aquatic, or at least at some portion of their life are dependent upon water for spore distribu-

Fig. 316.—Sporangiophore and sporangium of *Rhizopus* developed from zygote; note wall of zygote.

tion, on account of the development of motile spores (zoospores), whereas the Zygomycetes are principally aerial and produce non-motile spores.

6. The coenocytic hyphae and the form of the sporangia and gametangia in the Oomycetes strongly suggest a relationship between the Phycomycetes and such forms as the green alga *Vaucheria*.

ASCOMYCETES

Characteristics of the Group.—The Ascomycetes is the largest group of the fungi and includes a great variety of forms, over 37,000 in all, many of which cause diseases of economic plants.

The one outstanding characteristic of the group, and the one that suggested the name Ascomycetes, is the formation, somewhere in the life history, of spore sacs called **asci** (singular **ascus**) within each of which are produced a number of spores (generally eight) called **ascospores.** In addition to ascospores, conidiospores are also produced by many Ascomycetes. The hyphae of Ascomycetes differ from the coenocytic hyphae of the Phycomycetes in being septate, that is, divided by traverse walls into cells, each of which may contain one or more nuclei.

Fig. 317.—Leaf curl of peach caused by *Exoascus deformans*. At the left, branch with diseased leaves. At the right, healthy branch. (From Annual Report of the New Jersey Agricultural Experiment Station for 1913.)

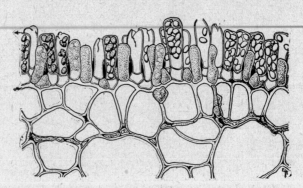

Fig. 318.—*Exoascus deformans*. Section of peach leaf showing layer of asci on the surface. (After Owens, from *Principles of Plant Pathology*.)

In *Exoascus*, which is parasitic on plums, peaches, and other related plants, causing a leaf curl and enlarged hollow fruits, the asci are not enclosed but are produced at the surface of the infected organ (Fig. 318). In most Ascomycetes the asci are produced in special, often large and fleshy, fruiting bodies, called **ascocarps**. In *Peziza* and *Sclerotinia*, and many other genera the asci are borne in a cup-shaped or saucer-shaped ascocarp, which is called an **apothecium**. In the powdery

FIG. 319.—A cluster of ripening peaches attacked by brown-rot (*Sclerotinia*). (After Barss, from Owens' *Principles of Plant Pathology*.)

mildews, the asci are formed within a more or less spherical ascocarp, called a **perithecium**, which is entirely closed. Thus ascocarps are either apothecia or perithecia.

In addition to many important parasitic Ascomycetes causing plant diseases, the group also includes such non-parasitic forms of economic importance as the blue and green molds, so common on preserves and decaying fruit, the yeasts and the truffles.

PEZIZA

One of the most common saprophytic Ascomycetes is *Peziza*, which belongs to one of the largest groups of the ascus fungi, in which the asci are borne in *apothecia*.

Plant Body.—The mycelium of the various species of *Peziza* generally grows in soils very rich in organic matter or in decaying wood. There arises from the mycelium a conspicuous apothecium which sometimes has a brightly colored lining. In one species, *Peziza coccinea*,

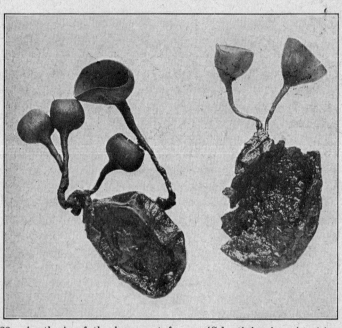

Fig. 320.—Apothecia of the brown-rot fungus (*Sclerotinia cinerea*) arising from prune "mummies." (After Barss, from Owens' *Principles of Plant Pathology*.)

the inside surface of the cup is bright red. A section through the **hymenium** (tissue lining the interior of the cup) shows numerous cylindrical asci each containing eight ascospores, and intermixed with the asci numerous sterile branches or hyphae known as **paraphyses**. The asci and paraphyses are perpendicular to the surface of the hymenium and parallel to each other. In such forms as *Peziza* and *Pyronema* the spores are discharged from the asci in great numbers and scattered over considerable distances by air movements.

Reproduction.—Although no gametangia have been found in *Peziza*, they have been discovered and carefully studied in the closely related

Fig. 321.—Apothecia of *Peziza sylvestris*. (After Seaver.)

form, *Pyronema*. In this the mycelium gives rise to female and male gametangia which are produced in close proximity. The female gametangium (sometimes called an **ascogonium** in this group) consists of a globular cell with a long tubular outgrowth, the **trichogyne,** which resembles the trichogyne of certain red algae. The female gametangium is multinucleate. The male gametangium is a cylindrical terminal cell, also multinucleate, which arises below the female gametangium. The tubular trichogyne curves toward the male gametangium and their tips come together; the intervening walls are broken down and the contents of the male gametangium move into the trichogyne and downward into the female gametangium. A union of male and female coenogametes ensues. In the female gametangium, the male and female nuclei come together in pairs, although there is yet no fusion. The fertilized female gametangium sends out a number of hyphae into each of which pairs of nuclei migrate. Then the hyphae are divided by cross walls into a varying number of compartments, in the apical one

Fig. 322.—The mature sporophore of a saprophytic ascomycete, *Helvella mitra*.

of which (destined to become an ascus) only one pair of nuclei occurs. These two nuclei now fuse, in which process there is, according to some investigators, a doubling of the chromosome number. Then there follow three successive divisions of the fusion nucleus to form eight daughter nuclei, each of which becomes the nucleus of an ascospore. One of the above divisions is a reduction division. The asci are intermingled with paraphyses which arise from beneath the female gametangium. Other sterile hyphae form the cup-shaped ascocarp.

POWDERY MILDEWS

The powdery mildews belong to a large family of Ascomycetes, all of which are strictly parasitic and produce their mycelium on the

Fig. 323.—Powdery mildew (*Uncinula salicis*) on willow (*Salix*) leaf. (After Owens, from *Principles of Plant Pathology*.)

surface of the host. The hyphae bear haustoria branches, which penetrate the host cells. Asexual spores of the conidial type, that is, formed by successive constrictions of a hyphal branch, are produced and asci are also developed in perithecia.

The conidiospores are produced in chains on the surface of the host, often in such tremendous numbers as to give a mealy or powdery

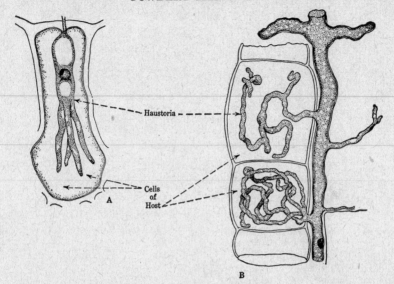

FIG. 324.—Haustoria of (*A*) a powdery mildew fungus (*Erysiphe graminis*) and (*B*) a downy mildew fungus (*Peronospora*). (*A* redrawn from C. C. Curtis, *B* from Smith.)

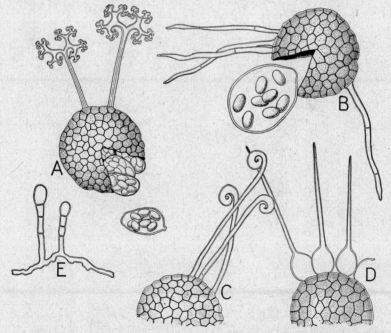

FIG. 325.—Fruiting stages of various genera of powdery mildew fungi. *A*, perithecium of *Microsphaera* from lilac leaf; *B*, perithecium of *Sphaerotheca* from gooseberry; *C*, perithecium of *Uncinula* from willow; *D*, perithecium of *Phyllactinia* from dogwood; *E*, conidial stage of a powdery mildew fungus growing on red clover. (After Owens, from *Principles of Plant Pathology*.)

appearance to the diseased structures and to suggest the name " powdery mildew." The conidiospores may germinate immediately after they are shed and thus the disease may spread rapidly from plant to plant.

Following the production of conidiospores the mycelium may form perithecia which are developed on the surface of the host plant. When mature they may be seen with the naked eye as black specks in a cobwebby mycelial growth.

Stages in the development of the perithecia are shown in Fig. 326. Two adjacent hyphae give rise to erect branches, which are unequal in size. A tip cell containing a single nucleus is cut off by a cross wall in each branch. The apical cell of the larger branch is the female gametangium, and that of the smaller branch is the male gametangium. These gametangia come in contact, there is a dissolution of a part of the wall separating the two, and the nucleus of the male gametangium enters the female gametangium and fuses with its nucleus. From the fertilized female gametangium there are formed more or less indirectly one or more asci. Sterile hyphae growing out from a cell beneath the female gametangium finally completely surround the ascus or asci to form a characteristic perithecium.

In some powdery mildews, such as *Sphaerotheca* and *Podosphaera*, a single ascus is borne in each perithecium; in others, as *Erysiphe*, *Microsphaera*, *Uncinula* and *Phyllactinia*, the perithecia contain more than one ascus. The perithecium often bears characteristic appendages, which are used as a basis for classification in this group. For example, in the genera *Sphaerotheca* and *Erysiphe*, the appendages are simple, flexuous and undivided at the tip; in *Podosphaera* and *Microsphaera*, they are dichotomously branched; in *Uncinula*, they are spirally rolled at the tip; and in *Phyllactinia*, they are swollen at the base.

BLUE AND GREEN MOLDS

These are well-known saprophytic ascomycetes found on a great variety of substances. *Aspergillus* and *Penicillium* are the two most common genera, and each has a number of species. *Aspergillus* species occur on decaying vegetables of all sorts, on moldy cereals, on jellies, old leather, paper, ensilage, etc. The mycelium produced is prolific and spores arise in tremendous numbers. Spores are developed on conidiophores, and arise by abstriction of terminal branches. The characteristic color of the mold appears when the conidiospores develop; in the different species there are various shades of green, brown, yellow, and red. The conidiospores, which are carried by air currents, and when in abundance impart a characteristic moldy odor to the atmosphere, are capable of immediate germination if they fall upon a suitable substratum.

Of the numerous species of *Aspergillus*, perithecia are known in only a few. The perithecium develops from two short hyphae which are spirally coiled about each other. Each of these hyphae consists of several cells. One of the hyphae is regarded as the female gametangium; and the other as the male gametangium. The fusion cell formed after a dissolution of the separating walls gives rise to hyphae which bear asci, each of which contains eight ascospores. The ascus-bearing hyphae

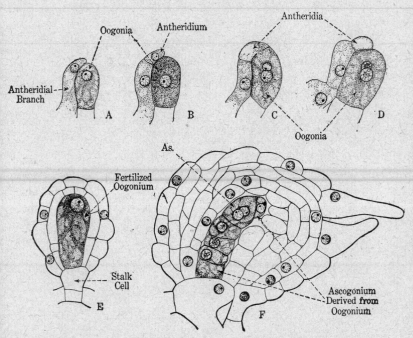

Fig. 326.—Stages in the development of a perithecium of a powdery mildew. *A*, antheridial and oogonial branches in contact. In *B* the antheridium and oogonium are cut off from the tips of the branches; *C*, movement of antheridial nucleus toward nucleus of oogonium; *D*, union of male and female nuclei, *E*, fertilized oogonium surrounded by hyphae derived from a cell just below the oogonium (stalk cell); multicellular ascogonium; *As*, cell which gives rise to the ascus. (Redrawn from Harper.)

become surrounded by other much branched, sterile hyphae which completely enclose them and form a perithecial wall.

Penicillium is the common blue mold on bread, cheese, lemons, etc. The conidiophores are branched, each branch bearing a chain of conidiospores. Sexual reproduction has been observed in several species of *Penicillium*, the process being very similar to that of *Aspergillus*.

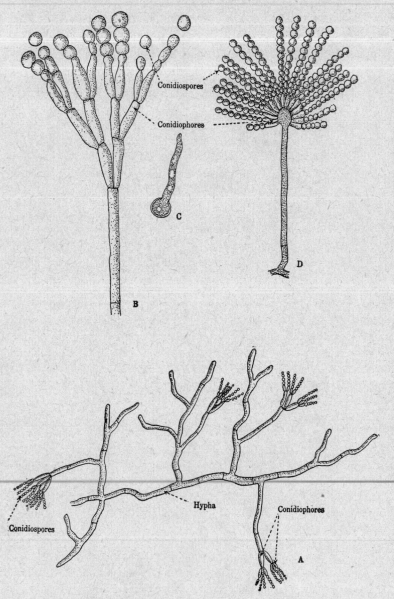

FIG. 327.—Blue and green molds. *A* and *B*, common blue mold (*Penicillium*). *C*, germinating conidiospore. *D*, green mold (*Aspergillus*).

Several species of *Penicillium* are of importance in the manufacture of certain kinds of cheese. For example *Penicillium Roqueforti* is the active agent in the ripening of Roquefort, Gorgonzola, and Stilton cheeses, and *Penicillium Camemberti* of Camembert cheese.

YEASTS

The position which the yeasts occupy in relation to other plants has long been a subject of debate. Usually, however, they are included with the Ascomycetes because of their production, under certain conditions, of structures which somewhat resemble asci.

The beer, cider and wine yeasts are included in the genus *Saccharomyces*, which has a number of species. *Saccharomyces cerevisiae* is by far the most important species, being the one employed in beer-brewing and bread-making.

Yeast cells may remain attached to form a short chain but they do not produce a true mycelium. The cells are usually egg-shaped or spherical and each cell is surrounded by a well-defined wall. Within the yeast cell may be discerned the nucleus, oil globules and vacuoles. One of the chief characteristics of the yeasts is their method of vegetative reproduction by "budding." In this process, a portion of the protoplasm of a cell forms a lateral outgrowth (bud) surrounded by a cell wall which finally may separate to form a a new individual.

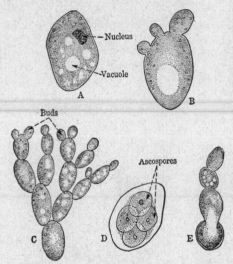

Fig. 328.—Yeast (*Saccharomyces cerevisiae*). *A*, single cell highly magnified. *B*, cell in process of budding. *C*, chain of cells formed as result of rapid budding and growth. *D*, formation of ascospores. *E*, germination of ascospore and the development of new plants by budding. (Redrawn from Curtis.)

Ascospores are produced only when there is an abundance of oxygen. In the production of ascospores the cell nucleus divides into several daughter nuclei, each one of which becomes the center of a spore lying within the original cell. The number of spores developed in a single yeast cell varies, but it is usually four. On disintegration of the wall of the original cell, the spores are liberated, and under proper conditions produce new yeast plants.

Fermentation.—The most important property of yeasts is their ability to cause alcoholic fermentation. The yeast cells absorb sugar, and within the protoplast this sugar is decomposed with the formation of carbon dioxide and ethyl alcohol. The sugars susceptible of alcoholic fermentation by yeast are the hexose sugars: glucose, fructose, mannose, and galactose. The chemical change which takes place in fermentation of glucose may be expressed as follows:

$$\underset{\text{glucose}}{C_6H_{12}O_6} \rightarrow \underset{\text{alcohol}}{2C_2H_5OH} + \underset{\text{carbon dioxide}}{2CO_2}$$

In the account of bacteria under the heading of carbohydrate fermentation (page 382) this transformation of certain sugars to alcohol and carbon dioxide was discussed.

The great economic importance of yeast is realized when we understand that on account of its power of producing a sugar-fermenting enzyme, it is indispensable in the making of bread, in the manufacture of commercial ethyl alcohol, and in the production of alcohol in fermented liquids used as beverages.

In bread making, yeast plants are mixed with a mixture of flour and water. The flour contains some sugar in addition to the starch. At a suitable temperature, the yeast cells multiply rapidly. Zymase is formed, and breaks down the sugar into alcohol and carbon dioxide. The bubbles of carbon dioxide gas are prevented from escaping by the dough, which, however, is caused to rise by the expansion of the bubbles. At baking temperatures, there is further expansion of the gas bubbles, and also a driving off of alcohol and water.

LICHENS

General Characteristics and Distribution.—The lichens constitute one of the most extraordinary groups of plants to be found in the plant kingdom. The plant body is made up of a fungus growing in intimate relationship with an alga. The fungus forms the greater bulk of the plant body, and is usually one of the Ascomycetes (in three genera of lichens the fungal component is a basidiomycete), as is evidenced by the fact that it reproduces by ascospores produced in an ascocarp. The alga in this plant complex belongs either to the Myxophyceae or simple Chlorophyceae. In some cases it is possible to make separate cultures of the alga and fungus which constitute the lichen, and then to bring them together and produce a lichen experimentally, the fungal threads enclosing the algal cells and forming a typical lichen body.

The co-partnership of the alga and the fungus in a lichen is an excellent example of symbiosis. The manufacture of food can be carried on only by the alga, and necessarily the fungus is dependent upon the alga, from which it absorbs food. However, the alga also derives some benefit from the presence of the fungus. The fungus absorbs water from the substratum upon which the lichen lives and also from fog and moist air, and passes it on to the alga. The fungus also protects the algal cells from fatal drying out when the air humidity is very low. It should be emphasized that in a lichen two definite species —an alga and a fungus—when grown together may produce a characteristic plant body which is different in form and appearance from either component grown separately. To this compound organism we must also give a generic and a specific name.

Lichens are world wide in their distribution. They are found in a great variety of situations, and are of many different forms and colors. Crustaceous and leaf-like forms occur on the surface of rocks, on the bark of trees and on the soil. Some lichens, such as the so-called reindeer moss (*Cladonia*) of arctic tundras, and *Usnea*, which is pendent from the branches of trees, grow to a large size. In many habitats lichens are exposed to the greatest extremes of temperature and humidity. In fact they are able to live in habitats—exposed rocks and tree bark, for example —where few other plants can maintain themselves. They can undergo extreme desiccation for a long period, and revive when favorable conditions recur.

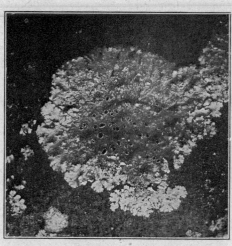

FIG. 329.—A foliose lichen showing the cup-shaped apothecia.

A few lichens are of some economic importance. Various pigments, including litmus, are manufactured from lichens, and some lichens are used for food by man and domestic animals. Reindeer and caribou on the northern tundras live in certain seasons, largely on " reindeer moss " (not a moss but a lichen). Lichens are also important agencies in the disintegration of rock upon which they grow.

Structure of Lichen Body.—The lichen body is a thallus, which in cross section is seen to possess an upper and a lower layer of fungal threads, between which is a region of looser hyphae. The algal cells may be scattered among the hyphae throughout the plant body, or as is more frequent, in a layer near the upper surface. Hyphae from the lower surface may act as absorbing and anchoring structures.

Reproduction.—In discussing reproduction of lichens it is necessary to distinguish between (1) the reproduction of the lichen as a whole, and (2) the reproduction of each of the two component organisms which make up the lichen.

In the case of many lichens, especially in pendent forms of *Usnea*, there is often considerable multiplication resulting from the tearing loose by the wind of relatively large fragments of thallus which may find lodgment in places favorable for their development into large

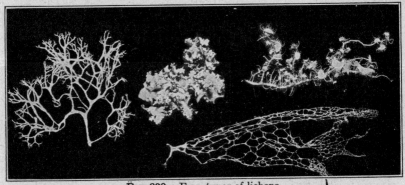

FIG. 330.—Four types of lichens.

thalli. In addition most lichens form special reproductive bodies called **soredia**, each of which consists of a few algal cells surrounded by fungous hyphae. They are produced in powdery or granular masses on the surface of the thallus or in some cases on special branches. When they fall from the lichen or are carried away by the wind they may develop into lichen thalli.

The algal component consists usually of simple unicellular plants, which reproduce within the body of the lichen by fission and thus increase in number as the thallus grows. The fungal component if, as in most cases, it is an Ascomycete, reproduces by means of ascospores. These are generally borne in apothecia which are very similar to those of *Peziza* and related Ascomycetes. Unless the ascospores germinate in close proximity to cells of the algal component, a new lichen will not be formed. A few lichens produce their asci within closed ascocarps (perithecia) which open by a small pore when the ascospores have reached maturity.

In certain species the ascocarps are formed as the result of a sexual reproductive process strikingly similar to that of certain Rhodophyceae. In other cases careful study has failed to show any evidence of a sexual process.

ASCOMYCETES—A SUMMARY

1. The group includes both parasitic and saprophytic forms. Organic matter of either plant or animal origin may be a source of food. Many of the representatives cause important diseases of cultivated plants.

2. The hyphae are septate, but each of the compartments thus formed may contain several nuclei.

3. In many cases conidiospores are produced.

4. In addition, characteristic spores (ascospores) are produced in an ascus (sac); in many cases it has been shown that sexual fusions are involved in the processes leading up to the formation of an ascus or group of asci, and that preceding the formation of ascospores a reduction division takes place.

5. The asci are generally produced in fruiting bodies, known as **ascocarps,** which may be open (apothecia) or closed (perithecia).

6. There is a close similarity between certain of the Ascomycetes and some of the Rhodophyceae as regards the structure of the gametangia and the behavior of the zygote. This similarity is suggestive of a relationship between the two groups.

BASIDIOMYCETES (BASIDIUM-FORMING FUNGI)

Characteristics of Group.—Thus far in our discussion of fungi we have dealt with the four classes: Bacteria (fission fungi), Myxomycetes (slime fungi), Phycomycetes (algal fungi), and Ascomycetes (sac fungi). There remains for us to consider one very important class of fungi, the Basidiomycetes. The class name is descriptive of the outstanding character of the group, which is the occurrence of a special type of structure, called a **basidium** (plural **basidia**), in the life cycle of these plants. It is a club-shaped hypha which produces spores (**basidiospores**) singly at the end of several (usually four) slender, pointed protuberances called **sterigmata** (singular **sterigma**). In some Basidiomycetes the basidium is divided by cross walls into a number of cells (generally four) but in other forms it is non-septate. In the early stages of development of the basidium there is a fusion of nuclei (as in the young ascus) to form a single diploid nucleus, and preceding the formation of basidiospores, a reduction division takes place.

The class Basidiomycetes is subdivided into the following three groups:

1. The smut fungi—Hemibasidiomycetes.
2. The rust fungi—Protobasidiomycetes.
3. The fleshy and woody fungi—Eubasidiomycetes.

HEMIBASIDIOMYCETES (SMUT FUNGI)

The smut fungi are regarded as the most primitive of the Basidiomycetes. All are parasites, occurring on a wide range of hosts, the most common hosts being the Gramineae, which include the grasses, and common cereals. The smuts annually destroy millions of dollars' worth of corn, oats, barley, wheat, rye, and other cereals. The estimated reduction of yield of cereals in the United States due to smuts during 1921 was 160,738,000 bushels.

Corn Smut.—The smut of corn (*Ustilago zeae*) may be selected as a type form. The mycelium of the fungus may occur in any part of the host (Fig. 332). It causes abnormalities of development and tumor-like swellings, sometimes of considerable size. These result from the abundant development of hyphae in the tissue of the host and from the resulting stimulation of the tissue of the affected organ to abnormally active growth. Later, practically all of the internal tissue of the diseased part of the host is used up by the growth of the smut hyphae, so that the whole deformed structure, except the surface layer, becomes a mass of fungal hyphae. These hyphae are then transformed into millions of black spores known as **chlamydospores.** Each of these spores is formed from a short segment of a hypha which becomes surrounded by a slightly thickened wall and then separates from the adjoining segments of the same hypha. Chlamydospores are capable of germination as soon as mature if conditions are favorable, or they may retain their vitality throughout the winter and germinate the next spring. Germination may take place on old corn stalks, soil, or manure. Each germinating chlamydospore produces a short hypha, called a promycelium or basidium, which is divided by cross walls into three or four cells. Each of these cells bears a single basidiospore which is generally spoken of as a **sporidium.** The sporidia are capable of multiplication by bud-

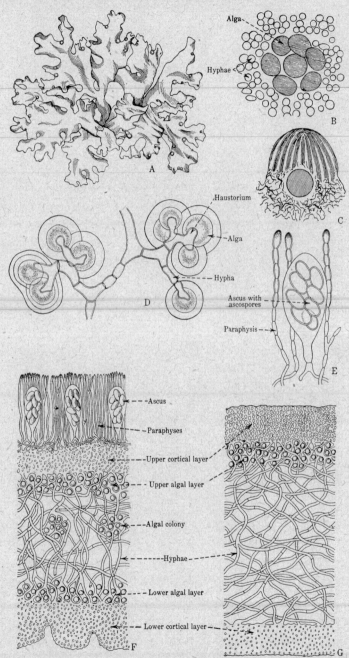

F~IG.~ 331.—A lichen.   A, plant slightly reduced.   B and C, soredia in different stages
of development.   D, algal cells surrounded by fungal cells with haustoria.
E, three paraphyses and a single ascus.   F, section of apothecium.   G, section
of vegetative portion of thallus.   (B and C, after Schwendener; E, F, and G,
after Schneider; D, after Bornet.)

ding, such budding often going on rapidly on barnyard manure. The sporidia are readily carried by the wind and may, if they fall upon any young tissue of a corn plant, send out short hyphae which will penetrate the epidermal cells and thus infect the plant. As a result of the infection

Fig. 332.—Common smut of corn (*Ustilago zeae*). Smut tumors on the ear. (After Jackson, *Del. Agr. Exp. Sta. Bul.* 83.)

there develop the tumor-like swellings already described. Each of these is the result of a separate infection.

Modes of Infection in Smuts.—Among the cereal smuts, three modes of infection are recognized, namely (1) **seedling infection**, (2) **flower infection**, (3) **general**

infection. In seedling infection, as illustrated by bunt (stinking smut) of wheat, covered smut of barley and all oat smuts, kernel smut of sorghums, and millet smuts, the spores adhere to the surface of the seed. When the seed germinates, the smut

Fig. 333.—Common smut of corn in the tassel.   (After Jackson, *Del. Agr. Exp. Sta. Bul.* 83.)

spores also germinate, and the smut hyphae penetrate the tissue of the seedling at once. The parasite keeps pace with the developing plant, becoming conspicuous as black, sooty masses of spores which partially or totally replace the flowering head. A smut of this sort may be held in control by treating the seed with a substance such as copper sulphate, copper carbonate, or formaldehyde, which will destroy adhering smut spores, but will not injure the embryo.

The loose smuts of wheats and barley infect their hosts through the flower, the spores being incapable of infecting any part of the plant except the ovary. There is a slight development of the mycelium in the embryo of the grain and there is no apparent injury to the grain. However, when the seed germinates, the dormant mycelium begins to grow, and as the young plant develops, the mycelium keeps pace with its host. It is possible by careful microscopic study to detect the hyphae of the smuts in the stem-growing point of the host (Fig. 339). Not until the flower head is forming does the presence of the parasite become evident. Then the tissues of the flowers which are infected by the mycelium of the fungus are transformed into a mass of black chlamydospores. These are readily scattered by the wind and may infect flowers in a less advanced stage of development.

It is obvious that the ordinary seed treatment which has for its object the destruction of smut spores adhering to the seed would be useless in controlling smuts which

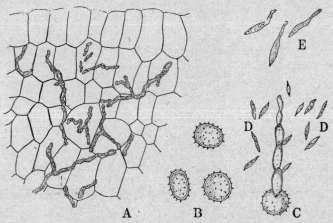

Fig. 334.—Corn smut (*Ustilago zeae*). *A*, hyphae in the tissue of the host. *B*, mature chlamydospores. *C*, a germinating chlamydospore, showing the 4-celled basidium, two cells of which are producing sporidia (basidiospores). *D*, sporidia. *E*, budding sporidia. (Redrawn from Freeman and Stakman, in Minnesota Agricultural Experiment Station Bulletin.)

have infected the flowers of the host, for in smuts of this type the hyphae are within the embryo. However, a hot-water method of seed treatment has been devised which will destroy the dormant mycelium but leave the embryo uninjured.

Corn smut is an example of the third, or general, type of infection. In this, young tissue of stem, leaves, flowers, and even roots may be infected. Since the parasite may gain entrance through any part of the plant, it is clear that seed treatment would be useless. Control of corn smut may be accomplished by removal from the field and burning of smut masses before they discharge the spores, and by a proper system of crop rotation.

PROTOBASIDIOMYCETES (RUST FUNGI)

The rusts are a group of fungi of great economic importance. They are parasites on a great variety of hosts, chiefly seed plants. Well-known diseases of economic plants which are caused by rusts are black

FIG. 335.—1, head of Little Club wheat affected with bunt or stinking smut (*Tilletia tritici*), and immediately to the right one kernel of wheat filled with chlamydospores of the parasite. 2, disease-free head of Little Club wheat, and to the left a normal wheat kernel. (From Mackie.)

stem rust of wheat, oats, barley and rye, asparagus rust, apple rust, orange rust of raspberry and blackberry, and blister rust of pines. The grain losses due to the black stem rust of cereals are sometimes enormous. Many epidemics of this disease have occurred, those of 1904 and 1916 in this country having been particularly destructive. According to one of the principal American authorities on cereal rusts, " the most conservative estimate places the loss of wheat in the United States due to the black stem rust in 1916 at 180,000,000 bushels, while the loss in Canada was estimated at about 100,000,000 bushels."

The rust fungi are striking examples of obligate parasites, that is organisms which are unable to live except in living tissue. They are

FIG. 336.—Loose smut of wheat (*Ustilago tritici*). Left, normal head of club wheat;
middle, head affected with smut before heading; right, spores beginning to blow
away. (From Mackie.)

incapable of living in culture media, even when these media are made
from the host plant upon which they thrive.

The mycelium of rusts is composed of septate hyphae which nearly
always grow in the intercellular spaces of the host tissue and are branched
and provided with haustoria. Five different types of spores may be
formed in rust fungi, but not all types are present in every species of
rust. These different forms of spores will be described in a later
paragraph.

One of the best-known genera among the rusts is *Puccinia*. It
has a number of very important species, chief of which is *Puccinia*

FIG. 337.—Smutted oats. At the left, head affected by loose smut (*Ustilago avenae*); at the right, head affected by closed smut (*Ustilago levis*). (From Colorado Agricultural College Extension Service Bulletin.)

FIG. 338.—*A*, kernels of normal wheat, and *B*, kernels of wheat filled with chlamydospores of *Tilletia*. The disease is bunt. (After Leach, in Colorado Agricultural Experiment Station Bulletin.)

graminis, the black stem rust of wheat, oats, barley, rye, and many grasses.

LIFE HISTORY OF PUCCINIA GRAMINIS (BLACK STEM RUST)

Most parasitic fungi require but a single host for their life cycle, but a few have two different host species and can not complete their life cycle unless both are present. *Puccinia graminis* is one of the latter, requiring a grass such as wheat as one host, and the barberry as the second or alternate host.[1]

Red-spore or Uredinial Stage.—The first visible evidence of this rust on cereals is seen on the stems and leaves as reddish-brown streaks or pustules, which make their appearance in the spring and summer. These are sori of minute yellowish spores formed just beneath the epidermis of the host. These spores are known as **urediniospores,** and the sori as **uredinia.** These spores are external evidence of the presence of a mycelium growing between the cells of the tissues of the host. The production of these spores is spoken of as the " red rust " stage of the disease. The mycelium which gives rise to the spores is intercellular and forms haustoria which penetrate the cells and absorb foods from the living protoplasts. Each urediniospore is stalked, one-celled and ovate, and has two nuclei and a rather thick wall which bears numerous small spiny projections. These spores are disseminated by the wind. They are capable of immediate germination, if they fall upon a wheat leaf or stalk, and if sufficient moisture is present. Infection takes place by the growth of the germ tube through a stoma into the host tissue (Fig. 340). Within the host tissues this hypha branches and forms a new mycelial growth. Within a short time the mycelium absorbs sufficient food from the host to form a new crop of **urediniospores.** Thus it

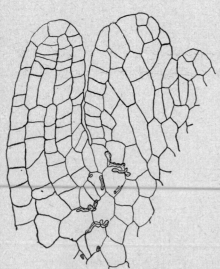

FIG. 339.—Portion of the tip of an infected barley stem showing hyphae of loose smut of barley in the tissue. (Redrawn after Freeman and Stakman, in Minnesota Agricultural Experiment Station Bulletin.)

[1] The account of the life history of *Puccinia graminis* has been revised and partly rewritten by Dr. Ruth Allen, Cytologist in Wheat Rust Investigations, U. S. Dep't of Agriculture.

is possible to have a number of successive crops of **urediniospores** in a season, and from one or a few infected plants the disease may spread over a large area. In fact, the red stage may thus repeat itself under favorable environmental conditions every seven to ten days. The epidemics of rust that occur in grain districts are chiefly due to weather conditions which are favorable to the development of successive crops of red rust spores, and thus make possible the rapid spread of the disease.

Black-spore or Telial Stage.—Usually in the late summer or fall when the grain begins to ripen, black pustules or sori appear on the same culms and leaves which produced the urediniosori. These sori produce dark-colored spores known as **teliospores.** The sori are called **telia.** One may sometimes find both urediniospores and teliospores in a single sorus. The teliospores are stalked, two-celled structures which are spindle-shaped and have a thick wall. Each of the cells of a young teliospore have 2 nuclei which fuse before the spore is ripe, thus giving rise to a diploid nucleus. They are unable to germinate at once as do the urediniospores, but after wintering in the open on stubble or on the soil, they germinate freely.

The Basidial Stage.—After the rest period, the teliospore germinates. The spore develops a hypha and the diploid nucleus migrates into it, divides twice (one division being the reduction division) giving rise to four haploid nuclei, two of which are *plus* and two *minus.* Septa divide the hypha forming the four-celled promycelium. Each of the four cells is capable of producing a single, colorless, uninucleate basidiospore on a short stalk (sterigma). Basidiospores are carried by the wind.

The Spermogonial Stage.—If the basidiospore comes to rest on a leaf, fruit, or young twig of certain species of barberry, including the common barberry (*Berberis communis*), the germ tube (young hypha) which is formed when the spore germinates, penetrates the epidermis of the barberry plant and develops mycelium in the tissue of the host. If the spore germinates on the surface of any plant except one of the susceptible species of *Berberis*, development of the hyphae of the rust fungus within the tissue of the plant does not take place. This mycelium, consisting of uninucleate cells, grows within the barberry leaf and in seven to ten days develops small flask-shaped structures called **spermogonia.** These are buried in the tissue of areas of the leaf which are thickened as the result of the presence of the rust mycelium within the leaf tissue. At maturity these spermogonia break through either the upper or the lower epidermis of the leaf and push out a tuft of stiff-looking hyphae, the paraphyses. The interior part of a spermogonium is lined with very fine hyphae at the tips of which small cells,

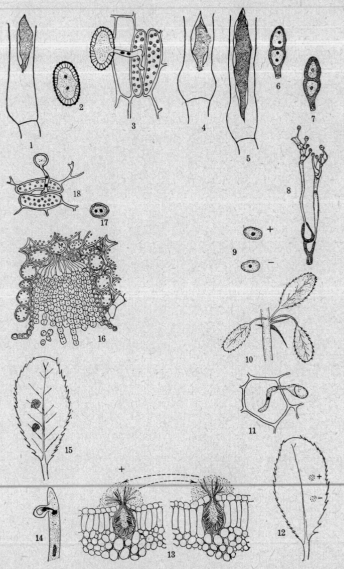

Fig. 340.—Life cycle of black stem rust (*Puccinia graminis*)—an heteroecious rust: 1, Uredinia on wheat stem. The red unrediniospores are produced early in the season. 2, A single urediniospore, a binucleate body. 3, Germinating uredinio-spore on the surface of the stem of the same or another wheat plant, its germ tube, with 2 nuclei, penetrating a stoma. As a result a mycelium, each cell of which is binucleate, is formed within the tissues of the host and soon another crop of urediniospores is borne in uredinia as shown in 4. Thus during a single season there may be successive crops of urediniospores, the disease thus spreading

the **spermatia,** are produced. These ooze out to the surface in a sweet-ish liquid of flower-like odor, attractive to insects.

It will be recalled that the basidiospores, like the asexual spores of *Rhizopus,* are of two kinds, *plus* and *minus.* A plus basidiospore results in a *plus* mycelium which bears *plus* spermatia. A *minus* basidiospore grows into a *minus* mycelium which bears *minus* spermatia. Neither, by itself, can proceed to the next part of the life cycle.

The Aecial Stage.—When a *plus* spermatium is carried to a *minus* infection or a *minus* spermatium is carried to a *plus* infection (achieved in nature by visiting insects) or when the hyphae of two adjoining infections of opposite sex overlap and become connected within the barberry leaf, fertilization takes place. *Plus* and *minus* nuclei meet but do not fuse. The further growth of the mycelium consists of binucleate cells, and aecia bearing binucleate aeciospores are now developed. The clustered aecia are cup-shaped structures opening upon the lower surface of the leaf and filled at maturity with chains of yellow one-celled, but binucleate **aeciospores.** These are scattered by the wind and if they fall upon the surface of a wheat plant or of any other species of grass susceptible to infection by the rust fungus, the spore pushes out a germ-tube, enters the host through a stoma and rust mycelium consisting of binucleate cells is developed within the tissue of the grass plant. This mycelium gives rise to the uredinia of the red-rust stage.

Spore Forms.—In the black stem rust of grasses and cereals which we have just described, there are four spore forms, namely:

---

rapidly over a field. 5, A telium produced later on wheat stems. The telio-spores which are liberated from the telia are 2-celled, each cell being binucleate. They remain alive on the soil or straw during the winter. 6, A single immature teliospore, two-celled, each cell binucleate. 7, A mature teliospore, each cell uninucleate. During the maturation of the teliospores, the two nuclei in each cell fuse. 8, A teliospore germinating the spring following its formation. Each cell is sending out a 4-celled promycelium (basidium) each cell of which may produce one basidiospore. The cells of the basidium and the basidiospores are each uninucleate. 9a and 9b, Basidiospores which will develop into plus and minus mycelia respectively, which will in turn give rise to plus and minus spermatia. 10, If the basidiospores fall upon a common barberry leaf (10), they germinate as shown in 11, and the germ tube penetrates the leaf epidermis and forms a mycelium within the tissue of the leaf. 12, A barberry leaf (upper surface), showing two groups of spermogonia. 13, Cross sections of two different parts of the same leaf, showing spermogonia in longitudinal section. One of these has developed from a plus mycelium, the other from a minus mycelium. At the tips of hyphae in the spermogonia, spermatia are produced. 14, Nucleus of a spermatium passing into a paraphysis. 15, The lower surface of a barberry leaf bearing the aecia or cluster cups. 16, Cross section of an aecium bearing aeciospores. 17, A binucleate aeciospore. 18, Hypha from a germinating aeciospore entering the stoma of a wheat leaf.

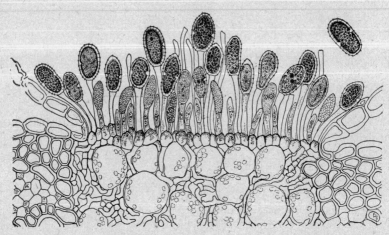

Fig. 341.—Section through a uredinium of *Puccinia graminis* on wheat stem, showing urediniospores in various stages of development. (After Owens, from *Principles of Plant Pathology*.)

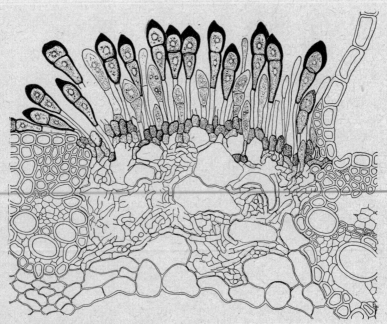

Fig. 342.—Section through a telium of *Puccinia graminis* on wheat stem, showing teliospores in various stages of development. (After Owens, from *Principles of Plant Pathology*.)

1. *Urediniospores*—in sori (uredinia) on the grass or cereal host.

2. *Teliospores*—in sori (telia) on the grass or cereal host.

3. *Basidiospores*—on a promycelium or basidium developing directly from the germinating teliospores on the soil or stubble.

4. *Aeciospores*—in cluster cups or aecia on the lower surface of the swollen areas of the barberry leaves.

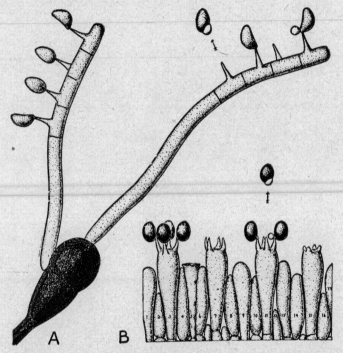

Fig. 343.—Spore-discharge in the Uredineae and the Hymenomycetes. *A*, a germinated teliospore of *Puccinia graminis* (from *Avena sativa*, bearing two basidia, one with four ripe spores and the other with spore-discharge going on.) *B*, a transverse section through the hymenium of *Psalliota campestris*, showing a basidium with four ripe spores and another basidium with spore-discharge going on. In both *Puccinia graminis* and *Psalliota campestris* a drop of water is excreted from the hilum of each spore just before discharge. Magnification the same both *A* and *B*, 880. (From Buller's *Researches on Fungi*.)

Heteroecism.—Parasitic fungi, which like *Puccinia graminis*, have two different host species and can not carry through their complete life cycle unless both hosts are present, are called heteroecious fungi. By far the majority of parasitic fungi, however, require but a single host in order to complete their life cycle. They are spoken of as autoecious fungi. A common autoecious rust is *Puccinia asparagi*, the asparagus rust.

Prior to 1865 the true relationship of the red rust stage, black rust stage, and barberry rust stage of *Puccinia graminis* was unknown. In fact, these three rusts were regarded as different species and given different generic names, *Uredo Puccinia*, and *Aecidium*, respectively.

The establishment of the fact that these were three different stages in the life history of a single organism is credited to the classical researches of the great German botanist, Anton de Bary.

Fig. 344.   Fig. 345.

Fig. 344.—Leaf of common barberry (*Berberis vulgaris*) showing clusters of aecia on the lower surface.   (From Buller's *Researches on Fungi*.)

Fig. 345.—Aecia of blister rust on white pine tree.   (After U. S. Dept. of Agr., from Owens' *Principles of Plant Pathology*.)

For a number of years, the great importance of the barberry in spreading rust has been recognized.   Denmark, in 1903, passed a barberry eradication law and since then almost all bushes have been eradicated from the country.   This has resulted in almost total elimination of black stem rust in Denmark.   In 1918, a vigorous barberry eradication campaign was initiated in this country by the Office of Cereal Investigations, of the United States Department of Agriculture, cooperating with the thirteen principal wheat-growing states.   Already, eradication has progressed so far in certain sections that the beneficial results are noticeable. It is not to be expected that destruction of all plants of those species of barberry which are subject to the disease will eradicate the disease in all localities. In regions where the winters are mild, urediniospores may survive the winter and infect cereals in the spring, thus continuing the disease without the alternate host.

White Pine Blister Rust (Cronartium ribicola).—This heteroecious rust, which has as alternate hosts certain species of white pines and certain species of *Ribes* (currants and gooseberries), although not a serious disease on *Ribes* species, has caused great losses of pines, chiefly *Pinus strobus* and other five-needled pines. The spermogonial and aecial stages occur on the pine, the uredinial and telial stages on *Ribes* species. On the pine the mycelium of the fungus grows in the tissue of the stem. From this mycelium there are developed on the surface of the bark small spermogonia from which spermatia exude in glistening drops of a sugary fluid. Also on the pine bark the aecia appear as orange-yellow blisters.

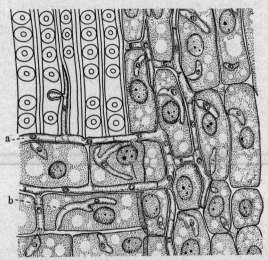

Fig. 346.—Relation of the mycelium of *Cronartium ribicola* in the stem of its host (*Pinus strobus*). *a*, hyphae passing above and at right between the cells of the parenchyma with their large nuclei, and at left passing between the tracheids with their large bordered pits, each cell of the hyphae with a nucleus; *b*, haustoria of various shapes, each with a nucleus. The nuclei of the host-cells are much larger than the nuclei of the fungus. (After Colley, from Arthur's *Plant Rusts*.)

Infection of the leaf of *Ribes* occurs as a result of the germination of aeciospores on the lower surface of the leaf. From the mycelium in the *Ribes* leaf there develop orange-yellow pustules (uredinia) on the lower surface, from which urediniospores are shed. These spores are borne throughout the summer and infect other *Ribes* plants. Teliospores may either arise from old uredinia or in separate sori. Teliospores germinate on any substratum where moisture is adequate. The germinating teliospore develops a five-celled promycelium, and on each of the four upper cells a sporidium is borne on a short sterigma. The sporidia are borne by the wind to the pine, where they germinate and infect the young leaf-bearing twigs. The first aecia do not appear until the second or third spring after infection. The mycelium spreads in the bark of pine, producing each season a new crop of aeciospores. As a result of the infection, large cankers are formed on the bark, which may finally girdle the branch upon which they are borne, and kill that portion of the tree above the girdle.

Fig. 347.—Telial stage of blister-rust on currant leaf. Natural size. (After Owens, from *Principles of Plant Pathology*.)

EUBASIDIOMYCETES (FLESHY AND WOODY FUNGI)

This group includes the most familiar representatives of the Basidiomycetes, such as the mushrooms, puff-balls, and many other fleshy and woody forms. A characteristic feature of the group is the conspicuous **sporophore** which may attain considerable size and which produces the **hymenium,** a compact layer of one-celled basidia (each with four basidiospores) and sterile filaments.

The Eubasidiomycetes consist of two subgroups:

1. Hymenomycetes—in which the hymenium is exposed.
2. Gasteromycetes—in which the hymenium is enclosed.

HYMENOMYCETES

The principal order of the Hymenomycetes is the *Agaricales*. This includes the gill fungi, the tooth fungi and the pore fungi.

A Common Gill Fungus.—Of all Eubasidiomycetes the gill fungi are

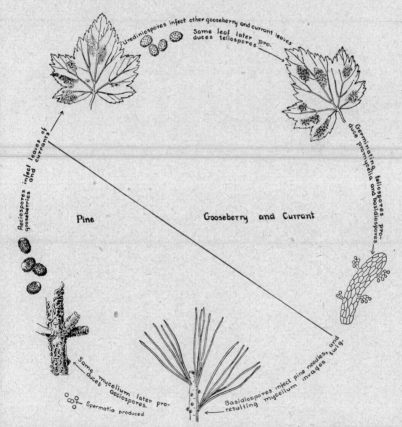

Fig. 348.—Diagrammatic representation of the life history cycle of white pine blister rust (*Cronartium ribicola*). (After Owens, from *Principles of Plant Pathology*.)

the best known. The most familiar gill fungus is the cultivated mushroom (*Agaricus campestris*). The mushroom as we ordinarily know it is not the whole plant but merely a reproductive structure or sporophore.   The vegetative part of the plant body is the mycelium which grows saprophytically in the soil or other substratum upon which the sporophores are produced.   It consists of extensively branched strands of hyphae which absorb and use as food organic material in the substratum.   On this account mushrooms are never found except in locations where there is an abundance of organic material, such as decayed leaves and twigs, or manure.   It is only after the mycelium has accumulated considerable stores of food that the sporophores are produced.

The mature sporophore, or fruiting body, consists of a stalk or **stipe** and an umbrella-shaped cap called the **pileus.**   On the under side of this cap there are borne thin plates called **gills** which radiate from the

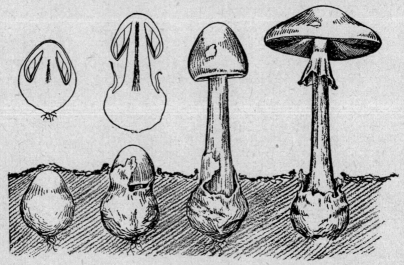

Fig. 349.—Stages in the development of a gill fungus (*Amanita*).   See explanation in text.   (After Longyear.)

stalk toward the margin of the pileus.   The whole surface of the gills is covered with a layer (the hymenium) made up of millions of basidia and sterile hyphae (paraphyses) all of which grow out at right angles to the surface of the gills.   At the free end of each basidium (see Figs. 350 and 351) basidiospores, usually four in number, are produced, one on the end of each of the four sterigmata.

Mushroom " spawn," as sold by seedsmen, usually consists of dried manure and decaying leaves containing the mycelium of mushrooms which have previously grown upon this material.   When a mushroom bed is being made this material is broken up, mixed with earth, and used to start the beds.   The partially dried mycelium in the spawn grows rapidly in the moist warm substratum of the mushroom bed. The sporophores originate from strands of the subterranean mycelium. The first evidence of these is in the form of small rounded masses of interwoven hyphae known as " buttons," which are usually formed just beneath the soil surface. Within the button the pileus and stipe develop, and when the stipe elongates and the cap expands, the " mushroom " (sporophore) quickly assumes its typical shape. In the young sporophore there is a thin layer of hyphae which extends from the margin of the cap to the stipe, covering the gills. As development proceeds this layer is torn, but remnants of it may cling to the stipe, forming a " ring." The presence of a " ring " on the stipe is characteristic of the common edible *Agaricus*, as well as a number of other gill fungi. The young sporophore is often covered with a membrane, which is ruptured by the expanding cap and stipe, and remains at the base of the stipe as a cup or **volva.**

Basidiospores are produced in immense numbers on the hymenium. It has been computed that a single sporophore of *Agaricus campestris*, measuring 8 cm. in diameter, may liberate as many as 1,800,000,000 spores and a single fruiting body of *Polyporus squamosus* as many as 11,000,000,000. In the latter case the spores are liberated at an average rate of at least one million a minute. The spores drop from the sterigmata of the basidia upon which they are borne, and are readily carried far and wide by air currents. Under favorable conditions they germinate and develop a new mycelium, but it has been estimated that in the common mushroom, *Agaricus campestris*, only about one spore in twenty billion actually germinates and grows into a mushroom plant.

Kinds of Gill Fungi.—The gill fungi are divided into five groups, based upon the color of the spores, as follows:

1. White-spored.
2. Rose-spored.
3. Ocher-spored.
4. Purple-brown-spored.
5. Black-spored.

Spore color is readily determined by making a spore print. This is made by cutting off the cap, laying it with gills down on a piece of smooth paper, and covering to prevent spores from being blown away. Within twenty-four hours or less, spores will have been discharged in sufficient numbers so that an imprint or copy of the gill arrangement is left and it is possible to determine the color of the spores.

White-spored gill fungi include the well-known genus *Amanita*, in which are found practically all the deadly poisonous species of gill fungi.

Amanita is distinguished by the following combination of characters:
1. White spores.
2. " Ring " on the stipe or stem.
3. Volva, or cup, at the base.

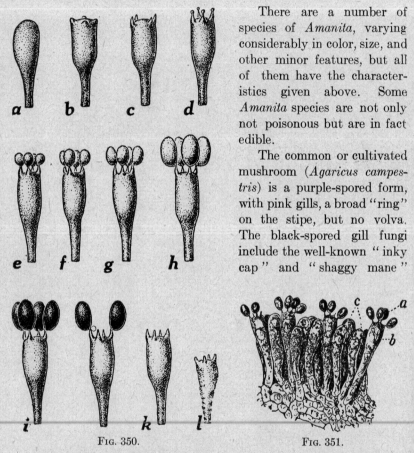

There are a number of species of *Amanita*, varying considerably in color, size, and other minor features, but all of them have the characteristics given above. Some *Amanita* species are not only not poisonous but are in fact edible.

The common or cultivated mushroom (*Agaricus campestris*) is a purple-spored form, with pink gills, a broad "ring" on the stipe, but no volva. The black-spored gill fungi include the well-known " inky cap " and " shaggy mane "

Fig. 350.

Fig. 351.

Fig. 350.—*Coprinus sterquilinus*. Stages in the development of a basidium and basidiospores, showing formation of basidium (*a–c*), development of spores (*d–i*), spore discharge (*j*), and degeneration of basidium (*k–l*). All of these stages are passed through in less than thirty-six hours. Magnification, 408 × (From Buller's *Researches on Fungi*.)

Fig. 351.—Small portion of a section through the spore-bearing layer (hymenium) of a mushroom. *a*, basidiospores; *b*, a basidium; *c*, paraphyses. (After Longyear, in Colorado Agricultural Experiment Station Bulletin.)

(*Coprinus* species). In these, the gills finally dissolve, forming a black inky liquid.

FIG. 352.—Semi-diagrammatic drawing of a section in a field illustrating the manner in which the spores of the Horse Mushroom (*Psalliota arvensis*) are liberated and dispersed. A slight lateral movement of the air is supposed to be carrying the spore-cloud away from the underside of the pileus. Reduced to ½. (From Buller's *Researches on Fungi*.)

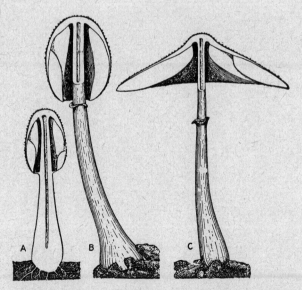

FIG. 353.—*Lepiota cepasestipes*. Sections of three fruit-bodies coming up among cinders, Sphagnum, etc., in a hothouse. *A*, in the morning, the gill-chamber still intact. *B*, in the afternoon, the pileus beginning to expand, an annulus left upon the stipe. *C*, at night, the pileus fully expanded and shedding spores. Natural size. (From Buller's *Researches on Fungi*.)

Tooth Fungi.—The members of this group have sporophores which are distinguished by the presence of teeth or spines which bear the hymenium. It includes both fleshy and leathery forms. *Hydnum* is the best-known genus in the family, several species of which cause wood rots.

Pore Fungi.—In this group, the spores are borne in open tubes or pits. Certain species of pore fungi are among the most destructive wood-rotting fungi. The fruiting body or sporophore is shelf-like in shape and frequently woody, leathery, or corky in texture. The sporophores of pore fungi are often found on trees and in some species may grow from year to year until they finally attain a large size.

Fig. 354.—Masses of mycelium of a dry rot fungus (belonging to the Polyporaceae) under the floor of a building.

GASTEROMYCETES—PUFF-BALLS

This assemblage of fleshy fungi has the hymenium enclosed within a covering known as the **peridium.** The puff-balls (Lycoperdales) are the best-known representatives. In some genera, the peridium consists of a single layer, whereas in others it has up to four layers. For example, in the earth-star (*Geaster*) the outer peridial layer splits open, when the spores are mature, into star-like lobes, and later those lobes become reflexed, whereas the inner layer opens by a terminal pore. The inside of a young, immature puff-ball consists of a white, fleshy tissue, which becomes chambered as development proceeds. In some genera, these chambers are filled with interwoven hyphae, the lateral branches of which end in basidia, whereas in other genera the walls are lined with basidia.

Other quite common representatives of the Gasteromycetes are the bird's nest fungi (Nidulariaceae) and the stink horns (Phallaceae).

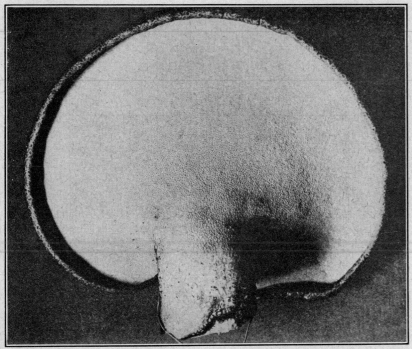

FIG. 355.—Under surface of fruit-body of *Polyporus squamosus* nearly full grown, showing the pores of the hymenial tubes and the reticulations on the stipe. The fruit-body was photographed immediately after it was cut; the involution of the edge of the pileus is quite natural. Photographed by R. H. Pickard. One-third natural size. (From Buller's *Researches on Fungi*.)

BASIDIOMYCETES—A SUMMARY

1. This group includes both parasitic and saprophytic fungi. Many cause destructive plant diseases.

2. The hyphae are septate and branched.

3. No motile spores are produced.

4. The characteristic feature of the class is the occurrence in the life cycle of a basidium, which produces asexual spores.

5. Gametangia have not been found. There are simple nuclear fusions, however, which serve as fertilization processes, and reduction divisions preceding the development of basidiospores.

FIG. 356.—An aspen trunk with several sporophores of the bracket fungus, *Fomes igniarius*. The vegetative mycelium is within the tissues of the stem. (After Von Schrenk and Spaulding, in *Journal of Agricultural Research*.)

6. The Basidiomycetes are considered to be the highest of the fungi, and to have been derived from the Ascomycetes. The basidium has a place in the life history similar to that of the ascus.

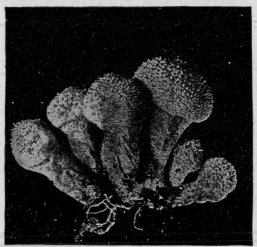

Fig. 357.—A cluster of puff-balls (*Lycoperdon*). (After Longyear.)

Fig. 358.—A sporophore of a puff-ball, *Lycoperdon pachydermum*. On the left an external view and on the right the sporophore in section showing the outer "shell" or peridium and the gleba, spore-bearing tissue within. At the base of the sporophore are the mycelial threads by which it is attached to the mycelium in the soil. (Photograph furnished by E. E. Morse.)

FIG. 359.—Sporophores of *Calvatia sculpta*, a puff-ball. (Photograph furnished by E. E. Morse.)

FIG. 360.—An "earth star," sporophore of *Geaster fornicatus*. (Photograph furnished by E. E. Morse.)

CHAPTER XIII

EMBRYOPHYTA

THE BRYOPHYTA (LIVERWORTS AND MOSSES)

It will be recalled that in the classification used in this book, the plant kingdom is divided into two subkingdoms: the Thallophyta (consisting of the Phycophyta and the Mycophyta), and the Embryophyta (consisting of Bryophyta, Pteridophyta, and Spermatophyta). In those members of the Thallophyta which have sexual reproduction, the zygote develops into one or more new plants which from the beginning of their development are independent and able to secure their own food. In the Bryophyta, Pteridophyta, and Spermatophyta, however, the zygote divides and produces a mass of cells, the **embryo**, which remains attached to and secures food from the haploid plant (gametophyte) which produced the zygote. Only after being thus dependent upon the haploid plant for some time does the embryo become an independent plant (in the Pteridophyta and Spermatophyta), and eventually produce spores. In the Bryophyta, the plant which develops from the embryo never becomes detached or entirely independent from the haploid plant.

On the basis of the production of an at least temporarily dependent multicellular structure, called the embryo, the three divisions, Bryophyta, Pteridophyta, and Spermatophyta, are grouped into the subkingdom, Embryophyta, whereas the Phycophyta (algae) and Mycophyta (fungi), which do not form embryos, make up the subkingdom Thallophyta.

GENERAL CHARACTERISTICS OF THE BRYOPHYTA

The algae, with very few exceptions, grow submerged in fresh or salt water, and those which do not grow submerged live on wet substrata or at least carry on an active existence only during periods when moisture is abundant. The Bryophyta, on the other hand, are truly terrestrial or land plants, although their adaptation to land conditions is so imperfect that few of them, if any, are able to complete their life cycle unless the plant is covered with water, at least for a short period. They are also unable to grow actively during dry periods, because of their relatively inefficient water-absorbing and conserving tissues.

Another very important characteristic of the Bryophyta is the fact that in all of them there is a distinct alternation of generations. It has been shown for many of the seed plants, for some algae, and a few other plants, and is probably true for all plants having sexual reproduction, that the zygote nucleus has twice as many chromosomes as the nuclei of the gametes, and that somewhere in the life cycle of all such plants there is a reduction division by which the double ($2n$ or diploid) chromosome number is reduced to the n or haploid number characteristic of the gametes. In the simpler algae having sexual reproduction, this reduction takes place soon after the formation of the zygote. Accordingly, " the plant " has nuclei with the haploid chromosome number.

It will be recalled that in a number of the Rhodophyceae the reduction division is delayed for a long time. Thus in the life cycle of *Polysiphonia* and many other red algae, there are two different plants which alternate with each other. These are (1) the asexual plant which has the diploid chromosome number and which produces tetraspores, the nuclei of which have the haploid chromosome number, and (2) the sexual plant arising from a tetraspore and having the haploid chromosome number in their nuclei. These sexual plants produce gametes whose fusion again doubles the number of chromosomes and again gives rise to asexual plants. This alternation of diploid and haploid plants, which is generally spoken of as **alternation of generations,** occurs also in some Phaeophyceae but it is by no means characteristic of the Thallophyta as a whole, for in most of the Thallophyta having sexual reproduction the doubling of chromosomes is soon followed by reduction and no " plant " with " $2n$ " chromosomes in its nuclei is produced. Alternation of generations is, however, characteristic of all the Bryophyta, Pteridophyta, and Spermatophyta.

The terrestrial habit, embryo formation, and the constant occurrence of alternation of generations in the life cycle are the most significant characteristics distinguishing the Bryophyta from most Thallophyta. The following is a summary of the principal characteristics of the Bryophyta:

1. With the exception of a few forms the Bryophyta are terrestrial or epiphytic and in general show marked preference for moist habitats. Those which grow in dry places often show a remarkable power to survive extreme desiccation, but they carry on their growth and other life processes actively only during wet or very moist periods.

2. Alternation of generations takes place in all the members of this division.

3. The asexual plant (**sporophyte**) is smaller than the sexual plant

(gametophyte).   It is permanently attached to and grows more or less parasitically upon the gametophyte, never establishing direct connection with the soil.

4. The epidermal cells are provided with a cuticle, which is lacking in the case of the Thallophytes.

5. No true roots are formed in this division, but the sexual or gametophyte plants produce organs called **rhizoids**, which perform the functions carried on by the roots of ferns and seed-bearing plants.

6. Sexual reproduction is heterogamous.   The female gametangium (called the **archegonium** in the Bryophyta and Pteridophyta) does not consist of a single cell (as in most of the Thallophyta), the protoplasm of which forms one or several female gametes (egg cells).   Instead it is a **multicellar** flask-shaped **organ,** and the single egg cell is surrounded by a wall made up of **many cells,** instead of being surrounded by a **cell wall only** as in the Thallophytes.

7. Multicellular antheridia (male gametangia) of the Bryophyta are also distinctly different from those of the Thallophyta, the wall surrounding the sperms produced by one antheridium being made up of a **layer of cells** instead of consisting, as in the Thallophyta, merely **of a cell wall.**

8. Fertilization can not take place unless the surface of the plants is wet, for it must be possible for the sperms to swim to the archegonia. The gametes have n chromosomes, the zygote $2n$.

9. The asexual spores of the Bryophyta (and the Pteridophyta and Spermatophyta as well) are formed in groups of four (**tetrads**), each tetrad being formed as the result of two divisions of a single cell (the spore mother cell).   The first of these two divisions is a reduction division.

The Bryophyta are divided into two classes, the Hepaticae or liverworts and the Musci or mosses.

THE HEPATICAE (LIVERWORTS)

The members of this class are in general more strictly confined to very moist habitats 'than are the Musci.   There are some species, however, notably certain forms growing in California and in other regions where there is a long dry season, which are able to survive months of almost complete desiccation.   The sporophytes of the liverworts are less complex than are those of the mosses and for the most part somewhat smaller.

We shall describe the structure, development, and reproduction of two representatives of the Hepaticae and call attention to some of the principal variations from these types.

RICCIA

This and the closely related genus *Ricciocarpus* have the simplest sporophytes (asexual phase) of all liverworts, although their gametophytes are not so simple as are those of certain other members of the class. *Riccia fluitans* is a species which frequently grows partially submerged in water whereas *Ricciocarpus natans* is generally found floating on the surface of water. Both of these species, however, can grow upon moist soil when the water dries up or recedes.

The Gametophyte.—The gametophyte of the land-living species of *Riccia* is a small, flattened, dorsiventral plant body or **thallus** which branches freely by dichotomy (forking) and thus frequently takes on a rosette form (Fig. 361). *Riccia* plants can often be found on bare moist ground in early spring. The middle line of the thallus is thickened and forms a sort of midrib, and there is a long depression on the upper side of the thallus along the middle line. From the underside of the thallus numerous rhizoids grow out. These are very similar to root hairs and are merely tubular extensions of certain of the cells of the lower surface of the thallus. They function as organs of attachment and also absorb water and soil solutes. In addition to the rhizoids there are borne on the under side of the thallus a series of broad overlapping scales. At the end of each branch of the thallus and at the bottom of the median furrow there is a single cell called the **apical cell**, which by its repeated division gives rise to daughter cells from which are formed all the new tissue of the growing branch. Thus the gametophyte grows at the tip as do the stems and roots of the higher plants, but the " promeristem " consists of a single cell instead of a group of cells as in the seed plants. If a cross section of the thallus (Fig. 362) be examined it is found that the upper or dorsal portion is made up of cells containing chloroplasts, while the lower or ventral part consists of colorless cells. In some species there are many clefts extending from the upper surface of the thallus down into the chlorophyll-bearing tissue. These function, like the stomata and intercellular spaces of leaves, in giving access of air to the cells which carry on photosynthesis. The colorless cells below the green layer serve for water and food storage.

The Gametangia.—Each antheridium and archegonium is sunk in a deep depression in the thallus, opening out into the median furrow. Antheridia and archegonia are usually found on the same gametophyte thallus. However, in many species of liverworts, mosses, and ferns, antheridia and archegonia are produced on different gametophytes which are therefore spoken of as **male gametophytes** and **female gametophytes.**

In *Riccia*, antheridia and archegonia in various stages of development may be found on a single plant, those nearest to the ends of the branches being at more immature stages of development than those farther back.

Antheridia.—These are more or less pear-shaped organs with a short stalk at the broader end. There is a single layer of sterile cells which forms the wall of the antheridium and encloses, in antheridia which are almost mature, several hundred cells with relatively large nuclei and dense cytoplasm. These latter are the sperm mother cells, each of which, by a single nuclear division and a subsequent oblique division of the protoplast, gives rise to two sperm cells. The protoplast of each sperm cell forms a single biciliate sperm.

Archegonia.—The female gametangia in *Riccia* are in no important particular different from those of other genera of the Hepaticae, and so may be taken as typical of the whole group. Each mature archegonium consists of an enlarged basal portion, the **venter**, and a slender and elongated tubular portion called the **neck**. The base of the venter is attached to the tissue at the bottom of the depression in which each archegonium is enclosed. The neck reaches almost or quite to the top of the depression where it opens into the median furrow of the thallus. Within the single layer of cells which forms the wall of the venter and neck is a single row of cells. The largest of these cells occupies most of the cavity of the venter. It has a large nucleus and dense cytoplasm and is the female gamete. The cell just above it is the **ventral canal cell**.

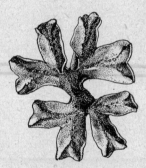

Fig. 361.—Thallus of a terrestrial species of *Riccia*. (Magnification about 8×.)

Though the ventral canal cell and the egg cells have been formed by the division of a single cell, the ventral canal cell never functions as a gamete. The other cells of the axial row are called the **neck canal cells**. They are four in number in *Riccia* but more numerous in some other liverworts. The walls separating the neck canal cells from each other generally break down before the archegonium is mature, and the protoplasts of the neck canal cells and ventral canal cells degenerate into a mucilaginous mass.

Fertilization.—The union of the male and female gametes can not take place in *Riccia*, nor in fact in any of the liverworts, mosses, or ferns, unless the gametophyte plants are wet. Even though fully developed, the archegonia and antheridia do not open except after the plants have been wet by rain or heavy dew. Furthermore, even if

freed from the antheridia, the sperms can reach the archegonia only by
swimming in water.   When gametophytes bearing mature archegonia
are wet, water is absorbed by the mucilaginous remains of the ventral
canal and neck canal cells, and as the result of the swelling of this
mucilaginous material the **cover cells**, closing the neck canal, are forced
apart.   The mucilage is soon dissolved away so that there is an open
passage down the neck canal to the cavity of the venter, where the
egg, a spherical, naked protoplast, awaits fertilization.   At the tip of
the antheridium some of the sterile cells forming the wall of the antheridium are forced apart as the result
of the swelling of the disorganized
walls of the sperm mother cells,
and through the resulting opening
the sperms escape.   Each sperm
is a small spirally twisted structure
made up mostly of nuclear ma-

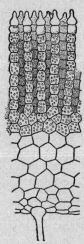

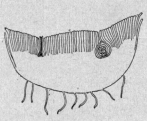

FIG. 362.   FIG. 363.

FIG. 362.—Cross section, somewhat diagrammatic, of the thallus (gametophyte) of
   Riccia showing on the left an unfertilized archegonium sunk in a deep depression.
   On the right is a sporophyte within the enlarged venter of an archegonium from
   the fertilized egg cell of which the sporophyte developed.   The chlorophyll-
   bearing tissue of the upper portion of the thallus is also shown as well as the
   colorless tissue of the lower part of the thallus, and the rhizoids.   (Magnification
   about 30×.)

FIG. 363.—A portion of a cross section of the thallus of a species of *Riccia* showing
   the chlorophyll-containing tissue, the colorless region, and the origin of a rhizoid.
   Magnification about 100×.   (Redrawn after Casares Gil.)

terial but including also some cytoplasm.   The two cilia are several
times as long as the body of the sperm.

The sperms have a tendency to move towards certain of the substances discharged from the archegonium neck (a phenomenon known
as **positive chemotaxis**), and so in their swimming they are directed
toward the archegonia.   On this account and because hundreds of
sperms are produced to one archegonium, few egg cells fail of being fertilized.   Though a number of sperms may find their way into a single
archegonium only one enters the egg and fertilizes it.   Almost imme-

diately upon the entrance of the sperm into the egg, a thin cellulose wall is formed about the resulting zygote. The nuclear material, which makes up practically the entire sperm, fuses with the nucleus of the egg, the resulting zygote nucleus having therefore twice the chromosome number characteristic of the gametophyte and gametes. The formation of the zygote marks the beginning of the sporophyte or asexual generation.

The Sporophyte.—The zygote now increases in size until it almost fills the venter of the archegonium and then by division becomes a two-celled embryo. By repeated cell divisions the embryo sporophyte grows into the mature sporophyte, a spherical mass of cells many times the size of the zygote. Meanwhile the venter of the archegonium enlarges as the sporophyte grows. The sporophyte, even after it has reached maturity, and the enlarged archegonium venter which surrounds it remain within the tissue of the gametophyte thallus. A short time before the sporophyte reaches maturity it consists of a wall made up of a single layer of flattened sterile cells and within this wall a number of free spherical cells with dense cytoplasm and large nuclei. Each of these cells is called a **spore mother cell**.

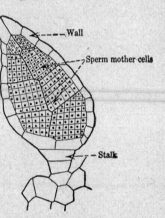

FIG. 364.—An antheridium of *Riccia* in longitudinal section.

Spore Formation.—Up to this point all the nuclei of the sporophyte, including the spore mother nuclei, have $2n$ chromosomes. Each spore mother cell undergoes two successive divisions and forms a spore tetrad or group of four spores. The first division of the spore mother nucleus is a reduction division and the two resulting nuclei have n chromosomes. They almost immediately undergo the second division which is, however, not a reduction division but an ordinary mitosis, so that the four spore nuclei have the haploid chromosome number. Each of these nuclei, together with some cytoplasm and considerable stored food, becomes surrounded by a thin wall which thickens as the spore ripens. By the time the spores have fully matured the single layer of cells forming the walls of the sporophyte and the cells of the enlarged archegonium venter have broken down.

Germination of Spores.—The spores are freed by the decay or shriveling of the gametophyte and under favorable conditions germinate to form new gametophyte plants. The coat of the mature spore consists of two layers, the **exine**, which is relatively thick and dark in color, and a thin and more delicate inner layer called the **intine**. At germination the protoplast of the spore absorbs a considerable quantity of water

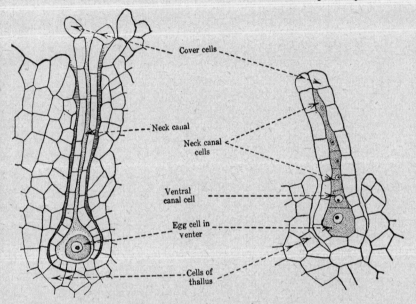

FIG. 365.—Archegonia of *Riccia* surrounded by the tissue of the thallus. To the right, an almost mature archegonium. To the left, an archegonium ready for fertilization. (Drawn from preparations of D. H. Campbell.)

and swells. As a result the exine is ruptured and the intine is stretched so that it protrudes in the form of a short, blunt germination tube. This soon grows, no doubt largely because of continued water absorption

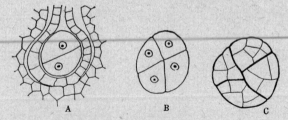

FIG. 366.—Successive early stages in the development of the sporophyte of *Riccia*.

and the resulting stretching of its wall, until it forms a tube of a length several times as great as the diameter of the spore. Most of the protoplasm of the spore, including oil drops and granules of other stored foods, passes out into the tube. Chloroplasts appear and increase in number, and soon the enlarged end of the germination tube is cut off by a transverse wall. By repeated division of the terminal cell a group of eight cells is formed. One of these cells becomes the apical cell. By successive divisions of this apical cell there are cut off cells from which all new tissue is derived. Thus a new gametophyte plant arises all the nuclei of which have *n* chromosomes.

Life Cycle of Riccia.—The following are the principal stages in the life cycle of *Riccia* (Fig. 369):

1. The gametophyte thallus which absorbs water and mineral salts from the soil and carbon dioxide from the air and which carries

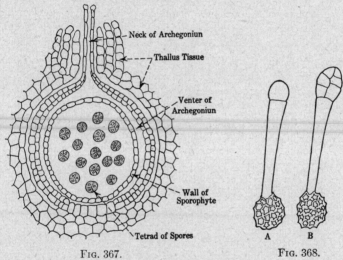

FIG. 367.

FIG. 368.

FIG. 367.—Diagrammatic figure showing in cross section, the mature sporophyte, enlarged archegonium, and thallus of *Riccia*.

FIG. 368.—Two early stages in the development of the gametophyte of *Riccia* from the spore. None of the cell contents has been shown.

on photosynthesis. All the nuclei of the gametophyte are haploid (having *n* chromosomes).

2. The development within this thallus of the gametangia (antheridia and archegonia).

3. The formation within each antheridium of hundreds of sperms and within each archegonium of one egg cell. Each gamete has *n* chromosomes.

4. The opening of the archegonia and antheridia after maturity and when the plants are wet.

5. Swimming of sperms to archegonia and fertilization of egg cell by a sperm.

6. The formation of the zygote with its $2n$ nucleus by the fusion of the two gametes.

7. Development from the zygote of a globular sporophyte consisting of a single outer layer of sterile cells enclosing a number of spore mother cells. All the cells of the sporophyte plant, including the spore mother cells, have diploid nuclei (each with $2n$ chromosomes).

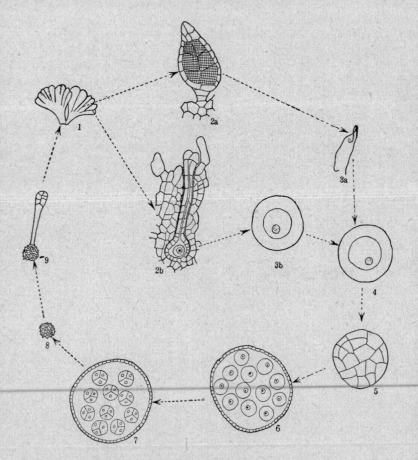

Fig. 369.—Diagram showing the life cycle of *Riccia*. 1, the gametophyte thallus (monoecious). 2a, an antheridium. 2b, an archegonium ready to open and permit the entrance of sperms (both antheridia and archegonia are sunk in the tissue of the thallus). 3a, a single sperm. 3b, an egg cell. 4, the fertilized egg cell or zygote. 5, an embryo sporophyte resulting from repeated divisions of the zygote. 6, the sporophyte with contained spore mother cells. 7, tetrads of spores each such group of four resulting from two divisions (the first a reduction division) of a spore mother cell. 8, a single ripe spore. 9, a very young gametophyte plant developed from a spore. Note that stages 4–6 and the wall cells in 7 belong to the sporophyte generation, the other structures to the gametophyte.

8. Reduction division of each spore mother nucleus to form two nuclei with n chromosomes.

9. Division of these by ordinary mitosis to form the nuclei of a tetrad of spores.

Fig. 370.—Thalli (male) of *Marchantia* as seen in natural habitat. A number of antheridial branches may be seen.

10. Liberation and germination of the spores and development of a new gametophyte.

MARCHANTIA

We have chosen *Riccia* as the first bryophyte type for discussion because it has the simplest sporophyte of all living Bryophyta, although a number of liverworts have much simpler gametophytes. As a second type we shall consider the relatively common and widely distributed *Marchantia* which has a considerably more complex sporophyte than *Riccia*.

The Gametophyte.—In *Marchantia* the gametophyte, like that of *Riccia*, is a dichotomously branched thallus bearing on the lower side rhizoids and thin scales. In *Marchantia*, the archegonia and antheridia are not borne on the same gametophyte thallus, but certain thalli bear archegonia and others antheridia (Figs. 372 and 373). Moreover, the gametangia, instead of being borne buried in depressions in the thallus as in *Riccia*, are produced on special erect thallus branches. The arrangement of the cells which carry on photosynthesis is quite different in the gametophyte of *Marchantia* from that of *Riccia*. Just below

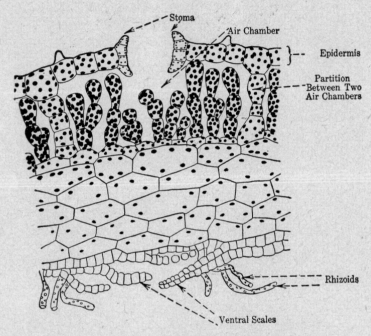

Fig. 371.—Cross section through a portion of the thallus (gametophyte) of *Marchantia*. Note in the air chambers the short, sometimes branched filaments of cells, provided with numerous and large chloroplasts.

the upper surface there are a large number of shallow air chambers. From the floor of each of these there arise short, sometimes branched filaments of cells which are provided with numerous and large chloroplasts and which are the principal carbohydrate-making cells. These chambers are completely roofed over by an epidermis except for a single pore which permits the ready entrance and exit of gases.

Reproduction by Gemmae.—*Marchantia* and a number of other related liverworts are capable of multiplying themselves asexually

without the formation of game-
tantia. This is accomplished by
means of outgrowths of the thallus
specially adapted to vegetative
reproduction (Fig. 373). They are
called **gemmae** and are borne in
structures called **gemmae cups**
which are produced on the upper
surface of the thallus. When separated from the gametophyte the
gemmae may grow into new gametophyte plants.

Antheridia and Archegonia.—
There is no essential difference in
the structure of the gametangia
in *Marchantia* and *Riccia*. The
antheridial branch has a slender
stalk surmounted by a disc with
lobed edge. Numerous antheridia are produced on each antheri-

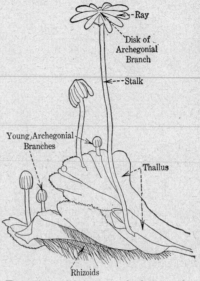

Fig. 372.—A portion of the female
gametophyte of *Marchantia*.

dial branch, each antheridium being enclosed within a cavity in the
disc. These cavities open on the upper surface of the disc and it has
been shown in the case of *Asterella*, a genus closely related to *Marchantia*, that, at the time the ripe antheridia open, their contents may
be projected several centimeters into the air. It is not unlikely that
this may occur also in *Marchantia*. When thus launched into the air
the male gametes are no doubt often carried some distance by air
currents and thus the chances of their reaching an archegonial plant
are somewhat increased, but fertilization is possible only when the
surface of the archegonial plant is covered with water.

The archegonial branch consists of a slender stalk surmounted
by a small disc with a number of radiating and drooping rays. The
archegonia are borne on the under side of the disc between the rays
and hang downward. At the time when the archegonia are just
mature the stalk of the archegonial branch is still only a few millimeters long, but it continues to lengthen even after the archegonia
are fertilized.

The Sporophyte.—In *Marchantia* the process of fertilization and the
early stages of the development of the embryo sporophyte from the
zygote (fertilized egg cell) are very similar to those in *Riccia*. The
mature sporophyte is, however, very different (Fig. 377). Instead of

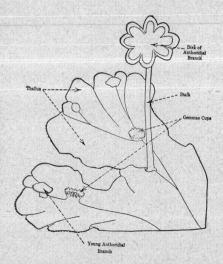

Fig. 373.—A portion of the male gameto-phyte of *Marchantia*, showing antheridia branches and gemmae cups. The latter are also sometimes produced on the femalel gametophyte.

consisting merely of a sphere of cells of which all but a single outer layer become transformed into spores, the mature sporophyte is made up of three distinct parts (the **foot, seta,** and **capsule**) and many of its cells are sterile, that is, do not give rise to spores. The foot is an expanded basal portion which attaches the sporophyte to the gametophyte tissue on the under side of the arche-gonial disc. The capsule is similar in structure to the whole sporophyte of *Riccia*, being oval in form and consisting of a single outer layer of sterile cells within which the spores are produced. By sterile cells is meant cells which are not directly concerned with reproduction. The seta is a short stalk which connects the foot and the capsule.

As the embryo sporophyte develops, the venter of the archegonium enlarges, keeping pace with the growth of the sporophyte and forming an envelope called the **calyptra.** This is not ruptured until just before the complete maturity of the sporophyte, when the seta elongates very rapidly. Meanwhile the foot of the sporophyte penetrates the tissue at the base of the archegonium and this tissue grows up around the foot. As a result the sporophyte becomes firmly attached to the gametophyte and is able to absorb the water and food which are necessary for its development. Not only are the cells forming the wall of the capsule, as well as all the cells of the seta and foot, sterile, but even within the capsule there are some sterile cells. These sterile cells which develop among the spores are the **elaters,** elongated spindle-shaped cells with spiral thickenings on the inner surface of the walls. The elaters are hygroscopic, and after the rupture of the capsule wall they bend and twist in response to changes in atmospheric humidity. These move-ments assist in the dissemination of the spores. The position of the sporophyte, hanging pendent from the under side of the rays of the archegonial branch, is also favorable to spore dissemination, for the

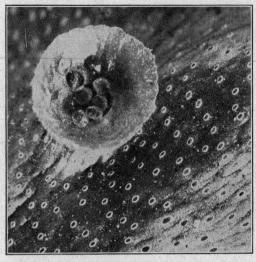

Fig. 374.—Photomicrograph of a portion of the upper surface of the thallus of *Marchantia*, showing a gemma cup in which may be seen a number of gemmae. Notice also the conspicuous openings (stomata) through the epidermis.

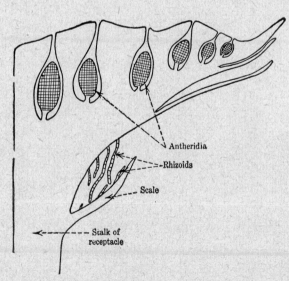

Fig. 375.—Diagram of half of an antheridial disk of *Marchantia*, showing the position of the antheridia. The antheridia are essentially the same in structure as those of *Riccia* as shown in Fig. 364 and have a wall one cell layer thick, not shown in this diagram, within which are great numbers of sperm-producing cells.

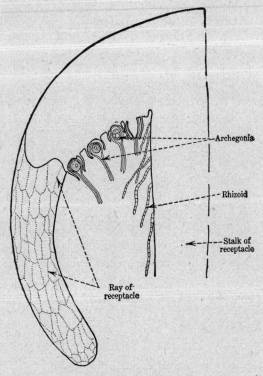

FIG. 376.—Diagram of half of an archegonial receptacle of *Marchantia*, showing the position of the archegonia.

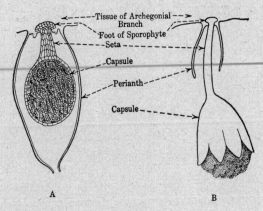

FIG. 377.—*Marchantia.* *A*, median longitudinal section of sporophyte. *B*, sporophyte, with capsule dehiscing. In both figures, a portion of gametophytic tissue is shown.

stalk of the archegonial branch may be as long
as 2 cm. at maturity. The spores falling from
the open capsule are very likely to be carried
away by air movements and thus distributed to
some distance.

**Germination of Spores and Development of
the Gametophyte.**—The development of spores
from the spore mother cells in *Marchantia* does
not differ in any important particular from the
same process in *Riccia*. It should be borne in
mind that in *Marchantia* as in *Riccia* all the
stages in development from the formation of the
zygote until the first division of the spore mother
cells belong to the diploid plant or generation,
the nuclei of which have $2n$ chromosomes. The
nuclei of the spores have the haploid (n) chromosome number, as do all the nuclei of the gametophyte plant. Spore germination and the development of the gametophyte in *Marchantia* do not
differ essentially from the corresponding processes
in *Riccia*.

Comparison of Marchantia with Riccia.—
The following are some of the most important
points of difference between the two liverworts
thus far discussed.

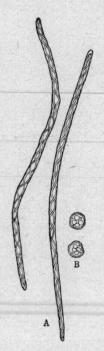

Fig. 378.—Elaters (*A*)
and spores (*B*) of
Marchantia.

1. The gametophyte of *Marchantia* is considerably more differentiated than the very simple gametophyte of *Riccia*.

2. In *Marchantia*. antheridia and archegonia are produced on different gametophyte plants instead of being borne on the same thallus
as in *Riccia*.

3. Antheridia and archegonia are borne on special branches of the
gametophyte in *Marchantia*, but in *Riccia* are merely sunk in the tissue
of the thallus proper.

4. The sporophyte of *Marchantia* is larger than that of *Riccia* and
more complex. It consists of a foot which acts as an organ for attachment and absorption, a stalk or seta, and the capsule within which
the spores are formed.

5. Much of the sporophyte of *Marchantia* is made up of sterile
cells, i.e., there is relatively much less sporogenous tissue in the
sporophyte of *Marchantia* than in *Riccia*. Even within the cap-

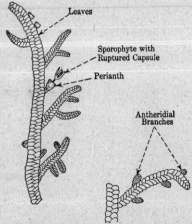

FIG. 379.—A leafy liverwort (*Porella*). At left, a portion of a female gametophyte; at right, a portion of a male gametophyte.

sule, some of the cells instead of forming spores develop into peculiar sterile cells called elaters.

6. In *Marchantia* there is rather effective provision for the distribution of spores, whereas such provision is lacking in *Riccia*. In the former plant the fact that the sporophyte is not buried in the gametophyte tissue, its attachment in a pendent position to the under side of the stalked archegonial branch, the presence of a seta, and the presence of elaters among the spores all favor dissemination. In *Riccia*, on the other hand, the spores, buried within the gametophyte, escape only by the disintegration of the tissue of the gametophyte.

OTHER LIVERWORTS

Both *Riccia* and *Marchantia* are thallose liverworts, but a very large number of the liverworts are leafy. In the leafy forms the gametophyte generally consists of a more or less prostrate dorsiventral stem bearing simple, generally close-set leaves and numerous rhizoids. There is not so great a variety of tissues as in such thallose forms as *Marchantia*, for the whole gametophyte is made up of very similar green parenchyma cells. The leaves are a single layer of

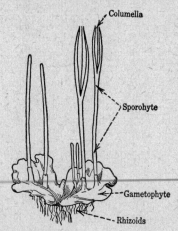

FIG. 380.—Plant of a species of *Anthoceros*, showing gametophyte thallus with attached sporophytes of which two (to the right) have split open at the ends.

thick cells and have no midrib. The antheridia and archegonia, which are borne upon the leafy branches, are not essentially different from those of the forms already described. The sporophytes resemble those of *Marchantia*, although generally the stalk or seta is relatively longer. *Porella*, one of the commonest of leafy liverworts, is shown in Fig. 379.

In all the liverworts thus far discussed and in fact in most liverworts, the sporophyte is parasitic upon the gametophyte, securing from it all its water and food. In striking contrast with these forms are the genus *Anthoceros* and two other closely related genera in which the sporophytes are green and able to carry on photosynthesis and thus to make their own food although they remain attached to the gametophyte and are dependent upon it for their supply of water and of salts from the soil. These sporophytes possess stomata which resemble those of ferns and flowering plants. The sporophyte has no seta but consists of a foot and a long cylindrical capsule which continues for some time to elongate by basal growth. Thus new spores are formed near the base while ripe ones are being discharged at the upper end where the capsule splits open. If these sporophytes only had rhizoids or roots by which they could absorb water and soil solutes

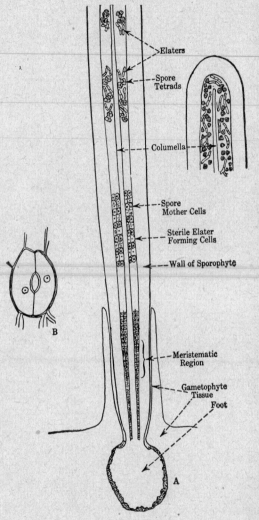

Fig. 381.—*Anthoceros*. *A*, diagram of a median longitudinal section of the basal portion of the sporophyte, including some gametophytic tissue to which the sporophyte is attached; and, to the right, of the apical part of the sporophyte. *B*, a stoma and guard cells from the sporophyte.

directly from the soil, they would no doubt be able to carry on an existence quite independent of the gametophyte plants.

THE MUSCI (MOSSES)

The Musci include many more genera than do the Hepaticae. Furthermore, the mosses are a much more conspicuous and important element of the flora than are the liverworts. There is, however, much more uniformity in the structure of both the vegetative and reproductive structures among the mosses than among the liverworts. The mosses are not so strictly limited to very moist habitats as are most of the liverworts. A few mosses are aquatic, many grow upon soil, and many others grow upon rocks, the bark of trees, and decaying wood.

The mature gametophyte of the mosses always consists of a stem having rhizoids at the lower end and bearing spirally arranged leaves. These leaves differ from the leaves of the leafy liverworts, which are borne in two rows, not only in their spiral arrangement but also in having a midrib. With the exception of two genera, all of the mosses belong to a single group, the Bryales. A single life history will be sufficient to illustrate the principal features of the structure and development of the plants of this order.

FUNARIA

Germination of Spores and Development of the Gametophyte.—The spores of this plant, as of most of the mosses, are produced in large numbers, are very small, and are easily borne to considerable distances by the wind. In the woods where all the vegetation of a larger or smaller area has been destroyed by fires, this and other mosses often arise in great numbers before competing species of plants with less efficient methods of dissemination can secure a foothold. When a spore germinates a leafy moss plant is not produced at once. Instead there develops a green filament made up of cells which lie end to end as in many of the green algae. These cells have numerous conspicuous chloroplasts. As this green filament grows, it branches freely and under favorable conditions may cover a considerable area of the substratum. This alga-like growth is called **protonema** and is characteristic of all the mosses. The food which makes possible the growth of the protonema is mostly that formed by photosynthesis carried on by the protonema itself, for the quantity of food contained in the minute moss spore is very little.

The leafy moss shoots (Fig. 382) arise as branches of the protonema. Near the end of these branches an oblique wall is formed,
cutting off an end cell. Two other oblique walls are soon formed.
These cut the first wall and thus form an apical cell having the form
of a three-sided pyramid of which the curved wall at the end of the
branch forms the base. From this cell new cells are cut off by walls
which are formed in succession parallel to the three sides of the pyramid.
These daughter cells in turn undergo divisions and thus the leafy
shoot grows. From the base of the leafy shoot numerous rhizoids
grow out. These serve to attach the leafy shoot to the soil or other
substratum and to absorb water and soil solutes. The rhizoids of
mosses are not tubular outgrowths of superficial cells like those of most
of the liverworts, but instead filaments of cells with cross walls which
are often oblique. The rhizoids branch freely, and under favorable
conditions they may give rise to a new protonema.

The leafy shoots are what we speak of as moss plants and they are
the most conspicuous part of the gametophyte. They are, however,
in reality, simply branches of the gametophyte and many leafy shoots
may arise from a protonema which has developed from a single spore.
Within the stem and in the midribs of the leaf there are somewhat
elongated cells which are apparently adapted for water conduction.

The gametangia (archegonia and antheridia) (Figs. 383 and 384)
are produced in groups at the ends of the leafy shoots. Though formerly
it was believed that in *Funaria* antheridia and archegonia are never
produced on the same gametophyte plant, it has been shown that the
leafy shoots which bear the antheridia develop first and that the shoots
bearing the archegonia develop later as branches of the shoots which
bore antheridia. There are, however, mosses which bear only antheridia
or only archegonia on a single gametophyte. In these species half of
the spores produced give rise upon germination to a protonema which
will produce only archegonia-bearing shoots, while the remainder of the
spores when they germinate will form a protonema with antheridia-
bearing shoots. In *Funaria* the shoots bearing antheridia are easily
recognized even without the use of a lens, for the leaves surrounding
the terminal cluster of antheridia are spread somewhat like the petals
of a flower. The group of antheridia can be seen as a distinctly orange
spot in the center of the "flower."

The Antheridia and Archegonia.—Although of different form the
antheridia of *Funaria* and other true mosses are essentially the same in
structure as those of the liverworts. The cells forming the wall of the
antheridium contain chloroplasts which become orange red (chromoplasts) when the antheridium ripens. The sperms are biciliate as in the

liverworts, whereas in the ferns and horsetails, two groups of the Pteridophyta, they are multiciliate. In another group of the Pteridophyta, the club mosses, the sperms are, however, biciliate as in the Bryophyta. Among the antheridia grow club-shaped, multicellular sterile hairs or paraphyses with conspicuous chloroplasts (Fig. 384). Paraphyses of a

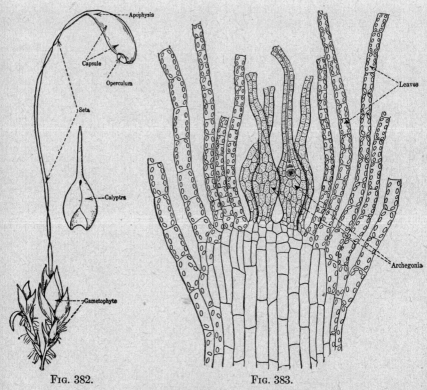

FIG. 382.   FIG. 383.

FIG. 382.—Portion of a gametophyte and attached sporophyte of a common moss, *Funaria hygrometrica.*

FIG. 383.—*Funaria hygrometrica.* Longitudinal section of tip of a female gametophore, showing archegonia. (Redrawn from Sachs.)

different type are found among the archegonia at the tips of the archegonial branches.

The archegonia have a conspicuous stalk and although they are essentially the same in structure as the archegonia of the liverworts they differ from them in having a longer neck and a larger number of neck canal cells (Fig. 387).

As in the liverworts, the opening of the antheridia and archegonia as well as the accomplishment of fertilization can take place only when the plants are wet. This is only one of several characteristics of the mosses which have been thought to indicate the aquatic origin and relatively imperfect adaptation of the mosses to life on land. Motility of the sperms or male gametes is a characteristic retained in all the ferns and fern allies and even in some primitive seed plants. It has been shown that, in some mosses at least, the sperms are chemotactic toward

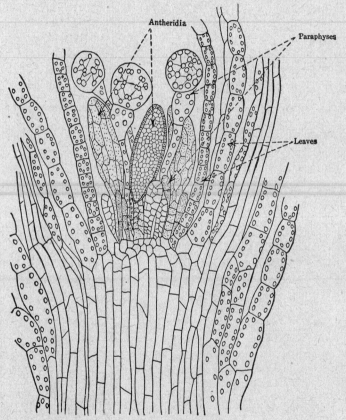

Fig. 384.—*Funaria hygrometrica.* Longitudinal section of tip of a male gametophore showing antheridia and paraphyses. (Redrawn from Sachs.)

certain substances, cane sugar for example, given out from open archegonia and are thus guided toward archegonia ready to be fertilized.

The Sporophyte.—The nucleus of the moss spore and the nuclei of the cells of the protonema, leafy shoots, gametangia, and gametes have n chromosomes. The fertilized egg cell or zygote, however, has the $2n$ chromosome number since it contains chromatin of two gametes.

Immediately after fertilization the naked zygote of *Funaria* produces a cellulose wall about itself and the formation of an embryo sporophyte begins. Growth and repeated cell divisions result in the formation of a spindle-shaped embryo with an apical cell at the upper end (Fig. 388 *C*). As this continues to grow the venter of the archegonium keeps pace with it, forming an envelope called the calyptra. Soon there begins a differentiation of the embryo sporo-

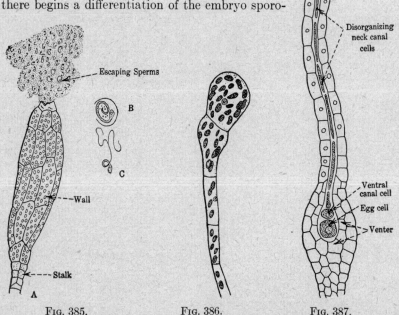

FIG. 385.   FIG. 386.   FIG. 387.

FIG. 385.—*Funaria hygrometrica*. *A*, mature antheridium discharging its sperms. These are at first held together by mucilage from the disorganized walls of the sperm-producing cells. *B*, a sperm still held in the mucilage. *C*, a sperm free from the mucilage. The chromoplasts shown in the wall cells of the antheridium (*A*) are orange in color.

FIG. 386.—A single paraphysis from a group of *Funaria* antheridia. The oval bodies in the cells are chloroplasts.

FIG. 387.—A mature archegonium of *Funaria*.

phyte into foot, seta, and capsule. The foot penetrates through the base of the venter of the archegonium into the apex of the leafy shoot. The seta becomes long and slender, and within it there is differentiated a central strand of elongated cells. It is when the seta elongates very rapidly, a short time before maturing of the sporophyte, that the base of the calyptra is torn away from the gametophyte. It remains for some time as a cap or hood over the capsule.

The capsule of *Funaria* and related mosses is a structure of much greater complexity than any yet met with among liverworts and mosses. It is approached in this respect only by the capsule of *Anthoceros* and a few closely related genera. It has a definite epidermis with stomata, a layer of chlorenchyma, and a complicated provision for opening the capsule and scattering the spores. The part of the capsule devoted to spore production is relatively very small. Fig. 390 shows the principal features of the anatomy of a mature capsule from which the calyptra has been removed. The outer layer of tissue is the epidermis, the cells of which have much thickened outer walls as in the flowering plants. It is in the epidermis of the basal portion of the capsule that stomata are found. In early stages of their development the stomata are similar in structure to those of the flowering plants, although when they are fully developed the cavities of the guard cells communicate with each other. Beneath the epidermis are several layers of wall cells, and next to this a zone of very large intercellular spaces crossed by branched filaments

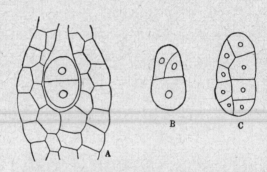

Fig. 388.—Early stages in the development of the sporophyte of *Funaria* from the zygote. *A*, after the first division of the zygote, the two-celled embryo still within the venter of the archegonium. *B* and *C*, later stages; in these the archegonium venter has not been shown. (*C*, drawn from a preparation of D. H. Campbell.)

of green cells. The center of the upper part of the capsule is made up of a more or less cylindrical mass of delicate, colorless, parenchyma cells called the **columella**. Just outside the columella is a narrow zone of sporogenous tissue and between this and the loose chlorenchyma are several layers of compact cells which supply food to the developing spores. It will be seen from the figure that the quantity of sporogenous tissue is very small as compared with the sterile tissue. As in the liverworts and in practically all of the ferns and their allies, and in the flowering plants as well, the spores are produced in tetrads, or groups of four. Each such group of four spores is derived from a single spore mother cell. Their formation is preceded by two nuclear divisions, of which the first is a reduction division. The spore mother cell is the last stage in the life cycle in which there are $2n$ chromosomes; it is the end of the sporophyte generation.   The spore nuclei have n chromosomes.

The upper end of the columella is a dome-shaped mass of parenchyma cells which projects out from the main mass of the capsule.   This part of the columella is not surrounded by a layer of sporogenous tissue but

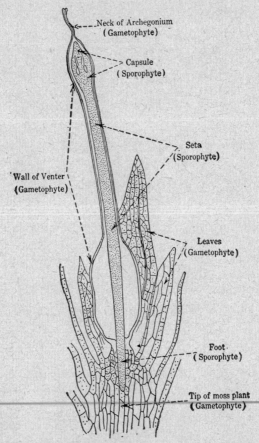

Fig. 389.—Tip of a female gametophyte branch and advanced sporophyte as seen in longitudinal section (semi-diagrammatic).   The shaded structure is the sporophyte.   (Adapted from Sachs.)

by several layers of sterile cells which form two peculiar structures, the **operculum** and the **peristome** (Fig. 390).   The operculum is a cap made up of the four or five outermost layers of cells.   When the capsule is mature and begins to dry up, the operculum is loosened from the tissues beneath it by a breaking down of certain thin cell walls, and it soon falls off.   Later a double fringe of long triangular teeth, the peristome, is formed by radial and tangential splitting of the layer of tissue just below the operculum and just outside the rounded extremity of the columella.   The edge or rim of the capsule to which these teeth are attached is made up of thick-walled cells and is called the **annulus.** By the time the spores are ripe and the operculum has been lost, most

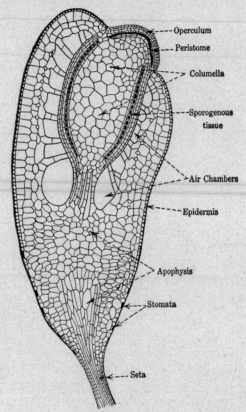

Fig. 390.—Longitudinal section of the capsule of the sporophyte of *Funaria hygrometrica.*

of the thin-walled cells within the capsule, including those of the colu-mella, collapse, leaving a cavity which is filled with a loose mass of spores.   The peristome teeth are rough by reason of the attached frag-ments of cell walls and they are highly hygroscopic.   When they are wet or the atmosphere humidity is very high, the peristome teeth bend inward and reach into the cavity of the capsule.   When they become dry they straighten out and lift out some of the spores which then are disseminated by air movements. If a spore comes to rest on a moist substratum and if the conditions of illumination and temperature are favorable, it germinates and forms a protonema as already described.

The Life Cycle. A Summary.— The life cycle of *Funaria* may be summarized in a few brief statements:

1. Germination of the spore from which develops a branched filamentous, alga-like growth called the protonema.

2. The formation of special protonema branches, and the setting up of an apical cell at the end of each branch.

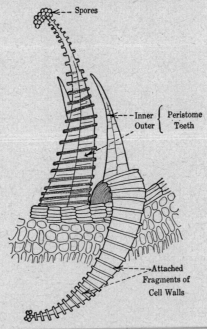

FIG. 391.—A portion of the peristome of a *Funaria* capsule, showing several of the inner and of the outer peristome teeth.

3. The growth of each of these branches or "buds" into a stem bearing rhizoids at the lower end and simple leaves above.

4. The formation at the tip of some of the leafy shoots of groups of antheridia and paraphyses.

5. The formation at the tips of other shoots (originating in *Funaria* as branches of shoots which formerly bore antheridia) of groups of archegonia and paraphyses.

6. The opening of antheridia and archegonia during a period when the plants are wet, and the escape of the sperms.

7. Swimming of some of the sperms to the archegonia whither they are probably directed by certain substances which diffuse outward from the open archegonia.

8. Fertilization, followed by the formation of a cell wall about the zygote. The zygote nucleus and all the nuclei of the sporophyte generation have 2n chromosomes.

9. The development of the zygote by growth and cell divisions into

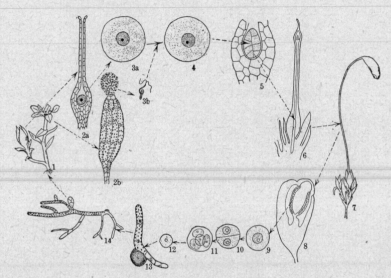

Fig. 392.—Diagram showing the life cycle of a typical moss (*Funaria*). 1, the leafy gametophyte plant (gametophore), showing an antheridial and an archegonial branch. 2a and 2b, an archegonium and an antheridium with mature egg and sperm. 3a and 3b, an egg and a sperm. 4, the zygote resulting from their fusion. 5, a young embryo sporophyte within the venter of the archegonium. 6, sporophyte in advanced stage of development, attached to the gametophyte and surrounded by the enlarged archegonium. 7, mature sporophyte attached to the gametophyte. 8, section of the sporophyte capsule showing the location of the spore mother cells. 9, spore mother cell. 10, two cells resulting from reduction division of the spore mother cell. 11, tetrad of spores resulting from division of the two cells. 12, a single spore. 13, germinating spore showing protonemal thread and rhizoid. 14, young gametophyte plant showing the buds which develop into leafy shoots of the gametophyte. The stages from 4 to 9 belong to the sporophyte generation. Those from 10 to 3 to the gametophyte generation.

an embryo sporophyte which is enclosed by the enlarged archegonium venter (calyptra) until just before the maturity of the sporophyte when the calyptra is torn away from its attachment to the leafy shoot.

10. The development of the embryo into the mature sporophyte consisting of (a) the foot which penetrates the tip of the stem of the

gametophore and serves as an organ of attachment and absorption, (b) the seta or stalk and (c) the capsule, a complex structure within which the spore mother cells are produced but which is mostly made up of sterile tissue.

11. The two successive divisions of each spore mother cell to form a tetrad of spores. The first division of the spore mother cells is a reduction division and marks the end of the diploid or sporophyte phase and the beginning of the haploid or gametophyte phase in which all the nuclei have n chromosomes.

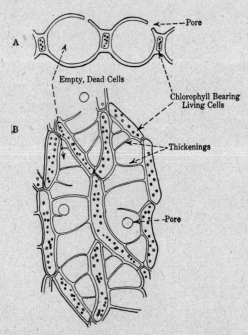

FIG. 393.—Sphagnum moss. A, portion of leaf in cross section; B, portion of leaf in surface view.

12. The drying out of the capsule, the loss of the operculum or capsule cover, and the escape, assisted by the hydroscopic movements of the peristome teeth, of the spores.

In Fig. 392 the life cycle of such a moss as *Funaria* is represented in the form of a diagram.

THE SPHAGNUMS

Distinctly different from *Funaria*, which is typical of most mosses, are the sphagnums or peat-mosses. These belong to a single genus and are mostly restricted to the swampy land in the vicinity of northern lakes where they often cover large areas and form "peat bogs." The leafy shoots are of a much paler color than those of the common mosses. When dry they can absorb great quantities of water or other liquids. This fact led to the use of dry sphagnums during the world war as a substitute for absorbent cotton in certain kinds of surgical dressings.

The principal particulars in which the members of the genus *Sphagnum* differ from such common mosses as *Funaria*, are:

1. The protonema is an irregular flat thallus instead of a system of branching filaments.

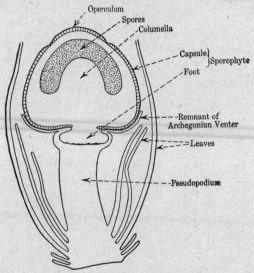

Fig. 394.—A mature sporophyte of *Sphagnum* in longitudinal section showing its attachment to the tip of the gametophyte branch.

2. Most of the leaves, except when very young, consist of a network of small chlorophyll-bearing cells, the spaces between which are filled by large empty cells which generally have a circular opening in the cell wall (Fig. 393). It is these large colorless cells which are responsible for the light green color of the leaves and it is chiefly because of the presence of these large empty cells that dry sphagnum has so great a capacity for the absorption of liquids.

3. The sporophyte has no seta but is raised somewhat by the elongation (pseudopodium) of the tip of the gametophyte stem below the region to which the foot is attached. The sporogenous tissue surrounds not only the sides of the columella but the upper end as well.

SUMMARY OF THE BRYOPHYTA

The forms which have been described in this chapter, although they are not to be considered as successive stages in evolution, do illustrate in all probability some of the principal steps which took place in the evolution of the sporophyte. The following is a summary of the most significant facts to be learned from a brief study of the Bryophyta:

1. Although certainly not aquatic plants like their probable ancestors, the algae, the Bryophyta show evidence of their origin from aquatic plants and of their incomplete adaptation to life on land.

2. The single most important distinction between these plants and the algae is the alternation in the life cycle of all of them of a sexual (gametophyte) generation with nuclei having n chromosomes and an asexual (sporophyte) generation whose nuclei have $2n$ chromosomes.

3. The adoption of a land habitat by these plants has necessitated certain structural and physiological adaptations to the great difference in the environment of land plants and that of submerged aquatics.

(A) The most important points of difference between the aquatic and the terrestrial habitats are:

(a) That on land only part of the plant is in contact with a medium (the soil) from which it can absorb water and essential salts.

(b) That the land plant is partly exposed to a medium (the atmosphere) to which it is continuously losing water.

(c) That whereas aquatic plants (submerged) are largely supported (buoyed up) by water, the atmosphere does not yield any appreciable mechanical support to the parts of land plant which grow in the air.

(d) That on account of the low specific gravity of the atmosphere it is a less efficient agency for distribution of gametes and many spores than is water.

(B) Some of the principal characteristics of the Bryophyta and of higher land plants which are apparently related to these differences in environment are:

(a) Special structures for the absorption of water and minerals from the soil are developed by all typical land plants—the rhizoid of lower land plants (Bryophyta) and the roots and root hairs of ferns and flowering plants. The rhizoids of the Bryophyta are, however, not very efficient organs for water absorption.

(*b*) The parts exposed to the air are protected from excessive water loss by the production of a superficial layer (epidermis) having an outer wall which, with its cuticle, is very resistant to the passage of water vapor. It is important that this should not prevent the entrance of the gases needed for photosynthesis and respiration. The epidermis among the higher plants, accordingly, has openings through it, called stomata; these are also found in the epidermis of the sporophyte of some liverworts (*Anthoceros*) and mosses. In all but the smallest land plants there are conductive tissues which provide for the rapid transfer of water from the water-absorbing structures to the parts exposed to the dry atmosphere.

(*c*) The more primitive land plants either grow prone upon the ground or, if erect, seldom attain a height of more than a centimeter or two, since they are lacking in mechanical tissue. Higher land plants have developed mechanical tissues and some of them are able to support a stem hundreds of feet high.

(*d*) In the Bryophyta and in the Pteridophyta as well, fertilization can take place only when the gametophytes are wet, because the sperms can move only in water. By various means the spores of land plants are adapted to efficient dissemination by air instead of water. Small size and the development of ridges or spines on the outer spore wall are among the principal provisions which favor wide distribution by air currents. The discharge of spores into the air from elevated structures, such as the long-stalked capsules of the mosses and many liverworts, makes it more likely that they will be carried to some distance by air currents before they fall to the ground.

4. In all the Bryophyta the gametophyte is "the plant," that is to say, the gametophyte is the conspicuous and independent plant, which alone is able to absorb water and to which the function of food manufacture is entirely or largely restricted. It is among the Bryophyta (in *Marchantia* and similar liverworts and in the mosses) that the gametophyte reaches its highest development among plants. There is a well-developed epidermis with specialized air pores in *Marchantia*, and rudimentary conductive tissue in the mosses. The gametophyte at its best, however, never becomes an efficient land plant.

5. Among living bryophytes the sporophyte ranges in complexity

from that of *Riccia*, which consists of a mass of spores with a single surrounding layer of sterile cells and which has no provision for spore dissemination, to the complex sporophyte of the mosses, in which sporogenous tissue is much reduced and tissues for photosynthesis and special provision for spore dissemination are present. However, the sporophyte's possibilities of development are limited by reason of the fact that it is restricted in the quantity of water and salts it can secure by the limited ability of the gametophyte for absorption and conduction.

6. In the next class, the Pteridophyta, the gametophyte is even simpler than in the Bryophyta, but the sporophyte is much more complex than in the mosses and liverworts. Moreover, it develops entirely new sporophyte organs, a root and a stem with leaves. The presence of a root makes it possible for the sporophyte to secure adequate supplies of water and salts, and thus to become a structure of great size and complexity.

CHAPTER XIV

EMBRYOPHYTA

PTERIDOPHYTA (FERNS AND FERN ALLIES)

GENERAL CHARACTERISTICS

The ferns and their allies constitute a large assemblage of plants which have certain resemblances to the liverworts and mosses on the one hand, and to the seed plants on the other. They resemble the Bryophyta in the following important particulars: (1) They produce ciliated male gametes; (2) they require water in order that fertilization may take place; and (3) they have gametangia which are essentially of the same structure as those of the liverworts and mosses. They resemble the Spermatophyta in that their sporophytes all have roots and can therefore live independent of the gametophyte, and in that they possess well developed vascular tissue.

We have seen that in the Bryophyta the sporophyte is entirely dependent for its supply of water and mineral salts upon the gametophyte, which alone possesses organs (rhizoids) for absorbing water and soil solutes from the soil. In many of the Bryophyta the sporophyte is unable to manufacture any of its own food, even when supplied by the gametophyte with these raw materials. But there is a certain approach to independence of the sporophyte in *Anthoceros* and in most mosses. The sporophytes of these plants have developed chlorophyll-bearing tissue and could probably live entirely independently if they possessed rhizoids or a root.

It is within the Pteridophyta that complete independence of the sporophyte is first attained. Although the sporophyte of the ferns and fern allies is at first attached to the gametophyte by a foot and is for a short time dependent upon it for water and food as well, it soon develops a root which attaches it directly to the soil. By virtue of having a root, the sporophyte is no longer dependent upon the gametophyte for its supply of water and mineral salts. Moreover, food-manufacturing tissue also is well developed in the sporophyte, so that this generation has attained complete independence.

The Pteridophyta have carried tissue differentiation in the sporophyte much further than any of the Bryophyta. The sporophyte has, among other specialized tissues, a well-developed vascular system. This, together with an efficient epidermis, abundant chlorophyll-bearing tissue, and a root which can penetrate into the deeper and relatively moister layers of soil, has enabled it successfully to carry on an independent terrestrial existence, which is not possible for the sporophyte of any of the Bryophyta.

The roots of the Pteridophyta and Spermatophyta, although performing the same functions as rhizoids, are far more complex structurally and are capable of indefinite growth.

As to the origin of the Pteridophyta, it is the generally accepted opinion that they and the mosses represent two distinct lines of development from some liverwort ancestor. The mosses have the most complex and highly differentiated sporophyte of any existing plants below the Pteridophyta, but there is little ground for the assumption that the Pteridophyta have arisen from the mosses even though the mosses are in some respects intermediate between the liverworts and the ferns.

A study of fossil plant remains reveals the fact that the ferns and their allies appeared on the earth earlier than the seed plants. During the carboniferous period (geological age when the great coal beds were deposited) they were very abundant; in fact they dominated the vegetation of that time.

The following are the principal groups of Pteridophyta which exist upon the earth today:

1. The Lycopodineae (Club Mosses). 2. The Equisetineae (Horsetails). 3. The Filicineae (Ferns).

THE FERNS (FILICINEAE)

Although probably both the club mosses and the horse-tails arose before the ferns by evolution from lower plants and are to be considered as older than the ferns, we shall use as our first and principal pteridophyte type a representative of the Filicineae, which is the largest group of the living Pteridophyta and includes the most familiar plants of this division of the plant kingdom.

Distribution and Habitat.—Ferns are widely distributed over the surface of the earth. They flourish most luxuriantly in moist, shady habitats, but there are some species which grow in very dry situations. Ferns reach their greatest size in the tropics, where certain tree ferns grow to a height of 15 meters or more. The stems of such tree ferns are erect, woody, and unbranched, and each bears at its apex a cluster of compound leaves (fronds). Most of the ferns, however, have a horizontal or short erect stem (rhizome) which is developed underground.

Life History of Polypodium.—This genus is selected as a type for detailed discussion because it is widely distributed and its life history is quite representative of the ferns with which we are most familiar.

The familiar fern plant, as we know it, with its roots, stem and leaves (fronds) is the asexual or sporophyte generation. The cells of this

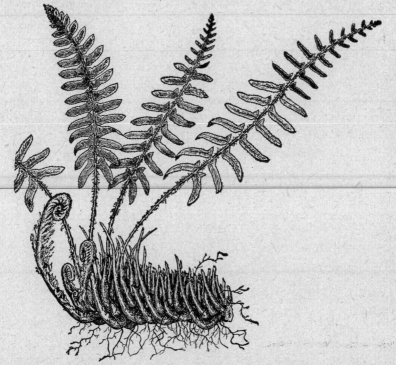

Fig. 395.—Sporophyte of Christmas fern (*Polystichum*), showing the horizontal rhizome bearing at the tip young coiled leaves, the expanded leaves of the previous season, each with a stalk or stipe prolonged to form the rachis from which pinnae (leaflets) arise laterally, and the fibrous roots which arise from the lower side of the rhizome. The older parts of the stem are covered with the petioles of dead leaves. (After Curtis.)

generation have nuclei with the diploid ($2n$) number of chromosomes. The sexual or gametophyte generation is a small independent plant which is devoid of roots, stem and leaves, is seldom more than a few millimeters in diameter, and is even simpler in structure than the gametophytes of mosses and most liverworts. It is often spoken of as a **prothallium** (Fig. 397). The cells of the gametophyte generation have nuclei with the haploid (n) number of chromosomes.

Spores.—There often occur, on the under side of the frond, brownish "dots," which are clusters of sporangia or spore cases. Within each of these cases there are a number of spores.

In *Polypodium* all the spores are similar in size and appearance, and accordingly *Polypodium* is said to be **homosporous**, in contrast to those pteridophytes which produce two kinds of spores differing in size and in other respects and which are therefore said to be **heterosporous.**

Spore Germination.—The spores of *Polypodium* have two coats or wall layers. The outer layer (exine) is hard, brown, and rough; the inner (intine) is thin and delicate. Under favorable conditions of moisture and temperature, water is absorbed by the spore, the exine is ruptured, and the spore contents, surrounded by the intine, protrude as a short tube.

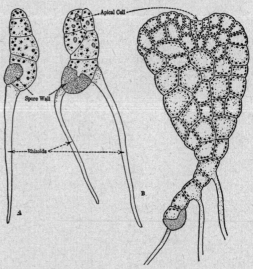

This germination tube is cut off by a cell wall as a stout, green cell, at the base of which the first rhizoid appears. By rapid growth, the cell elongates and soon by divisions in one plane comes to form a row of green cells.

The Gametophyte (Prothallium).—After a time, the terminal cell of

Fig. 396.—Early stages in the development of the gametophyte of *Polypodium.* (See explanation in text.)

this short filament becomes divided by an oblique wall into two cells of unequal size. This division is succeeded by the formation of a similar oblique wall in the larger of the two cells. There is thus formed an apical cell which is triangular in longitudinal section. This divides by the formation alternately of walls parallel to each of the original oblique walls. By the divisions of this apical cell the prothallium develops into a flat, green plate of cells. If growth is unhampered, the structure becomes more or less heart-shaped, with the apical cell at the bottom of the notch. During its growth, many unicellular rhizoids are developed on the under (ventral) surface. The mature gametophyte is one layer of cells in thickness, except in a region just back of the apical notch, where a cushion of cells is formed.

In *Polypodium* and in most other ferns, each prothallium bears both antheridia and archegonia. Some species, however, have the male and female gametangia on different gametophytes. In such species,

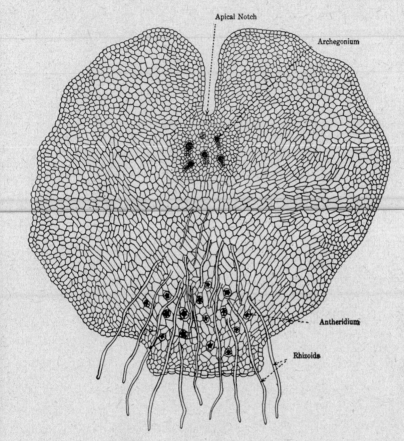

FIG. 397.— Mature gametophyte (prothallium) of fern, as seen from the ventral surface.

for example in *Onoclea*, the antheridia-bearing or male gametophytes are frequently smaller than the archegonial or female gametophytes.

The gametangia are borne on the ventral surface of the gametophyte, the antheridia being scattered among the rhizoids, and the archegonia are located just below the apical notch, where the prothallium is several cells thick. The antheridia develop earlier than the archegonia.

Antheridia.—The antheridium is spherical in shape and is not stalked, as are the antheridia of the Bryophyta. It consists of a single layer of chlorophyll-bearing cells, enclosing a group of sperm mother cells, usually thirty-two in number. Each of these sperm mother cells develops into a sperm, a spirally coiled structure consisting mostly of nuclear material, and bearing, not two cilia, as in the Bryophyta, but a large number.

Archegonia.—The archegonium is a flask-shaped structure resembling that of the bryophytes except that it is shorter and that the venter is embedded in the tissue of the gametophyte. There are one or two neck-canal cells, a single ventral-canal cell, and a large egg cell. At maturity, the neck-canal cell or cells and ventral-canal cell disintegrate into a mucilaginous mass, and a passageway is formed to the egg.

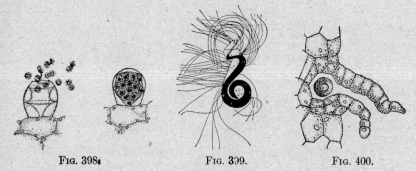

FIG. 398.   FIG. 399.   FIG. 400.

FIG. 398.—Antheridia of a true fern, one showing escape of sperms after rupture of antheridium wall. (After Atkinson.)

FIG. 399.—*Onoclea struthiopteris.* Ripe sperm. the nucleus black. (After Steil.)

FIG. 400.—Mature archegonium of a true fern.

Fertilization and Embryo Development.—The rupturing of the archegonia and antheridia takes place only in the presence of water, as described in the case of Bryophyta; the mucilaginous material in the neck-canal cell of the archegonium swells and the cover cells open. The sperms are set free from the antheridia in the presence of water. They swim to the neck of the archegonium, and move down the neck-canal to the egg. A number of sperms may be attracted to one archegonium and may pass down the neck-canal, but only one fuses with the egg. The zygote remains in the venter and germinates there.

It has been shown that the principal substances which attract the sperms to the egg in the species studied are malic acid and its salts.

At fertilization, the number of chromosomes is doubled so that the zygote has $2n$ chromosomes and hence is to be considered as the first cell of the sporophyte generation. In the diagrams in Fig. 409 are shown gamete fusion in the fern, the doubling of the chromosome number to $2n$ at the time of zygote formation, and the reappearance of $2n$ chromosomes which occurs at mitosis of the zygote nucleus and all other divisions of $2n$ nuclei previous to the reduction division. The diagram applies as well to the same processes as they occur in seed plants and most other plants having alternation of generations.

After fertilization the zygote begins its development into " the fern plant " (sporophyte). It forms a wall about itself and by two successive divisions becomes a four-celled body. This is spoken of as the

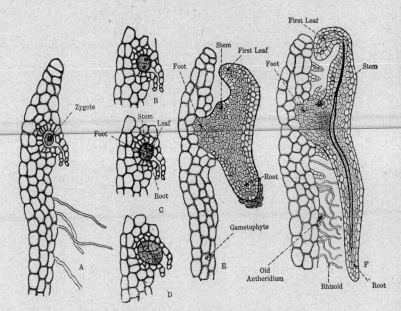

Fig. 401. —Stages in the development of the fern sporophyte.

quadrant stage of embryo development. From these four quadrants, four distinct primary growing points are formed, from which are developed the primary organs of the embryo, namely:

1. The *foot*, which is a mass of small cells embedded in the tissue of the prothallium, and which absorbs food and water for the young embryo from the prothallium.

2. The *root*, which grows downward into the soil.

3. The *primary leaf*, which is a temporary organ little resembling the

permanent leaves but serving as the first photosynthetic organ of the sporophyte.

4. The *stem*, which becomes the rhizome from which the fronds and adventitious roots arise.

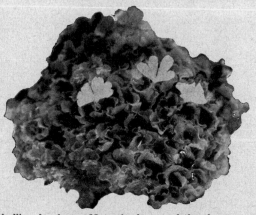

FIG. 402.—Prothallia of a fern. Note the leaves of the three young sporophytes.

These organs develop in the order given. In the early stages of embryo development the young sporophyte is completely parasitic upon the gametophyte, just as in the case of the liverworts, obtaining its food and water through the foot. However, as soon as the primary root and leaf are developed, it becomes an independent organism. The gametophyte soon withers and then the foot ceases to function. Of the four structures mentioned, only the stem (rhizome) is permanent. It soon develops leaves (fronds) and adventitious roots, and the primary root and primary leaf die.

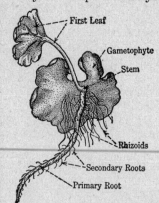

FIG. 403.—Fern sporophyte after its root has entered the soil and its first leaf has begun to carry on photosynthesis but before the death of the gametophyte.

The Mature Sporophyte. The Stem (**Rhizome**).—In *Polypodium*, as in most common ferns of temperate regions, the stem or rhizome is subterranean and generally grows horizontally a few inches beneath the surface of the ground. It usually branches sparingly, and at the ends of these branches are the terminal buds which are protected, as a rule, by a dense growth of scales and epidermal hairs. Increase in length of the rhizomes continues from year to year by growth of these buds. Hence, the rhizome is perennial. Each year new adventitious roots arise from the lower side of the rhizome and new leaves from its upper side. The leaves generally die at the close of each growing season. Examination of the other portions of the stem shows them to be covered by the bases of the petioles of dead fronds. By the death of older parts of the rhizome, branches become disconnected from the main rhizome and continue their development as separate new plants. In this way vegetative reproduction is accomplished. Ferns are propagated commercially both by division of the rhizomes and by sowing spores and later transplanting the young sporophytes after they have become independent of the gametophyte.

The stem of ferns is much more complex in structure than any organ

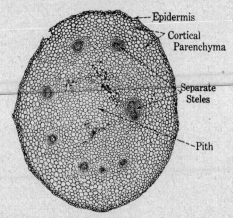

Fig. 404.—Photomicrograph of a cross section of a rhizome of a species of *Polypodium*.

found in the Bryophyta. Its outstanding structural feature is a water and food-conducting system (vascular system). A cross section through the internode of the rhizome of *Polypodium* shows the following tissues:

1. *Epidermis.*—This consists of a single layer of thick-walled cells.

2. *Mechanical Tissue.*—Just beneath the epidermis are several layers of **sclerenchyma** cells, and there are two or three distinct masses of this tissue nearer the center of the stem.

3. *Vascular Bundles.*—A varying number of these, some large and some small, are found near the center of the stem. They are separated from each other, and each is surrounded by an **endodermis**. The vascular bundles possess pericycle, xylem and phloem, but no cambium. In the bundles, the phloem surrounds the xylem. The vascular bundles or their branches extend throughout the leaves and roots.

4. *Parenchyma Tissue.*—This forms the ground tissue of the stem. The principal function of this tissue is storage of food and water.

The Root.—The roots are small and fibrous, and except for the primary root, which soon dies, all roots are adventitious and arise from the lower side of the stem. They originate not at the surface of the stem but deep in the stem tissue, just as branch roots of the seed plants have their origin deep in the tissue of the main root. The roots have root hairs and a root cap. The structure of the root is similar to that of

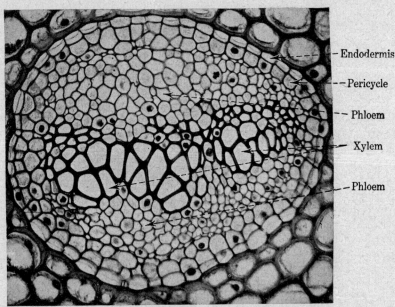

FIG. 405.—Photomicrograph of a single vascular bundle from the cross section of a rhizome of a species of *Polypodium*, shown in Fig. 404.

other vascular plants. There is a single, central stele, surrounded by a broad cortex which often contains much sclerenchyma tissue.

The Leaf.—The frond of *Polypodium* and most common ferns consists of a stalk or petiole, which is prolonged to form the **rachis**, from which arise laterally a number of **pinnae** (leaflets). Leaf primordia may be observed as small swellings near the growing point of the rhizome. These leaf primordia grow very slowly, in fact in some species it is not until the spring of the third year following their origin that the leaves appear above the ground.

Fern leaves continue to grow at the apex until their full size is reached. In this particular they differ from the leaves of seed plants, in which growth is apical only while the leaves are very young. They are of much the same structure as those of seed plants, having an upper and lower epidermis, stomata, chlorenchyma tissue, and vascular bundles (veins). The stomata are usually confined to the under surface. The chlorenchyma is generally not sharply differentiated into palisade and spongy parenchyma.

The Sporangia.—The sporangia of *Polypodium* grow in groups on the under side of the leaves, which are accordingly spoken of as **sporophylls.** The sporangia form small, brownish groups called **sori** (singu-

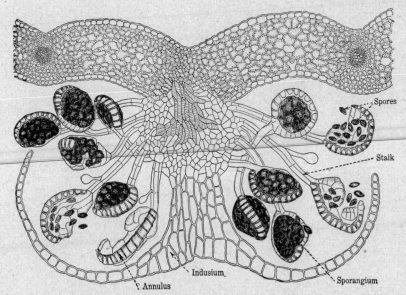

Fig. 406.—Cross section of fern leaf, through a sorus. Note the epidermal layers, chlorenchyma and veins of the leaf, as in higher plants. Different views of the sporangia are shown. (Redrawn from Kny.)

lar **sorus**). In certain ferns the sorus is covered by an outgrowth from the sporophyll called the **indusium** (Figs. 406 and 416).

In *Polypodium* all the fronds bear spores; that is to say, the functions of photosynthesis and spore production are combined in all the leaves and there is no differentiation into sporophylls and vegetative leaves.

In *Polypodium* each sporangium consists of a **stalk** and a **capsule.** The wall of the capsule is composed of a single layer of thin-walled cells except for the **annulus,** a row of cells extending from the stalk over the top of the capsule and part way down the other side. The inner and radial walls of the cells composing the annulus are much thickened, while the outer walls are relatively thin. This structural arrangement is of importance as will be seen when the opening of the sporangium is described. Between the end of the annulus and the stalk are a few thin-walled cells, two of which, the **lip cells,** are narrow and radially elongated. At maturity the sporangium wall splits between these two-lip cells.

In *Polypodium* the sporangium originates from a single epidermal cell. By repeated division of this cell, the sporangium is developed. Besides the single-layered wall there are one or two layers of cells forming a nutritive tissue known as the **tapetum** (Fig. 408), and a central mass of sporogenous tissue. The sporogenous tissue (tissue which is to give rise

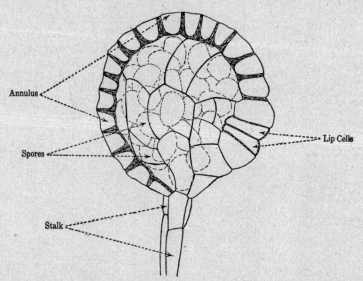

Fig. 407.—Surface view of a sporangium of *Polypodium*, before dehiscence. The spores within the capsule can be seen through the transparent wall which consists of a single layer of thin-walled cells. (Adapted from drawing by D. H. Campbell.)

to the spores) of each sporangium becomes organized into a number (usually sixteen) of large cells, rich in protoplasm, which are called **spore mother cells.** By two successive divisions, the first of which is a reduction division, each spore mother cell forms a tetrad (group of four) of spores.

Soon after the formation of the spore mother cells, the walls of the tapetal cells break down and the spore mother cells come to float in the tapetal protoplasm which escapes into the cavity of the sporangium. The spore mother cells and later the young spores absorb food from the tapetal protoplasm.

Reduction Division.—Reduction in the number of chromosomes takes place during the first of the two successive divisions of the spore mother cell which result in the formation of a tetrad of spores. Thus, the spore mother cells have diploid nuclei and belong to the sporophyte generation, whereas the spores have haploid nuclei and belong to the gametophyte generation.

In the chapter on the cell (pages 79 to 82), the process of mitosis was described in some detail. In that description it was shown how in the division of the nucleus, the two daughter nuclei each receive an equal amount of chromatin and each has a number of chromosomes

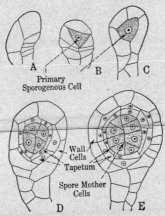

FIG. 408.—A series of stages in the development of the sporangium of *Polypodium*. *A*, just before the formation of the wall which cuts off (as shown in *B*) the primary sporogenous cell from the other cells of the young sporangium. *C*, a somewhat later stage; two of the cells surrounding the primary sporogenous cell have divided. *D*, tapetal cells have been cut off from the primary sporogenous cell and some of these tapetal cells have divided tangentially; within the tapetal layer four cells have been formed which will divide further to form spore mother cells as shown in *E*. (*D* and *E*, drawn from microtome sections prepared by D. H. Campbell.)

equal to that of the mother cells. Thus in an ordinary mitosis there is no reduction in the number of chromosomes. It will be recalled that in all plants having sexual reproduction a reduction division takes place somewhere in the life cycle. In the reduction division, the division of the nucleus is by **meiosis,** a process briefly described on page 80. We shall now describe the reduction division of a spore mother cell of a fern, which in its principal features is essentially the same as the reduction division in most plants in whose life cycle such a division takes place. This description applies also to the reduction division of the pollen mother cells and to the reduction division which occurs in the young ovule.

This is a continuous process which it is, however, convenient for purposes of discussion to divide into the following stages which are numbered to correspond with the figure numbers in Fig. 410.

1 and 2.   *The chromatin of the resting nucleus of the spore mother cell is*

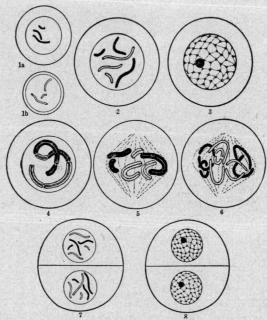

Fig. 409.—Diagrams showing the chromosomes contributed to the zygote (2 and 3) by the gametes (1A and 1B), and the splitting (6) of each of these chromosomes during the first division of the zygote. Each of the resulting nuclei (7 and 8) of the two-celled embryo contains the same number and kind of chromosomes as the zygote nucleus (2). All later divisions of sporophyte nuclei in ferns, seed bearing plants and most other plants having sexual reproduction, proceed as shown in diagrams 3–7. The (paternal) chromosomes contributed by the male gamete are shown in white, those (maternal) contributed by the female gamete in black. In order to simplify the diagrams three has been chosen as the haploid chromosome number (1A and 1B) and accordingly six is the diploid number (2–7), although most plants have larger chromosome numbers. Corresponding (homologous) chromosomes (members of pairs of chromosomes, one paternal and one maternal, which control the same inherited characteristics) from sperm and egg cell correspond in length. The chromosomes do not lose their individuality while the nucleus is in the resting condition, between divisions, although the chromatin is scattered. The diagrams 1A and 1B are so drawn as to show the chromosomes present in the gamete nuclei even though these nuclei are actually in the resting condition when they unite.

evenly distributed.   At the beginning of the reduction division the homologous chromosomes (the pairs of chromosomes, one maternal and one paternal, which contain the same inherited characteristics), *in close contact, appear as long threads.*   It should be pointed out here that in the division

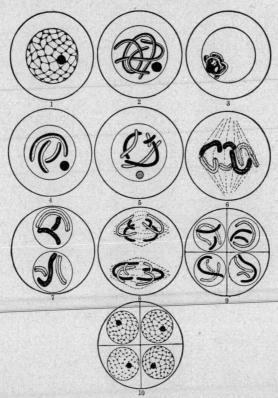

FIG. 410.—Diagrams showing chromosome behavior during the reduction division which occurs at the time of spore formation in ferns and in most other plants which have sexual reproduction. As also in Fig. 409, the chromosomes shown in white are paternal chromosomes, those in black, maternal chromosomes. Homologous chromosomes (corresponding maternal and paternal chromosomes) are of corresponding length. As the result of the process here shown, the spore mother cell (in the resting condition in 1) gives rise to a tetrad (group of four spores) as shown in 10. The mother nucleus (1) has the diploid chromosome number (in this case six) as is shown in 7 of Fig. 409, which is characteristic of the cells of the sporophyte. These six consist of three pairs of homologous chromosomes, one of each pair having come from the male gamete and one from the female gamete in the last fusion of gametes (2, 5 in Fig. 409). Note that in 410, 2, the three pairs, with the chromosomes of each pair in close contact, are lying within the nuclear membrane. In 3 the paired chromosomes have shortened and have become closely "knotted" whereas in 4 they have become "unraveled" and have undergone further shortening. In 5 the members of each pair have separated but are still in close proximity. In 6 the nuclear membrane and the nucleolus have disappeared and the six chromosomes, each now showing evidence of a later lengthwise splitting, have been separated into two groups of three. *This is the actual reduction division.* As shown in 7, only one chromosome of each homologous pair is present in each of the resulting nuclei which are therefore different in their chromosome "stock." Each of these nuclei now undergoes a second division (8) with a splitting of each of its chromosomes, so that there are two kinds of nuclei in the tetrad (shown in 9), two having the same chromosomes as the upper nucleus in 7 and two having the same chromosomes as the lower nucleus shown in 7.

of the zygote and in the subsequent divisions, resulting in the multicellular sporophyte, the chromosomes contributed by the male gamete
(paternal chromosomes) and by the female gamete (maternal chromosomes) maintain their individuality. It is, however, only at the time
of reduction division that the separate identity of the maternal and
paternal chromatin becomes apparent.

3. *The long paired chromosomes contract and then undergo a characteristic knotting.* There is evidence that during the loose union of the
paired threads an interchange of chromatin may take place between
maternal and paternal chromosomes.

4. *The paired chromosomes again become distinct, and become still
shorter.* The number of pairs of chromosomes is seen to be one-half the
diploid number. (See Fig. 410.)

5. *The chromosomes of each pair separate, but still lie close together.*

6 and 7. *At about this time the spindle is formed, and the nucleoli and
nuclear membrane disappear. One partner of each pair of chromosomes
moves toward one pole,
and the other partner of
the pair toward the op-
posite pole.* At least by
this time each chromo-
some shows evidence of
the splitting which will
be completed in the sub-
sequent division (6 of
Fig. 410). Thus each
daughter nucleus has
one-half the diploid
number of chromosomes
and each one of the
daughter nuclei receives
either a paternal or a
maternal chromosome
from each pair. How-
ever, it is only by
chance that the chro-
mosomes of a daughter

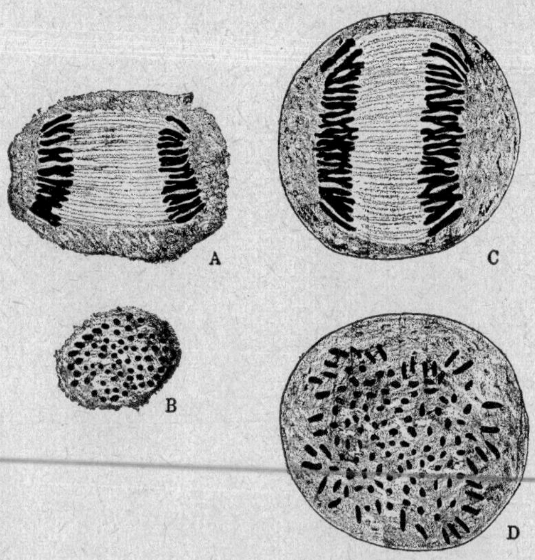

FIG. 411.—Nuclei from the gametophyte (*A* and *B*)
and of the sporophyte (*C* and *D*), of *Nephrodium*
during mitosis, showing 64 and 128 chromosomes
respectively. (Redrawn from Yamanouchi.)

nucleus are all paternal or all maternal. Each of the chromosomes
now shows clearly that it is double in nature.

8. *Each daughter nucleus resulting from the first division of the mother
cell promptly undergoes a second division of the ordinary type, which
does not involve any reduction in chromosome number, nor any separation
of maternal from paternal chromosomes.*

9. *Each of the four haploid nuclei thus formed, together with part of the cytoplasm, is surrounded by a wall and becomes a spore.*

Dehiscence.—As the sporangium becomes progressively drier, the annulus begins slowly to straighten out, and as it does so the weak lip

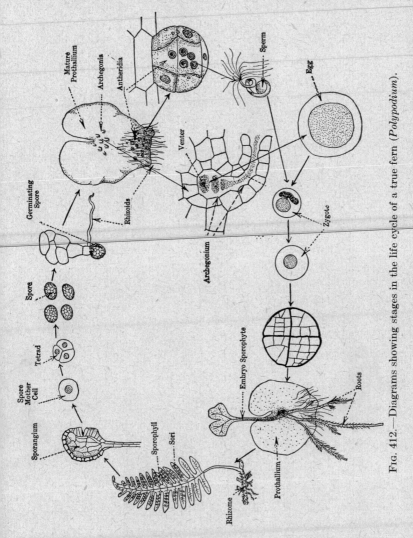

Fig. 412.—Diagrams showing stages in the life cycle of a true fern (*Polypodium*).

cells and the thin side walls of the sporangium are torn. Finally, the annulus may almost double back upon itself, pulling with it a mass of ripe spores. Suddenly the annulus returns to its original position, at the same time dispersing the spores. In their dry condition the spores are easily disseminated by wind.

Summary of Life Cycle.—The life history of *Polypodium* may be summarized as follows:

1. The spores, which have the haploid (*n*) number of chromosomes, are discharged from the sporangia, which are borne in clusters on the under surface of the sporophyll.

2. Under proper conditions of moisture and temperature, the spores germinate, each producing a short green filament.

3. By a series of divisions of an apical cell, the green filament grows into a flat, heart-shaped structure, the prothallium (gametophyte) which is attached to the soil by numerous rhizoids.

4. Antheridia and archegonia are borne on the ventral surface of the prothallium (gametophyte). In *Polypodium*, antheridia and archegonia occur on the same prothallium.

5. Each antheridium usually produces thirty-two multiciliate-sperms, and each archegonium develops a single egg-cell.

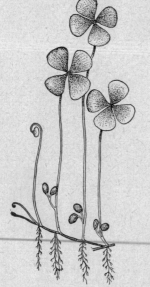

6. Fertilization of the egg-cell takes places in the venter of the archegonium. At fertilization the *n* chromosomes of the egg and

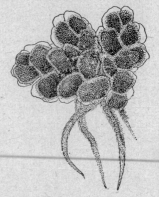

FIG. 413.—Habit drawing of *Marsilia quadrifolia*, one of the water ferns. Note the oval sporocarps. (After Wettstein.)

FIG. 414.—Plant of *Azolla*, one of the water ferns, magnified about eight times.

sperm nuclei are united in the zygote nucleus, which has, therefore, the diploid (2*n*) number of chromosomes, half of which are maternal and half paternal. The zygote is thus the beginning of the sporophyte generation all the nuclei of which have 2*n* chromosomes.

7. Successive divisions of the zygote result in the development of the embryo sporophyte, consisting of foot, root, primary leaf and stem

The foot is a temporary structure absorbing, during a short time only, food from the prothallium to which it is attached. The foot dies after the primary root and leaf have developed to the point where they can supply sufficient water and food for the young sporophyte. And, after leaves and adventitious roots have developed on the stem, the primary leaves and roots also die, so that only one of the four primary organs (the stem) is permanent. The mature sporophyte consists of a rhizome, bearing roots and fronds. On the under side of the fronds, sporangia are borne in clusters called **sori.**

8. The sporogenous tissue of each sporangium forms, in *Polypodium*, sixteen spore mother cells. Each of these, by two successive divisions, the first of which is a reduction division, gives rise to four spores with haploid nuclei. At the reduction division the maternal and paternal chromosomes of any pair are separated from each other and pass to different daughter cells.

Polypodium and most of the other true ferns (Filicineae) are homosporous, but a few members of this group are heterosporous, producing two kinds of spores—small spores (**microspores**) which give rise to male gametophytes, and large spores (**megaspores**) which produce female gametophytes. (The terms *microspore* and *megaspore* are used in heterosporous Pteridophyta and in Spermatophyta to designate respectively those spores which give rise to the male gametophyte and to the female gametophyte, but it should be pointed out that in certain cases the microspore may equal or exceed in size the megaspore.) Examples of heterosporous Filicineae are the water ferns including the genera *Salvinia, Azolla, Marsilia,* and *Pilularia.* This habit of heterospory also occurs in *Selaginella,* a genus of the more primitive pteridophyte group, Lycopodineae.

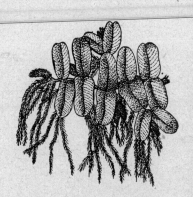

Fig. 415.—Habit sketch of *Salvinia natans,* a water fern. (After Wettstein.)

In *Polypodium,* as in most common ferns, it will be recalled that all fronds are similar and may produce sporangia. In such ferns as the cinnamon fern (*Osmunda cinnamonea*), the sensitive fern (*Onoclea sensibilis*), and others, there are, however, two sorts of leaves: (1) ordinary foliage leaves which never produce sporangia, and (2) spore-bearing leaves which are much smaller and the cells of which contain very little chlorophyll.

In many ferns, the sori are covered by a membranous outgrowth of the epidermis, known as an **indusium.** The form and arrangement of sori and indusia are characters which are much used in the classification of ferns. In *Polypodium* and many other genera, indusia are absent, and the sori are said to be **naked.** A so-called "false indusium," formed by a folding over the margin of the frond so as to cover the sporangia, occurs in the common bracken (*Pteris aquilina*) and in related ferns such as the maiden-hair fern (*Adiantum*).

The heterosporous ferns are a group of aquatic or amphibious forms known as the "water ferns." They differ from *Polypodium* and other common ferns in the production of two kinds of spores, small (microspores) and large (megaspores) which give rise to male prothallia and female prothallia respectively. The microsporangia and megasporangia are borne in characteristic spherical or oval bodies known as **sporocarps.** The sporangia resemble in general structure those of *Polypodium*, which we have described, except that they have no annulus. In water ferns, the gametophytes are short-lived and greatly reduced structures. They do not possess chlorophyll, and their supply of food is restricted to that which was present in the spores from which they developed and which was supplied by the sporophyte. The gametophytes are therefore entirely dependent upon the sporophyte generation. In the extreme reduction and complete dependence of the gametophyte generation these heterosporous ferns are similar to the heterosporous genus *Selaginella,* which will later be described, and to the seed plants. Although the seed plants (*Spermatophyta*) probably evolved from heterosporous pteridophyte ancestors, neither the water ferns nor any plant closely related to *Selaginella* were among the ancestors of the Spermatophyta. Heterospory has developed quite independently in several different groups of the Pteridophyta.

EQUISETINEAE (THE HORSETAILS)

General Characteristics.—The Equisetineae or horsetails, is represented among living plants by only a single genus, *Equisetum,* of which there are about thirty species. That the Equisetineae were formerly a much more important element in the flora of the earth than they are today is shown by the considerable number and variety of such plants of which fossil remains have been found. The fossil Equisetineae include species of the genus *Equisetum* which greatly exceeded the living species in size and which were tree-like in form. In addition there are fossil remains of several other genera including the genus *Calamites.* Some of the latter plants and other fossil Equisetineae were heterosporous and produced, like the water ferns, two kinds of spores, microspores and megaspores, which gave rise respectively to male and female gametophytes.

The living equisetums vary greatly in size; for example, the South

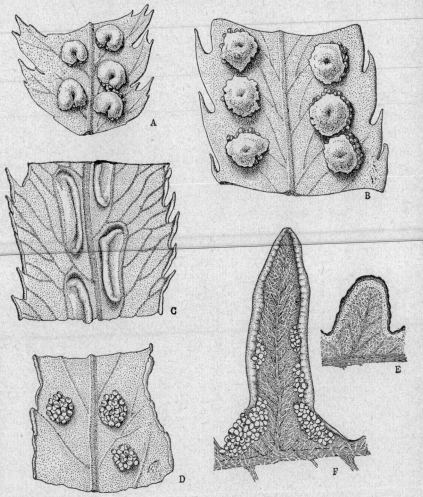

Fig. 416.—Sori and indusia of various types. *A*, sori of *Dryopteris* with kidney-shaped indusia. *B*, shield-shaped indusia of *Polystichum* sori. *C*, linear indusia covering the sunken sori of *Woodwardia*. *D*, naked sori of *Polypodium* which are without indusia. *E*, and *F*, a young and an older pinnule of *Pteris* showing the false indusium (inrolled margin of the leaf) characteristic of *Pteris* and several related genera.

American species, *Equisetum giganteum*, may grow to a height of 30 feet though its stem diameter is only a few centimeters, whereas certain species, like *Equisetum sciripodes*, seldom exceed 20 cm. in height.

In the Equistineae as in the Filicineae, the sporophyte is the conspicuous generation. It is made up of a branched system of horizontal underground rhizomes from which, each season, erect aerial shoots are sent up. The most striking characteristics of the sporophyte plant are:

1. The heavy impregnation of the outer tissue with silica.

2. The reduced, scale-like leaves.

3. The distinct hollow internodes of the aerial stems.

4. The peculiar form of the sporophylls and the grouping of these at the tips of aerial shoots into cone-like structures called **strobili.**

The siliceous deposit gives to the shoots a harsh texture, and on this account the plant was formerly used for cleaning and polishing metal utensils and given the name of "scouring rush." On account of the reduced size of the leaves, photosynthesis is carried on principally by the green stems. The horsetails grow for the most part along the margins of streams or lakes or in other moist locations.

The commonest species, *Equisetum arvense*, is very widely distributed throughout the northern hemisphere. We shall use it as a type of the group and briefly describe its life history.

FIG. 417.—The sporophyte of horsetail (*Equisetum arvense*) showing green vegetative shoots (left) and spore-bearing shoots (right) and the rhizomes from which these aerial shoots arise. Note the whorls of scale leaves, and on the vegetative shoot the whorls of green branches.

Life History of Equisetum. Gametophyte.—The asexual spores are all morphologically alike. The spores are globular and green in color. In addition to the usual two intine and exine wall layers there is developed outside of the exine a third layer called the **perinium.** In the mature spore, the perinium ruptures in such a way that two ribbon-like appendages (**elaters**) are formed which remain attached to the spore at one place about halfway between the ends of the elaters, and coil

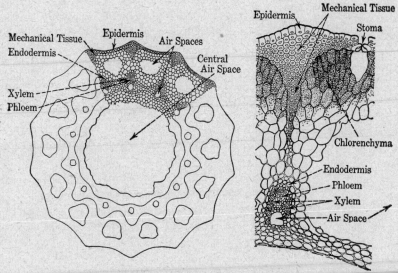

FIG. 418.—Left, cross section of the aerial stem of *Equisetum hyemale*; right, a portion of a cross section of an aerial stem of the same species, more highly magnified. Drawings by Carl Sharsmith.

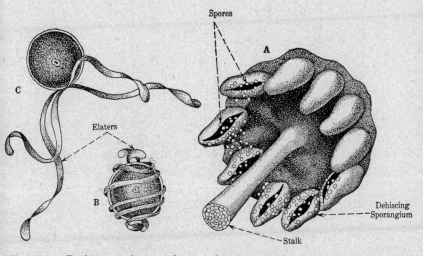

FIG. 419.—*Equisetum. A,* ventral view of a sporophyll. *B,* mature spore with elaters coiled about the spore body. *C,* spore with elaters uncoiled. (Redrawn from Wettstein, after Dodel-Port.)

around the spore. These elaters are very sensitive to changes in atmospheric humidity; when the air is dry, they uncoil; when it is humid they again coil around the spore and thus the air-borne spores are deposited in moist places favorable for their germination. The movements of the elaters also assist the escape of the spores from the sac-like sporangia which are attached to the lower side of the sporophylls (see Fig. 419) and which split along one side when the spores are ripe. As might be expected, these spores have the n chromosomes. The ripe spores are capable of germination as soon as they are shed from the sporangium.

In all the species of *Equisetum* thus far critically studied, the spores develop into gametophytes which may produce either antheridia or archegonia, depending upon the size of the gametophytes. If the gametophyte remains small and but one cell layer in thickness, probably as a result of poor nutrition, it bears antheridia only; on the other hand, if the gametophyte grows to relatively large size, and develops a cushion of cells several layers thick, both archegonia and antheridia may develop on the same gametophyte.

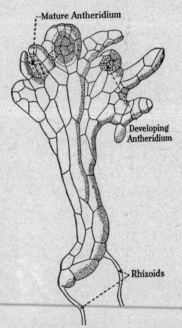

The archegonia and antheridia of *Equisetum* are not essentially different from those of the ferns, and the sperms are multiciliate as in the Filicineae (Figs. 420 and 421).

Liberation of the sperms, opening of the archegonia, and fertilization, take place much as in the ferns, and the development of the sporophyte from the zygote does not differ in any important particular from that in *Polypodium*. The sporophyte is dependent upon the gametophyte for a short period only.

Fig. 420.—*Equisetum*. Gametophyte bearing antheridia. (Redrawn from Hofmeister.)

The Sporophyte.—The mature sporophyte consists of a perennial rhizome which grows in the soil and from which roots and aerial shoots are produced. The aerial stems have a rough surface, and their division into nodes and internodes is very distinct. The internodes are hollow and are marked with a number of longitudinal grooves. At each node there is a whorl of small, pointed structures, the very much reduced foliage leaves which are joined at their bases, forming a sheath around the stem.

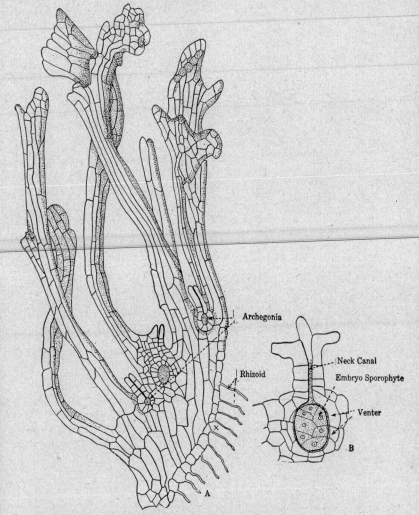

Fig. 421.—*Equisetum.* *A*, Gametophyte, bearing archegonia. *B*, embryo sporophyte in venter of archegonium. (*A*, redrawn from Hofmeister. *B*, redrawn from Sadebeck.)

In *Equisetum arvense* there are two kinds of aerial shoots: reproductive and vegetative. In the early spring there are sent up from the rhizomes, simple, unbranched reproductive shoots, each of which bears at the tip a single, terminal, cone-shaped, whitish group of sporo-phylls (strobilus). These spore-bearing shoots die down soon after spore production, and are succeeded by slender, green, sterile shoots which send out numerous branches in whorls at the nodes.

Strobilus and Sporangium.—The strobilus consists of an axis with much shortened internodes. At the nodes there arise shield-shaped structures (**sporophylls**) which bear spo-rangia.

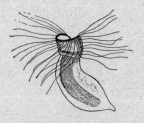

The sporangia are long sacs on the under side of the sporophyll. In the developing sporangium there is, as in the fern sporan-gium, a tapetum consisting of two or three layers of cells. Each sporophyll bears five to ten sporangia. At maturity the spo-rangia dehisce longitudinally, and the spores are shed.

Fig. 422.—Sperm of *Equise-tum*. (Redrawn from Be-lajeff.)

There are two points in this life history of *Equisetum* worthy of special emphasis: (1) the sporangia are produced on specialized sporophylls. (2) The spores are similar as are the spores in the majority of true ferns, but certain extinct forms related to *Equise-tum* were heterosporous.

LYCOPODINEAE (THE CLUB MOSSES)

General Characteristics.—The Lycopodineae, like the Equisetineae, constitute a class which was formerly represented by much larger, more numerous, and more highly differentiated species than exist today. The number of species of living Lycopodineae greatly exceeds, however, the living species belonging to the Equisetineae, the two common genera *Lycopodium* and *Selaginella* including nearly six hundred species.

Remains of certain fossil representatives of this class are abundant in the coal beds. Among the most interesting of these fossil relatives of the modern club mosses are the arborescent genera, *Lepidodendron* and *Sigillaria*. Fossil *Lepidodendron* trunks having a length of over 30 meters have been found. Some of the extinct Lycopodineae had stems in which secondary growth in thickness took place through the activity of a cambium, much as in present-day gymnosperms and dicotyledons. In spite of this similarity of the stems of fossil Lycopodineae to the stems of seed plants, and in spite of certain similarities in the reproduction of *Selaginella* (a living representative of the Lycopodineae) to the repro-duction of seed plants, **there is no reason to believe that any members of the Lycopodineae were ancestors of the seed plants.**

Most of the species of *Lycopodium* and *Selaginella* are found growing as terrestrial plants in temperate or tropical regions or as epiphytes in moist tropical forests but they do not constitute a very important element in the flora of the temperate and colder parts of the earth.

The Lycopodineae differ from the Filicineae and the Equisetineae principally in that:

1. The sperms are biciliate instead of multiciliate.

2. The sporophylls, though resembling the vegetative leaves as in most of the true ferns, are grouped in strobili.

3. There occurs in the life cycle a temporary sporophyte organ (the **suspensor**), lacking in other pteridophytes but found in the seed-bearing plants.

Selaginella is a type of living pteridophyte showing well-marked heterospory, and a very greatly reduced gametophyte, even though it is in many respects a much more primitive form than the ferns. On account of the much-reduced character of the gametophytes, which are not visible to the naked eye, we shall begin our account of the life history of *Selaginella* with the sporophyte, which as in all the Pteridophyta is the more conspicuous generation.

Life History of Selaginella. The Sporophyte.—In the creeping species of *Selaginella* the shoot is dorsiventral, the leaves are small and arranged on the axis in four longitudinal rows. In some species, leafless branches (known as **"rhizophores"**) grow downward from the leafy stems and give rise to roots when they come into contact with the soil. The leaves have a loose, spongy mesophyll and a well-developed epidermis with stomata which are usually confined to the under surface. The chloroplasts are large and few in number, and in some species there is only one in each cell.

Strobilus and Sporangia.—The strobili are branches on which the leaf-like sporophylls are borne, generally in four rows so that a rather compact four-angled or club-shaped structure is formed.

Attention has already been called to the fact that *Selaginella* is heterosporous, like the water ferns which were mentioned earlier in this chapter. Heterospory, which is the habit of producing small spores which give rise to male gametophytes and larger spores from which the female gametophytes develop, arose apparently independently in several groups of Pteridophyta including some groups now extinct. Although it is not common among living ferns and fern allies, it is universal among the spermatophytes or seed-bearing plants.

Corresponding to the difference between the two kinds of spores (**microspores** and **megaspores**) of heterosporous plants are differences in the sporangia (**micro-** and **megasporangia**) and in the sporophylls upon which the sporangia are borne (**micro-** and **megasporophylls**). The strobili of *Selaginella* are bisporangiate in that they are made up of both microsporophylls and megasporophylls.

In *Selaginella* each of the megasporophylls bears a single megasporangium within which four large spores (the megaspores) are produced. The microsporophylls also bear solitary sporangia (microsporangia), within which, however, there are formed numerous (generally sixty-four) spores (microspores).

Development of Spores.—Up to the formation of the spore mother cells the development of the microsporangia and megasporangia is the same, and not essentially different from that of the sporangia of true ferns. Each sporangium consists of a short stalk and an enlarged portion within which the spores are produced. The wall of the sporangium consists of three layers of cells, of which the innermost is a tapetal layer similar to that found in the ferns (Filicineae) and in *Equisetum*. Generally the same number of spore mother cells (usually sixteen) is formed in both the micro- and megasporangia.

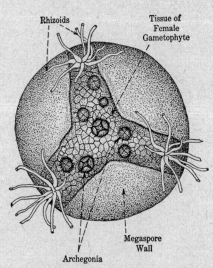

Rhizoids

Tissue of Female Gametophyte

Megaspore Wall

Archegonia

Fig. 423.—Female gametophyte of *Selaginella* partly enclosed by megaspore wall. (Redrawn from Bruchmann.)

Each microspore mother cell gives rise to four spores, so that sixty-four spores are generally produced in each microsporangium. One of the two divisions of the mother cell by which the four spores are produced is a reduction division. The first division of the functioning spore mother nuclei in both microsporangia and megasporangia is a reduction division, the nucleus of the spore mother cell dividing by meiosis. This division marks the end of the sporophyte and the beginning of the gametophyte generation.

In most species of *Selaginella*, only one of the spore mother cells in the megasporangium divides; accordingly the number of megaspores is four in most species. The nucleus of each of these spores contains n chromosomes. The other spore mother cells undergo disorganization and their protoplasm furnishes food for the developing spores which are accordingly better nourished than are those of the microsporangium and are able to attain a very much larger size.

The Male Gametophyte.—The microspores begin to germinate before they are shed from the micro-
sporangium. This is in marked contrast with conditions in other pteridophytes which we have studied; in most other pteridophytes the spores do not normally begin to germinate while still within the sporangium. In all the Spermatophyta the germination of the microspores is initiated before their release from the

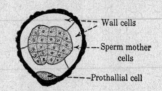

FIG. 424.—Male gametophyte of *Selaginella*.

sporangium and probably this was true also in the extinct heterosporus plants which were the ancestors of the present-day seed plants. The male gametophyte of *Selaginella* is formed entirely within the microspore. After the di-
vision of the nucleus of the microspore, at the time of its germination, a wall is formed which divides the spores into two cells of very unequal size. The spores are usually shed in this two-celled condition. Subsequently the larger cell of the two goes through a series of divisions which result in the formation of a cen-
tral group of cells, and a single layer of wall cells. (See Fig. 424.) The protoplast of each cell of the central group develops into a single sperm. The smaller cell of the first two formed (i.e., the **prothallial cell**)

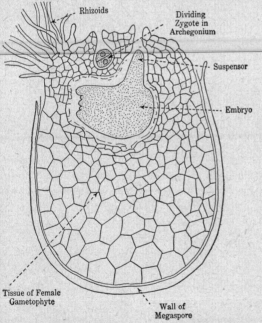

FIG. 425.—Longitudinal section of female gametophyte of *Selaginella*, partly surrounded by the rup-
tured megaspore wall. One embryo sporophyte is well developed; a second, in its first stage. (Redrawn from Bruchmann.)

is considered to be homologous with the vegetative cells which make up the greater part of the fern prothallium. All the rest of the gametophyte is believed to represent a single antheridium. The **prothallial cell** is merely a vestigial structure; it does not possess chlorophyll, and probably plays no essential part in the life history of the plant. The gametophyte is unable to carry on photosynthesis and is entirely dependent for food upon the supply which the microspore received from the sporophyte plant. This is just the reverse of the condition existing in most liverworts where the sporophyte is completely dependent upon the gametophyte, since the sporophyte can absorb water and solutes only from the gametophyte and is unable to carry on photosynthesis.

The Female Gametophyte.—Germination of the megaspores, which generally commences **before** they are shed from the megasporangium, begins by the division of the single megaspore nucleus into two nuclei, between which no wall is formed. By continued free division of the nuclei, there are formed within the megaspore a large number of nuclei most of which accumulate at one end of the spore. Then walls are formed simultaneously between the nuclei, and thus a mass of tissue (the female gametophyte) is formed within the megaspore. The gametophyte grows and by its growth the megaspore wall is finally ruptured at one end and gametophytic tissue is exposed. Several archegonia develop upon this exposed surface. In some species, rhizoids (which do not function), are produced from the exposed tissue and there may be some development of chlorophyll in this region of the gametophyte.

The archegonia do not differ from those of the true ferns and *Equisetum* in any important particular. Each consists of a venter containing the egg, a single ventral-canal cell, a single neck-canal cell and a neck, composed of two tiers of four cells each. All this development of the female gametophytes takes place, at least in many species, while they are still within the megasporangium which remains attached to a megasporophyll of the strobilus.

Transfer of Microspores and Fertilization.—It will be recalled that the male gametophyte is enclosed by the microspore wall at the time when the microspores are shed. In some species of *Selaginella* the microspores (usually in the two-celled stage when shed), sift down between the megasporophylls, which generally occupy a lower position in the strobilus than the microsporophylls, and come to lie very near the megasporangia. About this time the development of the male gametophyte is completed and, if the plant is wet about this time by rain or heavy dew, water is absorbed by the microspore. As a result the walls separating the sperms break down, the contents of the microspore swell, the microspore wall is ruptured, and the biciliate sperms are set free. Previous to this time, the megasporangium wall has opened, but not sufficiently to allow the female gametophytes to escape. The sperms swim to the archegonia, which are by this time ready for fertilization. It should be emphasized here that the presence of water is essential if the sperms are to reach the archegonia, a condition which gives indication of the origin of *Selaginella* from aquatic ancestors.

The fertilized egg is the beginning of the sporophyte or diploid generation, the zygote nucleus having $2n$ chromosomes. The zygote generally starts its development into an embryo sporophyte at once. The first division of the zygote is by a wall which is at right angles to the axis of the archegonium and results in the formation of an outer cell, known as the **suspensor cell,** and an inner cell, the **embryo cell,** from which the embryo proper develops. The suspensor cell elongates considerably, pushing the developing embryo down into the deeper tissue of the female gametophyte, from which nourishment is absorbed.

The suspensor cell may divide several times, but it takes no part in embryo formation. The suspensor is a structure which distinguishes the Lycopodineae from the homosporous ferns, but a similar structure has developed, entirely independently, in the seed plants. The young embryo (Figs. 425 and 426), embedded in the tissues of the female gametophyte and still enclosed within the megaspore wall, consists of a foot, a rudimentary root, and a rudimentary stem, with two cotyledons (first leaves). In

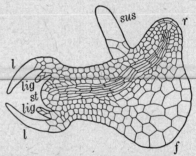

Fig. 426.—Embryo sporophyte of *Selaginella. sus,* suspensor; *r,* young root; *l,* first leaves; *lig,* ligules; *st,* growing point of stem; and *f,* foot. (Redrawn after Bruchmann.)

some species the megaspores are not shed until after the growing stem and root of the embryo have begun to emerge from the female gametophyte or have even forced their way out through the sporangium wall.

Soon after, the female gametophyte is shed from the strobilus, the root of the embryo sporophyte enters the ground, the stem elongates, leaves are developed, and the young sporophyte becomes independent. By this time the suspensor and foot, which served to absorb food from the female gametophyte as the sporophyte grew, cease to function.

Summary of the Life History of Selaginella.

1. Germination of microspores, the initial stages taking place within the sporangium. Shedding of the two-celled male gametophyte enclosed within the microspore wall.

2. Further development of male gametophyte, which at maturity consists of a single prothallial cell and a central group of antheridial cells, each cell of which gives rise to a single sperm, and a single layer of wall cells surrounding the central group.

3. Rupture of microspore wall and liberation of biciliate sperms. The nuclei of the sperms and of all the cells of the male gametophyte and of the microspores have n chromosomes.

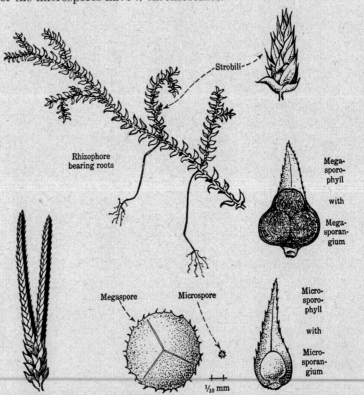

Fig. 427.—A species of *Selaginella* showing habit, strobili, microsporophyll, microsporangia, microspore, megasporophyll, megasporangium and megaspore. At the lower left-hand corner are shown two strobili from a different species of *Selaginella*. The $\frac{1}{10}$-mm. scale refers only to drawings of the spores.

4. Germination of each megaspore within the sporangium to form a female gametophyte, which by its growth ruptures the spore wall at one side. At maturity the female gametophyte consists of a mass of small cells at the exposed end which develop archegonia, and a group of large cells at the opposite end. Early in the formation of the female gametophyte the nuclei multiply by free nuclear division. The nucleus

of the megaspore, presumably the nuclei of the female gametophyte, and the nucleus of the egg have n chromosomes.

5. Swimming of some of the sperms, if water is present, to the archegonia, and fertilization of the egg, followed by the formation of a cell wall about the zygote. The zygote nucleus has $2n$ chromosomes.

6. Formation from the zygote, and within the female gametophyte tissue and megaspore wall, of a suspensor and an embryo consisting of foot, root, and stem with two cotyledons.

7. Further development of the sporophyte, during which the root enters the ground, the stem grows longer, and leaves (in some species) bearing peculiar leafless branches (rhizophores) and forming roots at their ends are produced.

8. Formation, after a vegetative period, of strobili bearing both mega- and microsporophylls.

9. Development of microsporangia on microsporophylls, which usually occur near the apex of the strobili, and of megasporangia on megasporophylls, which usually occur near the base of the strobili.

10. Formation of four microspores by two successive divisions from each spore mother cell in the microsporangium. During the first division, the chromosome number is reduced; this reduction and the similar reduction during the formation of megaspores mark the end of the diploid (sporophyte) generation.

11. Formation of four megaspores, by two successive divisions (one a reduction division), from only one spore mother cell of the many in the megasporangium, the remaining spore mother cells disorganizing and furnishing nourishment for the single tetrad of spores.

Significant Points in the Life History of Selaginella.—Some of the most significant facts relative to *Selaginella* are:

1. The production of two kinds of spores (heterospory)—microspores and megaspores.

2. The grouping of the sporophylls to form a strobilus.

3. The extreme reduction of the male and female gametophytes, most marked in the male gametophyte which consists of a single antheridium and one vegetative cell.

4. Retention of the spores and contained gametophytes within the sporangia until their development is far advanced.

5. Development of the new sporophyte from one of the two cells resulting from the first division of the zygote. From the upper cell there is developed a new structure called the suspensor, which resembles a structure also called the suspensor which has been **entirely independently developed** in the seed plants.

6. Dependence of the gametophytes upon the sporophyte which is

just the reverse of the condition existing in mosses and liverworts where the gametophyte is the independent generation and the sporophyte is totally or partially dependent upon it.

Lycopodium.—The two most common living genera of the class Lycopodineae are *Selaginella* and *Lycopodium*. In *Lycopodium*, which is homosporous, the stem branches extensively, the leaves are generally small and scale-like, and are arranged spirally on the stem. In some species of *Lycopodium* the gametophytes are small, chlorophyll-free structures, which live saprophytically under ground, but in other species they are green and develop on the surface of the soil. In no case are they dependent on the sporophyte.

SUMMARY OF THE PTERIDOPHYTA

1. Alternation of generations is well developed in all Pteridophyta.

2. In all of them the sporophyte possesses a root and thus frees itself early in its development from all dependence upon the gametophyte.

3. In addition, the sporophyte possesses leaves, organs which never occur upon the sporophyte of the Bryophyta.

4. Spores are produced not in a single terminal capsule, but in many sporangia borne on sporophylls.

5. Probably because the sporophyte of ferns and their allies is better adapted to life on land than the gametophyte of liverworts and mosses, the pteridophytes are larger and more successful plants than any bryophytes.

6. Heterospory has arisen independently in several groups of pteridophytes, living and extinct. Most of the living species of this group are homosporous.

7. In the formation of spores in all Pteridophyta, the same essential change takes place as in spore formation in the Bryophyta, i.e., the development of a tetrad from each spore mother cell. This tetrad is the result of two successive divisions of the spore mother cell; during one of these two divisions meiosis occurs and the chromosomes are reduced to the haploid number.

8. As contrasted with the Bryophyta, the Pteridophyta show a marked reduction of sporogenous as compared to vegetative tissue.

9. In all ferns, as also in Bryophyta, the structure of the gametangia is essentially the same as is also the method of fertilization.

10. Fertilization in all ferns is dependent, as in the Bryophyta, upon the presence of water.

11. In general, the gametophytes of the Pteridophyta are much

smaller and simpler than those of the mosses and liverworts, and the sporophytes are larger and less simple in structure.

12. In some of the heterosphorous Pteridophyta the female gametophyte and the young sporophyte are retained for some time within the sporangium.

13. In certain Pteridophyta—*Selaginella* and *Lycopodium*—a new structure, the suspensor, is developed from one of the first two cells formed from the zygote. The **presence of a somewhat similar structure in the seed plants is not, however, to be considered as indicating that these plants are ancestors of the seed plants.**

CHAPTER XV

EMBRYOPHYTA

THE SPERMATOPHYTA (SEED PLANTS)

The Spermatophyta by far exceed in importance, both economically and as a component of the earth's flora, all other living plants. The spermatophytes are the dominant plants of our time and exceed in number of known species all other groups of plants taken together.

The reason for the dominance of the Spermatophyta is the fact that they are more effectively adapted to the land habitat than any other plants. Although the types of plants which we have discussed in the preceding chapters of Part II, or the groups to which they belong, certainly do not represent an actual evolutionary series which has culminated in the production of the seed-bearing plants, they do illustrate what were probably some of the principal changes which took place during the evolution of the Spermatophyta.

It will be recalled that among the forms thus far studied the following progressive changes have taken place:

1. An increase in the size, complexity, differentiation, and independence of the sporophyte and in its adaptation to life on land.

2. A reduction in the quantity of the sporogenous tissue of the sporophyte relative to those tissues concerned with vegetative activity.

3. In plants above the bryophytes, a reduction in the size and an increase in the simplicity of the gametophyte generation. In heterosporous Pteridophyta, this progressed so far that the gametophyte became dependent upon the sporophyte, much as the sporophyte was dependent upon the gametophyte in the liverworts and mosses.

4. The retention of the megaspores within the megasporangium after their germination, in *Selaginella* and in certain other Lycopodineae and in the water ferns. In these plants the megaspores and contained female gametophytes remain within the sporangium until after fertilization has taken place, and in some species even until the embryo sporophyte is far advanced in its development. This is in striking contrast to the shedding of the spores before germination in most other pteridophytes.

5. Increasingly effective provision for spore dissemination.

The tendencies just enumerated reach their culmination in the seed plants, for:

1. The sporophyte of the seed plants may attain a length of hundreds of feet; it has the most highly complex differentiated tissues found among plants, and is dependent upon the gametophyte for a very short period only.

2. Although an immense number of spores may be produced, the (sporogenous) tissue which is devoted to spore production is greatly reduced relative to the vegetative tissues and is generally a very small fraction of the tissue of the sporophyte.

3. The male gametophyte (pollen grain) is finally reduced in flowering plants to three cells, and the female gametophyte (embryo sac) in some of the higher seed plants to eight cells, and both derive their food entirely from the sporophyte. Antheridia and archegonia, if represented at all, are very much reduced.

4. Fertilization is not conditioned by the presence of water, for the male gametophyte (shed microspore or pollen grain), carried by wind or insects to the vicinity of the megaspore, develops a tube (pollen tube) down which the male gametes pass to the female gametophyte. Except in a few very primitive seed plants, the male gametes have no cilia. With the loss of cilia by the male gametes there disappear the last structures which give direct evidence of the aquatic origin of the higher plants.

5. The megaspore (usually one in each megasporangium) is never released from the megasporangium (nucellus). The megaspore gives rise to the female gametophyte, and within this is developed the embryo sporophyte. The young sporophyte, together with gametophytic tissue and sometimes a mass of nutritive tissue, eventually becomes the seed.

CHIEF DISTINGUISHING CHARACTERISTICS OF SPERMATOPHYTA

The two characteristics which most sharply differentiate the Spermatophyta from all other plants are (1) **the formation of a pollen tube** and (2) the **production of seeds**. These two characteristics have probably been of great importance as factors making for the success of the seed plants, first, because the pollen tube has released them from dependence upon water for fertilization, and second, because the seed is an extremely efficient structure for reproduction and multiplication, being able to retain its vitality for many years (in some cases no doubt for as many as a hundred) and very resistant to desiccation and to great extremes of temperature. Seeds are also well adapted for wide dissemination, and, on account of the well-advanced state of development of the embryo sporophyte within the seed and the supply of stored food available to it, the new plant after germination is able to become well established before it must become self-supporting. These facts and the possession of very efficient organs and tissues for absorption, conduction, and conservation of water make it possible for seed plants to thrive in habitats which are much drier than those to which the Bryophyta and Pteridophyta are for the most part restricted.

The seed-bearing plants include species which are adapted to a wide range of conditions. By far the majority are autophytic, but a few are heterophytic, as for example, such saprophytes as Indian pipe (*Monotropa*) and the Sierran snow plant (*Sarcodes*), and such parasitic forms as

Fig. 428.— Mistletoe (*Phoradendron flavescens*), a parasitic flowering plant in dense clumps on the branches of an oak tree. The picture was taken in the spring before the tree had developed its leaves.

Fig. 429.—Mistletoe (*Phoradendron villosum*) on a branch of an oak tree. (After Owens, from *Principles of Plant Pathology.*)

dodder (*Cuscuta*) and mistletoe (*Viscum* and *Phoradendron*). Autophytic seed-bearing plants are to be found in almost every location where organisms can exist at all. They are lacking in the following habitats:

1. The open sea, though many grow entirely or partially immersed in the shallow water along the seacoast.

2. The most precipitous of smooth, rocky cliffs, though some seem actually to prefer steep, rocky slopes.

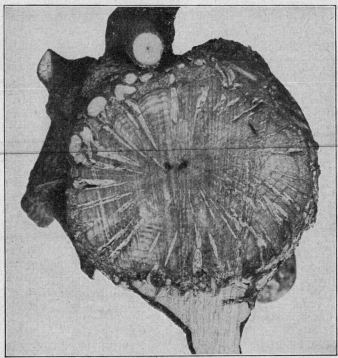

FIG. 430.—Cross section of an oak branch parasitized by mistletoe. The wood of mistletoe is lighter in color than oak wood; the wedge-shaped masses of tissue of the parasite may be seen penetrating the host along the medullary rays. (After Owens, from *Principles of Plant Pathology*.)

3. The deeper parts of large bodies of fresh water, though they are found along the shores and extending some distance into lakes, ponds, and slow-flowing rivers.

4. The driest parts of certain deserts, where there is no rainfall.

5. Regions of perpetual snow, such as the summits of some peaks and certain parts of the polar regions.

In addition to the typical terrestrial forms there are many aquatics, such as the water weed (*Elodea*) and marine eel-grass (*Zostera*), and a large number of epiphytes, mostly tropical or subtropical, such as the so-called Florida moss (*Tillandsia*), a member of the pine-apple family, and many orchids.

The seed plants have in all probability descended from pteridophyte ancestors, through forms long extinct which were intermediate between certain of the living ferns and the most primitive of the Spermatophyta. Inasmuch as the first part of this book was devoted very largely to an account of the morphology and the physiology of the sporophyte of the seed-bearing plants, we shall not discuss those subjects here. In this chapter we shall restrict ourselves for the most part to an account of the gametophyte generation of several types of the seed plants, a description of sexual reproduction and the origin of the new sporophytes (embryos of the seeds) in these plants, and to a statement of the homologies which exist between these plants and the Pteridophyta and Bryophyta.

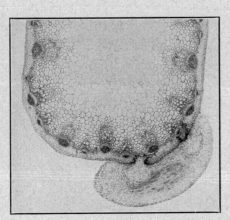

Fig. 431.—Photomicrograph showing a cross-section of a clover stem, and at the right a portion of the stem of the parasitic plant, dodder (*Cuscuta*), in section with a haustorium penetrating the tissues of the host.

The Spermatophyta consist of two well-marked classes, the Gymnospermae (gymnosperms) and the Angiospermae (angiosperms). These two class names are based upon one of the best-defined distinctions between the two groups. The seeds of the Gymnospermae (naked-seeded plants) are borne **upon the surface** of the megasporophyll (carpel or cone scale), whereas the seeds of the Angiospermae (covered-seeded plants) are always formed **within a closed structure** (the ovary) formed by the union of the margins of one or more megasporophylls (carpels).

GYMNOSPERMAE

The gymnosperms are all woody, perennial forms and, with few exceptions, are evergreen plants. They are of great economic importance as sources of timber, rosin, and turpentine. The group is a relatively small one, including only about 500 species, whereas there are more than 125,000 species of angiosperms. Among the best-known gymnosperms are the pines (*Pinus*), spruces (*Picea*), firs (*Abies*), larches (*Larix*), junipers (*Juniperus*), frequently but incorrectly called cedars, the so-called Douglas fir (*Pseudotsuga*), and the redwood and big tree (*Sequoia*). We shall use the genus *Pinus* as a type of this group since its life history is better known than that of any other gymnosperm.

LIFE HISTORY OF PINUS (PINE)

The Sporophyte.—The familiar pine tree is the sporophyte plant and is homologous with the attached, dependent sporophyte (foot, seta, and capsule) of a moss and with the familiar fern plant (root, rhizome, and fronds). The most striking characteristics of the pine sporophyte are as follows: (1) excurrent branching; (2) retention of the leaves during the winter; and (3) the grouping of the long and slender needle-like foliage leaves in clusters or fascicles generally of two to five. Excurrent branching and the evergreen habit are characteristics of most gymnosperms, but the fascicles of leaves closely held together at the base by a circle of scales is peculiar to the pines. As in most of the common gymno-

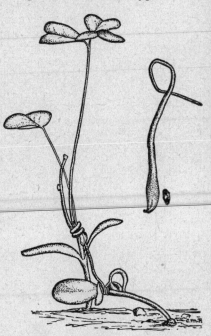

FIG. 432.—Dodder (*Cuscuta*), a parasitic angiosperm. To the right, a seed and a seedling of the parasite before its separation from the soil and its attachment to the host. To the left, two alfalfa seedlings already parasitized and the parasite no longer attached to the soil. (From Robbins and Eggington, Colorado Experiment Station Bulletin.)

sperms, the wood contains no vessels but consists mostly of tracheids with many bordered pits. The linear form of the leaves, their very thick cuticle, and the depressed stomata show the pines to be xerophytic plants as are most of the gymnosperms.

The Strobili.—The sporophylls are borne in strobili or cones. There are two kinds of strobili, megasporangiate and microsporangiate, bearing megasporophylls and microsporophylls, respectively (Fig. 433, and Figs. 435 and 436). Because of the general use of the terms carpels

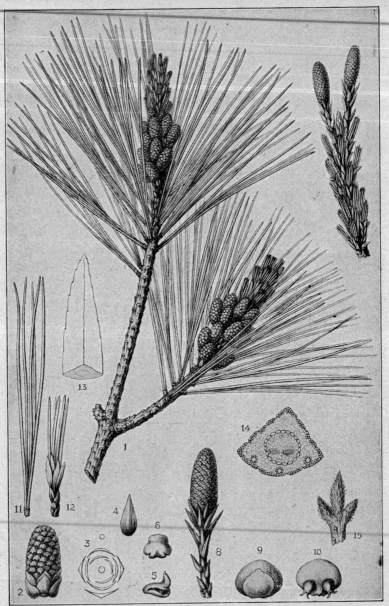

FIG. 433.—Sugar pine (*Pinus lambertiana*). 1, twigs showing last year's foliage leaves, staminate (microsporangiate) strobili, and young leaves of this year's foliage; 2, a single staminate strobilus; 3 to 5, bracts and microsporophylls; 8, carpellate (megasporangiate) strobili; 9, megasporophyll as seen from below and showing the bract and the ovuliferous scale; 10, the same from above showing the megasporangia (ovules); 11 to 14, arrangement and structure of the needles (foliage leaves); 15, end of a twig showing one terminal and two lateral buds. (From Sargent's *Silva of North America*.)

for megasporophylls and stamens for microsporophylls among the flowering plants (angiosperms), the two kinds of strobili in the gymnosperms
are often spoken of respectively as **carpellate** and **staminate** strobili or
cones. They are borne upon the same individual plant.

Megasporangiate Strobili and Megasporophylls.—The familiar pine
cones are the carpellate or megasporangiate strobili. They remain on
the tree for the greater part of two years in all pines, and in some for
many years. These cones first make their appearance at the beginning
of the growing season when the parts within the buds develop, and
growth in length of the twigs begins. At the time there may be found
near the tips of certain branches the newly formed miniature cones.

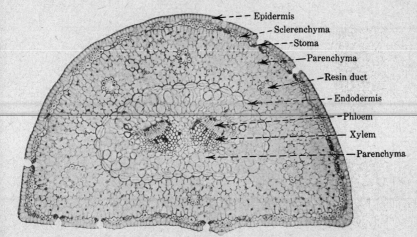

FIG. 434.—Photomicrograph of cross-section of pine needle. In the endodermal cells
note the Casparian strips.

They seldom exceed a centimeter in length and are generally deep red
or flesh color. They consist of a central axis upon which the megasporophylls are spirally arranged. If one of the megasporophylls is removed
from a strobilus and examined with a lens, it will be found to consist
of a very short stalk and a scale to which a bract is attached on the
lower side (Figs. 433, 9 and 10, and 437). On the upper side and near
the base of the scale are two rounded or oval swellings. These are the
ovules which eventually become the seeds. Sections cut lengthwise
through an ovule show that it consists of an oval mass of tissue (the
nucellus or **megasporangium**) surrounded by a single integument and
with a micropyle which is directed toward the base of the scale (Fig.
438*A*). At the opposite end from the micropyle, the tissue of the
integument and nucellus is continuous with that of the scale.

Microsporangiate Strobili and Microsporophylls.—The staminate or microsporangiate strobili are produced in much larger numbers than the carpellate cones and are smaller in size. They are found in clusters near the ends of some of the branches. Like the megasporangiate strobilus, the microsporangiate strobilus consists of a short axis on which the microsporophylls are arranged spirally. They generally make their appearance soon after the beginning of the growing season.

The microsporophyll consists of a stalk, bearing at the end an expanded scale-like portion. To the under side of this scale and to the side of the stalk the two microsporangia (pollen sacs) are attached. Generally the microspores (pollen) are shed within a few weeks after the strobili have made their appearance, whereupon the strobili, having performed their function, wither and soon fall from the tree.

Megasporangium and Megaspores.—Quite early in the development of the cone, sections of the nucellus (megasporangium) show near its center a single cell, the **megaspore mother cell,** which is considerably larger than the surrounding cells and which has dense cytoplasm and a large nucleus. (See Figs. 438, *A* and *B*.) The

Fig. 435.—Tip of a branch of Monterey Pine (*Pinus radiata*), showing two megasporangiate strobili (carpellate cones) a short time after their appearance in the spring and about the time pollination takes place.

conspicuous spore mother cell within the nucellus of *Pinus* soon undergoes two successive divisions and thus four megaspores are formed. Instead of being arranged in a tetrahedral group as are the spores of all the Bryophyta and Pteridophyta and the microspore of the seed plants, these four spores lie in a row as shown in Figs. 438, *D* and 445. All vegetative

cells of the pine and those of the carpellate strobili, including the spore
mother cell, belong to the sporophyte generation and their nuclei have $2n$
chromosomes.   The first of the two nuclear divisions by which the

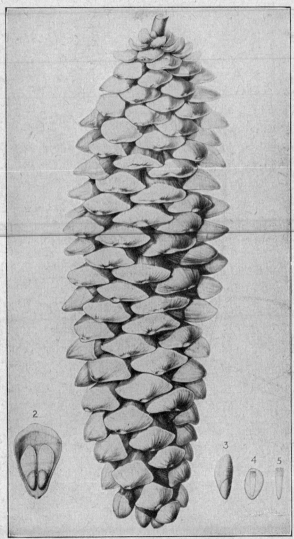

Fig. 436.—Sugar pine (*Pinus lambertiana*). 1, mature cone; 2, single carpellate
scale with two seeds attached; 3, single mature seed; 4, longitudinal section of
seed, showing embryo embedded in endosperm; 5, embryo separated from seed,
showing many cotyledons.   (After Sargent from *Silva of North America*.)

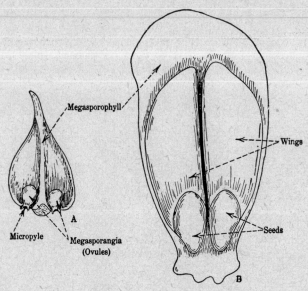

Fig. 437.—Megasporophylls of *Pinus*. *A*, about the time of pollination. *B*, after the seeds have matured.   Note that the two drawings are made from different species.

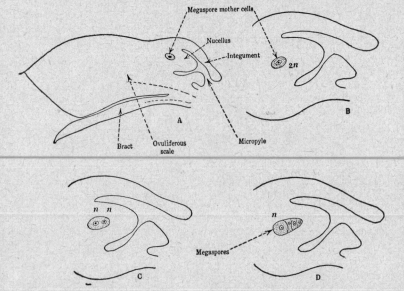

Fig. 438.—Diagrams showing the megasporophyll of pine in longitudinal section and four stages in the production of megaspores from the spore mother cell. (*A*, redrawn after Coulter and Chamberlain.)

megaspore mother cell gives rise to four megaspores is a reduction division (in which nuclear division is by meiosis) such as we have already described in our account of the life history of a true fern. Accordingly, the nucleus of each megaspore has n chromosomes. One

Fig. 439.—Tip of a branch of *Pinus* bearing microsporangiate strobili (staminate cones). The strobili near the base of the cluster have already shed part of their pollen while in those in the upper part of the cluster the microsporophylls have not separated and no pollen has been liberated.

of the four megaspores, the one farthest from the micropyle, now enlarges at the expense of the other three, which are finally completely absorbed.

Microsporangium and Microspores.—The development of the

microspores within the microsporangia in *Pinus* is not essentially different from spore production in the ferns. In order to study the early stages in the development of the sporangia and the spores, the rudimentary strobili must be dissected out of the terminal buds before the beginning of the season of active growth. In *Pinus Laricio*, at Chicago, microspore mother cells were found as early as October of the year preceding the opening of the buds and the appearance of the strobili. The sporangium wall consists of several layers of cells, of which the innermost at least is a tapetal layer such as is found surrounding the spore mother cells in the mosses and pteridophytes. The reduction division which reduces the chromosome number to *n* and the second division take place early in the spring and results in the formation of a tetrad of microspores from each microspore mother cell (Fig. 444 *B*).

Fig. 440.—Photomicrograph of median lengthwise section of microsporangiate (staminate) cone of pine.

Germination of Microspores and Development of Male Gametophyte. —The pollen grains or microspores of *Pinus* germinate (that is, undergo nuclear divisions and thus begin the formation of the male gametophyte) as much as a month before they are shed from the microsporangia. We shall describe the germination of the microspore before taking up the development of the female gametophytes, since it occurs months before the germination of the megaspore.

The microspore just before its germination consists of an oval cell with a single large nucleus (Fig. 444 *C*). Each microspore has two balloon-like (Fig. 444 *C–F*) wings which are formed by the separation of the exine layer of the wall from the intine at two places and an inflation of the spaces thus formed between the two layers. The wings are air-filled and each may at this stage be almost as large as the spore proper. Of the two nuclei formed by the first division of the single nucleus of the spore (Fig. 444*D*), one becomes flattened out against the spore wall and is soon cut off from the other daughter nucleus and

from most of the cytoplasm of the spore by a thin cell wall.   This
nucleus, which we shall call the **first vegetative nucleus,** rapidly degenerates.   Its sister nucleus has meanwhile undergone a second mitosis.
Of the two resulting nuclei (Fig. 444*E*), one is the **second vegetative
nucleus,** which behaves like the first vegetative nucleus, and the other,

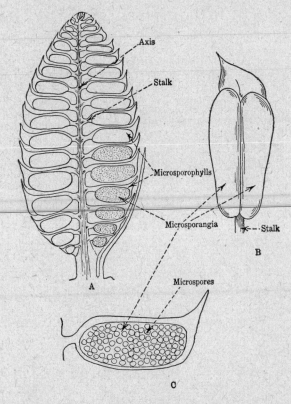

Fig. 441.—Microsporangiate strobilus and microsporophylls of *Pinus*.   *A*, strobilus
  in longitudinal section.   *B* and *C* two views of a microsporophyll, the latter in
  longitudinal section.

together with the cytoplasm surrounding it, is called the **antheridial
cell.** The two vegetative cells apparently perform no function but are
merely vestigial cells corresponding to the vegetative cells which make
up the greater part of the gametophyte of the ferns and to the single
vegetative cell of the male gametophyte which develops within the
microspore of *Selaginella*. A short time before the microspores are
shed the antheridial cell undergoes division into a smaller cell, the

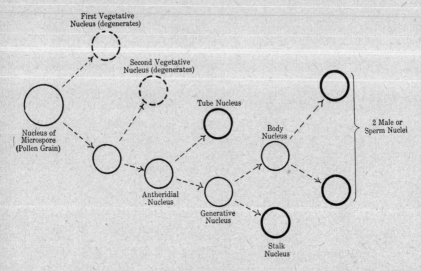

First Vegetative
Nucleus (degenerates)

Second Vegetative
Nucleus (degenerates)

Tube Nucleus

Body
Nucleus

2 Male or
Sperm Nuclei

Nucleus of
Microspore
(Pollen Grain)

Antheridial
Nucleus

Generative
Nucleus

Stalk
Nucleus

FIG. 442.—Diagram showing nuclei formed during development of the male gametophyte from a microspore of a pine.

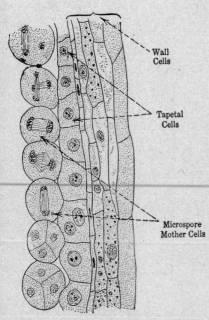

Wall
Cells

Tapetal
Cells

Microspore
Mother Cells

FIG. 443.—Part of a young microsporangium of *Pinus* showing divisions of the pollen mother cells. (Redrawn in part from Coulter and Chamberlain.)

generative cell (cut off against the second vegetative cell), and a larger cell, the tube cell (Fig. 444*F*).

Pollination.—About this time the microsporangia dehisce longitudinally and the pollen grains (microspores) are liberated. The quantity of pollen produced is astonishingly large. That shed by a single Scotch pine may be as much as a liter. It is yellow in color and resembles the finely powdered form of sulphur called "flowers of sulphur." There are records of pine pollen having been borne for hundreds of miles by the wind. Microscopic examination, at the time of pollenshedding and for weeks after, of water, soil, or the surface of plants anywhere in the vicinity of pines, will almost unfailingly reveal the characteristic pine microspores.

As in all wind-pollinated plants, by far the greater part of the pollen is wasted. Some does, however, reach the carpellate cones, the mega-sporophylls of which at this time are slightly separated, so that some

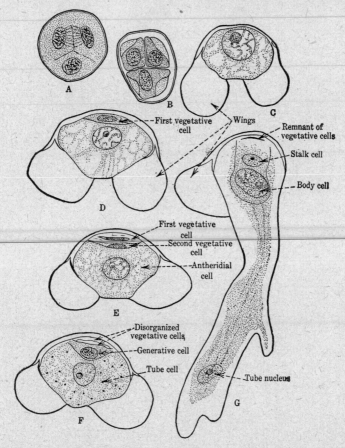

Fig. 444.—Successive stages in the development of the microspore and male gameto-phyte of *Pinus laricio*. *A*, showing the telophase of the second division of the spore mother cell. *B*, showing three of the four spores of a tetrad some time before maturity. *C*, a mature microspore. *D* to *F*, successive stages in the development of the male gametophyte up to the time the spores are shed. *G*, about a year after pollination and some time before fertilization. Figure 442 shows diagrammatically the nuclear divisions and other nuclear changes which accompany the development of the male gametophyte of *Pinus*. (Redrawn from Coulter and Chamberlain.)

of the pollen grains sift down between them and come to lie in close proximity to the micropyles of the ovules. Just at this time the nucellus in each ovule exudes a quantity of a sticky fluid, which protrudes through the micropyle so that it comes in contact with some of the microspores. As the drop dries up, the pollen grain or grains are drawn down through the micropyle and come in contact with the nucellus itself. Pollination is accordingly different from that of the flowering plants (angiosperms) in that the pollen grain, instead of being brought into contact merely with the stigma (tip of the carpel or carpels), is, in *Pinus* and many related gymnosperms, brought into *direct contact* with the megasporangium (nucellus of the ovule).

Subsequent Changes up to Fertilization.—It will be recalled that at the time of pollination the pollen grain contains a male gametophyte consisting of two flattened and much-disorganized vegetative cells, the generative cell, and the tube cell (Fig. 444*F*). The ovule is at this time in the condition already described, the nucellus of the megasporangium proper being surrounded by a single integument and enclosing a single functional megaspore which is larger than the surrounding cells but lacks any thick spore wall such as is found in *Selaginella* and the water ferns. In *Pinus Laricio*, at Chicago, pollination was found to take place about the middle of June.

Very soon after pollination, the scales of the carpellate cone are pressed together as the result of their growth and are sealed together by an exudation of pitch, and the whole cone is inverted by the curvature of its stalk. During the subsequent eleven months the male gametophyte does not develop to any considerable extent. A short pollen tube is formed by each pollen grain. This tube, which may branch somewhat, penetrates the tissue of the nucellus and grows downward very slowly until cold weather comes on.

Development of Female and Male Gametophytes.—During the year following pollination there is developed from the megaspore a considerable mass of tissue which is the female gametophyte and is often spoken of as the endosperm, but which, however, is not homologous with the endosperm in the seeds of flowering plants. Its cells differ from those of the surrounding nucellar tissue in that their nuclei have but half the chromosome number of the cells of the nucellus, since the first division of the nucleus of the megaspore mother cell (see page 542 was by meiosis. The manner of development of this female gametophyte, or endosperm, is as follows: The megaspore first enlarges considerably at the expense of the nucellar tissue which surrounds it. It then germinates, i.e., undergoes division of its nucleus into two nuclei. These two nuclei are not separated by a wall, however, and they undergo repeated division without wall formation. After this (free nuclear) division has continued for some time, walls are formed between the nuclei and there results a solid mass of gametophyte tissue which has displaced a considerable amount of the tissue of the nucellus.

Late in the spring of the following year (nearly a year after pollination), there are formed at the end of the female gametophyte nearest the micropyle a number of archegonia, generally two or three, which are quite different in appearance from those of the Pteridophyta or Bryophyta. The number of archegonia is much greater in certain gymno-

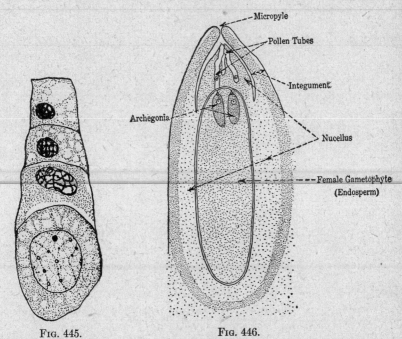

FIG. 445.   FIG. 446.

FIG. 445.—*Pinus austriaca.* Four megaspores which have arisen by the divisions of the megaspore mother cell within the nucellus. The large basal cell is farthest from the micropyle and is the one which gives rise to the female gametophyte. (Redrawn after Ferguson.)

FIG. 446.—Ovule of pine at about the time of fertilization. (Redrawn after Coulter and Chamberlain.)

sperms, sixty for example in *Sequoia sempervirens.* Each archegonium has its origin in a single superficial cell of the gametophyte, and no part of it projects above the surface of the gametophyte. When fully developed, each archegonium consists of eight small neck cells in two tiers of four, the ventral-canal cell, and a very large cavity containing the egg cell, which almost fills it. The ventral-canal cell disorganizes before fertilization. Neck-canal cells are entirely lacking. The cavity in which the egg lies is surrounded by a layer of cells, the **jacket cells,** which have dense cytoplasm and large nuclei and suggest the tapetal cells in sporangia. Although the function of the jacket cells seems to be similar to that of tapetum, it must be borne in mind that the tapetum is made up of sporophyte cells and nourishes the spore mother cells and spores, whereas the jacket cells belong to the gametophyte and supply food to the egg cell and later to the embryo. The jacket cells are therefore not homologous with tapetal cells.

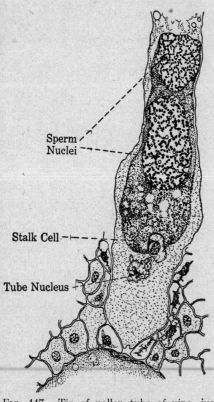

Sperm Nuclei

Stalk Cell

Tube Nucleus

FIG. 447.—Tip of pollen tube of pine, just before it enters the archegonium. (After Ferguson.)

The archegonium is not fully developed and ready for fertilization until about a year after pollination. During the second spring the pollen tube, which has ceased development during the cold winter months, has been growing slowly downward and penetrating the nucellar tissue which caps the apical portion of the female gametophyte. The tube nucleus has by this time passed from the body of the spore into the tube. Meanwhile, the generative cell has divided into a **stalk cell** and a **body cell** (Fig. 444 *G*), which also soon pass into the tube. In the tube the nucleus of the body cell divides into two nuclei which are the **sperm nuclei** and correspond to the sperms of the Pteridophyta and Bryophyta. Thus, the fully developed male gametophyte consists of two disorganized vegetative cells in the body of the spore and four nuclei, with a quantity of surrounding cytoplasm, which lie in the tube. These four nuclei in the tube are (1) the tube nucleus, (2) the stalk nucleus, and (3) two male or sperm nuclei. The stalk nucleus is surrounded by cytoplasm about which is a definite membrane, so that we may speak of the stalk cell. The nuclei of the gametes are large and stain more densely than do the other nuclei in the tube, and their cytoplasm is quite clearly differentiated

Fertilization.—When the tip of the pollen tube reaches the surface of the female gametophyte, it destroys the neck cells and discharges the four cells which it contains into the cytoplasm of the egg.

The nucleus of one (the functioning) male cell now moves toward the large egg nucleus which lies deep in the cytoplasm of the egg cell, and fusion of the two gamete nuclei takes place. The non-functioning male nucleus and the tube and stalk nuclei soon undergo disorganization, their material becoming part of the food store of the zygote.

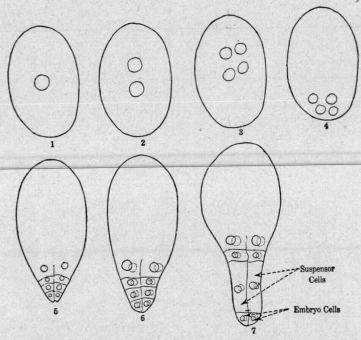

Fig. 448.—Diagrams showing stages in the development of the pro-embryo of *Pinus* from the zygote; 1, shows the zygote before the first division of the fusion nucleus; 2 to 7, see explanation in the text.

Formation of the Embryo.—Immediately after the fusion of the functioning male nucleus and the egg nucleus, the first division of the zygote nucleus begins. In this division twenty-four chromosomes (the sporophyte number) of which twelve (the gametophyte number) were contributed by the nucleus of the male cell and twelve by the egg nucleus, are involved. These split so that each daughter nucleus of the zygote receives twenty-four chromosomes. A second mitosis then takes place and thus four free nuclei are formed. These pass to the base of the egg cell where each nucleus divides again. During this division, walls are formed between the resulting eight nuclei which lie in two tiers of four. By later divisions sixteen cells (four tiers of four) are produced, of which the uppermost four are not cut off from the cytoplasm of the egg (Fig. 448, 5, 6). This group of sixteen cells is called the **pro-embryo.** Of the four tiers of cells of the pro-embryo, those in the next to the lowest tier elongate to ten or twelve times their original length (Figs. 448, 7 and 449, *A*). They are called **suspensor cells,** and their elongation causes the four cells of the lowermost tier to be pushed deep down into the endosperm (female gametophyte tissue) below the archegonium. The eight cells of the two upper tiers remain within the cavity of the original egg cell and serve to absorb food for the nourishment of the four embryo cells, each of which develops into an embryo. Since there may be three archegonia within a single pine ovule, as many as twelve young embryos may thus be formed. Before their development has progressed far, one generally surpasses the others and finally develops at their expense into the one functioning embryo of the seed.

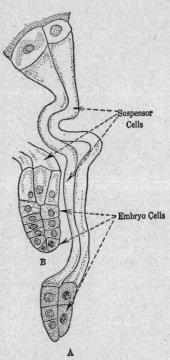

FIG. 449.—Further development of the pro-embryo of pine, showing early stages (*A* and *B*) in the development of the embryos. (Redrawn after Coulter and Chamberlain.)

The Seed.—Even after fertilization the endosperm continues to grow, encroaching upon the tissue of the nucellus and absorbing it. Accordingly, in the ripe seed nothing remains of the nucellus but a brown, papery layer capping the endosperm at the micropylar end of the seed. Buried in the endosperm of the mature seed is the embryo, which consists of the **radicle,** the **hypocotyl,** three to many **cotyledons,** and the **plumule.** The seed coat ("shell") of the pine seed is formed by changes in the tissue of the integument. After fertilization and while the ovule is developing into a seed, the whole carpellate cone grows to many times its previous size and the tissues of the cone scales become woody and hard and lose most of their water. In most species the scales separate after the seeds have become mature, and permit the seeds to fall from the cone.

In many pines a layer of tissue from the upper surface of the cone scale splits off to form a wing, which remains attached to the base of the seed when it is shed. This imparts a spinning motion to the seed as it falls, and slows up its rate of descent so that in a moderate breeze the seeds may be carried some distance from the tree on which they are produced. The germination of pine seeds does not differ in any very

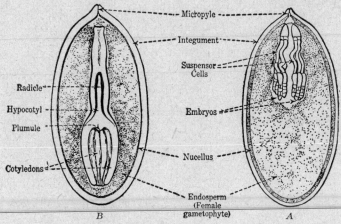

FIG. 450.—Two stages in the development of pine seed, shown in longitudinal section. *A*, more highly magnified than *B*, and showing an earlier stage of development. Note the numerous embryos in *A* and the single surviving embryo in *B*, also the greater relative reduction of the nucellus in the older seed. (Redrawn from Curtis.)

significant particular from that of the angiosperm seeds discussed in an earlier chapter.

SUMMARY OF THE PRINCIPAL FEATURES OF THE LIFE HISTORY OF PINE

1. **Formation of microspore mother cells within the microsporangia** (two microsporangia are borne upon each microsporophyll of the staminate strobilus).

2. **Formation of a tetrad of microspores from each microspore mother cell** by two divisions, of which the first is a reduction division and marks the beginning of the male gametophyte, the nuclei of the microspores having therefore *n* chromosomes.

3. **Germination of the microspores within the microsporangium.** At the time these spores are shed the male gametophyte consists of two disorganized vegetative cells, a tube cell and a generative cell.

4. **Appearance within the ovule** (which consists of the megasporangium or nucellus and an integument) **of a single conspicuous megaspore mother cell.**

5. **Division of this cell to form a row of four megaspores,** the first division being a reduction division (so that the nucleus of each megaspore has n chromosomes) and marking the beginning of the female gametophyte generation, and the development of one of these megaspores at the expense of the other three until it becomes the sole functioning megaspore.

6. **Escape of microspores, and pollination by wind.** The microspores sift down between the megasporophylls and come to lie near the megasporangia. They are drawn in through the micropyle to the surface of the megasporangium (nucellus) by the retraction, as it dries, of a mucilaginous drop protruding from the micropyle at the time of pollination.

7. **Formation of a pollen tube, which grows slowly downward through the tissue of the nucellus.** It develops short, irregular branches which appear to act as haustoria and absorb food from the tissue of the nucellus. The growth of the pollen tube ceases during the winter but is resumed the following spring.

8. **Germination of the megaspore and growth of the female gametophyte** (endosperm) at the expense of the tissue of the nucellus. **Formation at the apical end of the female gametophyte of several archegonia** of much simpler form than those of the Pteridophyta.

9. **Entrance of the pollen tube into the archegonium and discharge of its contents into the egg cell.** This takes place about a year after pollination. The contents of the pollen tube consist of the stalk cell, the tube nucleus, and two sperm nuclei (the latter three derived from the generative cell mentioned in 3 above) and some cytoplasm. One male nucleus fertilizes the egg nucleus (this initiates the sporophyte generation), and the other nuclei disorganize.

10. **Immediate development of the zygote into a pro-embryo of sixteen cells,** four of which are embryo cells and four suspensors. These latter four cells elongate and thrust the embryo cells deep into the tissue of the endosperm (female gametophyte). Each embryo cell begins to develop into an embryo, but one of the many embryos gains the upper hand and becomes the single functioning embryo of the seed.

11. **Development of the ovule into a seed,** involving growth of the embryo, further growth of endosperm with almost complete disappearance of the nucellus, and formation of the hard outer layer or "shell" of the seed from the integument.

12. **Germination of the seed.**

13. **Growth into a mature sporophyte plant** producing each season microsporangiate strobili and megasporangiate strobili.

Other Gymnosperms.—What has been said of the structure and life history of *Pinus* applies in its principal features to most of the common gymnosperms which belong to the Order Coniferales. To point out the principal variations from the *Pinus* type within this group would be beyond the scope of this book. The other three orders of the living Gymnosperms (Cycadales, Ginkgoales, and Gnetales) differ in a number of interesting and important particulars from *Pinus*, and nearly related genera. We shall give special attention to the Cycadales because they are probably the most primitive of living Gymnosperms. However, there are important extinct groups of Gymnosperms (Cycadofilicales, Bennettitales, and Cordaitales), represented only by fossil remains, some of which, chiefly representatives of the Cycadofilicales, are more primitive than the Cycadales. The Cycadofilicales resembled ferns in

FIG. 451.—Plants of a species of *Zamia* showing (center and right) two microsporangiate strobili and on the left a megasporangiate strobilus. Photograph furnished by C. J. Chamberlain.

their external appearance, and the microsporangia were very similar to those of living heterosporous pteridophytes, but the megasporangia were very different from those of present-day heterosporous Pteridophyta, and a well-developed ovule was formed. The occurrence of a combination of pteridophyte and spermatophyte characteristics in Cycadofilicales has led to the conclusion that representatives of this group were probably the most primitive seed plants.

In Cycadales or Cycads the plant body (sporophyte) consists of a stout stem which branches sparingly or not at all and bears a rosette of leaves at the ends of the stems. The plants have the appearance of tree ferns or palms.

In the cycads the microsporophylls and megasporophylls are borne upon different individual plants.   The microsporophylls bear numerous microsporangia (as many as 750 in the genus *Dioon*) and thus are in striking contrast with those of *Pinus* which bear only two microsporangia.   In some of the Cycadales the megasporophylls show a distinct resemblance to vegetative leaves.   In most of the genera only two megasporangia are borne on each megasporophyll.   In *Cycas*, *Zamia*, and other genera of the Cycadales as well as in *Ginkgo biloba*, the only living species of the Ginkgoales, the male gametes have cilia and are motile like the sperms of the Pteridophyta and Bryophyta.   These gymnosperms with motile sperms partly bridge the gap between the heterosporous Pteridophyta and the seed-bearing plants.

We shall discuss briefly the life history of *Zamia*, a typical cycad.

The megasporangium consists of a nucellus enclosed by a relatively thick integument.   Formation of the megaspore mother cell and of four megaspores, of which only one functions, is essentially the same as in *Pinus*.   The megaspore on germination gives rise to a mass of tissue, the female gametophyte, consisting of small cells at the micropylar end, and of larger cells, nutritive in function, at the opposite end.   Usually four archegonia, similar in most respects to those of *Pinus*, are found in each gametophyte.

The microsporangia and the development of the microspore tetrads are not essentially different in *Pinus* and *Zamia*.   The principal differences in the male gametophyte are that in *Zamia* (1) only one vegetative cell is produced, (2) this vegetative cell does not degenerate at once but remains alive until the time of fertilization, and (3) the sperms or male gametes are provided with a large number of cilia and swim around for a time before fertilization takes place in the liquid which fills the small depression which occurs next to the micropyle at the end of the nucellus.

After fertilization there is rapid free nuclear division resulting in many nuclei, which move towards the lower end of the egg.   Walls are formed about the nuclei in this region, giving rise to a tissue known as the **pro-embryo.**   In the upper part of the egg, numerous nuclei remain free for a period.   Certain cells in the pro-embryo now begin to elongate, forming a **suspensor,** which pushes the tip cells of the pro-embryo deep into the tissue of the female gametophyte (endosperm), from which they obtain nutriment.   The cells at the end of the long suspensor develop into the embryo which has two cotyledons, a stem growing point between them, a short hypocotyl, and a radicle.

In the mature seed, the embryo sporophyte lies embedded in the endosperm (remnant of the female gametophyte) which is surrounded by the remains of the nucellus, which in turn is enclosed by the seed coats, consisting of an inner stony layer and a soft outer one.

In certain particulars *Zamia* is a plant with characters intermediate between those of the Pteridophyta and those of the higher Gymnosperms, of which *Pinus* is a type. Features of the Cycadales, reminiscent of Pteridophyta, are as follows:

1. Pinnate foliage leaves, which are inrolled before maturity and continue to grow at the apex until their full size is reached.
2. Concentric vascular bundles in leaf veins and in the axes of the strobilus.
3. Leaf-like megasporophylls in certain groups.
4. Motile sperms.

Characters of the Cycadales which are similar to those of the higher gymnosperms are as follows:

1. Vascular bundles in the stems of a gymnosperm type.
2. Reduced gametophytes.
3. Woody sporophylls in certain groups.
4. Pollen tube.
5. Pro-embryo.
6. Seeds.
7. Complete elimination of neck-canal cells in archegonia.

Ginkgo biloba (order Ginkgoales) is the so-called " maidenhair tree," long cultivated in China and Japan and now to a considerable extent in this country. It is different from the Cycadales in being freely branched and bearing simple leaves which are fan-shaped and strongly suggest the leaflets of the maidenhair fern. Ginkgo is dioecious, and the microsporophylls and megasporophylls are much reduced and not leaf-like.

The Gnetales in several respects are more like the angiosperms than are any of the other gymnosperms. Thus they have true vessels in the secondary wood; the groups of microsporophylls and megasporophylls are usually borne on the same plant; and in two of the three genera (*Tumboa* and *Gnetum*) no archegonia are formed and the female gametophyte shows striking resemblances to the embryo sac (female gametophyte) of the angiosperms.

ANGIOSPERMAE

The second class of the Spermatophyta, the Angiospermae, far exceed in number of species and in their importance to man any other class in the plant kingdom. In fact, in the number of described species the angiosperms exceed all the other plant groups taken together. The group includes, with the exception of certain gymnosperms which furnish timber, turpentine, and rosin, practically every plant which is utilized by man as a source of food, clothing, or materials for use in industry and in the arts. Although they include some very simple forms which have evolved by reduction from more highly differentiated

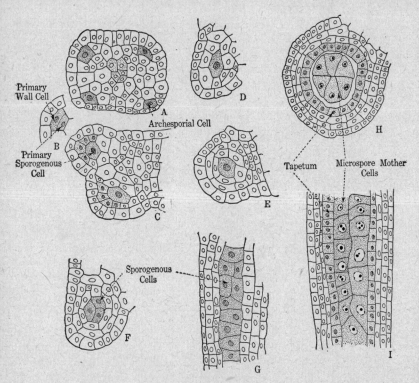

FIG. 452.—Stages in the development of the anther of wheat. A, cross section of young anther. B, first division of archesporial cell. C, D, E and F, cross sections of anthers showing subsequent division. G, longitudinal section of F. H and I, cross and longitudinal sections of a locule of a young anther, showing mature microspore mother cells. (Redrawn from Percival.)

ones, they represent without question the highest point in the evolution of plants.

The angiosperms as a class are better adapted to the land habitat than any other class of plants, and accordingly are not only the most important and conspicuous element in the flora of the earth but are represented in practically every part of the world where plants can live at all.

Distinction between Gymnosperms and Angiosperms.—Although angiosperms have much in common with the gymnosperms, the two groups are quite distinctly marked off from each other. The principal points of contrast are:

1. Whereas the gymnosperms are all woody, perennial plants, the angiosperms also include, in addition to such forms, many herbaceous annual and biennial plants.

2. In typical angiosperms, microsporophylls (stamens) and megasporophylls (carpels) generally are borne together in groups (flowers); in the gymnosperms, as we have already learned, they are borne in different groups (staminate and carpellate strobili).

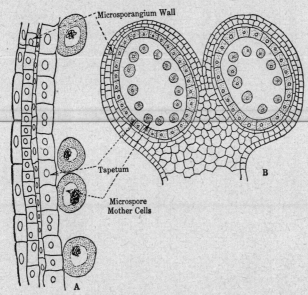

Fig. 453.—*A*, longitudinal section of a portion of the wall of the anther of wheat. *B*, transverse section of an anther lobe of wheat. (Redrawn from Percival.)

3. With very few exceptions, vessels occur in the xylem of all angiosperms, but they are lacking in the xylem of all living gymnosperms except the *Gnetales*.

4. Angiosperm seeds are borne within a closed structure (ovary) presumably resulting from the fusion of the edges of one or more megasporophylls, whereas the seeds of the gymnosperms are borne naked on the surface of megasporophylls, which do not form ovaries.

Life History of Wheat (*Triticum*).—In our discussion of the different major groups of plants, it has been the plan to trace in detail the life history of some one genus, which is fairly representative of the group under consideration. This has been supplemented by a statement of the principal departures, which occur within that group, from the type representative. Among the several thousand genera of angiosperms, there is for the most part marked uniformity in the essential stages of their life history. As the angiosperm representative we have chosen a member of the Gramineae or grass family, *Triticum aestivum* (common wheat), not only because its life history has been rather completely worked out, but also because it is one of the most important and familiar plants in the world.

As in the Pteridophyta and Gymnospermae, the sporophyte of wheat, and of other angiosperms, is the conspicuous generation in the life history; i.e., the sporophyte is "the wheat plant."

Inasmuch as the first half of this book was almost entirely devoted to an account of the structure and physiology of flowering plants, it will not be necessary for us to describe here the mature angiosperm sporophyte. It will be recalled that the plant body of an angiosperm consists of a root, and shoot, the latter made up of the stems and leaves, and that in addition to foliage leaves there are floral leaves.

The principal features of the grass flower were described on pages 250-254. The stamens and carpels are respectively homologous with the microsporophylls and megasporophylls of *Pinus* and heterosporous pteridophytes. In this chapter we shall use the terms microsporophylls and megasporophylls rather than the synonymous terms stamens and carpels which originated long before the homology of these structures with the spore-bearing leaves of the gymnosperms and pteridophytes was first suspected.

Microsporophylls and Microsporangia.—The anther consists at first of a small mass of meristematic cells (Fig. 452). There are early differentiated in this mass four separate groups of cells which by further development will become the microsporangia. Each of these groups of cells has its origin in a longitudinal row of cells just beneath the epidermis. Each cell of this row divides, by a wall parallel to the surface of the anther, to form two rows of cells. By further division of the cells of the outer row, several layers of cells are formed, and these, together with the epidermis, make up the wall of the microsporangium. The innermost wall layer is the tapetum. The cells of the tapetum break down during the development of the microspores, their protoplasm escaping into the cavity of the microsporangium (pollen sac) furnishing food for the development of spores. By repeated division of the cells of the inner of the two longitudinal rows, microspore mother cells are formed. Each mother cell now undergoes two successive cell divisions, during the first of which there is a reduction in the number of chromoьomes. Thus, each mother cell gives rise to four microspores (pollen grains), the nucleus of each having n chromosomes.

Megasporophylls and Megasporangia.—The megasporangium (nucellus) has its origin in a small mass of undifferentiated cells which protrude from the placenta. From the base of this projection arise two rings of tissue which grow up about the developing megasporangium. These two layers of tissue (the integuments) finally entirely envelop

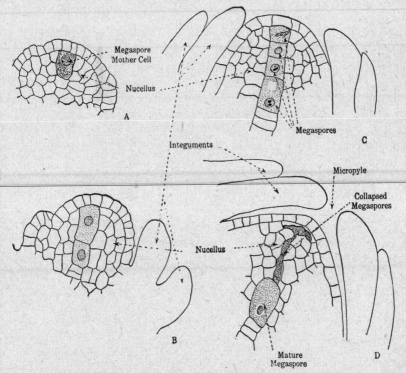

Fig. 454.—Median lengthwise section of young ovules of wheat, showing development of the megaspores and the degeneration of all but one of these. (Redrawn from Percival.)

the megasporangium proper, except for a small opening (micropyle) at the free end of the ovule (Fig. 454, *D*).

While the megasporangium is still very small, one of the cells just below the epidermis of the nucellus becomes differentiated from the surrounding cells in size and in the appearance of its contents. This is the megaspore mother cell, and the nucellar tissue surrounding it constitutes the megasporangium wall. No tapetal layer is formed.

The nucleus of the megaspore mother cell now undergoes two suc-

cessive divisions and thus four potentital megaspores are produced.
These spores are not arranged in the characteristic tetrahedral groups,
as are the spores of all Bryophyta and Pteridophyta and the microspores
of seed plants, but in a single row. As the first of the divisions by which

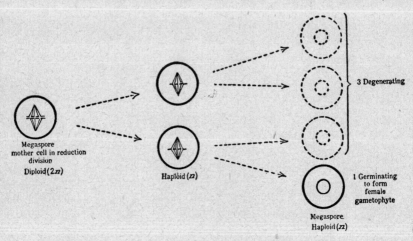

Fig. 455.—Diagram showing the development of megaspores from a megaspore
mother cell. Compare with Fig. 458.

the four spores arise is a reduction division, the spore mother cell is
the last cell in the life cycle having the diploid chromosome number,
the nucleus of each of the four spores having *n* chromosomes. Definite
walls are formed around each mega-
spore. Soon the basal megaspore
begins to enlarge at the expense of
the other three, and finally these three
are completely absorbed, leaving a
single large functioning megaspore, as
in *Pinus*.

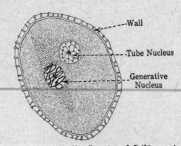

Fig. 456.—Pollen grain of *Lilium* at
the time of shedding. Early stage
of a male gametophyte enclosed
within the microspore wall.

The Male Gametophyte.—**Germination of the microspore** begins while it
is still within the microsporangium.
For convenience we shall consider the
germination of the microspore and
the development of male gametophyte as taking place in the following
stages:

(1) **Division of the protoplast of the microspore into a tube cell and
a generative cell.** The cytoplasm of these two cells is clearly differentiated, but they are not separated by a wall. (See Fig. 456.)

(2) A little later, and before the shedding of the microspores, the **division of the generative cell which produces two male gametes or sperms.** (In many angiosperms the second division does not take place until after the pollen tube is formed.)

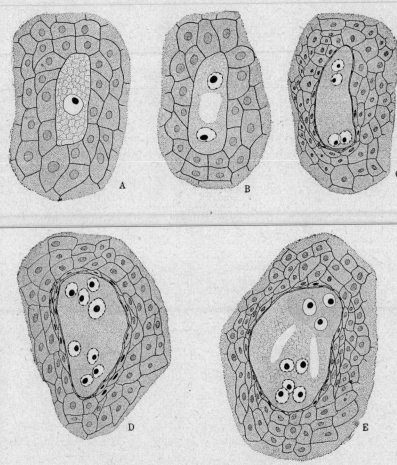

Fig. 457.—Stages in the development of the female gametophyte (embryo sac) of corn. Longitudinal sections. *A*, 1-celled embryo sac (megaspore). *B*, 2-celled embryo sac. *C*, 4-celled embryo sac. *D*, 8-celled embryo sac at time the polar nuclei have started to migrate. *E*, 8-celled embryo sac after the polar nuclei have migrated. The megaspore mother cell and embryo sacs are embedded in nucellar tissue. (Redrawn from Miller, in *Journal of Agricultural Research*.)

(3) **Following pollination, the formation of the pollen tube.**

(4) **Migration of the two male gametes into the pollen tube,** and the migration of the tube nucleus as well.

The mature male gametophyte (pollen grain) consisting of three nuclei and some associated cytoplasm, is even more reduced than that of *Pinus*, for in the latter case there are, in addition to the two sperm nuclei, the remnants of two vegetative cells, a tube cell, and a stalk cell.

The Female Gametophyte (Embryo Sac).—The protoplast of the surviving megaspore, as in *Pinus*, the Cycadales, and some heterosporous pteridophytes, now undergoes free nuclear division. There results a female gametophyte consisting of eleven to fifteen nuclei lying free in a mass of vacuolate cytoplasm. In contrast with *Pinus*, cell walls are not subsequently formed between the nuclei of the female gametophyte in the angiosperms.

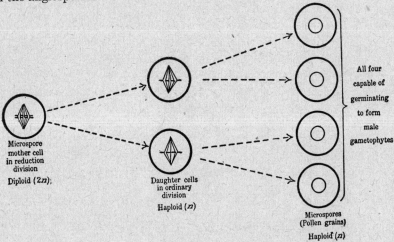

All four capable of germinating to form male gametophytes

Microspore mother cell in reduction division

Diploid (2*n*);

Daughter cells in ordinary division

Haploid (*n*)

Microspores (Pollen grains)

Haploid (*n*)

FIG. 458.—Diagram showing the development of microspores from the microspore mother cell.   Compare with Fig. 455.

This process of development of the female gametophyte may be conveniently divided into the following states:

(1) The **first division of the megaspore nucleus results in two nuclei, which promptly separate,** and one of which moves to the micropylar end of the sac and the other to the opposite (antipodal) end of the sac.

(2) **Each of these two nuclei divides,** so that there are **two nuclei at the micropylar end, and two at the antipodal end.**

(3) Following this second division, **each of the four nuclei divides,** resulting in eight nuclei, **four at the micropylar end** and **four at the antipodal end.**

(4) Now, **a single nucleus from each group** of four **moves toward the center of the embryo sac.** The two nuclei (polar nuclei) lie in contact with one another without fusing until the time of fertilization.

(5) **The three nuclei at the end opposite the micropyle divide, forming a group of six to ten antipodal nuclei.** Although not separated from one another by cell walls, each of these nuclei has about it a quantity of cytoplasm set off from that of neighboring nuclei by a thin membrane, so that we may speak of them as cells (the antipodal cells). In most angiosperms there are only three antipodal cells, and accordingly, the embryo sac generally contains only eight nuclei.

(6) Of the **three nuclei remaining at the micropylar end,** one is the **egg nucleus, and the** other two are the **synergid nuclei.** Each of these nuclei has associated with it a quantity of cytoplasm, which is separated by a limiting membrane from the rest of the embryo sac. Thus at the time of fertilization the female gametophyte of wheat and also of Indian corn as shown in Fig. 460 consists of:

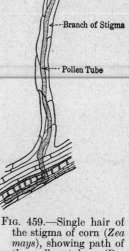

(*a*) **Two synergid cells** or "helper cells" at the micropylar end of the embryo sac.

(*b*) **A single egg cell** near the synergids.

(*c*) **Two polar nuclei,** usually near the center of the embryo sac.

(*d*) **Six to ten antipodal cells,** at the end of the embryo sac opposite the synergids.

Pollination and Development of the Pollen Tube.—The pollen of wheat is carried to the plume-like stigma by the wind. Within one and a half to two hours after pollination, the pollen tube begins to develop. It penetrates the tissue of the stigma and, entering the style, grows downward into the ovary, and

Fig. 459.—Single hair of the stigma of corn (*Zea mays*), showing path of the pollen tube. (Redrawn from Miller, in *Journal of Agricultural Research.*)

makes its way to the micropyle. After passing through this opening, it penetrates the tissue of the nucellus and enters the embryo sac.

There is considerable variation in different angiospermous plants as to the length of the interval between pollination and fertilization. In wheat the union of the gamete with the egg nucleus has been observed between thirty and forty hours after pollination. In most herbaceous angiosperms, the interval is a few hours or days. In the elms, oaks, beeches, walnuts, orange and other species of *Citrus*, and many other woody plants, the interval may vary from one to eleven months.

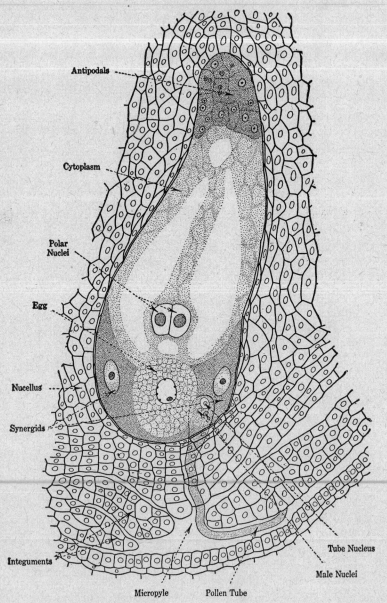

Antipodals

Cytoplasm

Polar
Nuclei

Egg

Nucellus

Synergids

Integuments

Tube Nucleus

Male Nuclei

Micropyle   Pollen Tube

FIG. 460.—Longitudinal section of a mature embryo sac of corn (essentially similar
to that of *Triticum*) (*Zea mays*) just prior to fertilization. (Redrawn from
Miller, in *Journal of Agricultural Research*.)

Fertilization.—After entering the embryo sac, the pollen tube grows towards the egg nucleus. The tip of the tube is then ruptured and its contents discharged. **One of the sperm nuclei fuses with the egg nucleus, forming the zygote nucleus,** and the **second sperm nucleus unites with the polar nuclei to form the endosperm nucleus.**

At the union of a sperm nucleus with the egg nucleus, there is a **doubling of the number of chromosomes,** and the **resulting zygote, the nucleus of which has $2n$ chromosomes, marks the beginning of the new sporophyte generation.** At the union of the second sperm nucleus with the two polar nuclei, there is a trebling of the number of chromosomes. The resulting " **triple fusion nucleus** " and the cytoplasm of the embryo sac associated with it develops into endosperm ($3n$ tissue).

By the union of the sperm with the egg, the zygote is furnished with one set of chromosomes from the male parent and another set from the female parent. These two sets are associated in all the cells of the sporophyte. That is, in the first division of the zygote nucleus and in all subsequent divisions of sporophytic cells, chromosomes of paternal origin (contributed by the sperm nucleus) and those of maternal origin (contributed by the egg nucleus), split

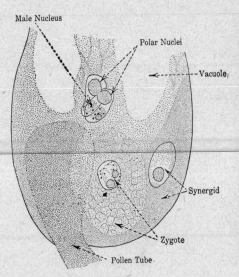

Fig. 461.—Longitudinal section of the lower portion of the embryo sac of corn at the time of fertilization. One male nucleus is shown fusing with the two polar nuclei, and the other male nucleus is shown fusing with the egg nucleus. (Redrawn from Miller, in the *Journal of Agricultural Research.*)

longitudinally and each daughter nucleus receives an equal amount of both maternal chromatin and paternal chromatin. There is reason to believe that the chromatin of all the chromosomes contributed by the male and female gametes maintains its individuality in the nuclei of all sporophyte cells.

The synergids degenerate at about the time of fertilization. During the growth of the embryo and endosperm, the antipodal cells also slowly degenerate.

Development of Embryo Sporophyte.—The fertilized egg (zygote) becomes by repeated division a multicellular embryo sporophyte. In wheat, the zygote undergoes division into two cells a few hours after fertilization. This two-celled body is the **pro-embryo.** One cell of the pro-embryo is the suspensor, and from the other cell the embryo develops. A depression appears at one side of the **embryo,** marking the position of the growing point of the stem. The scutellum (single cotyledon) arises from the tissue above this depression. The origin and development of the other organs of the embryo are shown in Fig. 465.

Development of the Endosperm.—It will be recalled that in *Pinus* and in most other gymnosperms the nutritive tissue of the seed, **the endosperm, is the female gametophyte,** a mass of tissue developed by repeated divisions of the megaspore nucleus and subsequent cell-wall formation. Even at the time of fertilization, this gametophyte tissue makes up a considerable part of the ovule, and after fertilization it continues to grow until it finally displaces all the tissue of the nucellus (megasporangium). In wheat and all other angiosperms, the endosperm has an entirely different origin. It is initiated, not by the germination of the megaspore as in *Pinus,* but by the division of the endosperm nucleus which is the product of the fusion of three haploid nuclei (two polar nuclei and a sperm nucleus). Accordingly the endosperm in most angiosperms is neither sporophyte tissue with $2n$ chromosomes in the nuclei, nor gametophyte tissue with nuclei having n chromosomes. Unless there are irregularities in the nuclear division of the endosperm cells they would be expected to have nuclei with $3n$ chromosomes.

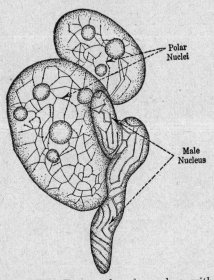

Polar Nuclei

Male Nucleus

Fig. 462.—Fusion of male nucleus with two polar nuclei, in *Lilium aurantum,* to form the primary endosperm nucleus, ×1260. (Redrawn from Blackman and Welsford.)

Although the first division of the zygote is followed by wall formation and all the cells of the embryo are enclosed in cell walls, the endosperm develops at first by **free nuclear division.** This phenomenon of repeated division of nuclei without cell-wall formation has already been met with in the development of the female gametophyte of *Pinus,* the Cycadales, and certain heterosporous pteridophytes. In wheat, walls are later formed about the free nuclei, and a more or less compact endosperm tissue results, the cells of which are largely filled with starch and protein.

It will be recalled that in many plants, such as peas, beans, alfalfa, squash, sunflower, and many others, the endosperm is completely absent in the mature seed owing to its absorption by the developing embryo. In wheat, as in all other grasses, and in the castor-oil plant, and many other angiosperms, the endosperm constitutes a large part

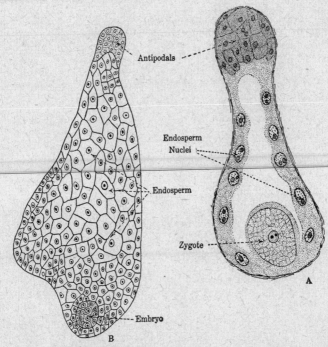

Fig. 463.—*A*, longitudinal section of the embryo sac of corn 12 hours after fertilization. *B*, 36 hours after fertilization. (After Miller, in *Journal of Agricultural Research*.)

of the mature seed, continuing to perform its function of supplying food to the embryo after germination begins.

The Seed.—The development of the angiosperm seed was discussed at length on pages 258–266. The student is referred to those pages in order to refresh his knowledge of this process, which, as described there, is very similar in its essential features to that which takes place in wheat. In the enlargement of the embryo and endosperm, the tissue of the nucellus is encroached upon and either partly or totally absorbed. In the mature wheat seed, the nucellus constitutes a thin layer of cells,

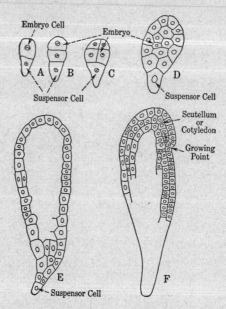

FIG. 464.—Longitudinal sections of young embryos of wheat. In *E* and *F*, some of the cells have been omitted. (Redrawn from Percival.)

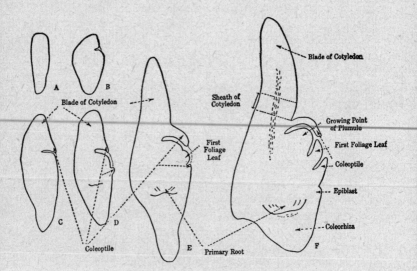

FIG. 465.—Longitudinal sections of the embryo of wheat in various stages of development. (Redrawn from Percival.)

covering the outer surface of the endosperm. In the young wheat seed, there are two integuments of two layers of cells each. In the maturing of the seed, the outer integument is entirely absorbed, so that the mature seed coat consists of two rows of cells belonging to the inner integument. It will be recalled that the so-called " seed " or grain of wheat is in reality a one-seeded fruit, in which the ovary wall has become firmly attached to the ovule.

Thus it is seen that as a result of nuclear fusions in the embryo sac, which is embedded in the megasporangium (nucellus) of the ovule, there follows a series of changes, involving all tissues of the ovule, which result in the production of a structure termed the seed. The mature wheat grain possesses tissue belonging to (1) **the parent sporophyte,** (2) **the embryo sporophyte,** and (3) also an **endosperm,** which can not properly be designated either as sporophytic or gametophytic. The seed coats and the nucellus consist of sporophyte tissue.

SUMMARY OF THE PRINCIPAL FEATURES IN THE LIFE HISTORY OF WHEAT

1. **Formation of the microspore mother cells** within the microsporangium (pollen chamber) borne upon the microsporophyll (stamen).

2. **Formation of a tetrad of microspores from each microspore mother cell by two successive divisions,** of which the first is a reduction division so that the microspore nuclei have n chromosomes.

3. **Germination of the microspore, which begins within the microsporangium (pollen sac), to form the male gametophyte,** which at the time of shedding of the pollen grain consists of two sperm nuclei and a tube nucleus, together with some cytoplasm.

4. **Differentiation within the megasporangium (nucellus) of a single megaspore mother cell.**

5. **Division of the megaspore mother cell to form a row of four megaspores,** the first division being a reduction division so that the nucleus of each megaspore has n chromosomes. Only one of these megaspores develops, and at the expense of the other three.

6. **Germination of the megaspore, which by three successive divisions gives rise to eight free nuclei: one egg nucleus, two polar nuclei, two synergids, and three antipodals.** The **antipodal nuclei** undergo further divisions **giving rise to six to ten or more nuclei.** The mature female gametophyte then consists of eleven to fifteen nuclei. Each of the synergid nuclei, the egg nucleus, and each of the antipodal nuclei is surrounded by cytoplasm, and separated from the others and from the rest of the megaspore by a thin membrane, so that we may speak of the synergid cells, the egg cell, and the antipodal cells.

7. **Escape of the pollen grains (microspores with contained male gametophytes)** and their dissemination by the wind. Adherence of pollen grains to stigma of pistil.

8. **Further development of the male gametophyte and growth of the pollen tube,** through the stigmatic and stylar tissue to the micropyle of the ovule, its penetration of the nucellus and embryo sac, and **discharge of the tube nucleus and two sperm nuclei into the embryo sac.**

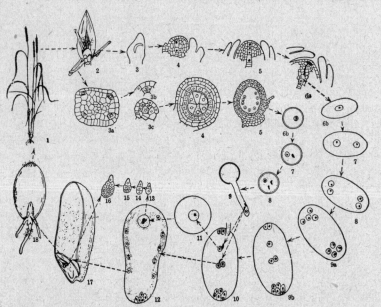

Fig. 466.—Diagrams showing stages in the life cycle of wheat. 1, mature sporophyte; 2, single flower; (outer circle) 3, 4, 5 and 6a and 6b, stages in the development of the megaspore; (inner circle), 3a, 3b, 3c, 4, 5, and 6b, stages in the development of the microspore; (outer circle), 7, 8, 9a and 9b, stages in the development of the female gametophyte; (inner circle), 7, 8 and 9, development of the male gametophyte and germination of pollen grain; 10, process of double fertilization; 11, zygote; 12, developing zygote and endosperm within the embryo sac; 13, 14, 15, 16, early stages in the development of the embryo sporophyte; 17, mature grain in longitudinal section showing mature embryo and endosperm (dotted); 18, germinating embryo.

9. **Union of one sperm nucleus with the egg nucleus.** The resulting zygote is the beginning of the sporophytic generation. **Union of the other sperm nucleus with two polar nuclei.** The resulting triple-fusion nucleus by its division initiates the formation of the endosperm.

10. **Development of the embryo sporophyte** by repeated division of the zygote. In this development a pro-embryo is formed, consisting of a suspensor and a terminal or embryo cell. From the latter the embryo proper develops.

11. **Development of the endosperm** by the free nuclear division of the triple-fusion nucleus, followed by wall formation and subsequent growth.

12. **Development of the ovule into a seed,** involving growth of the embryo and the endosperm, almost complete disappearance of part of the nucellus, and changes in the inner integuments to form the seed coat.

13. **Germination of the seed.**

14. **Growth into a mature sporophyte plant.**

Important Points of Contrast between Gymnosperms and Angiosperms.

1. The seeds of gymnosperms are borne upon the surface of the megasporophyll; the seeds of angiosperms are always formed within a closed structure, the ovary, formed by the union of the margins of one or more megasporophylls.

2. Gymnosperms are all woody, perennial forms, and with few exceptions are evergreen. Angiosperms include both herbaceous and woody plants, and annual, biennial, and perennial forms.

3. In almost all angiosperms, the xylem has vessels; in all gymnosperms, except the *Gnetales*, vessels are lacking.

4. In gymnosperms, the pollen comes into direct contact with the megasporangium (nucellus), whereas in angiosperms the pollen comes in contact with the tip of a structure, the pistil (consisting of one or more megasporophylls or carpels), which is directly connected with the megasporangium.

5. In contrast to gymnosperms, angiosperms usually have sepals and petals associated with the megasporophylls and microsporophylls, the whole forming a characteristic structure called the flower.

6. In gymnosperms, the first divisions of the zygote result in a number of free nuclei; in angiosperms such free nuclear division does not occur.

7. The male gametophyte of angiosperms is somewhat more reduced than that of gymnosperms.

8. The female gametophyte of gymnosperms is an extensive tissue consisting of many thousands of cells separated by walls and giving rise to archegonia. The female gametophyte of angiosperms is usually an eight-nucleate structure (embryo sac), generally without separating cell walls, which never develops archegonia.

9. The more primitive gymnosperms produce motile male gametes; such gametes are not formed in any angiosperms.

10. In the gymnosperm embryo there are generally three to eight cotyledons; in angiosperms either one (monocotyledons) or two (dicotyledons).

11. In the angiosperms, the endosperm is a tissue arising from a triple-fusion cell. In gymnosperms there is no counterpart to this tissue, the endosperm of gymnosperms being female gametophyte, and therefore haploid.

Evolution among the Angiosperms.—There are approximately 150,000 species of flowering plants (Angiosperms) in about 8000 genera and 300 families. Flowering plants are the predominant vascular plants in the world today. In the group as a whole there is much variation in the degree of specialization, as concerns both vegetative and reproductive structures, but this is particularly noticeable in the case of the flowers.

We have seen that the angiosperm flower probably had as its morphological forerunner the strobilus of the pteridophytes. In fact the angiosperm flower has been quite appropriately defined as a " shoot beset with sporophylls." It is quite generally believed that the primitive floral type is that one which most nearly approaches the strobilus in its structure. In such a type of flower we should expect (1) **an elongated floral axis,** (2) **all, or at least some, of the flower parts spirally arranged,** and (3) **stamens** (microsporophylls) **and carpels** (megasporophylls) **numerous and separate** (not coalescent or adnate). This combination of characteristics occurs in the buttercups (*Ranunculus*), representatives of the Crowfoot Family (*Ranunculaceae*). For these and other reasons these plants are regarded as being primitive angiosperms, from which the other groups of flowering plants probably have evolved.

PRINCIPAL TENDENCIES IN THE EVOLUTION OF THE FLOWER

The principal tendencies in the evolution of the flower from the primitive type as represented by the buttercup flower are:

1. **From a spiral arrangement of flower parts to a whorled arrangement of flower parts.** Plants with the spiral arrangement are considered to be more primitive than those with the whorled arrangement, and there is little doubt that the plants bearing whorled flowers have evolved from ancestors with flower parts spirally arranged. Thus (among plants belonging to the Ranunculaceae or closely related families) the white water-lily (*Nymphaea alba*) has its petals and stamens spirally arranged; in the magnolia the carpels are spirally attached, and the buttercup has both stamens and carpels spirally disposed. In most angiosperms, however, the flower parts are arranged in whorls or circles, not spirally.

2. **From a condition in which the flower is hypogynous to a condition in which it is perigynous or epigynous.** Hypogyny occurs in the buttercups, pinks (*Caryophyllaceae*), mustards (*Cruciferae*), and many

other relatively primitive forms; perigyny is well illustrated by the plum and cherry, and epigyny by the orchids (*Orchidaceae*), the honeysuckles (*Caprifoliaceae*), and the asters (*Compositae*).

3. **From a condition in which the carpels are separate** (each of the several pistils consisting of a single carpel) **to a condition (syncarpy) in which the carpels are united.** The compound pistil is regarded as the more advanced type. The buttercups, water-lilies, and magnolias are good examples of flowers in which the carpels are separate, whereas most flowering plants have, like the lilies, primroses, gentians (*Gentianaceae*), and mints (*Labiatae*), syncarpous flowers.

4. **From a condition in which the petals are lacking or, if present, separate, to one in which the petals are united** (sympetaly). The willows (*Salix*), buckwheat, and beet are a few of the many plants in the families the flowers of which have petals lacking; the rose, apple, and mustard belong to families whose flowers have separate petals, and the mints, morning glories, and potato are examples of plants with sympetalous flowers.

5. **From a condition of radial symmetry of the flower, as in the lily, rose, and morning glory, to bilateral symmetry, as in the snapdragons** (*Scrophulariaceae*), **orchids, and mints.** It appears that plants with bilaterally symmetrical flowers were evolved from plants with radially symmetrical flowers.

6. **From a condition in which there are five whorls of flower parts to a condition in which there are four whorls of flower parts, or to still further reduction of floral whorls.** For example, in the primroses (*Primulaceae*), there are five sepals, five petals, two whorls of stamens of five each, and five carpels (united), thus making five whorls or cycles. The flowers of the gentians (*Gentianaceae*), morning glories (*Convolvulaceae*), and phloxes (*Polemoniaceae*), on the other hand, are tetracyclic, having only four whorls, the arrangement being in general five sepals, five petals, five stamens, and two carpels (united into a single pistil).

As already stated, the buttercup flower may be regarded as the primitive type of angiosperm flower. In it there is a combination of the following primitive characteristics: **spiral arrangement of stamens and carpels, indefinite number of stamens and carpels, radial symmetry, no elevation of the corolla or other whorls relative to the carpels.**

From this primitive type of flower there seem to have been at least three main lines of advance. These three lines culminated in forms represented respectively by the **orchids** (*Orchidaceae*), the **mints** (*Labiatae*), and the **asters** (*Compositae*). In these three families there is a combination of advanced characteristics, namely: **whorled arrangement of flower parts, a definite number of stamens and carpels, bilateral**

**symmetry, both coalescence and adnation of flower parts, and an eleva-
tion of the corolla** (the ovary being inferior).

Intermediate between the buttercup type of flower and the flower
type of each of these three families are the flowers of other families of
angiosperms showing various degrees of advancement above the primitive buttercup type.

Fig. 467 [1] shows diagrammatically the three principal lines of
evolution of flower type as illustrated by a few important angiosperm
families. One of these lines of descent passes through the lilies (*Liliaceae*) and the irises (*Iridaceae*) to the orchids (*Orchidaceae*); a second
through the roses (*Rosaceae*), saxifrages (*Saxifragaceae*), and honeysuckles (*Caprifoliaceae*) to the asters; and the third through the geraniums (*Geraniaceae*) and phloxes (*Polemoniaceae*) to the mints (*Labiatae*).

For an understanding of this diagram it is essential to know the
number and arrangement of the parts of the flowers of each of the families mentioned. This information is supplied by the flower " formula "
given below the common name in each case. In these formulae Ca
stands for sepals, Co for petals, S for stamens, and P for carpels. Figures (exponents) placed after the symbols for any flower part indicate
how many such parts are found in the flower, ∞ standing for " numerous." Parentheses enclosing an exponent means that the parts in question are more or less coalesced (united). When all the symbols are
written in a single line, as in buttercups, lilies, and geraniums, it indicates that none of the parts are raised above others. When certain of
the symbols are written above certain others it indicates that the upper
ones are raised above the others in the flower. When the exponents
are written thus, $Co^{(5+0)}$, or $Ca^{(3+2)}$, instead of merely Co^5 or Ca^5, the
flower is bilaterally symmetric (not radially symmetric).

The floral formula for the buttercups indicates that there are 5 to
15 calyx segments (Ca), 0 to 15 corolla segments (Co), numerous (∞)
stamens (S), and numerous (∞) carpels (P); moreover, there is no
union of flower parts as is indicated by the absence of parentheses around
the exponents 5–15 or 0–15, and there is no elevation of parts, as is shown
by the writing of the four symbols in a line. It is seen from the chart
that the typical rose type of flower (family *Rosaceae*) has essentially
the same structure as that of the buttercup, except that in roses the
corolla segments and stamens are elevated, that is, are inserted on the
margin of a disc which is an outgrowth of the receptacle. This eleva-

[1] The chart method of showing family relationships was originated by F. E. Clements,
on the basis of the Besseyan system. Reference is made here to Clements and Clements,
Rocky Mountain Flowers. This chart method is also used in *Flower Families and Ancestors,*
and in *Flowers of Coast and Sierra* by the same authors.

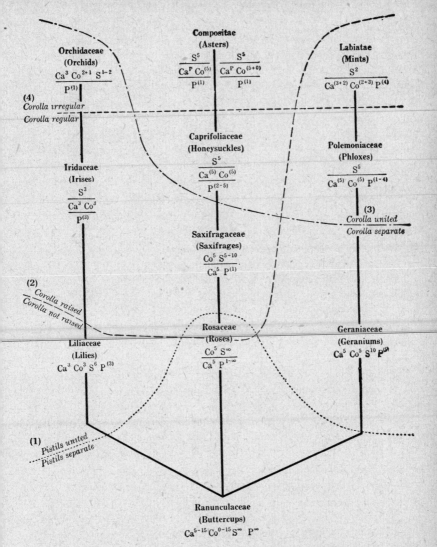

Fig. 467.—Chart showing the principal lines of descent and tendencies in the evolution of insect-pollinated angiosperm flowers. In the flower formulae, Ca stands for sepals, Co for petals, S for stamens and P for carpels. The exponents give the number of the flower parts in the different whorls. Parentheses enclosing exponents indicate that the flower parts of the whorl in question are more or less united with each other (coalescent). When there are two exponents for a single whorl with a plus sign between them the flower parts are in two groups, as in the Labiatae where the corolla is two-lipped, one lip consisting of two petals, the other of three. When the symbols for certain flower parts are separated from others by a horizontal line those above the line are raised in the flower above those below the line.

The position of any family in the chart and its flower formula do not in all cases hold for all the genera and species of the family but are characteristic of the family as a whole.

tion of the petals and stamens is shown in the floral formula by writing their symbols (Co^5S^∞) above a line, below which is $Ca^5P^{1-\infty}$.

The rose-saxifrage line of advance culminates in the asters (family *Compositae*), the flowers of which were described on page 247. The second dicotyledonous branch from the buttercups includes, among others, the geraniums (family *Geraniaceae*) and phloxes (family *Polemoniaceae*) and culminates in the mints (family *Labiatae*). The principal tendencies in the evolution of the flower are also shown in this branch, except that there has been an elevation of the stamens only, the corolla not being raised (i.e., the flowers are hypogynous). In the formula for the *Labiatae*, $Ca^{(3+2)}$ indicates that the calyx is 2-lipped with 3 lobes in one lip and 2 lobes in the other, and the parentheses about the exponents indicate the union of calyx segments; likewise $Co^{(2+3)}$ indicates a 5-toothed sympetalous 2-lipped corolla. In the monocotyledonous branch, from the buttercups, through lilies (family *Liliaceae*), irises (*Iridaceae*), to orchids (*Orchidaceae*), there has been a reduction in the number of parts in each floral whorl to 3, which is characteristic of most monocotyledonous flowers.

Orchid flowers are noted for their pronounced bilaterial symmetry, which character contributes to their peculiar beauty and grotesqueness. The perianth is composed of two whorls of three members each. The three segments of the outer whorl (sepals) are usually similar in shape and texture, but one member of the inner whorl (petals) is highly modified to form a prominent lip and spur, or a peculiar sac or pouch. In the ancestors of present-day orchids the stamens were six in number, but in most extant orchids there is but one functional stamen. The ovary consists of three united carpels and is inferior, all the other parts being raised above it.

The chart shows that, in each of the three lines of development there are four tendencies in the evolution of the flower: namely, (1) **from pistils separate to pistils united**; (2) **from corolla not raised to corolla raised**; (3) **from corolla separate to corolla united**; and (4) **from corolla regular to corolla irregular.** Although this chart shows but a few angiosperm families, it may be used to ascertain roughly the position and relationship of the families. For example, examination of the flower of a typical representative of the potato family (*Solanaceae*) shows it to have 5 united sepals, 5 united petals, 5 stamens inserted on the corolla, and 2 carpels united into a single pistil. Its floral formula is therefore, $\dfrac{S^5}{Ca^{(5)}Co^{(5)}P^{(2)}}$. Examination of the chart indicates that this family is quite closely allied with the phloxes (*Polemoniaceae*).

In Fig. 468 a more complete chart is given, showing many more

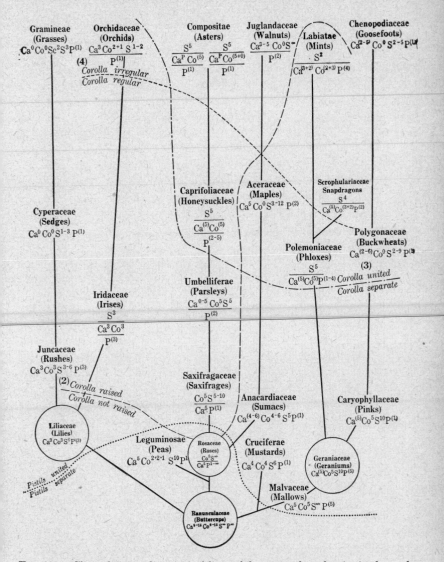

FIG. 468.—Chart showing the principal lines of descent and tendencies in the evolution of flowers in the angiosperms and the relationships of twenty-five important families. Each of the three principal lines of descent represented in Fig. 467 are here shown to consist of two more or less parallel lines, one made up of insect-pollinated, the other of wind-pollinated plants. Thus, of the two series having their origin in the Liliaceae the one culminating in the Graminae consists of wind-pollinated plants, that ending in the Orchidaceae of insect-pollinated plants. Similarly the two series leading up to the Compositae and the Labiatae are made up of plants mostly pollinated by insects and the Juglandaceae and the Chenopodiaceae lines are wind-pollinated. This and the simpler chart (Fig. 467) are adapted from charts by Clements and Clements in *Rocky Mountain Flowers* and other publications.

families and also, in each of the three lines of descent, two main branches, one made up of insect-pollinated families with conspicuous flowers and one of families with wind-pollinated flowers. The wind-pollinated series ends, in the lily line, with the grass family (*Gramineae*), in the rose line with the walnuts (*Juglandaceae*), and in the geranium line with the goosefoots (*Chenopodiaceae*).

The chart may be used to ascertain the family to which a flowering plant belongs, or at least to determine quite closely what are the relationships of the family to which it belongs to other families, and thus greatly to simplify determination of its genus and species. An important consequence of such use is to focus attention upon the various family types so that an increasing number of these come to be recognized upon sight by means of their distinctive earmarks. In utilizing the chart for this purpose it is essential at the outset that the floral formula of the flower of the plant in hand be carefully worked out. "The steps of advance which affect the pistil must be the first to be considered in ' placing ' the flower in its proper place.[2] Of these steps affecting the pistil, the union of simple pistils into a compound one must be considered first and then, second, the elevation of the corolla on the ovary. The other two changes affect the corolla also, and of these the union of the petals into a bell or tube is of the most importance and should be considered next. The change in shape of the corolla (corolla regular to corolla irregular) is of the least weight in determining flower relationships. This is because irregularity of corolla, though characteristic of all of the highest groups, may occur occasionally in almost any group, even the buttercups. For this reason, the steps of advance must be followed in the order in which they occur across any of the three lines of development and no one can be ' skipped ' in order to reach a farther one. Since the ovary is the keynote to the family relationships, one must be very careful to determine with certainty whether it is simple or compound, and if the latter, exactly how many cells or locules it has. This must be done by a cross section of as mature an ovary as possible, and determined not from one specimen but from several. It is well to study the other parts from several specimens also, as variations from the normal may occur in any one and so spoil results."

Apart from its practical value as a guide to family types, perhaps the chief merit of the chart lies in the graphic survey it affords of the vast group of flowering plants, and in the consequent grasp of the major features of their evolution and relationship. As an epitome of the process of evolution, the arrangement of flowering plants in the chart

[2] This sentence and the remainder of this paragraph are quoted from the instructions for the use of the chart for plant determination in Clements and Clements, *Rocky Mountain Flowers*, and the following was prepared for this book by F. E. Clements.

is hardly to be matched in any other class of organisms, plant or animal, a value that is enchanced by the frequent contacts which its use involves with flowers in garden and field. Probably no other aspect of botanical study is so readily transmuted into everyday terms and thus rendered available for the understanding and appreciation of life in general as well as in particular. This may be illustrated by the wide range of uses derived from the fruits and seeds of flowering plants. The advantage to the plant of having receptacle and calyx contribute to the fleshy pulp of the fruit, as in flowers with the corolla raised, is shown by the success man has achieved in utilizing the fruits of the rose and melon families. Furthermore, when man turned to plants for his chief supply of food in the form of starch, his choice was largely restricted to grasses and especially to corn, which is to be ranked as the most highly specialized and hence the most advanced of all plants. Even the secondary flour-producing plants, such as buckwheat, sunflower, and oats, belong to the great terminal groups with single-seeded fruits characterized by maximum storage of food for the embryo.

Distinctions between Monocotyledons and Dicotyledons.—In the use of the chart method, or any other method, for the determination of the family to which a plant belongs, the student should bear in mind the important differences between the two classes of the angiosperms; they are briefly:

1. The leaves of monocotyledons are generally parallel-veined and almost always have entire margins whereas the leaves of dicotyledons are generally net-veined and are very frequently toothed, lobed or compound.

2. With few exceptions the number of flower parts of any one kind, i.e., carpels, stamens, petals, or sepals, is three or some multiple of three in the monocotyledons. In the dicotyledons it is generally four or five or some multiple of four or five.

3. In the stems of monocotyledons the conducting tissue is in numerous vascular bundles scattered through the stem but not arranged in a single ring. Dicotyledonous stems have the conducting or vascular tissue either in a hollow cylinder surrounding the pith and increasing in width as the stem grows older or distributed in separate bundles arranged in a single circle.

4. The embryos of the seeds of monocotyledons have only one cotyledon or seed leaf whereas in the dicotyledonous embryos there are generally two cotyledons.

In the first chart (Fig. 467) monocotyledonous families are shown on the line of descent which is farthest to the left. In the chart in Fig. 468 they are on the " wind-pollinated " line culminating in the *Gramineae* and the " insect-pollinated " line leading up to the *Orchidaceae*.

CHAPTER XVI

EVOLUTION AND HEREDITY

Evolution.—The evolution of plants and animals is a subject of very great popular and scientific interest. In discussions of the subject, however, there has frequently been confusion of two quite different things: the fact of evolution and the means by which it is brought about. It has long been held by those concerned with the scientific study of plants and animals that all the thousands of species of plants and animals which exist today, or have existed in the past, have originated from previously existing species, and that they all therefore have arisen by the process we call evolution from one or a few original kinds. Although it is one of the principles of scientific thinking that such a theory as that of evolution is to be accepted as true only in the sense that it is highly probable, it can safely be said that no biological theory is better substantiated by the evidence than that of organic evolution. To accept evolution as a fact does not necessarily involve the endorsement of Darwin's theory of how evolution has been and is being brought about, or of any other particular theory as to the method of evolution. At the same time, this problem of how new species evolve must be recognized as one of the most important of all problems having to do with living things.

Accepting the fact of evolution, we shall attempt in this chapter to summarize, so far as is possible in a few pages, the principal theories as to the method of evolution and some of the most important facts bearing upon these theories.

Heredity and Variation.—It is inconceivable that the many species of plants and animals which exist about us could have evolved were it not for two remarkable tendencies which are characteristic of all organisms. These two tendencies are **heredity** and **variation**. Heredity may be defined as the tendency of the progeny to be like the parents and therefore to resemble each other. Heredity is a conservative tendency, in the absence of which there could be no such things as species, for a species is a group of very similar individuals related by descent. Variation, on the other hand, is the tendency of the progeny to differ from the parents and therefore from each other. It is clear that without variation no new species could ever have arisen from preëxisting species.

That like begets like is one of the most obvious facts in human experience. Even primitive peoples recognize the fact that characteristics are passed on from parents to children, and that acorns always grow into oaks and never into pines or apple trees. In fact, this similarity between parents and progeny is so obvious, at least among organisms other than human beings, that it is commonly assumed to be much more complete than it really is and only the most conspicuous differences are recognized at all.

It is among the individuals of our own species that the non-conservative tendency (variation) is most obvious, at least to those who are not students of heredity. Except in the case of some twins having unusually close resemblance, there is always sufficient variation among the children of a single family, aside from differences in age and sex, to make it easy to distinguish them from one another. Moreover, in the rare cases where two individuals of the same or different families show very close likeness, it is only necessary to employ fairly accurate methods of measurement to show that many differences exist between them. Thus it is literally true that no two individuals of our species are exactly alike. The variations which exist among other species than our own are less apparent, but close examination of the individuals of any species, whether of plants or animals, reveals differences between them.

There immediately suggests itself, in connection with heredity and variation, the question of the actual cause of these tendencies. Why do the progeny tend to be like the parents and why are they often quite unlike and always slightly different from the parents? The cause can be stated more briefly and simply for heredity than for variation. The progeny generally closely resemble the parents because their living substance is derived from the parents. If the new individuals have arisen by vegetative methods, as in stem cuttings and bulb formation, it is clear that all the protoplasm of the new plant came originally from the single parent. In sexual reproduction the new individual develops from a fusion cell or zygote in which are combined a protoplast from one parent with a protoplast, or at least a nucleus, from the other parent. In either case there is continuity of living material from parent to progeny, and the tendency to likeness must be due to this continuity. The fact that in many seed plants only the nucleus, and apparently none of the cytoplasm, of the male gamete, fuses with the egg cell, indicates that at least in these cases it is the nuclei which make possible the reappearance of parental characters among the offspring.

Chromosome Theory of Inheritance.—Within recent years a great deal of study has been devoted to the subject of the relation of the nucleus to inheritance. Out of this study has grown the chromosome theory of inheritance, according to which the chromatin of the resting nuclei and of the chromosomes of dividing nuclei bear the inherited characters. It will be recalled that the number of chromosomes is constant for each species, except for the fact that the number is doubled at fertilization and halved again at the reduction division. There is

Fig. 469.—Leaf variations in *Artemisia vulgaris*. The leaves in each vertical row are from a single plant and thus show variation in one individual. Thus 1a is from near the base of a given plant, 1b from about half way up the stem of that plant and 1c from near the tip of the same plant. The leaves in each horizontal row are from corresponding parts of three different plants and thus show variations between different individuals. (Redrawn from Clements and Hall's *The Phylogenetic Method in Taxonomy*.)

very good reason to believe that the identity of these chromosomes is not lost in the period between nuclear divisions. In fact, there is little doubt that each chromosome which a daughter nucleus receives in a late stage of one mitosis is reassembled in an early stage of the next division. It has been shown very conclusively in a few organisms, and it is probably true in all, that each of the chromosomes of a haploid nucleus is the bearer of a different group of inherited elements. It is also very probable that each chromosome is actually made up of a linear series of elements, genes, each of which is concerned in the development of one or several characters. It follows, then, that the chromosomes of a haploid nucleus all differ in the character-conditioning units which they carry.

In the diploid nucleus, on the other hand, there are two chromosomes which condition the same group of characters. One of these we shall call the maternal and the other the paternal chromosome, since they were contributed respectively by the female and the male gamete when the zygote was formed at fertilization. Since these two chromosomes correspond in the characters which they condition and in the order in which the genes or hereditary units are arranged, they are called **homologous chromosomes** (Fig. 475). Each of the pairs of chromosomes

Fig. 470.—A series of pinnae of various bud mutants of the Boston fern (*Nephrolepis exaltata bostoniensis*), itself a bud mutant. The pinnae shown are: 1, *var. bostoniensis*, the original mutant form, and 2, *Piersoni*; 3, *Whitmani*; 4, *Goodi* (or *gracillima*); 5, *magnifica*; 6, *Craigi*; 7, *Amerpohli*. (From *Genetics in Relation to Agriculture* by Babcock and Clausen, McGraw–Hill Book Co.)

which appear at meiosis consists of two homologous chromosomes which are separated from each other at the anaphase. Accordingly, each of the daughter nuclei, resulting from the reduction division, *contains one from each pair* of homologous chromosomes but *does not contain any pair* of homologous chromosomes. It contains one chromosome for each group of characters, but only one instead of two as do the diploid nuclei. It follows, therefore, that the nuclei of the megaspores and microspores of the seed-bearing plants, and the nuclei of the embryo sac and pollen tube including the egg cell and sperm, likewise contain only a single chromosome for each group of characters. Although there are a few cases in which characters are apparently conditioned by the cytoplasm it is probable that with rare exceptions inheritance is due to the continuity of chromatin from one generation to another.

Kinds of Variations.—The differences (variations) which exist between the individuals of a species or race may be conveniently grouped into three kinds:

(1) Modifications (*developmental variations*).
(2) Combinations (*Mendelian variations*).
(3) Mutations.

Modifications.—Modifications are variations which are not inherited and which are due to differences in the external conditions (environmental factors) to which different individuals are exposed. It is a matter of common observation that plants of the same species, even if grown from seeds of the same fruit, may be quite unlike when grown in very different habitats. Thus when plants of moist valleys are grown from seed or by transplantation in alpine regions, their internodes are generally shorter, their leaves are smaller and thicker, and their flowers are larger than when they grow in their natural habitat. If the seeds of these plants are planted in the natural habitat again, it will be found that the modifications which the species displayed when grown in an alpine habitat have not been inherited. Much less conspicuous environmental differences than those which are characteristic of the habitats just mentioned may call forth considerable modifications. This is evident from the great differences which are frequently noticeable between plants of the same variety in different parts of a grain field, and which are due to differences in such environmental factors as soil moisture, soil fertility, and illumination. It is probable that these differences in environment do not bring about any change in the chromatin of the plants and therefore are not inherited.

Combinations.—It is known that there are often **heritable** differences of varying degree between the individuals of a species or variety. These may combine in various ways in the progeny of two such individuals, thus giving rise to variations which are spoken of as combinations. Thus when plants of two different species or varieties are crossed (hybridized), as when one variety or species is pollinated with pollen from another, there may be among the progeny some individuals which resemble one parent, some which resemble the other parent, and still others which on account of a combination of characters are, in some respects, unlike either of the parents.

Mutations.—Mutations are sudden and sometimes relatively large differences which occasionally make their appearance in a few individuals out of many hundreds or thousands. It is only when such changes appear among individuals which are not of hybrid origin that their occurrence may be attributed with certainty to mutation. The characters arising by mutation are heritable except in the case of certain bud mutations which are to be discussed later. This type of variation (mutation) is apparently not due to the combination of different parental characters but to changes in the nuclear material. These changes are of two general categories: (1) an alteration in a single hereditary element, gene, in a particular chromosome; (2) irregularities in the distribution of the chromosomes in cell division so that whole chromosomes or pieces of chromosomes are lost from or added to the normal chromosome complement. Mutations occur not only from plants raised from seeds—the so-called seed sports—but may also arise from one or a few of the buds of a normal plant. Such cases are spoken of as bud mutants or bud sports. Some of the most valuable varieties of ornamental and other economic plants have originated as bud mutations. In the case of many, but not necessarily all, bud sports, the seeds produced by the flowers of a sport branch, even though pollinated by pollen from the same branch, do not give plants having the characteristics of the sport or bud mutant. That is to say, most bud sports do not "breed true," and must be propagated vegetatively by means of cuttings or by some method of grafting.

There are not many familiar varieties of economic plants which can be stated definitely to have had their origin in seed sports (mutations). This is in part due to the fact that most of the widely known varieties of economic plants originated long ago, and accordingly little is known as to their origin. Today, however, plant breeders are constantly on the lookout for such mutations and recognize them as possibly furnishing the material for the production of desirable new varieties. The sweet pea (*Lathyrus odoratus*) is a domesticated plant as to whose history, since the beginning of its culture, we are well informed. A number of new and desirable character differences are known to have originated in seed sports or mutations of sweet peas. In the two centuries and over since the sweet pea was first used as a horticultural plant, at least a dozen distinct color mutations have thus arisen, as well as several mutations which involved changes in the size and form of the flowers and in the number of flowers borne upon a flower stalk. By no means all of the many hundred varieties of this plant have, however, arisen as seed mutations. The greater number have arisen by hybridizing or crossing of different varieties which originally arose by mutation.

Among the many varieties of economic plants which have arisen as bud mutants are the copper beech, the numerous variegated kinds of *Coleus*, various forms of the Boston fern (*Nephrolepis exaltata bos-*

toniensis), itself a bud mutant of the tropical *Nephrolepis exaltata*, and a few varieties of oranges, apples, and other fruits (Figs. 470 and 471).

Theories as to the Origin of Species.—Having discussed the phenomena of heredity and variation which are fundamental to any explanation of the method of evolution, we shall give a brief account of some of the principal theories of evolution.

Long before Darwin's remarkable studies of the origin of species, which aroused such wide popular and scientific interest in evolution, a number of theories had been advanced as to the method of evolution.

Direct Response to Environment.—According to the theory of Geoffroy St. Hilaire, the French naturalist (1772–1844), new species have arisen in direct response to changes in the environment. That is to say, as climatic and other conditions on the surface of the earth have slowly altered, these changes have directly modified the individuals of certain species and have thus called forth variations. A succession of such variations in a species, if inherited, might result in the production of a new species. St. Hilaire believed some of these changes to have been favorable, or at least, not unfavorable, and that the individuals which underwent these changes survived and produced progeny like themselves. Others were unfavorable and resulted in the destruction of the individuals.

Use and. Disuse.—Jean de Lamarck, another French naturalist, proposed an explanation of evolution which is commonly spoken of as the theory of " use and disuse." It is a familiar fact that, in the case of individuals, the continued use of a part of the body, as, for instance, the muscles of the arm of a blacksmith, results in a development of that organ which makes it better able to do the work habitually required of it. It is also true that persistent disuse of an organ is apt to result in its partial degeneration or even suppression. Now, Lamarck believed that changes in the environment might bring certain organs into disuse and increase the extent to which other organs were used, and thus bring about degeneration of certain organs and build up or modify others. Moreover, and this was the most important feature of his theory, he regarded the characters thus acquired during the life of an individual as heritable. Thus the environment might, by reduction or suppression of certain organs and development of others, cause new species to arise. Among numerous illustrations of his theory, he used the neck of the giraffe. He assumed that the ancestors of the giraffe were grazing animals with short necks, and that some change in the environment made it necessary or advantageous for them to feed upon the leaves of trees. This, he believed, called forth a slight elongation of the neck which was transmitted by the individuals to their progeny.

By inheritance and continued use (reaching upward for leaves), the elongation became greater from generation to generation until the remarkably elongated neck of the giraffe had been evolved.   Lamarck's theory was founded on three assumptions: (1) that the environment changes, (2) that use and disuse may alter the character of an individual, and (3) that such alterations can be inherited.   The first two assumptions are recognized as correct, but there is no convincing evidence to indicate that acquired characters (modifications) can be inherited.

Orthogenesis.—Another theory, which has been advanced by different men and in different forms, is that there is inherent in certain

Fig. 471.—Fruits of the Washington navel orange 1, and of four strains that have originated from it by bud variation; 2, Thomson navel; 3, yellow navel; 4, corrugated; 5, ribbed.   (From *Genetics in Relation to Agriculture* by Babcock and Clausen, McGraw-Hill Book Co.)

species and perhaps in all species a tendency to vary in a certain definite direction.   If variation in this direction does not result in the individuals' becoming less favorably adapted to their environment, new species will arise and these in turn will give rise to others.   Otherwise, the variations will not persist.   The principal objections to this theory are as follows: (1) It has never been shown that such a persistent tendency to vary in a certain direction does exist.   (2) No explanation has ever been given as to the driving force or principle which is responsible for the assumed tendency.

Darwin's Theory of Natural Selection.—The best known of the theories of evolution is Charles Darwin's theory of natural selection. The principal features of this theory are as follows:

1. **Plants and animals in nature produce many more progeny than can possibly survive.** Long before Darwin's time it was computed by Linnaeus that if an annual plant produced two seeds each year, and each of these grew into a plant which in turn produced two seeds— and so on, there would be after twenty years more than a million plants. The common shepherd's purse (*Capsella*) may produce upon a single plant as many as 64,000 seeds, and a tobacco plant may have more than 360,000 seeds annually. There are plant species of which an individual may develop, in a single year, 74 or 75 million seeds, and one tropical fern which may produce 200 billion spores annually per individual. Actually, a very small proportion of these seeds or spores ever germinate, and only a few of the seedlings grow to maturity.

Fig. 472.—de Lamarck (1744–1829), an early evolutionary biologist best known for his theory of the inheritance of acquired characteristics. (From Shumway after Pirsson and Schuchert.)

2. **On account of this production of individuals far beyond the earth's facilities to support them, there is a struggle for existence.** That is to say, there is an intense competition in nature for water, light, food, and raw materials. This competition is going on (*a*) between different individuals of the same species, (*b*) between the individuals of one plant species and those of other species of plants, and (*c*) between certain plant species and certain animal species. Darwin found that of 357 seedlings which came up in a cleared piece of land, 3 by 2 feet square, 295 were destroyed, principally by insects.

3. **Individual organisms or different species differ in their fitness for a given environment.** Clearly, the water-lily is not fitted to live in a desert or the cactus to grow in a pond. Also, among plants living in a given habitat, some are better fitted for that environment than others.

4. **Through the struggle for existence, there is a natural selection which results in the survival of the fittest, or to put it conversely, in the**

destruction of the unfit. Thus nature may be said to determine which individuals will survive and give rise to successive generations.

5. **The individuals of a species are not all alike and even among the progeny of the same parents there are always at least slight variations** (a fact already discussed earlier in this chapter). Darwin assumed these variations to be heritable. He also believed that by the

Fig. 473.—Charles Darwin.
Reproduced from the *Beagle Diary* by permission of the Cambridge University Press and Professor A. C. Seward.

destruction of the individuals whose variations reduced their fitness, and by the selection for survival and reproduction of those with variations which better fitted them for the environment, the original differences might be increased so that a new species would result.

Darwin collected and published a great mass of data in support of his theory of natural selection, and his publications led many to the acceptance of his theory of the origin of species. Although, at the present time, many biologists do not accept in its entirety his "theory of the origin of species by natural selection," it is certainly true that his work has done more to stimulate workers in the field of biology than that of any other man who has ever lived.

It is now quite generally accepted that natural selection is a most important factor in evolution, but there are a number of serious objections to Darwin's particular theory of evolution by natural selection. We shall discuss briefly some of the most important of these objections. (1) The variations which, according to Darwin, provide the material for natural selection are of the type called **continuous** or **fluctuating variations**. Illustrations of this kind of variation can be secured by measurements of any organ or structure in many individuals of a given species of plant or animal. Thus if the length of all the beans in a lot is measured, and if all those having approximately the same length be sorted out, the following relation will be found to exist: The number of the beans having the least length will be very few. Those having the greatest length will also be very few. Between these extremes the numbers will increase as we approach the length halfway between the two extremes, at or near which we will find the largest number of individuals. Now it is known that if the variations in question are heritable (and some fluctuating variations can be inherited), it is possible, for instance, by selection through some generations to increase the average length of the beans. Thus the length characteristic of the greatest number of beans in any generation would be displaced in the direction of the extreme length. There is no reason, however, for believing that the extremes would change. Instead, the greatest length and the shortest length would remain the same, and unless the extremes of variations can be shown to be changed by selection nothing new has been produced. In short, natural selection of fluctuating variations can not push the range of variation beyond certain boundaries which are characteristic of a species.

(2) Another important objection to Darwin's theory is that the variations upon which Darwin believed natural selection to act are scarcely of sufficient degree to be of life-and-death importance, as would be necessary if his theory were correct.

(3) Furthermore, many of the characters which differentiate one species from another can scarcely be conceived of as having anything to do with the fitness for the environment.

(4) It has also been pointed out that by far the greater number of the individuals which succumb in the struggle for existence do so in the very early stages of their development (seedlings and young animals) and thus before many of their characteristic differences have appeared.

The Mutation Theory of Evolution.—Hugo de Vries, the great Dutch student of mutation, has pointed out that the principal objections to Darwin's theory are removed if we abandon the idea that species can be originated by natural selection of small fluctuating variations. He suggests that new forms originate by mutation rather than by natural selection. The principal features of de Vries' theory of evolution are the following: (1) There arise from time to time, among the individuals of a species, forms which differ relatively widely in one or more characters from typical individuals. (2) The distinguishing characters of these mutant individuals are inherited, at least in many cases. (3) These mutations arise quite independently of fluctuating variations. (4) Mutations may take place in any direction. (5) The mutants (mutating individuals), at least in many cases, differ sufficiently from typical plants to make them subject to natural selection. (6) Accordingly, in nature all unfit mutants are likely to be eliminated by natural selection.

The mutation theory of the present day lays emphasis upon small rather than large mutations on the ground that in nature radical changes from the types of old-established species will tend to be eliminated at once by natural selection; but that minute mutations which are either neutral or advantageous in their effects may gradually accumulate, first causing new varieties to appear, then new subspecies, and finally new species. At any point in the process natural selection may operate to preserve or eliminate the new forms.

For many years all attempts to produce mutations artificially were unsuccessful but recently it has been found possible to cause mutations to arise by subjecting organisms or their reproductive cells to X-rays, or radium, or to higher temperatures than those to which they are ordinarily exposed. These newly discovered methods by which mutations can be artificially produced furnish us with a means, previously lacking, for the experimental study of these variations.

Mendelian Inheritance.—A large part of the work which is being done today in the experimental study of evolution, as well as of the practical work of the plant and animal breeder, is based upon the remarkable discoveries of the Austrian monk, Gregor Johann Mendel. His experiments had to do with the manner of inheritance of certain characters by the individuals resulting from the crossing (hybridizing) of two organisms differing in one or more characters. His most important work was with the garden pea (*Pisum sativum*). His discoveries, the outcome of eight years of breeding experiments, were published in an obscure scientific periodical in 1866. Partly on that account and partly because the time was not yet ripe for a proper appreciation of its significance, his work remained practically buried for thirty-five years. In 1900, sixteen years after Mendel's death, his publication was discovered almost simultaneously by three botanists who had been led by their own studies to conclusions similar to his.

A discussion of his work can best be introduced by an account of some of his experiments.

His first experiments were made by crossing two varieties of garden peas, a dwarf variety (20–45 cm. high) and a tall variety (175–200 cm.

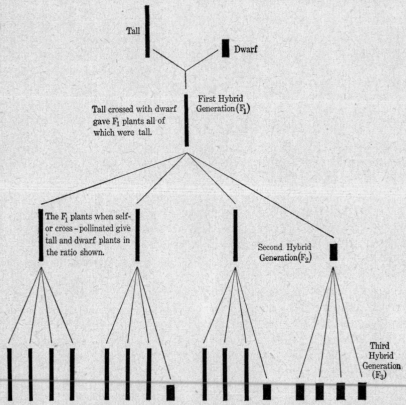

Tall

Dwarf

First Hybrid Generation (F₁)

Tall crossed with dwarf gave F₁ plants all of which were tall.

The F₁ plants when self- or cross-pollinated give tall and dwarf plants in the ratio shown.

Second Hybrid Generation (F₂)

Third Hybrid Generation (F₃)

FIG. 474.—Diagram to illustrate inheritance in a monohybrid cross between tall and dwarf peas.

high). That is to say, he grew plants of these two varieties and used the pollen from each to pollinate the flowers of the other variety. Peas were favorable plants for his study because the pea is a species which is naturally self-pollinated. On that account, it was reasonably certain, since the seeds produced naturally by the tall variety and the dwarf variety always produce plants which are respectively tall and dwarf, that the varieties were pure as regards tallness and dwarfness.

Mendel kept a very careful record of the progeny of all his hybrids. He found that, whether he used pollen from a dwarf plant to pollinate the stigma of a tall plant, or vice versa, the seeds formed gave on germination only tall plants. In different form, these results may be stated thus: When the dwarf variety was crossed with the tall variety all of the individuals of the first (hybrid) generation, commonly spoken of as the F_1 (first filial) generation, were tall (Fig. 474, second row from top of figure).

In the F_2 (second filial generation), secured by allowing F_1 individuals to self-pollinate, about one-quarter of the individuals were dwarf and about three-quarters tall (third row, Fig. 474). Mendel secured

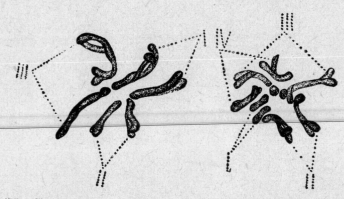

FIG. 475.—Chromosome individuality as shown in *Crepis capillaris* (left) and *C. setosa* (right). The two chromosomes connected by dotted lines to a single Roman numeral are homologous. Each of the chromosomes has already begun to split since the stage of mitosis shown is the metaphase of somatic (2x) nuclei. The chromosomes are shown as seen from a point on the axis of the spindle. Note the similarity in size and form of the two chromosomes in each homologous pair. The use of the same numerals in the left-hand and the right-hand part of the figure is not meant to indicate corresponding chromosomes. Compare text, page 569. (From Collins and Mann, in *Genetics in Relation to Agriculture* by Babcock and Clausen, McGraw-Hill Book Co.)

787 tall to 277 dwarf plants. When the F_2 dwarf plants were self-pollinated, all their progeny were dwarf plants. These dwarf F_2 and F_3 plants were like the dwarf plants which were crossed with the tall plants at the beginning of the experiments and they never gave any tall plants as long as they were bred with dwarf plants. Two-thirds of the tall plants of the F_2 generation (that is, one-half of all the F_2 individuals), when self-pollinated, gave one-quarter dwarf and three-quarters tall plants. The remaining tall F_2 plants, when self-pollinated, gave nothing but tall plants, which, like the dwarf F_2 plants, gave nothing but tall plants when self-pollinated. In short, although the F_2 plants appeared

to be only of two kinds, dwarf plants and tall plants, there were actually three kinds of plants (bottom row, Fig. 474):

1. Dwarf plants (about one-quarter of all) which gave only dwarf plants when self-pollinated.

2. Tall plants (about one-half of all the F_2 plants) which, when self-pollinated, gave one-quarter dwarf and three-quarters tall plants.

3. Tall plants (about one-quarter of all of the F_2 plants and in appearance like the other tall plants) which gave only tall plants when self-pollinated.

For these three kinds of plants it is convenient to use the following designations, the meaning of which will shortly be made clear:

(1) **Pure recessive,** (2) **hybrids,** and (3) **pure dominants.**

It is important to bear in mind that the pure recessives, when self-pollinated or cross-pollinated among themselves, will never give anything but pure recessives, in this case dwarf plants; that the hybrids, when self-pollinated or crossed among themselves, will give the three classes in the proportion $1 : 2 : 1$; and that the pure dominants, when self-pollinated or crossed among themselves, will give only pure dominants.

Mendel also secured $1 : 2 : 1$ ratios in the F_2 generation when he crossed a variety of pea having a smooth seed coat, and one having a wrinkled coat, and also when a variety with green and yellow cotyledons were crossed.

Such characters as those of tallness and of dwarfness in Mendel's peas, when inherited, remain distinct and are thus transmitted as integral units. From the fact that the tall F_1 plants gave some dwarfs when self-pollinated, it is clear that the character for dwarfness was transmitted through the tall F_1 plants as a unit which was not affected by its association with the character for tallness.

One of the most remarkable facts about Mendel's breeding experiments with tall and dwarf peas is that although the F_1 plants had received both the character for dwarfness and the character for tallness, the plants were actually tall; that is to say, the character for tallness prevented the opposite character form coming to expression. On this account, the character for tallness is spoken of as a **dominant character,** and that for dwarfness as a **recessive character.** This prevention of the expression of a recessive character by a dominant character is by no means universal in Mendelian inheritance. For instance, when the red-flowered variety of the common garden four o'clock is crossed with the white-flowered variety, the F_1 plants are pink, neither color being completely dominant.

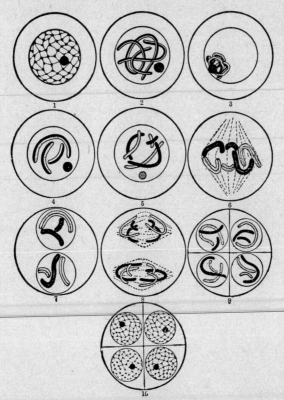

FIG. 476.—Diagrams showing chromosome behavior during the reduction division which occurs at the time of spore formation in ferns and in most other plants which have sexual reproduction. As also in Fig. 409, the chromosomes shown in white are paternal chromosomes, those in black, maternal chromosomes. Homologous chromosomes (corresponding maternal and paternal chromosomes) are of corresponding length. As the result of the process here shown, the spore mother cell (in the resting condition in 1) gives rise to a tetrad (group of four spores) as shown in 10. The mother nucleus (1) has the diploid chromosome number (in this case six) as is shown in 7 of Fig. 409, which is characteristic of the cells of the sporophyte. These six consist of three pairs of homologous chromosomes, one of each pair having come from the male gamete and one from the female gamete in the last fusion of gametes (2, 5 in Fig. 409). Note that in Fig. 476, 2 the three pairs, with the chromosomes of each pair in close contact, are lying within the nuclear membrane. In 3 the paired chromosomes have shortened and have become closely "knotted" whereas in 4 they become "unraveled" and have undergone further shortening. In 5 the members of each pair have separated but are still in close proximity. In 6 the nuclear membrane and the nucleolus have disappeared, and the six chromosomes, each now showing evidence of a later lengthwise splitting, have been separated into two groups of three. *This is the actual reduction division.* As shown in 7, only one chromosome of each homologous pair is present in each of the resulting nuclei which are therefore different in their chromosome "stock." Each of these nuclei now undergoes a second division (8) with a splitting of each of its chromosomes, so that there are two kinds of nuclei in the tetrad (shown in 9), two having the same chromosomes as the upper nucleus in 7 and two having the same chromosomes as the lower nucleus shown in 7.

Explanation of Mendel's Results on the Basis of Chromosome Behavior.—It will be recalled that, with a few exceptions, inherited characters are conditioned by genes which are transmitted from one generation to the next through the chromosomes. That is to say, the progeny have a certain character which was possessed by one or both parents because the nuclei of the new plants contain chromosomes received from the parents. Now, there can be little doubt that there is a certain definite and fixed part (genetic **factor** or **gene**) of one of the chromosomes, at least, which is the carrier of each of the two characters which distinguished Mendel's dwarf and tall varieties. The nuclei of the dwarf sporophyte plants, in his first cross, contained two homologous chromosomes each with the factor for dwarfness. In these nuclei, there were no factors for tallness. That is to say, these plants were **homozygous** for this character. The original tall plants were also homozygous because their nuclei contained no chromosomes containing a factor for dwarfness but two homologous chromosomes bearing the factor for tallness. Since these plants are naturally self-fertilized, there is little possibility, under normal conditions, of the introduction into the nuclei of the progeny of dwarf plants of a chromosome with the factor for tallness. Accordingly, they produce only dwarf plants, i.e., "breed true." For the same reason, the original tall plants would also breed true under normal conditions.

Fig. 477.—Gregor Mendel (1822–1884), whose plant breeding experiments laid the foundation for modern genetics. (From Curtis and Guthrie, *A Textbook of General Zoology*.)

The student will also recall that in the reduction division, a little before the formation of microspores (pollen grains) and megaspores (one of which is the cell which divides and forms the embryo sac), the members of each pair of homologous chromosomes are separated from each other and pass to opposite ends of the spindle. Accordingly, the megaspores and microspores (and the same is true of the sperm nuclei and egg nucleus) each contain only one chromosome from each pair existing in the sporophyte nuclei. Since both the chromosomes of the homologous pair carrying the factors for stature in the sporophyte of the dwarf plants carry the factor for dwarfness, the egg nuclei and the sperm nuclei are all alike with respect to the factors for stature. Similarly, all the sperm nuclei and egg nuclei produced by the tall plants are alike in that they have the factor for tallness only.

It will make the rest of our explanation somewhat easier to grasp if we substitute the capital letter T for the expression " factor for tallness," and the small letter t for the expression " factor for dwarfness," the capital letter indicating that the corresponding character is dominant, and the small letter that the alternative character which it represents is recessive. It will also be convenient to designate the gametes bearing one of these factors as T sperm, T egg, t sperm and t egg, and the zygotes resulting from their fusion as tT zygotes, tt zygotes and TT zygotes.

The fact already stated, that Mendel's original dwarf plants bred true, can be restated thus, using the designations just mentioned. Since, in the case of the sporophytes of the dwarf variety, both members of the pair of homologous chromosomes controlling stature bear the factor for dwarfness, only t sperms and t eggs will be produced by the dwarf plants produced by self-pollination or crossing with other dwarf plants. Therefore all the zygotes which are formed by the fusion of these gametes will be tt zygotes and will give dwarf plants.

As stated in earlier chapters, the double number of chromosomes in the zygote of any plant consists of pairs of homologous chromosomes, one chromosome of each pair having come from the sperm and one from the egg cell.

The F_1 Generation.—Now when dwarf and tall plants are crossed, pollen from the dwarf variety may be used to pollinate stigmas of the tall variety, in which case t sperm $\times$ T egg $= tT$ zygote; or pollen from the tall variety may be used to pollinate stigmas of the dwarf variety, in which case T sperm $\times$ t egg $= tT$ zygote.

In both cases the zygote contains a pair of homologous chromosomes, each of the members of which bears one of the alternative factors. Accordingly, the F_1 plants developed from these zygotes will be **heterozygous**, and on account of the dominance of the tall character will be tall plants. Now at the reduction division of the microspore mother cell, the t chromosome and the T chromosome, which have been associated as homologous chromosomes in all the nuclei of the sporophyte plants, are separated thus:

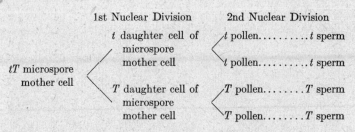

As a result, the pollen grains and the sperm cells are of two kinds, T and t, produced in equal numbers. Similarly there are produced T eggs and t eggs in equal numbers, as is shown in the following diagram.

$$tT \text{ megaspore mother cell} < \begin{array}{l} t \text{ daughter cell of megaspore mother cell} < \begin{array}{l} t \text{ megaspore}\ldots\ldots t \text{ egg} \\ t \text{ megaspore}\ldots\ldots t \text{ egg} \end{array} \\ T \text{ daughter cell of megaspore mother cell} < \begin{array}{l} T \text{ megaspore}\ldots\ldots T \text{ egg} \\ T \text{ megaspore}\ldots\ldots T \text{ egg} \end{array} \end{array}$$

FIG. 478.—Spreading and erect pure lines of Gypsy wheat, 1907. (From Williams in *Genetics in Relation to Agriculture* by Babcock and Clausen, McGraw-Hill Book Co.)

Such separation, at the time of the reduction division, of the two members of a pair of homologous chromosomes bearing alternative factors, so that half of the gametes have the factor for one character, and half the factor for the other character, is spoken of as **segregation**. The resulting purity of the gametes is one of the most important features of Mendelian inheritance.

The F_2 Generation.—Now, when an F_1 plant is self-pollinated or cross-pollinated with other F_1 plants, there will be four possible combinations of sperm and egg, since there are two kinds of sperms and two kinds of eggs; and these combinations, by the law of probability, will occur in equal proportions. These combinations are:

(1) T sperm $\times$ T egg giving TT zygote.
(2) t egg $\times$ T sperm giving tT zygote.
(3) T egg $\times$ t sperm giving Tt zygotes, and
(4) t sperm $\times$ t egg giving tt zygotes.

These four combinations and their origin may be shown graphically by the following checkerboard diagram.   In this the two kinds of sperms are placed in the horizontal row, and the two kinds of eggs in the vertical row, the possible combinations of gametes are shown in the four squares:

	T sperms	t sperms
T eggs	**TT** 1 zygote	**Tt** 3 zygote
t eggs	**tT** 2 zygote	**tt** 4 zygote

Let us consider briefly the result of these four combinations as they are expressed in the individuals of the F_2 generation. Combinations 2 and 3 are identical, since in both there is a chromosome bearing the factor for dwarfness and a chromosome with the factor for tallness. These zygotes are said to be **heterozygotes**. Together, these plants will make up half of all the plants. They will all be tall plants on account of the dominance of tallness. In fact, these plants are the ones which we designated earlier as the **hybrid F_2 plants.** They are identical with the F_1 plants in appearance and in their behavior when interbred.

The zygotes resulting from combination 4 will develop into plants homozygous for this character, since in this case both the members of the pair of homologous chromosomes governing stature bear the same factor. They will be dwarf plants, since the dominant character is entirely absent, and on the same account tall plants can never arise from them as long as they are interbred. These are the plants which were designated in an earlier paragraph as **pure recessive plants.** They are indistinguishable in appearance, and in their behavior when inter-bred, from the original dwarf plants used at the beginning of the experiment.

The zygotes resulting from combination 1 will be homozygous also, and will correspond in their behavior with the pure recessives, except that they and their progeny will all be tall plants instead of dwarf. They are the plants that were spoken of in an earlier paragraph as the **pure dominants** and are indistinguishable from the original tall plants used at the beginning of the experiment.

We have described at some length the simplest possible case of Mendelian inheritance. Reference has already been made to other cases, such as varieties of peas with green and yellow cotyledons and those with smooth and wrinkled seeds. Crosses between such plants as these, which differ in one pair of contrasting characters, are called **monohybrid crosses.**

Dihybrid.—Mendel also carried on experiments in which two pairs of contrasting characters were involved, instead of one pair only. He crossed a variety which produced yellow, wrinkled seeds when self-pollinated, with another variety producing green, smooth peas. Such a cross is known as a **dihybrid cross.** Mendel could judge of the nature of the F_1 plants of this cross without planting the seeds, for the characters involved were really characters of the embryo sporophyte within the seeds and not characters which, like stature, could be judged only after germination had taken place and the embryo sporophytes had grown to some size. All the F_1 seeds from Mendel's dihybrid cross of yellow wrinkled and green smooth were yellow smooth peas. Accordingly it is clear that the characters for green color and wrinkled surface are recessive and those for yellow color and smoothness are dominant.

Now, in every nucleus of the embryo sporophyte and later of the mature sporophyte of these F_1 plants, there must have been a chromosome carrying the factor for yellow, one carrying the factor for wrinkled surface (these two chromosomes being from one parent), a chromosome carrying the factor for green color, and one carrying that for smooth surface (these two chromosomes having come from the other parent). Of these four chromosomes, the ones carrying the color factors would constitute a homologous pair, and the other two also a homologous pair. When these seeds were germinated and the resulting plants had flowered, there would be, at the reduction divisions, as in the monohybrid case, a separation of the chromosomes of the homologous pairs, and accordingly a separation of the factors which these chromosomes carried. There would result, however, not two kinds of eggs and two

FIG. 479.—Typical heads from seven pure lines of Defiance Wheat. (From *Genetics in Relation to Agriculture* by Babcock and Clausen, McGraw–Hill Book Co.)

kinds of sperms but four kinds of each, thus: *YS* eggs, *Yw* eggs, *gS* eggs, and *gw* eggs; and *YS* sperms, *Yw* sperms, *gS* sperms, and *gw* sperms.

It is possible to prophesy what would be the various combinations resulting from the self-pollination of the F_1 plants or from crossing them with each other. The checkerboard diagram on page 588 shows the various combinations in the simplest fashion possible. In a vertical row to the left of the checkerboard are indicated the four different kinds of eggs, and in a horizontal row above the checkerboard are shown the four types of sperms. In the sixteen blocks of the checkerboard are shown the various possible combinations which might result in the zygotes.

Examination of the diagram shows the combinations which should result and the number of each (on the average) among sixteen zygotes or F_2 seeds.

Merely for convenience in pointing out the different combinations, the squares of the checkerboard are numbered from 1–16. It will be clear that the order in which the factors are given in the different combinations is of no significance. Thus *YSYw* (square 2) is identical

	YS sperm	Yw sperm	gS sperm	gw sperm
YS egg	$YSYS$ 1	$YwYS$ 5	$gSYS$ 9	$gwYS$ 13
Yw egg	$YSYw$ 2	$YwYw$ 6	$gSYw$ 10	$gwYw$ 14
gS egg	$YSgS$ 3	$YwgS$ 7	$gSgS$ 11	$gwgS$ 15
gw egg	$YSgw$ 4	$Ywgw$ 8	$gSgw$ 12	$gwgw$ 16

with $YwYS$ (square 5). The following are the combinations theoretically possible:

I. $YYSS$ (square 1)—**one zygote out of sixteen**—homozygous for both color and surface—**the seed yellow and smooth**.

II. $YYSw$ (squares 2, 5)—**two zygotes out of sixteen**—homozygous for color but heterozygous for surface—**the seed yellow and smooth**—the latter on account of dominance of the smoothness.

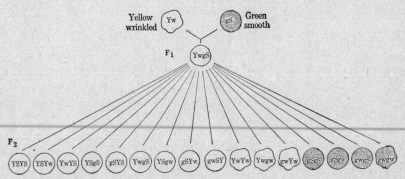

Fig. 480.—Diagram to illustrate inheritance in a dihybrid cross between a pea which would have produced yellow wrinkled seeds if self-pollinated and one which would have produced green smooth seeds if self-pollinated. Wrinkled seeds are distinguished from smooth by their outline and green from yellow by the shading of the former. The letters show the various combinations of factors.

III. $YgSS$ (squares 3, 9)—**two zygotes out of sixteen**—homozygous as to surface character but heterozygous for color—**the seeds yellow and smooth**—the former on account of the dominance of yellow color.

IV. *YgSw* (squares 4, 7, 10, 13)—**four zygotes out of sixteen**—heterozygous as to the characters both for color and surface—**the seeds yellow and smooth**—on account of the dominance of these characters.

V. *YYww* (square 6)—**one zygote out of sixteen**—homozygous as to both color and surface—**the seeds yellow and wrinkled** because of the absence of chromosomes bearing either the factor for green color or for smooth surface.

VI. *Ygww* (squares 8, 14)—**two zygotes out of sixteen**—heterozygous for color and homozygous for surface—the seeds **yellow** on account of the dominance of yellow and **wrinkled** because no chromosome with the factor for smoothness is present.

VII. *ggSw* (squares 12, 15)—**two zygotes out of sixteen**—heterozygous as to surface and homozygous as to color—**the seeds smooth** on account of the dominance of this character and **green** because of the absence of any factor for yellow.

VIII. *ggSS* (square 11)—**one zygote out of sixteen**—homozygous both as to color and surface—**the seeds therefore green and smooth**.

IX. *ggww* (square 16)—**one zygote out of sixteen**—homozygous both as to color and surface—seeds therefore **green and wrinkled**.

Now, although there are nine different sorts of zygotes in respect to chromosomes present in their nuclei, the seeds, as regards the characters which will be visible, fall into four classes only, as follows:

Classes according to the appearance of the seeds	Combinations of factors
A. Yellow smooth (9 seeds)............	1. *YYSS* —1 seed 2. *YYSw*—2 seeds 3. *YgSS* —2 seeds 4. *YgSw* —4 seeds
B. Yellow wrinkled (3 seeds)...........	5. *YYww*—1 seed 6. *Ygww* —2 seeds
C. Green smooth (3 seeds).............	7. *ggSw* —2 seeds 8. *ggSS* —1 seed
D. Green wrinkled (1 seed).............	9. *ggww* —1 seed

In the case of classes A, B, and C, all the plants (seeds) in any one class, which are alike in all obvious characters although they may differ in some recessive characters, are said to have the same **phenotype**. If they are also alike in all other characters, that is, in those characters which do not come visibly to expression but can be demonstrated only by breeding experiments, they are said to have the same **genotype**. Thus the individuals of any single one of the nine sorts listed under " Combinations of factors " have the same genotype. Altogether, there are nine genotypes represented. For example, seeds corresponding to the combinations *YYSS* and *YgSw*, have the same phenotype, because they are all yellow and smooth. However, they differ genotypically since those corresponding to the combinations *YYSS* have no factor for green color and wrinkled surface, whereas the other seeds, corresponding to the combination *YgSw*, have these factors but do not manifest their presence because the characters for yellow color and smooth surface are dominant.

An examination of the nine combinations listed above will show that not only *YYSS* (the pure dominant) and *ggww* (the pure recessive) will breed true, but also the combinations *ggSS* and *YYww*. In other words, all will breed true in which only two factors (one for color and one for surface) are present. All the others will give various combinations when self-fertilized. These combinations can be definitely foretold on the basis of the checkerboard diagram on page 604.

Clearly, when trihybrid crosses are made, that is, crosses of individuals differing in regard to three pairs of contrasting unit characters, a much more complex situation will result in the F_2 than in the case of dihybrids. It will, however, be possible to prophesy all the resulting combinations, just as in the case of a dihybrid cross.

This account of the results of monohybrid and dihybrid crosses illustrates the manner in which many new combinations of characters may be established by crossing plants differing in relatively few characters. Thus the crossing of forms differing in two such pairs of contrasting characters gives four possible combinations of characters. Eight combinations of factors result when the forms crossed differ in three pairs of contrasting (alternative) characters, and sixteen if four pairs are involved. It is thus that new characters such as those which have originated in the sweet pea by mutation have been utilized in producing numerous varieties.

Fossil Plants.[1]—Fossils are the evidences of life buried in the rocks. The oldest known fossils are plants which are referred to the subkingdom Thallophyta; they lived in the sea more than half a billion years ago during the era known by paleontologists as the Proterozoic.[2] Aquatic plants similar to them are still living in the warmer parts of the ocean,

---

[1] This section on fossil plants was prepared by Ralph W. Chaney, Professor of Paleontology in the University of California.

[2] Geologists divide the history of the earth into five eras, the Archeozoic during which no life is known to have existed, the Proterozoic in which the beginnings of life appear, the Paleozoic during which ancient life became well established, the Mesozoic in which life began to assume a modern aspect, and the Cenozoic in which plants and animals of modern types became dominant.

where they form calcareous reefs with structures similar to those of their remote ancestors.

The greatest development and diversity of plant life have occurred upon the land. The first land plants date back several hundred million years to the beginning of the Devonian period, which falls in the middle of the Paleozoic era. The oldest plants upon the land were for the most part small and simply organized, with creeping stems and without well-developed roots and leaves; like most plants which live in water or moist places, they reproduced by means of spores. Although they are definitely referable to the division Pteridophyta, these primitive plants are unlike any now living; because of their resemblance to the Psilotales, a simple order with two living examples in the tropics and the southern hemisphere, they are placed in the order Psilophytales. Fossil plants of this extinct order have recently been found in the Devonian of Montana, in association with the remains of fish known as ostracoderms which represent the most primitive vertebrates. Related plants occur as fossils elsewhere in North America, in many parts of Europe, in China, in South Africa, Australia, and the Falkland Islands. Some of them have structures suggesting their ancestry in the division Bryophyta, which is intermediate between the Pteridophyta and the Thallophyta, and whose geologic history is practically unknown.

In later Devonian and Carboniferous time, more advanced types of Pteridophytes form the dominant element of the land vegetation. Stems, roots, leaves, and fruiting structures of plants known as calamites are abundant in the layers of shale associated with coal-beds; except for their much greater size, they resemble our present-day *Equisetum*, whose jointed stems are of common occurrence in many parts of the world today; calamites are placed with *Equisetum* in the order Equise-tales, and like this modern relative appear to have lived in swamps. A second order, the Lycopodiales, whose living representatives are the small club-mosses or ground-pines of our moist forests, had abundant Paleozoic species of trees reaching a height of over 100 feet. Although all parts of these plants occur in the fossil record, the most characteristic remains are of the stems; these show rows of leaf scars, and are referred to the genera *Lepidodendron* (scale-tree) and *Sigillaria* (seal-tree). (Fig. 481, 1–3.)

Many true ferns, of the order Filicales, also occur in later Paleozoic rocks, but most of the fern-like plants reproduced by means of seeds rather than by spores and are placed in the division Spermatophyta. They are known as seed-ferns (Pteridosperms), and make up one of the most varied elements of the Carboniferous floras. Another type of seed-plant occurring in the Paleozoic falls in the extinct order Cordai-

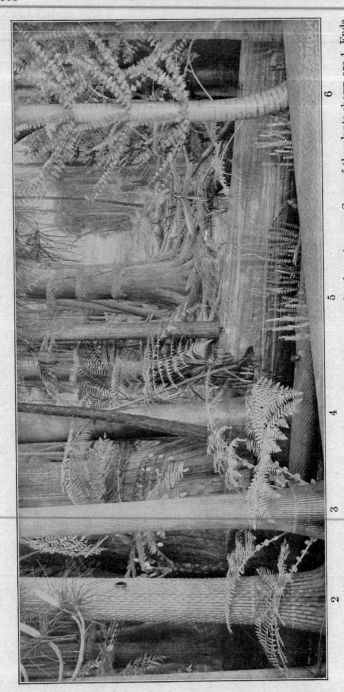

Fig. 481.—Reconstruction of a part of a Carboniferous forest, based upon fossil specimens. Some of the plants shown are 1, Ends of branches of *Lepidodendron clypeatum*. 2 and 3, stems of *Sigillaria rugosa* and *saulli*. 4, Frond of *Neuropteris heterophylla*. 5, (Small plants) *Sphenophyllum emarginatum*. 6, (tree) *Calamites species*. *Lepidodendron* and *Sigillaria* belong to the Lycopodiales, *Calamites* and *Sphenophyllum* to the Equisitinae, and *Neuropteris* to the Cycadofilicinae. (Photograph furnished by the Field Museum of Natural History, Chicago.)

tales; they were tall trees with long, strap-shaped leaves, whose stems show a general resemblance to the modern Gymnosperm known as *Araucaria*. No flowering plants have as yet been found in rocks of Paleozoic age.

The Permian period which brought to a close the Paleozoic era witnessed great changes in the distribution of sea and land; broad shallow seas, like Hudson Bay in eastern Canada, which covered much of the United States, were drained, and much of the continent of North America became dry land as we now know it. The resultant draining of the swamps, in which the plants of the Carboniferous lived, together with widespread glaciation and aridity especially in the southern hemisphere, inaugurated living conditions unsuited to most of the Paleozoic plants and resulted in their extinction. Some of the seed-ferns, and giant horsetails and lycopods, survived into the early part of the following era, which is known as the Mesozoic because its life was of a type intermediate between the Paleozoic and the more recent. But for the most part these ancient plants disappeared, and their places were taken by large-leafed ferns, conifers, and cycads. The Mesozoic is sometimes referred to as the Age of Cycads because of the abundance of these plants, which are placed in the Gymnospermae although their general appearance is more like that of the palm. Cycads occur today in the warmer parts of both hemispheres, and represent the last of a group of plants which was widespread from Antarctica to Greenland during the middle of the Mesozoic. At this time there appeared the immediate ancestors of modern conifers—trees like our pine and redwood of the northern hemisphere, and *Araucaria* of the southern. There are abundant impressions of leaves so like those of the living *Ginkgo* or maidenhair tree that there can be no question that this tree, now found in the temple grounds of China and Japan as a single surviving species, was formerly widespread in many parts of the world. More perhaps than at any other time in the history of the earth, the same general type of vegetation covered wide areas in which the forests of today are wholly different; this has led paleontologists to conclude that the climate of middle Mesozoic time was much more uniform than it is at present; a flora which is widespread and essentially uniform in many parts of the world is known as a cosmopolitan flora.

The plants of the Paleozoic and the first half of the Mesozoic were probably rather monotonous in aspect, since they lacked the structure known as the flower which gives color to our modern vegetation. Angiosperms, or flowering plants, make their first appearance in the Cretaceous, which is the last period of the Mesozoic era. Leaves similar to the sycamore (*Platanus*), *Magnolia*, *Sassafras*, legumes, and

Fig. 482.—Fossil leaves of redwood and alder (approximately 40 million years old) on a sla volcanic shale of Miocene age, from the John Day Basin of eastern Oregon. In Mio time redwoods, which are now restricted to a limited area along the Pacific Coast, were tributed over much of the northern hemisphere, including Asia, Europe, and North Ame (Photograph furnished by R. W. Chaney.)

palm of today have left their impressions in sediments deposited in valleys and lakes during the Cretaceous, long before man or his relatives lived upon the earth. Since some of these plants are considered by botanists to represent a high stage in evolution among angiosperms, it is evident that their ancestors must have lived during an earlier part of the Mesozoic under conditions not favorable to their preservation as fossils. There is much indirect evidence for the assumption that the earliest flowering plants lived in the uplands, far away from places where their leaves and stems might become buried and preserved, and that their history may have extended back into the closing days of the Paleozoic era; but there is no direct evidence of their history prior to the Cretaceous, when they appear first in Greenland, and shortly later in Europe and North America. From their earliest occurrence in high northern latitudes, most paleontologists believe that flowering plants, and the mammals which fed upon them, had their origin in the land mass known as Holarctica, including northern Eurasia, North America, and the arctic islands.

The last of the great eras of geologic time, the Cenozoic, which has extended down into the present, is the Age of Flowering Plants; during this time they have become the most abundant element in the vegetation of the world. The once dominant Pteridophytes and cycads have gradually come to occupy an unimportant place, and occur for the most part in the warmer parts of the world. Even the gymnosperms have become restricted in distribution and numbers, but the angiosperms have adapted themselves to a wide range of living conditions and greatly outnumber all other types of plants. The changes in flowering plants during the Cenozoic era, which extends over the last one hundred million years of earth history, are not so much in kind as in distribution. Because of their small size, softer structures, and less regularly deciduous habit, herbs do not commonly occur as fossils, but their absence from the record can not be interpreted as indicating that they did not live in the past. Most of the common families of trees and shrubs are well represented in the fossil record, and the restriction of their range as a result of earth changes forms one of the most striking chapters in the history of vegetation.

During the early part of the Cenozoic, the forest in western North America was made up of trees whose closest living equivalents now occupy the subtropical portions of Mexico and Central America; figs (*Ficus*), laurels (*Nectandra, Ocotea*), cinnamon (*Cinnamomum*), custard-apple (*Anona*), and ebony (*Diospyros*) are among the many fossils whose modern relatives are restricted to the warmer parts of the world. The gradual cooling and drying of the climate, together with a slow uplift of the mountains in western America, made it impossible for these trees to survive in California and Oregon, but their closely related descendants have continued down to the present in the regions to the south.

During the middle portion of the Cenozoic, a strictly temperate forest was widespread over much of the northern hemisphere. Its most characteristic species was the redwood (*Sequoia*), and many common associates of the modern redwood, such as the alder (*Alnus*), tan-oak (*Lithocarpus*), California laurel (*Umbellularia*), and maple (*Acer*) left their leaves, fruits, and stems in the deposits of that day. From its close resemblance to the redwood forest of coastal California, which lives under temperate climatic conditions characterized by high rainfall and uniform temperature, it is possible to conclude that a similar climate was widespread from California around the Pacific Basin to China. The intermigration between Asia and North America of many plants and animals has long been indicated by the fossil record; the recent finding of redwood fossils on St. Lawrence Island halfway between the continents in the Bering Sea indicates the former presence of a land connection over which the life of the past was enabled to migrate. In addition to the typical redwood element of this fossil forest, there are species of plants whose nearest living relatives no longer occur upon the Pacific coast of North America; such trees as the beech (*Fagus*), basswood (*Tilia*), chestnut (*Castanea*), and elm (*Ulmus*) not only ranged into western North America but extended with the redwood into Greenland, Spitzbergen, and other parts of the North. These records of the plant life of the past emphasize the great changes which have occurred over the surface of the earth in geologic time, and help to explain some of the peculiarities in distribution of modern plants.

During this latter portion of the Cenozoic era in which we live, plants which require mild moist climate have been further restricted. A continued trend toward cooling and drying, with the accompanying uplift of the mountains in western America, has confined the redwood forest to a narrow strip along the California coast. Fossil floras of late Cenozoic age contain poplars (*Populus*), willows (*Salix*), sycamores (*Platanus*), and other trees which live still in the interior of western America where the temperature and rainfall are not well suited to the growth of dense forests. Over wide areas grasslands have invaded the territory once occupied by forests, and it seems clear that further climatic changes along this trend of cooling and drying may be expected to limit forests to an even greater extent. Whether the trend will continue, or whether as indicated by events of the past there will be a return to moist mild climate, it is not possible to predict. It seems certain, however, that the plant life on a changing earth will continue to change in the future as it has in the past, and that the forests of geologic time which lies ahead will differ as much from those which we know as those of today differ from the ancient vegetation of the Carboniferous with its giant club-mosses and horsetails.

APPENDIX

BOOKS FOR REFERENCE AND COLLATERAL READING

General References

KERNER: *The Natural History of Plants*. English translation by Oliver. Henry Holt & Co., New York, 1895.

FITTING, JOST, SCHENCK, and KARSTEN: *Strasburger's Textbook of Botany*, Fifth English Edition. Macmillan & Co., London, 1923.

BOWER: *The Botany of the Living Plant*, Second Edition. Macmillan & Co., London, 1923.

COULTER, BARNES, and COWLES: *Textbook of Botany*, Vol. I, Revised Edition. American Book Co., New York, 1930.

SMITH, OVERTON, GILBERT, DENNISTON, BRYAN, and ALLEN: *A Textbook of General Botany*, Revised Edition. The Macmillan Co., New York, 1931.

SINNOTT: *Botany, Principles and Problems*. McGraw-Hill Book Co., New York, 1935.

WODEHOUSE: *Pollen Grains*. McGraw-Hill Book Co., New York, 1935.

HILL, OVERHOLTS, and POPP: *Botany, a Textbook for Colleges*. McGraw-Hill Book Co., New York, 1936.

External Morphology of Seed-Bearing Plants

GRAY: *The Elements of Botany*. American Book Co., New York, 1887.

LEAVITT: *Outlines of Botany*. American Book Co., New York, 1901.

Plant Anatomy

HABERLANDT: *Physiological Plant Anatomy*. Macmillan & Co., London, 1914.

JEFFREY: *The Anatomy of Woody Plants*. University of Chicago Press, 1917.

STEVENS: *Plant Anatomy*, Fourth Edition. P. Blakiston's Son & Co., Philadelphia, 1924.

EAMES and MACDANIELS: *An Introduction to Plant Anatomy*. McGraw-Hill Book Co., New York, 1925.

Plant Cytology

WILSON: *The Cell in Development and Heredity*, Third Edition. The Macmillan Co., New York, 1925.

SHARP: *An Introduction to Cytology*, Third Edition. McGraw-Hill Book Co., New York, 1925.

SEIFRIZ: *Protoplasm*. McGraw-Hill Book Co., New York, 1936.

Plant Physiology

PALLADIN: *Plant Physiology*, Third American Edition. Translated and edited by Livingston. P. Blakiston's Son & Co., Philadelphia, 1926.

SPOEHR: *Photosynthesis*. The Chemical Catalog Co., New York, 1926.

WAKSMAN and DAVISON: *Enzymes.* The Williams & Wilkins Co., Baltimore, 1926.

COULTER, BARNES, and COWLES: *A Textbook of Botany*, Vol. II, *Physiology.* Revised by Shull. American Book Co., New York, 1930.

KOSTYCHEV: *Chemical Plant Physiology.* English translation by Lyon. P. Blakiston's Son & Co., Philadelphia, 1931.

RABER: *Principles of Plant Physiology*, Revised Edition. The Macmillan Co., New York, 1933.

CURTIS: *The Translocation of Solutes in Plants.* McGraw-Hill Book Co., New York, 1935.

BOYSEN-JENSEN: *Growth Hormones in Plants.* McGraw Hill Book Co., New York, 1936.

LOOMIS and SHULL: *Methods in Plant Physiology.* McGraw-Hill Book Co., New York, 1937.

WENT and THEIMANN: *Phytohormones.* The Macmillan Co., New York, 1937.

MILLER: *Plant Physiology*, Second Edition. McGraw-Hill Book Co., New York, 1938.

MEYER and ANDERSON, *Plant Physiology.* D. Van Nostrand Co., New York, 1939.

Chemistry of Plants and Plant Products

HAAS and HILL: *The Chemistry of Plant Products*, Third Edition. Longmans, Green & Co., London, 1921.

ONSLOW: *Principles of Plant Biochemistry*, Part I. Cambridge University Press, 1931.

Plant Ecology

CLEMENTS: *Plant Succession; An Analysis of the Development of Vegetation.* Carnegie Institution of Washington, 1916.

WARMING: *Ecology of Plants.* Clarendon Press, Oxford, England, 1909.

TANSLEY: *Practical Plant Ecology.* Dodd, Mead & Co., New York, 1923.

WEAVER and CLEMENTS: *Plant Ecology.* McGraw-Hill Book Co., New York, 1929.

The Plant and the Soil

RUSSELL: *Soil Conditions and Plant Growth.* Longmans, Green & Co., London, 1921.

The Algae

WEST and FRITSCH: *Treatise on British Fresh Water Algae.* The Macmillan Co., New York, 1927.

SMITH: *The Fresh-water Algae of the United States.* McGraw-Hill Book Co., New York, 1933.

SMITH: *Cryptogamic Botany*, Vol. I, Algae and Fungi. McGraw-Hill Book Co., New York, 1938.

The Fungi

BULLER: *Researches on Fungi*, Vols. 1–5. Longmans, Green & Co., London, 1909–1933.

MACBRIDE: *North American Slime Moulds*, Second Edition. The Macmillan Co., New York, 1921.

MARSHALL and OTHERS: *Microbiology for Agricultural and Domestic Science Students*, Third Edition. P. Blakiston's Son & Co., Philadelphia, 1921.

FRED and LÖHNIS: *Textbook of Agricultural Bacteriology.* McGraw-Hill Book Co., New York, 1923.

Conn and Conn: *Bacteriology*, Second Edition. Williams & Wilkins, Baltimore, 1924.

Stevens: *Plant Disease Fungi*. The Macmillan Co., New York, 1925.

Gwynne-Vaughan and Barnes: *The Structure and Development of the Fungi*. The Macmillan Co., New York, 1927.

Gaumann-Dodge: *Comparative Morphology of Fungi*. McGraw-Hill Book Co., New York, 1928.

Owens: *Principles of Plant Pathology*. John Wiley & Sons, New York, 1928.

Arthur: *The Plant Rusts*. John Wiley & Sons, New York, 1929.

Fitzpatrick: *The Lower Fungi, Phycomycetes*. McGraw-Hill Book Co., New York, 1930.

Henrici: *Molds, Yeasts, and Actinomycetes*. John Wiley & Sons, New York, 1930.

Clements and Shear: *The Genera of Fungi*. H. W. Wilson Co., New York, 1931.

Heald: *Manual of Plant Diseases*, Second Edition. McGraw-Hill Book Co., New York, 1933.

Melhus and Kent: *Elements of Plant Pathology*. The Macmillan Co., New York, 1939.

MacBride and Martin: *The Myxomycetes*. The Macmillan Co., New York, 1934.

Bessey: *Textbook of Mycology*. P. Blakiston's Son & Co., Philadelphia, 1935.

Heald: *Introduction to Plant Pathology*. McGraw-Hill Book Co., New York, 1937.

Smith: *Cryptogamic Botany*, Vol. I, Algae and Fungi. McGraw-Hill Book Co., New York, 1938.

Mosses, Liverworts, and Ferns

Campbell: *Mosses and Ferns*, Third Edition. The Macmillan Co., New York, 1918.

Smith: *Cryptogamic Botany*, Vol. II, Bryophytes and Pteridophytes. McGraw-Hill Book Co., New York, 1938.

Morphology of the Reproductive Structures of Seed-Bearing Plants

Coulter and Chamberlain: *Morphology of Gymnosperms*, Revised Edition. University of Chicago Press, 1917. *Morphology of Angiosperms*. D. Appleton & Co., New York, 1903.

Eames: *Morphology of Vascular Plants*. McGraw-Hill Book Co., New York, 1936.

The Botany of Economic Plants

Robbins: *Botany of Crop Plants*, Third Edition. P. Blakiston's Son & Co., Philadelphia, 1933.

Robbins and Ramaley: *Plants Useful to Man*. P. Blakiston's Son & Co., Philadelphia, 1933.

Stanford: *Economic Plants*. Appleton-Century Co., New York, 1934.

Muenscher: *Weeds*. The Macmillan Co., New York, 1935.

Hill: *Economic Botany*. McGraw-Hill Book Co., New York, 1937.

Muenscher: *Poisonous Plants of the United States*. The Macmillan Co., New York, 1939.

Systematic Botany of the Seed-Bearing Plants

General

Rendle: *The Classification of Flowering Plants*. Cambridge University Press, 1904–1924.

Bailey: *Manual of Cultivated Plants*. The Macmillan Co., New York, 1924. *Standard Cyclopedia of Horticulture*. The Macmillan Co., New York, 1927.

HUTCHINSON: *The Families of the Flowering Plants*. The Macmillan Co., New York, 1926.

REHDER: *Manual of Cultivated Trees and Shrubs*. The Macmillan Co., New York, 1927.

CLEMENTS and CLEMENTS: *Flower Families and Ancestors*. The H. W. Wilson Co., New York, 1928.

SWINGLE, D. B.: *A Textbook of Systematic Botany*. McGraw-Hill Book Co., New York, 1928.

POOL: *Flowers and Flowering Plants*. McGraw-Hill Book Co., New York, 1929.

HITCHCOCK: *Manual of the Grasses of the United States*. U.S.D.A. Misc. Publ. 200, 1935.

FOR THE NORTHEASTERN AND CENTRAL STATES

BRITTON: *Manual of the Flora of the Northern States and Canada*. Henry Holt & Co., New York, 1905.

GRAY: *A Handbook of the Flowering Plants and Ferns*, Seventh Edition. American Book Co., New York, 1908.

FOR THE SOUTHEASTERN STATES

SMALL: *Flora of the Southeastern United States*, Second Edition. The Author, New York, 1933.

FOR THE ROCKY MOUNTAIN REGION

COULTER: *New Manual of the Botany of the Central Rocky Mountains*, Revised by Nelson. American Book Co., New York, 1909.

FOR THE PACIFIC COAST

JEPSON: *The Trees of California*, Associated Students Store, University of California, 1909. *A Flora of the Economic Plants of California*. Same publisher, 1924. *A Manual of the Flowering Plants of California*. Same publisher, 1925.

SUDWORTH: *Forest Trees of the Pacific Slope*. U.S.D.A., Forest Service, Washington, 1908.

FRYE and RIGG: *Elementary Flora of the Northwest*. American Book Co., New York, 1914.

ABRAMS: *Illustrated Flora of the Pacific States*, Vol. I. Stanford University Press, California, 1923.

McMINN and MAINO: *Illustrated Manual of Pacific Coast Trees*. University of California Press, Berkeley, 1935.

MUNZ: *A Manual of Southern California Botany*. Claremont College, Scripps Publishing Fund, Claremont, California, 1935.

McMINN: Illustrated Manual of California Shrubs. J. W. Stacey, San Francisco, 1939.

History of Botany

GIBSON: *Outline of the History of Botany*. A. & C. Black, London, 1919.

HAWKS: *Pioneers of Plant Study*. The Sheldon Press, London, 1928.

Evolution and Heredity

DARWIN: *On the Origin of Species*. Various publishers.

BABCOCK and CLAUSEN: *Genetics in Relation to Agriculture*, Second Edition. McGraw-Hill Book Co., New York, 1927.

MORGAN: *A Critique of the Theory of Evolution.* Princeton University Press, 1925. *The Scientific Basis of Evolution.* W. W. Norton & Co., New York, 1932.

SINNOTT and DUNN: *Principles of Genetics.* McGraw-Hill Book Co., New York, 1932.

Plant Geography

SCHIMPER: *Plant-Geography upon a Physiological Basis.* English translation by Fisher. Oxford Press, 1903.

CAMPBELL: *An Outline of Plant Geography.* The Macmillan Co., New York, 1926.

GLOSSARY

GLOSSARY OF TECHNICAL TERMS INCLUDING THEIR ORIGIN

Abscission (or **absciss**) **layer** (of leaf), (L. *abscissus*, cut off), zone of delicate, thin-walled cells extending across base of petiole.

Accessory buds (L. *acessio*, an addition or appendage), referring to extra buds in the leaf axil.

Achene, simple, dry, one-seeded, indehiscent fruit, with seed attached to ovary wall in one point only.

Actinomorphic (Gr. *aktis*, ray + *morphe*, form), having flowers of a regular or star pattern, capable of bisection in two or more planes into similar halves.

Adnation (L. *adnatus*, p.p. of *adnascor*—*ad*, to + *nascor*, be born), referring to flowers in which two or more whorls may become grown together to a greater or less extent.

Adventitious bud, one which arises anywhere on the plant except in the axils of the leaves.

Aeciospore (Gr. *oikion*, a little house + *spora*, a seed), yellow one-celled spores of rust fungi formed in special clusters called aecia.

Aecium (plural **aecia**), (Gr. *oikion*, a little house), in rust, a cluster cup which produces aeciospores.

Alternate, referring to bud or leaf arrangement in which there is one bud or one leaf at a node.

Ammonification (Ammon, Libyan Jupiter—first found near his temple—a pungent gas + L. *facio*, I make), decomposition of amino acids, resulting in the production of ammonia.

Anatropous (Gr. *ana*, up + *trepo*, turn, *anatrepo*, turn upside down), the ovule reversed, with micropyle close to the side of the hilum and the chalaza at the opposite end.

Androsporangia (Gr. *aner*, gen. *andro*, a man + *spora*, a seed) sporangia (spore cases), which produce zoospores of a type that develop into dwarf males.

Annual (L. *annualis*, within a year), plant which completes its life cycle within one year's time and then dies.

Annual ring, one year's growth of wood (xylem).

Annulus (L. *anulus* or *annulus*, a ring), in ferns, row of specialized cells in capsule of ferns of importance in opening of capsule; in mosses, thick-walled cells along the rim of the capsule to which the peristome is attached.

Anther (Gr. *antheros*, flowering), pollen-bearing portion of stamen.

Antheridium (Gr. *antheros*, flowering, cf. *anthos*, a flower + dimin.—*idion*), male gametangium or sperm-bearing organ.

Anthocyanins (Gr. *anthos*, a flower + *kyanos*, dark-blue) water-soluble pigments, usually red or blue, sometimes purple.

Apical growth, growth restricted to the apex of an organ.

Apophysis (Gr. *apophysis*, offshoot, protuberance), in moss capsule, the swelling at base.

Apothecium (Gr. *apo*, from + *thekion*, a small case, cf. *apotheke*, a storeroom), cup-shaped or saucer-shaped open ascocarp.

Archegonium (Gr. *arkhe*, beginning + *gonos*, a seed), female gametangium or egg-bearing organ, in which egg is protected by a jacket of sterile cells.

Ascocarp (Gr. *askos*, a bag + *karpos*, fruit), fruiting body (in ascomycetes) in which asci are produced.

Ascogonium (Gr. *askos*, a bag + *gonos*, a seed), female gametangium of the Ascomycetes.

Ascomycetes (Gr. *askos*, a bag + *myces*, fungus), a large group of fungi in which the characteristic spores are of the type known as ascospore.

Ascospore (Gr. *askos*, a bag + *spora*, a seed), spore produced by an ascus.

Ascus (plural **asci**), (Gr. *askos*, a bag), a spore sac, within which are produced a number of spores (generally 8) called ascospores.

Asexual (L. *a*, without + *sexualis*, sexual, *sexus*, sex), reproduction which does not involve the union of protoplasts.

Assimilation, transformation of digested foods into protoplasm.

Atropous (Gr. *atropos*, unbending; from *a*, not + *trepo*, turn), an ovule with a straight axis, the chalaza being at the insertion and the micropyle at the opposite end, farthest from the hilum.

Auricles (L. *auricula*, dimin. of *auris*, ear), ear-like structures; in grasses, small projections which grow out from the opposite side of the sheath at its upper end where it joins the blade.

Autophyte (Gr. *auto*, self + *phyton*, a plant), a plant which can make its own food.

Axile placentation, type in which placentae are on the axis of the ovary.

Axillary bud (L. *axilla*, arm pit), bud in the axil of a leaf.

Banner (Low L. *bandum*, a standard), large, broad, and conspicuous petal of legume type of flower.

Basidiomycetes (N.L. *basidium*, a little pedestal, plural *basidia*), group of fungi characterized by the production of spores on a special structure, the basidium.

Basidiospores (N.L. *basidium*, a little pedestal + *spora*, a seed), special asexual type of spore borne by basidia in the Basidiomycetes.

Basidium (N.L. *basidium*, a little pedestal, plural *basidia*), special club-shaped type of conidiophore in Basidiomycetes.

Benthon (Gr. *benthos*, depth), attached aquatic plants and animals, collectively.

Berry, simple fleshy fruit, the ovary wall fleshy and including one or more carpels and seeds.

Biennial (L. *biennium*, a period of two years), plant which completes its life cycle within two years and then dies.

Bifacial (leaf), (L. *bis*, twice + *facies*, face), upper and lower surfaces distinctly different.

Biology (Gr. *bios*, life + *logos*, word, speech, discourse), science which deals with living things.

Botany (Gr. *botane*, Latin from *botania*, grass, herb), science dealing with plant life.

Bryophyta (Gr. *bryon*, moss + *phyton*, plant), group of plants including the true mosses and the liverworts.

Bulb (L. *bulbus*, a modified bud, usually underground), short, flattened, or disc-shaped underground stem, with many fleshy scale leaves filled with stored food.

Bundle scar, scar left where conducting strands passing out of the stem into the leaf stalk were broken off when the leaf fell.

Callus (L. *callus*, hard skin), mass of large, thin-walled cells, usually developed as the result of wounding.

Calyptra (Gr. *kalyptra*, a veil, covering), in liverworts, an envelope covering the developing sporophyte, formed by growth of the venter of the archegonium.

Calyx (Gr. *kalyx*, a husk, cup), sepals collectively; outermost flower whorl.

Cambium, a layer, usually regarded as one cell thick, of persistently meristematic tissue.

Campylotropous (Gr. *kampylos*, bent + *trepo*, turn), applied to an ovule, one side of which has grown faster than the other, so as to bring its micropyle near the hilum.

Capillitium (L. *capillus*, a hair), in Myxomycetes, simple or branching tubes or threads within the sporangium.

Capsule (L. *capsula*, dimin. of *capsa*, a case), simple, dry, dehiscent fruit, with two or more carpels.

Carpel (Gr. *karpos*, fruit), a floral leaf bearing ovules.

Carpogonium (Gr. *karpos*, fruit + *gonos*, producing), female gametangium (in red algae).

Carpospore (Gr. *karpos*, fruit + *spora*, seed), the spore produced in a carpogonium.

Caruncle (L. *caruncula*, dimin. of *caro*, flesh, wart), a spongy outgrowth of the seed coat, especially prominent in the castor-bean seed.

Caryopsis (Gr. *karyon*, a nut + *opsis*, appearance), simple, dry, one-seeded, indehiscent fruit, with pericarp firmly united all around to the seed coat.

Catkin (cat + dimin.—kin), type of inflorescence, really a spike, generally bearing only pistillate flowers or only staminate flowers, which eventually falls from the plant entire.

Central placentation, type in which ovules are borne on the axis of a unilocular ovary.

Chalaza (Gr. *chalaza*, small tubercle), the region on a seed at the upper end of the raphe where the funiculus spreads out and unites with the base of the ovule.

Chemosynthesis, the manufacture of food by use of energy secured from a chemical reaction, such as oxidation of ammonia, nitrite, hydrogen, etc.

Chemotropism (Gr. *chemia*, art of transmuting metals + *tropos*, turn), a growth movement, the stimulus of which is a chemical substance.

Chlorenchyma (Gr. *chloros*, green + *enchyma*, infusion), tissue possessing chloroplasts.

Chlorophyceae (Gr. *chloros*, green + *phykos*, seaweed), a group of algae, the so-called green algae.

Chloroplastid (chloroplast), (Gr. *chloros*, green + *plastos*, formed), green plastid; specialized protoplasmic bodies containing chlorophyll.

Chondriosomes (Gr. *chondros*, dimin.—*chondrion*, a grain + *soma*, a body), small, rod-shaped, living bodies or filaments found in the cytoplasm of cells.

Chromatin (Gr. *chroma*, color), substance in the nucleus which readily takes artificial staining; also that portion which bears the determiners of hereditary characters.

Chromatophore (Gr. *chroma*, color + *phoros*, bearing), plastid which bears a pigment.

Chromoplastic (chromoplast), (Gr. *chroma*, color + *plastos*, formed), specialized protoplasmic body containing yellow or orange pigments.

Chromosomes (Gr. *chroma*, color + *soma*, body), protoplasmic bodies of definite number formed during nuclear division.

Cilia (L. *cilium*, an eyelash), whip-like filaments of protoplasm.

Circumscissile dehiscence (L. *de*, off + *hisco*, I open; L. *circum*, around + *scindo-scissus*, split), capsule which splits along a circular horizontal line.

Coalescence (L. *coalescere*, to grow together), a condition in which there is union of separate parts of any one whorl of flower parts.

Coenocyte (Gr. *koinos*, shared in common + *kytos*, a vessel), a plant or filament whose protoplasm is continuous and multinucleate and without any division by walls into separate protoplasts.

Coenogamete (Gr. *koinos*, shared in common + *gamos*, marriage), a multinucleate gamete, with no walls separating the many nuclei.

Coleoptile (Gr. *koleos*, sheath + *ptilon*, down, feather), in grasses, a sheath which surrounds the plumule.

Coleorhiza (Gr. *koleos*, sheath + *rhiza*, root), sheath which surrounds the radicle of grasses.

Collenchyma (Gr. *kolla*, glue + *enchyma*, infusion), a stem tissue composed of cells which fit rather closely together and with walls thickened at the angles of the cells.

Columella (L. *columella*, a small pillar), in liverworts, a core of sterile tissue occupying the axis of the sporophyte; in mosses, a mass of parenchyma-like cells, nonsporogenous, in the capsule of the sporophyte; in bread mold, a dome-shaped central structure in the sporangium.

Complete flower, one which has the usual flower parts (sepals, petals, stamens, carpels).

Compound leaf, leaf blade made up of a number of separate parts, or leaflets.

Compound pistil, a pistil composed of two or more carpels.

Conceptacle (L. *conceptaculum*, a receptacle), cavities or chambers of the fronds (of *Fucus*, for example) in which gametangia are borne.

Conidiophore (Gr. *conis*, dust + *phoros*, bearing), conidium-bearing branch of hypha.

Conidiospore (Gr. *conis*, dust + *spora*, a seed), spore formed by abstriction.

Conjugation (L. *conjugatus*, united), process of sexual reproduction involving the fusion of isogametes.

Connective, a band of tissue uniting the two lobes of an anther.

Corm (Gr. *kormos*, a trunk), short, solid, vertical, enlarged underground stem in which food is stored.

Corolla (L. *corolla*, dimin. of *corona*, a wreath, crown), petals, collectively; usually the conspicuous colored flower whorl.

Cortex (L. *cortex*, bark), tissue of a stem or root bounded externally by the epidermis and internally by the pericycle.

Corymb (L. *corymbus*, a cluster of flowers), flat-topped type of inflorescence, main axis of which is elongated but the pedicels of the older flowers longer than those of the younger flowers, so that flowers are all approximately in one plane.

Cuticle (L. *cuticula*, *cutis*, the skin), waxy layer on outer wall of epidermal cells.

Cutin (L. *cutis*, the skin), waxy substance which is very impermeable to water and to water vapor or other gases.

Cutinization, impregnation of cell wall with a substance called cutin.

Cyanophyceae (Gr. *kyanos*, dark blue + *phykos*, seaweed, algae), a group of algae known as the blue-green algae.

Cyme (Gr. *cyma*, a wave, a swelling), type of inflorescence in which the flowers at the apex are the first to mature and open.

Cytology (Gr. *kytos*, a hollow (cell) + *logos*, word, speech, discourse), the science dealing with the cell.

Cytoplasm (Gr. *kytos*, a hollow vessel + *plasma*, form), protoplasm of the cell surrounding the nucleus.

Deciduous (L. *deciduus*, falling), referring to trees and shrubs which lose their leaves in the fall.

Dehiscent (L. *dehiscere*, to split open), opening spontaneously when ripe, splitting into definite parts.

Deliquescent (L. melting away), referring to a method of branching in which it is impossible to pick out any one main stem.

Dentrification (L. *de*, from + *nitrum*, nitre + *facio*, I make), conversion of nitrates into nitrites, or into gaseous oxides of nitrogen, or even into free nitrogen.

Diastase (Gr. *diastasis*, standing apart), enzyme which brings about the hydrolysis of starch with the formation of sugar.

Dichotomy (Gr. *dicha*, in two, apart + *tome*, a cutting), a method of branching by forking.

Diclinous (Gr. *dis*, twice + *klino*, incline), unisexual, having the stamens in one flower and pistils in another.

Dicotyledon (Gr. *dis*, twice + *kotyledon*, a cup-shaped hollow), a plant whose embryo has two cotyledons.

Digestion (L. *dis*, apart + *gerere*, to carry), a process in which insoluble substances are rendered soluble and diffusible.

Dihybrid, a cross involving two pairs of contrasting characters.

Dioecious (Gr. *dis*, twice + *oikos*, house), unisexual, the male and female elements in different individuals.

Diploid (Gr. *diplous*, two-fold), applied to the $2x$ generation, the chromosomes being double as many as in the haploid generation.

Dorsal suture (L. *dorsum*, the back + *sutura*, a seam), the line of a carpel corresponding to the midrib of the floral leaf (carpel).

Dorsiventral (L. *dorsum*, the back + *venter*, the belly), (*leaf*) upper and lower surfaces are distinctly different.

Drupe (L. *drupa*, a stone fruit), simple, fleshy fruit, derived from single carpel, one-seeded, in which exocarp is thin, mesocarp fleshy, and endocarp stony.

Ecology (Gr. *oikos*, home + *logos*, discourse), the study of plant life in relation to environment.

Egg, female gamete.

Elater (Gr. *elater*, driver), in *Equisetum*, ribbon-like appendage attached to mature asexual spore; elongated, spindle-shaped, sterile, hygroscopic cells in the capsule of liverwort sporophyte.

Endocarp (Gr. *endon*, within + *karpos*, fruit), inner layer of fruit wall (pericarp).

Endodermis (Gr. *endon*, within + *derma*, skin), the layer of ground tissue which abuts on the stele, being differentiated as a sheath around it.

Endosperm (Gr. *endon*, within + *sperma*, seed), tissue in seeds in which food is stored.

Enzyme (Gr. *en*, in + *zyme*, yeast), an organic catalyst which is able to alter the rate of a chemical reaction.

Epiblast (Gr. *epi*, upon + *blastos*, sprout), a leaf of the plumule of grasses, a rudimentary second cotyledon.

Epidermis (Gr. *epi*, upon + *derma*, skin), the outermost layer of cells of young plant organs.

Epigyny (Gr. *epi*, upon + *gyne*, female), a condition in which the receptacle surrounds and fuses with the ovary so that other flower parts appear to arise from the top of the ovary.

Epipetaly (Gr. *epi*, upon + *petalon*, leaf), referring to a condition in which stamens are borne upon the petals.

Excurrent (L. *ex*, out + *curro*, I run), a type of erect shoot growth in which there is a single main stem, usually with many lateral branches, as in the pine.

Exine (L. *exterus*, outside), outer coat of spore.

Exocarp (Gr. *exo*, without, outside + *karpos*, fruit), outermost layer of fruit wall (pericarp).

Facultative parasite (L. *facultas*, capability; Gr. *parasitos*, one who lives at another's expense), a saprophyte which may be able to exist for a time as a parasite.

Facultative saprophyte (L. *facultas*, capability; Gr. *sapros*, rotten + *phyton*, a plant), a parasite which may be able to exist for a time as a saprophyte.

False indusium (L. *falsus*, untrue; L. *indusium*, woman's undergarment), in ferns, a covering of sporangia formed by a folding-over of the margin of the frond.

Fertilization (L. *fertilis*, capable of producing fruit), the sexual process involving the fusion of heterogametes.

Filament (L. *filum*, a thread), stalk of stamen bearing the anther at its tip.

Fission (L. *fissilis*, easily split), asexual reproduction involving merely the division of a single-celled individual into two new single-celled individuals of equal size.

Flagellum (L. *flagellum*, a whip), (plural, flagella), long slender whip of protoplasm.

Follicle (L. *folliculus*, dimin. of *follis*, bag), simple, dry, dehiscent fruit, with one carpel, splitting along one suture.

Foot, in liverworts, an expanded basal portion of the sporophyte which attaches it to the gametophyte.

Free nuclear division, division of nucleus without cell-wall formation.

Fucoxanthin (Gr. *phykos*, seaweed + *xanthos*, yellowish brown), a brown pigment found in brown algae.

Funiculus (L. *funiculus*, dimin. of *funis*, rope or small cord), stalk of the ovule.

Gametangium (Gr. *gametes*, spouse; *gamete*, wife + *angeion*, a vessel), organ-bearing gametes.

Gametes (Gr. *gametes*, a spouse), protoplast which fuses with another protoplast to form the zygote in the process of sexual reproduction.

Gametophyte (Gr. *gametes*, a spouse + *phyton*, a plant), the sexual or gamete-producing plant.

Gel (L. *gelatus*, congealed; also L. *gelo*, freeze), jelly-like colloidal mass.

Gemma (L. *gemma*, a bud), (plural gemmae), a small mass of vegetative tissue, an outgrowth of the thallus; in liverworts, borne in gemmae cups, capable of growing into new gametophyte plants.

Gene (Gr. *genos*, race, offspring), a material substance in the chromosome which determines or conditions one or more hereditary characters.

Geotropism (Gr. *ge*, earth + *tropos*, turning), a growth curvature induced by gravity.

Glucoside (Gr. *glykys*, sweet + *-ides*, like), a substance which on decomposition yields glucose and certain other compounds.

Glume (L. *gluma*, husk), outer and lowermost bracts of a grass spikelet.

Ground meristem (Gr. *meristos*, divisible), a primary meristem which gives rise to cortex, pericycle, pith rays, and pith.

Guttation (L. *gutta*, drop, exudation of drops), exudation of water in the liquid form.

Halophyte (Gr. *hals*, salt, the sea + *phyton*, a plant), a plant able to grow in salt marshes or on alkali soils.

Haploid (Gr. *haplous*, single + *-ides*, like), the organism with the single number of chromosomes, the haploid or *x* generation, the gametophyte.

Haustorium (plural, haustoria), (L. *haustor*, a drawer), projections of hyphae which act as penetrating and absorbing organs.

Head, type of inflorescence, typical of composite family, in which flowers are grouped closely on a receptacle.

Hermaphrodite flower (Gr. *hermaphroditos*, a person partaking of the attributes of both sexes, represented by Hermes and Aphrodite), one having both stamens and pistils.

Hesperidium (Gr. *hesperides*, women), simple, fleshy fruit, a type of berry with leathery rind.

Heterocyst (Gr. *heteros*, other + *cystis*, a bag), enlarged colorless cell which may occur in the filaments of certain blue-green algae.

Heteroecism (Gr. *heteros*, other, different + *oikizo*, colonize), referring to fungi which cannot carry through their complete life cycle unless two different host species are present.

Heterogametes (Gr. *heteros*, other + *gametes*, a spouse), gametes dissimilar in size and behavior.

Heterophyte (Gr. *heteros*, other + *phyton*, a plant), a plant which must secure its food ready made.

Heterospory (Gr. *heteros*, other + *spora*, seed), the condition of producing microspores and megaspores.

Heterothallic (Gr. *heteros*, other + *thallos*, a sprout), referring to species in which male gametangia and female gametangia are produced in different filaments or by different individual plant bodies.

Hilum (L. *hilum*, a trifle), scar on seed which marks the place where the seed broke from the stalk.

Homospory (Gr. *homos*, one and the same + *spora*, seed), production of but one kind of spore, in opposition to heterospory.

Homothallic (Gr. *homos*, one and the same + *thallos*, a sprout), referring to species in which male gametangia and female gametangia are produced in the same filament or by the same individual plant body.

Hormogonia (Gr. *hormos*, necklace + *gonos*, offspring), (singular, hormogonium), in certain blue-green algae, short sections of filaments delimited by special cells known as heterocysts.

Hormone (Gr. *hormon*, pres. part. of *hormaein*, to excite), substance which is produced in one part of an organism, is moved to another part, and there is capable of influencing a specific physiological process, even though the substance is present in very minute quantities.

Humidity (relative), (L. *humidus*, moist), the weight of water vapor in any quantity of air, compared with the total weight of water vapor which the air is capable of holding at the temperature in question.

Humus (L. *humus*, the ground), decomposing organic matter in the soil.

Hydathode (Gr. *hydor*, *hydatos*, water + *hodos*, way), special structures (sometimes modified stomata) of leaves through which water of guttation can easily escape.

Hydration (Gr. *hydor*, water + *tion*, act of), absorption of water by a substance with attendant swelling.

Hydrolysis (Gr. *hydor*, water + *lysis*, loosing), union of a compound with water, attended by decomposition into less complex compounds.

Hydrophyte (Gr. *hydor*, water + *phyton*, a plant), a plant which lives in water or in very wet soil.

Hydrotropism (Gr. *hydor*, water + *tropos*, turning), a growth curvature due to the stimulus of water.

Hymenium (Gr. *hymen*, a membrane), spore-bearing tissue in various fungi.

Hypha (Gr. *hyphe*, a web), (plural, hyphae), a fungal thread or filament.

Hypogyny (Gr. *hypo*, under + *gyne*, female), a condition in which the receptacle is convex or conical, and the whorls of flower parts are situated one above another in the following order, beginning with the lowest: sepals, petals, stamens, carpels.

Imperfect flower, flower lacking either stamens or pistils.

Inclusion, non-living structure within the cytoplasm.

Incomplete flower, one which lacks one or more of the four kinds of flower parts.

Indehiscent (L. *in*, not + *dehisco*, I split open; *de*, off + *hisco*, I open), not opening by valves or along regular lines.

Indusium (L. *indusium*, a woman's undergarment), (plural, indusia), membranous outgrowth of the epidermis of a fern leaf which covers the sori.

Inflorescence (L. *inflorescere*, to begin to bloom), a flower cluster.

Integument (L. *integumentum*, covering; *in*, upon + *tego*, cover), coat of ovule.

Intercalary growth (L. *intercalaris*, to be inserted), growth not restricted to the apex of an organ.

Internode (L. *inter*, between + *nodus*, a knot), the region of a stem between two successive nodes.

Intine (L. *intus*, within), the innermost coat of a pollen grain.

Irregular flower, one in which one or more members of at least one whorl are of different form from other members of the same whorl; zygomorphic.

Isobilateral (Gr. *isos*, equal + L. *bis*, twice, two-fold + *lateralis*, pertaining to the side), (leaf), upper and lower surfaces essentially similar.

Isocyclic (Gr. *isos*, equal + *kyklos*, circle), a flower having whorls with equal number of parts.

Isogametes (Gr. *isos*, equal + *gametes*, a spouse), gametes similar in size and behavior.

Keel (AS. *ceol*, ship), a structure of the legume type of flower made up of two petals loosely united along their edges.

Lactase (L. *lac, lactis*, milk), enzyme which brings about the hydrolysis of lactose with the formation of two sugars, glucose and galactose.

Lamella (L. dimin. of *lamina*, thin plate), the membrane or primary septum between any two cells.

Lamina (L. *lamina*, a thin plate), blade or expanded part of a leaf.

Lateral bud, bud which grows out from the side of a stem.

Latex (L. *latex*, juice), a milky secretion.

Leaf axile, angle formed by the leaf stalk and the stem.

Leaflet, separate part of the blade of a compound leaf.

Leaf primordium (L. *primordium*, the beginning), an outgrowth from the promeristem of the growing point of the stem.

Legume (L. *legumen*, pulse), a simple, dry, dehiscent fruit with one carpel, splitting along two sutures.

Lemma (Gr. *lemma*, a husk), lower bract which subtends a grass flower.

Lenticel (L. *lens, lentis*, a lentil), structure of the bark which permits the passage of gas inward and outward.

Leucoplastid (leucoplast), (Gr. *leukos*, white + *plastos*, formed), colorless plastid.

Liana (Sp. *liar*, to tie), a plant which climbs upon other plants depending upon them for mechanical support; a plant with climbing shoots.

Lignification (L. *lignum*, wood + *facio*, I make), impregnation of cell wall with a substance called lignin.

Ligule (L. *ligula*, dimin. of *lingua*, tongue), in grass leaves, an outgrowth from the upper and inner side of the leaf blade where it joins the sheath.

Lobed (leaf), (Gr. *lobos*, lower part of the ear), divided by clefts or sinuses.

Locule (L. *loculus*, dimin. of *locus*, a place), a cavity of the ovary in which ovules occur.

Loculicidal dehiscence (L. *loculus*, dimin. of *locus*, a place + *caedo*, I cut), capsule splits open along the middle of each carpel.

Lodicules (L. *lodicula*, a small coverlet), two scale-like structures which lie at the base of the ovary of a grass flower.

Megasporangium (Gr. *megas*, large + *spora*, a seed + *angeion*, a vessel), sporangium which bears megaspores.

Megaspore (Gr. *megas*, large + *spora*, a seed), large asexual spore which gives rise to a female gametophyte.

Megasporophyll (Gr. *megas*, large + *spora*, a seed + *phyllon*, leaf), sporophyll (spore-bearing leaf) bearing megasporangia.

Meiosis (Gr. *meiosis*, reduction), applied to reduction divisions of chromosomes.

Meristem (Gr. *meristos*, divisible; *merizo*, divide), undifferentiated tissue the cells of which are capable of active division.

Mesocarp (Gr. *mesos*, middle + *karpos*, fruit), middle layer of fruit wall (pericarp).

Mesophyll (Gr. *mesos*, middle + *phyllon*, leaf), tissue of leaf between epidermal layers.

Mesophytes (Gr. *mesos*, middle + *phyton*, a plant), Warming's term for those plants which are intermediate between hydrophytes and xerophytes, avoiding both very moist and very dry environmental conditions.

Micropyle (Gr. *mikros*, small + *pyle*, orifice, gate), pore leading from the outer surface of the ovule between the edges of the two integuments down to the surface of the nucellus.

Microsporangia (Gr. *mikros*, little + *spora*, seed + *angeion*, a vessel), sporangium which bears microspores.

Microspore (Gr. *mikros*, small + *spora*, a seed), small asexual spore which gives rise to a male gametophyte.

Microsporophyll (Gr. *mikros*, little + *spora*, a seed + *phyllon*, leaf), sporophyll (spore-bearing leaf) bearing microsporangia.

Middle lamella (L. *lamella*, a thin plate or scale), original thin membrane separating two adjacent protoplasts.

Mixed bud, bud containing both rudimentary leaves and flowers.

Monocotyledon (Gr. *monos*, solitary + *kotyledon*, a hollow), a plant whose embryo has one cotyledon.

Monoecious (Gr. *monos*, solitary + *oikos*, house), the stamens and pistils in separate flowers, but borne on the same individual.

Monohybrid (Gr. *monos*, solitary + L. *hybrida*, a mongrel), a cross involving one pair of contrasting characters.

Morphology (Gr. *morphe*, form + *logos*, discourse), the study of form and its development.

Multiciliate (L. *multus*, many + *cilium*, an eyelash), a spore or sperm which has many cilia.

Myxomycetes (Gr. *myxa*, mucus + *myces*, mushroom), "slime fungi."

Naked bud, bud not protected by bud scales.

Nectary (Gr. *nektar*, the drink of the gods), a nectar-secreting gland.

Net venation, veins of leaf blade visible to unaided eye branch frequently and join again, forming a network.

Nitrification, change of ammonium salts into nitrates through the activities of certain bacteria.

Node (L. *nodus*, a knot), slightly enlarged portion of the stem where leaves and buds arise, and where branches originate.

Nucellus (L. *nucella*, a small nut, kernel of an ovule or seed), tissue composing the chief part of the young ovule, in which embryo sac develops; megasporangium.

Nucleolus (L. dimin. of *nucleus*, nut, kernel), dense protoplasmic body in the nucleus.

Nut (L. *nux*, a hard, indehiscent, one-seeded fruit), a dry, indehiscent, hard, one-seeded fruit, generally produced from a compound ovary.

Obligate parasite, an organism which is obliged to live strictly as a parasite.

Obligate saprophyte, an organism which is obliged to live strictly as a saprophyte.

Oogonium (Gr. *o(i)on*, an egg + *gonos*, offspring, seed), female gametangium or egg-bearing organ, characteristic of the thallophytes.

Oomycetes (Gr. *o(i)on*, egg + *myces*, mushroom), those fungi which reproduce sexually by antheridia and oogonia, the result being an oospore.

Oospore (Gr. *o(i)on*, an egg + *spora*, a seed), zygote resulting from the fusion of heterogametes.

Operculum (L. *operculum*, a lid), in mosses, cap of capsule.

Opposite, referring to bud or leaf arrangement in which there are two buds or two leaves at a node.

Osmosis (Gr. *osmos*, a pushing), the passage of a solvent from a quantity of pure solvent or a dilute solution through a semipermeable membrane into a more concentrated solution.

Ostiole (L. *ostiolum*, a little door), a small opening or pore.

Ovary (Gr. *o(i)on*, L. *ovum*, an egg), enlarged basal portion of pistil which becomes the fruit.

Palea (or palet), (L. *palea*, chaff), upper bract which subtends a grass flower.

Palmately veined (L. *palma*, palm of the hand), leaf blade with several principal veins spreading out from the upper end of the petiole.

Panicle (L. *panicula*, a tuft), type of inflorescence, the main axis of which is branched, and the branches bear loose racemose flower clusters.

Pappus (L. *pappus*, plant down), scales or bristles representing a reduced calyx in composite flowers.

Parallel venation, type of venation in which veins of leaf blade that are clearly visible to unaided eye are parallel to each other.

Paraphysis (Gr. *paraphysis,* a growth at the side), (plural paraphyses), slender, multicellular hair (*Fucus,* etc.); sterile branches or hyphae associated with asci in the fruiting body of certain fungi.

Parasite (Gr. *parasitos,* one who lives at another's expense), an organism deriving its food from the living body of another plant or an animal.

Parenchyma (Gr. *parenchyma,* something poured in at the side; *para,* beside + *enchyma,* infusion), a tissue composed of cells which usually have thin walls of cellulose, and which fit rather loosely together, leaving intercellular spaces.

Parietal placentation (L. *paries,* wall, *placenta,* a cake), type in which placentae are on the ovary wall.

Parthenocarpy (Gr. *parthenos,* virgin + *karpos,* fruit), the development of fruit without fertilization.

Parthenogenesis (Gr. *parthenos,* virgin + *genesis,* origin), division and subsequent development of a gamete without activation by another gamete.

Pedicel (L. *pediculus,* a little foot), stalk or stem of the individual flowers of an inflorescence.

Peduncle (L. *pedunculus,* a late form of *pediculus,* a little foot), stalk or stem of a flower which is borne singly; or the main stem of an inflorescence.

Perfect flower, one having both stamens and pistils; hermaphroditic.

Perianth (Gr. *peri,* around + *anthos,* flower), petals and sepals taken together.

Pericarp (Gr. *peri,* around + *karpos,* fruit), fruit wall, developed from ovary wall.

Pericycle (Gr. *peri,* around + *kyklos,* circle), tissue of a stem or root bounded externally by the cortex and internally by the phloem (or in primary roots by both xylem and phloem).

Peridium (Gr. *peridion,* a little pouch), (plural peridia), covering to the hymenium of certain fungi, chiefly puffballs; in Myxomycetes, the hardened envelope which covers the sporangium.

Perigyny (Gr. *peri,* about + *gyne,* a female), a condition in which the receptacle is more or less concave, at the margin of which the sepals, petals, and stamens have their origin, so that these parts seem to be attached around the ovary.

Perinium (Gr. *peri,* about + *is, inos,* muscle), layer outside of exine and intine of asexual spores of *Equisetum.*

Peristone (Gr. *peri,* about + *stoma,* a mouth), in mosses, a fringe of teeth which facilitates by hygroscopic movement the dissemination of spores from the capsule.

Perithecium (Gr. *peritheke,* a cover; *peri,* around + *theke,* a box), spherical closed ascocarp.

Petal (Gr. *petalon,* a flower leaf), usually the conspicuous colored flower parts.

Petiole (L. *petiolus,* a little foot or leg), stalk of leaf.

Phaeophyceae (Gr. *phaios,* dusky + *phykos,* seaweed), a group of algae characterized by a brown pigment.

Phelloderm (Gr. *phellos,* cork + *derma,* skin), the innermost layer of the periderm.

Phellogen (Gr. *phellos,* cork + *-gen.,* the root of *gignomai,* be born), cork cambium, a cambium giving rise to cork and phelloderm.

Photosynthesis (Gr. *phos, photos,* light + *syn,* together + *tithemi,* place), a process in which carbon dioxide and water are brought together chemically to form a carbohydrate, the energy for the process being radiant energy.

Phototropism (Gr. *phos, photos,* light + *tropos,* turning), a growth curvature in which light is the stimulus.

Phycocyanin (Gr. *phykos,* seaweed + *cyanos,* blue), blue pigment, occurring in blue-green algae.

Phycoerythrin (Gr. *phykos,* seaweed + *erythros,* red), a red pigment occurring in red algae.

Phycomycetes (Gr. *phykos,* seaweed + *myces,* mushroom or fungus), a group of fungi which approach the algae in some characters.

Phytobenthon (Gr. *phyton,* a plant + *benthos,* depth), attached aquatic plants, collectively.

Phytoplankton (Gr. *phyton,* a plant + *planktos,* wandering), free-floating plants, collectively.

Pileus (L. *pileus,* a cap), umbrella-shaped cap of fleshy fungi.

Pinna (plural pinnae), (L. a feather), leaflet of fern leaf (frond).

Pinnately veined (L. *pinna,* a feather; L. *vena,* a vein), leaf blade with single midrib from which smaller veins branch off, somewhat like the divisions of a feather.

Pistil (L. *pistillum,* a pestle), central organ of the flowers typically consisting of ovary, style, and stigma.

Pistillate flower (L. *pistillum,* a pestle), one having pistils but no stamens.

Placenta (L. *placenta,* a cake), (plural placentae), the tissue within the ovary to which the ovules are attached.

Placentation (L. *placenta,* a cake + *tion,* disposition of), manner in which the placentae are distributed in the ovary.

Plankton (Gr. *planktos,* wandering), free-floating aquatic plants and animals, collectively.

Plasmodesma (Gr. *plasma,* anything formed + *desma,* a bond, a band), fine protoplasmic thread passing through the wall which separates two protoplasts.

Plasmodium (Gr. *plasma,* anything formed + *eidos,* shape, kind), in Myxomycetes, a slimy mass of protoplasm, with no surrounding wall and with numerous free nuclei distributed throughout.

Plasmolysis (Gr. *plasma,* anything formed + *lysis,* a loosing), the separation of the cytoplasm from the cell wall, due to removal of water from the vacuole.

Plastid (Gr. *plastos,* formed, *plasso,* form), a specialized cytoplasmic structure.

Polygamous (Gr. *polys,* much + *gamos,* marriage), having perfect pistillate and staminate flowers on the same individual or on different individuals.

Pome (L. *pomum,* a fruit), simple fleshy fruit derived from several carpels, the receptacle fleshy, outer pericarp fleshy, inner pericarp papery.

Poricidal dehiscence (L. *porus,* a passage, pore + *caedo,* I cut), capsule splits open by pores at the apices of the carpels.

Procambium (L. or Gr. *pro,* before + *cambio,* exchange), a primary meristem which gives rise to vascular bundles.

Pro-embryo (L. *pro,* for + *embryon,* a foetus), a group of cells arising from the division of the fertilized egg cell, some of which are the so-called suspensor cells, and others are embryo cells.

Promeristem (Gr. *pro,* before + *meristos,* divisible; cf. *merizo,* divide), a rounded cone of meristematic tissue at the growing point.

Prothallium (Gr. *pro,* for + *thallos,* a sprout), in ferns, the sexual or gametophyte generation.

Protoderm (Gr. *protos,* first + *derma,* skin), a primary meristem which gives rise to epidermis.

Protonema (Gr. *protos*, first + *nema*, a thread), (plural protonemata), algal-like growth, an early stage in development of the gametophyte of mosses.

Protoplasm (Gr. *protos*, first + *plasma*, anything formed), living substance.

Protoplast (Gr. *protoplastos*, formed first), the organized living part of a single cell.

Pseudopodium (Gr. *pseudes*, false + *pous*, *podos*, a foot), in Myxomycetes, arm-like process from the body by which the plant creeps over the surface; in mosses, elongation of the tip of the gametophyte stem below the region to which the foot of the sporophyte is attached.

Pteridophyta (Gr. *pteris*, fern + *phyton*, plant), a division of the plant kingdom including ferns and their allies.

Raceme (L. *racemus*, a bunch of grapes), type of inflorescence in which the main axis is elongated but the flowers are borne on pedicels which are about equal in length.

Rachilla (Gr. (*rhachis*, a backbone + L. dimin. ending *-illa*) shortened axis of spikelet.

Rachis (Gr. *rhachis*, a backbone), main axis of spike; axis of fern leaf (frond) from which pinnae arise; in compound leaves, the extension of the petiole corresponding to the midrib of an entire leaf.

Raphe (Gr. *rhaphe*, seam), ridge on seeds, formed by the stalk of the ovule, in those seeds in which the funiculus is sharply bent at the base of the ovule.

Raphide (Gr. *rhaphis*, a needle), a bundle of fine, sharp, needle-like crystals.

Receptacle (L. *receptaculum*, a reservoir), enlarged end of the pedicel or peduncle to which other flower parts are attached.

Regular flower, one in which the corolla is made up of similarly shaped petals equally spaced and radiating from the center of the flower; star-shaped flower; actinomorphic.

Rhizoid (Gr. *rhizoma*, a root + *-ides*, like), root-like structures which perform the functions of roots.

Rhizome (Gr. *rhizoma* (*rhiza*), root), elongated underground, horizontal stem.

Rhizophores (Gr. *rhiza*, root + *-phor*, one of the roots of *phero*, bear), leafless branches which grow downward from the leafy stems of certain Lycopodineae and give rise to roots when they come into contact with the soil.

Rhodophyceae (Gr. *rhodon*, a rose + *phykos*, seaweed), a group of algae characterized by a red pigment.

Rootstock, elongated, underground, horizontal stem.

Runner, stem that grows horizontally along the ground surface.

Samara (L. *samara*, the fruit of the elm), simple, dry, one- or two-seeded indehiscent fruit with pericarp bearing a wing-like outgrowth.

Saprophyte (Gr. *sapros*, rotten + *phyton*, a plant), an organism deriving its food from the dead body or the non-living products of another plant or animal.

Sarcode (Gr. *sarx*, *sarkos*, flesh + *-(?) les*, like), name applied by Dujardin (1835) to the jelly-like substance observed in animal cells.

Schizocarp (Gr. *schizo*, split + *karpos*, fruit), dry fruit with two or more united carpels, which split apart at maturity.

Schizomycetes (Gr. *schizo*, to split + *myces*, mushroom), a group of fungi.

Scutellum (L. *scutella*, a dimin. of *scutum*, shield), single cotyledon of grass embryo.

Sepals (N.L. *sepalum*, a covering. Note: The word sepalum is a modern word formed by analogy with petalum, Gr. *petalon*), outermost flower structures which usually enclose the other flower parts in the bud.

Septate (L. *saeptum*, a hedge or enclosure), divided by cross walls into cells or compartments.

Septicidal, dehiscence (L. *saeptum*, an enclosure + *caedo*, I cut; *dehisco*, I split open; *de*, off + *hisco*, open), capsule splits open along the line of union of carpels.

Sessile (L. *sessilis*, pertaining to sitting; cf. *sedeo*, I sit), sitting, referring to leaf lacking a petiole.

Seta (L. *saeta*, a bristle), in liverworts, a short stalk of the sporophyte which connects the foot and the capsule.

Sexual (reproduction), reproduction involving the union of protoplasts.

Sheath, part of leaf which wraps around the stem, as in grasses.

Silique (L. *siliqua*, pod), the fruit characteristic of Cruciferae (mustards); two-celled, the valves splitting from the bottom and leaving the placentae with the false partition stretched between.

Sinus (L. *sinus*, a curve, fold, hollow), clefts in leaf blade.

Sol (see solution), liquid colloidal mass.

Soredium (Gr. *soros*, a heap), (plural soredia), special reproductive body of lichens consisting of a few algal cells surrounded by fungous hyphae.

Sorus (Gr. *soros*, a heap), (plural, sori), a cluster of sporangia.

Spermagonium (Gr. *sperma*, a seed + *gonos*, offspring), (plural, spermagonia), flask-shaped structure on upper surface of barberry leaf which bears spermatia.

Spermatium (Gr. *sperma*, seed), (plural spermatia), in rust fungi, a cell borne at the tip of hyphae which line the interior of spermagonia (on barberry leaves).

Spermatophyta (Gr. *sperma*, seed + *phyton*, plant), seed plants.

Spike (L. *spica*, an ear of grain), type of inflorescence in which the main axis is elongated and the flowers are sessile.

Spikelet (L. *spica*, an ear of grain + *dimin.* ending -*let*), the unit of inflorescence in grasses; a small group of grass flowers.

Sporangiophore (Gr. *spora*, a seed + *angeion*, a vessel + -*phore*, a root of *phero*, bear) a spore-bearing branch.

Sporangium (Gr. *spora*, a seed + *angeion*, a vessel), spore case.

Sporidium (Gr. dimin. of *spora*, a seed), the basidiospore of smut fungi.

Sporocarp (Gr. *spora*, a seed + *karpos*, a fruit), fruiting body of aquatic ferns which bear microsporangia and megasporangia.

Sporophore (Gr. *spora*, seed + -*phor*, a root of *phero*, bear), the fruiting body of fleshy and woody fungi which produces spores.

Sporophyll (Gr. *spora*, a seed + *phyllon*, leaf), spore-bearing leaf.

Sporophyte (Gr. *spora*, a seed + *phyton*, a plant), the asexual generation in those plants which show alternation of generations.

Stamen (L. *stamen*, warp in a loom, a thread), flower structure made up of an anther (pollen-bearing portion) and a stalk or filament.

Staminate flower, one having stamens but no pistils.

Sterigma (Gr. *sterigma*, a prop), (plural sterigmata), slender, pointed protuberance at the ends of a basidium which bear basidiospores.

Stigma (L. *stigma*, a prick, a spot, a mark), expanded tip of the style to which pollen adheres.

Stipule (L. *stipula*, dimin. of *stipes*, a stock or trunk), leaf-like structures from either side of the leaf base.

Stolon (L. *stolo*, a shoot), stem that grows horizontally along the ground surface.

Strobilus (Gr. *strobilos*, a cone), a sporophyll-bearing axis.

Style (Gr. *stylos*, a column), slender column of tissue which arises from the top of the ovary and through which the pollen tube grows.

Suberization (L. *suber*, the cork oak), impregnation of cell wall with a substance called suberin.

Sucrase (Gr. *sucre*, sugar), enzyme which brings about the hydrolysis of cane sugar with the formation of two hexose sugars, fructose, and glucose.

Syconium (Gr. *sykon*, fruit of the fig tree), the multiple fruit of fig, in which the receptacle is hollow and succulent, and lined on the inside with numerous seeds.

Symbiosis (Gr. *syn*, with + *bios*, life), an association of two different kinds of living organisms involving benefit to both.

Sympetaly (Gr. *syn*, with + *petalon*, leaf), a condition in which petals are united.

Synandry (*syn*, with + *aner* (*andr-*), male), a condition in which stamens are united.

Syncarpy (Gr. *syn*, with + *karpos*, fruit), a condition in which carpels are united.

Synergids (Gr. *synergos*, toiling together), the two nuclei at the upper end of the embryo sac, which, with the third (the egg) constitute the egg-apparatus.

Synsepaly (Gr. *sun*, with + *sepalum*, see sepals), a condition in which sepals are united.

Tapetum (Gr. *tapes*, a carpet), nutritive tissue in the sporangium.

Taxonomy (Gr. *taxis*, arrangement + *nomos*, law), systematic botany; science dealing with the describing, naming, and classifying of plants.

Teliospore (Gr. *telos*, completion + *spora*, a seed), black, two-celled winter spore in the life cycle of black stem rust.

Telium (Gr. *telos*), (plural telia), a sorus of teliospores.

Terminal bud, a bud at the end of a stem.

Testa (L. *testa*, a brick, potsherd, shell), the outer coat of the seed.

Tetrad (Gr. *tetradeion*, a set of four), a group of four, usually referring to the asexual spores of Bryophyta, Pteridophyta, and Spermatophyta.

Tetraspores (Gr. *tetra-*, four + *spora*, seed), spores formed by division of the spore mother cell into four parts.

Thallophyta (Gr. *thallos*, young branch + *phyton*, plant), a division of the plant kingdom including plants whose body is a thallus.

Thallus (Gr. *thallos*, a sprout), plant body without true roots, stems, or leaves.

Thigmotropism (Gr. *thigma*, touch + *tropos*, turning), growth curvature induced in climbing plants by the stimulus of contact.

Tissue, a group of cells of similar structure which performs a special function.

Trichogyne (Gr. *thrix*, *trichos*, a hair + *gyne*, a female), in the red algae a filament at the free end of the carpogonium which is receptive to the sperms; or in the ascomycetes the long tubular outgrowth of the ascogonium (female gametangium).

Triple-fusion nucleus, formed by union of two polar nuclei of embryo sac and one sperm nucleus, and developing into endosperm.

Tropism (Gr. *trope*, a turning), movement of curvature due to an external stimulus which determines the direction of movement.

Tuber (L. *tuber*, a bump, swelling), much enlarged, short fleshy underground stem.

Turgor pressure (L. *turgor*, a swelling), the pressure within the cell resulting from the absorption of water into the vacuole and the imbibition of water by the protoplasm.

Umbel (L. *umbella*, a sunshade), type of inflorescence, the axis of which is short and the pedicels of nearly equal length.

Urediniospore (L. *uredo*, a blight + Gr. *spora*, a seed), red, one-celled summer spore in the life cycle of black stem rust.

Uredinium (plural uredinia), (L. *uredo*, a blight), a sorus of urediospores.

Uredosorus (L. *uredo*, a blight + *soros*, a heap), a group of urediniospores.

Vacuole (L. dimin. of *vacuus*, empty), watery solution of various substances embedded in the cytoplasm.

Venation (L. *vena*, a vein), arrangement of veins in leaf blade.

Venter (L. the belly), enlarged basal portion of an archegonium in which the egg cell is borne.

Ventral canal cell, the cell just above the egg cell in the archegonium.

Ventral suture (L. *ventralis*, pertaining to the belly), the line of union of the two edges of a carpel.

Versatile (L. *versatilis*, movable), anthers attached near the middle to the filament in such manner that they swing freely.

Volva (L. *volva*, a wrapper), cup at base of stipe or stalk of fleshy fungi.

Whorl, a circle of flower parts, or of leaves.

Whorled, referring to bud or leaf arrangement in which there are three or more buds or three or more leaves at a node.

Wings, lateral petals of legume type of flower.

Xanthophyll (Gr. *xanthos*, yellowish brown + *phyllon*, leaf), a constituent of chlorophyll, a yellow coloring matter insoluble in water.

Xerophyte (Gr. *xeros*, dry + *phyton*, a plant), a plant very resistant to drought, or which lives in very dry places.

Zoology (Gr. *zoon*, animal + *logos*, speech), science having to do with animal life.

Zoospore (Gr. *zoon*, an animal + *spora*, a seed), motile asexual spore.

Zygospore (Gr. *zygotos*, yoked + *spora*, seed), zygote resulting from the fusion of isogametes.

Zygote (Gr. *zygotos*, yoked), protoplast resulting from the fusion of gametes (either isogametes or heterogametes).

Zymase (Gr. *zyme*, leaven), intracellular, sugar-fermenting enzyme.

INDEX

(Numbers in **bold-face** type indicate pages bearing illustrations.)

A

Abies (spruce), 537; absence of root hairs in, 166

Abscission layer, **203**; of leaves, 202

Absorption, 20, 65; by plant cells, a summary, 74; by roots, 25, 163, 172; in germination, 297; of dissolved substances into living cells, 73; of energy, 210, 211; of inorganic salts, 172; of solutes, 65, 73; of water, 170, 172; spectrum of chlorophyll solution, **208**

Accessory buds, 30

Accessory pigments, 348, 382

Acer (maple), leaf of, **185**; *saccharum*, wood of, in section, **120**; winged fruit of, **294**

Acetic acid fermentation, 396

Achene, 272, **276**, **280**; of buckwheat, **280**

Acids, 216; *see also* Acetic acid, Malic acid, etc.

Acorn, **281**

Acquired characters, inheritance of, 588

Active buds, 32

Active solute absorption, theory of, 73

Adaptations favoring dispersal of seeds by wind, water, and animals, 293

Adiantum (maiden-hair fern), 516

Adnation of flower parts, 234

Adventitious buds, 28

Adventitious roots, 154

Aecia, **446**, **448**; of blister rust on white pine tree, 437; on barberry leaf, **437**

Aecial stage of *Puccinia graminis* (blackstem rust), **449**

Aeciospores, 447

Aerial roots: of banyan, **177**; of corn, **175**

Aesculus (buckeye), bud scales and leaves of, **96**; twigs showing opening of terminal bud, **96**

After-ripening of seeds, 305

Agaricales, 453

Agaricus campestris (a mushroom), 453, 455, 456

Agave (century plant), in flower, **45**

Age of trees: determination of, 123; *Sequoia*, **116**

Aggregate fruits, 271, 273; of blackberry, **273**; of raspberry, **271**; of strawberry, **276**

Agriculture, 6

Agronomy, 6

Agropyron repens, rhizome of, 148

Air: composition of, 204; in soil, 319; movements as affecting transpiration rate, 220; temperature as affecting transpiration, 221

Albugo candida (white rust), **411**; asexual reproduction in, **410**; development of sporangia, **413**; sexual reproduction in, 410; zoospore formation and germinating zygote of, **413**

Alcoholic fermentation, 395

Alder (*Alnus*): fossil leaves of, **610**; old root of, in transverse section, **170**

Aleurone in grain, **291**, 292

Algae, 344, 347; alternation of haploid and diploid phases in, 384; and typical land plants, relative complexity of, 387; blue-green, 348; brown, 372; characteristics of, 347; classes of, 347; conditions favoring zoospore and gamete production in, 387; green, 352; origin and evolution of sex in, a summary, 386; red, 382; reduction division of, 356, 360, 365, 367, 381, 385